Waynesburg College Li
Waynesburg, Pennsylva
P9-DHP-304

*FAMOUS PROBLEMS*
*OF*
*MATHEMATICS*

OTHER *GRAYLOCK* PUBLICATIONS

ALEKSANDROV: *Combinatorial Topology*
*Vol. 1: Introduction. Complexes. Coverings. Dimension*
*Vol. 2: The Betti Groups*
*Vol. 3: Homological Manifolds. The Duality Theorems. Cohomology Groups of Compacta. Continuous Mappings of Polyhedra*

KHINCHIN: *Three Pearls of Number Theory*
*Mathematical Foundations of Quantum Statistics*

KOLMOGOROV and FOMIN: *Elements of the Theory of Functions and Functional Analysis*
*Vol. 1: Metric and Normed Spaces*
*Vol. 2: Measure. The Lebesgue Integral. Hilbert Space*

NOVOZHILOV: *Foundations of the Nonlinear Theory of Elasticity*

PETROVSKII: *Lectures on the Theory of Integral Equations*

PONTRYAGIN: *Foundations of Combinatorial Topology*

# FAMOUS PROBLEMS OF MATHEMATICS

**Solved and Unsolved**

**MATHEMATICAL PROBLEMS**

**From Antiquity to Modern Times**

BY

HEINRICH TIETZE

*Professor of Mathematics*
*University of Munich*

Authorized Translation from the Second (1959) Revised German Edition

Edited by
BEATRICE KEVITT HOFSTADTER and HORACE KOMM

*GRAYLOCK PRESS*
NEW YORK
1965

*Originally published in two volumes as*

Gelöste und ungelöste mathematische Probleme aus alter und neuer Zeit



*Library of Congress Catalog Card Number 64-8910*

*Manufactured in the United States of America*

*TO MY DEAR COLLEAGUES*

CONSTANTIN CARATHÉODORY
AND
OSKAR PERRON

DEDICATED IN GRATEFUL MEMORY
OF ALL THE YEARS
SPENT IN A COMMON EFFORT

## CONTENTS

## LIST OF PLATES

## LIST OF PORTRAITS

# PREFACE

"Jerome is to learn how to study,
He is to go to the university at Easter."

Wilhelm Busch
Illustrations to the Jobsiad, Chapter III.

One sometimes encounters quite curious conceptions as to what studying really means. If only everything is made quite palatable to the student, then, in the opinion of some, it ought to be an easy matter to advance to a mastery of the material, child's play to attain the loftiest heights of knowledge. It is thought to be an error if toil and effort are required on the way to the heights and that therefore, through the fault of the teacher, the goal is reached by only a few, and only slowly and gradually even by these. Of course everyone realizes that in, say, skiing or horseback riding it is not sufficient to listen to instructions on the motions and carriage of the body, in order to handle oneself properly from the beginning on the skis or in the saddle; rather, many a drop of sweat and an occasional tumble must precede the assurance sought for.

Why should it not be similar in the intellectual field, in the acquisition of a body of knowledge: that genuine success is accorded only to serious, persistent effort along with occasional correction of false conceptions? And that even the best teacher can indeed guide the student and help him to avoid unnecessary obstacles on the way to acquiring skills and knowledge, but neither can nor should spare him persistent work; and that in addition, where talent is lacking, the hardest labor of love must be content with modest results. In this respect the serious study of mathematics is hardly an exception.

When a learned man of antiquity was called before his king to explain mathematics to him, and the king, as soon as things became more difficult, asked whether there was not a simpler way of learning it, the scholar replied, "There is no royal road to mathematics." Whoever wants to climb the heights of this science simply has to work his way to the peak with his own power, gradually exercised and steeled. Not to mention those who are making their first ascent and wish to master a problem which is still unsolved and has resisted all previous efforts. One who has merely looked out from the compartment window of an alpine railway or of a comfortable alpine hotel, will not thereby become a proficient mountaineer. A mathematical work that attempted to glide over all the difficulties of the subject matter would be completely unfit for training a reader in mathematical thinking and giving insight into this special field.

But we would not be willing to dispense with mountain railways either—unless there were too many of them. We are not speaking here of those people who use them and take them for granted, scarcely reflecting that the entire business of constructing a railroad could be done only by engineers and workmen of high competence in the building of mountain railroads; of those who, from the hotel terrace, esteem the alpine scenery as no more than a somewhat altered background for the unaltered horizon of interests they have brought up with them from the lowlands and who are incapable of any inward elevation by the world of the mountains. For many, however, the heart does beat higher, and even though they themselves may not feel the strength to climb mountains, they nevertheless convey to others their love for the mountain world. And some little boy who, has been brought along by his parents, receives an ineradicable impression, and will perhaps some day become an inspired and eminent alpinist.

*This book seeks to resemble such a convenient alpine railway up into the world of mathematics.* It can give nothing to the man in whom no chord vibrates responsively to the peculiar harmonies of this realm of thought, who accepts with inward indifference the technological and scientific acquisitions which he uses every day of his life, and which were made possible only by the fruitful contributions of mathematics. But we venture to hope that there will also be readers who will not remain entirely untouched by the aura which breathes in this realm that affects most people as being so unapproachable. It is possible, if fate so wills it, that there may even be some young man with unspent energies and with the necessary ability, who will feel the urge to pursue the subject more seriously, spurred by the distant vision offered to him here. For I confess that what is offered here will not be able to satisfy him, nor should it. From the railway route along which we here guide the reader are excluded, because of their difficulty of access, many of the most important mountain heights and lines of advance.

If then our book takes up the task, first of all of giving to outsiders a more accurate and perhaps a more appealing image of the nature of mathematics than one commonly finds; and if the notes offered at the end, part of which are addressed to readers with more advanced knowledge, are intended to supply supplementary material and a bibliography for more detailed study of the subject; at the same time we have had, in publishing this material, an additional goal before us which is of utmost seriousness.

It has to do with the recruitment of successors in our field.

As late as the early 1930's our lecture halls were still overfilled, and even the best students found entry into the profession obstructed for years ahead by the many, all too many graduates of earlier classes. If institutions of higher learning almost took pride in outdoing their own and each other's records on numbers of students enrolled, that was an unhealthy phenomenon (and a difficult one to resist, for reasons which are not under discussion here), in which quality of teaching results gave way to quantity. Nevertheless, in a course with 200 students you might easily count on finding twenty competent students, some of them eminently talented. To be sure, the overflow was afterwards brought under control.

When the same course was offered again later, there were only twenty students instead of 200, and if the consequent selection had brought into the lecture hall the best students of their class-year, one might expect a considerable improvement in the quality of their work. This did *not* occur. And although the students actually worked harder than earlier classes had done, the average achievement sank instead of rising. First-rate talents which might some day show capacity for original research seemed to be extinct. Instead of being able to cover the material faster because of the elimination of the 180 average and weak students, the teacher had to slow down his tempo from year to year if he wished to maintain contact with his students at all. This could not help but give one pause.

This brings us back to the introductory question: how an extensive, far-reaching field of study is to be mastered. An essential requisite for successful study at the university level is the thorough, firmly fixed propaedeutics acquired in the secondary school—received and inwardly digested with a certain love by those who are talented in the field. Even more important is that the student should have already learned what study at an intellectual level really is. Whoever comes to the university without this must be a failure, like the aspirant Hieronymus Jobs in C. A. Kortum's satyrical epic, which inspired Wilhelm Busch to retell it in illustrated verses.

In a profession like ours the vocation must have been awakened by teachers who have themselves experienced it. Much of the aversion to mathematics comes from instruction given by a teacher who himself was not in complete command of his subject, and was not filled by that warmth for the inner beauty of his specialty which would enable him to communicate it to others. Everyone will concede that a fondness and natural gift for a specific field of knowledge are not always conjoined with pedagogical talent. At the same time, the competence first mentioned must be the driving force for the good teacher of the future in his choice of a profession.

There are of course cases where it cannot be predicted who will become a competent or preeminent research man, even after he has completed the usual university studies, let alone before then. A rapid and thorough advance in the acquisition of professional knowledge is of itself no guarantee of a productive vein. We have seen enough of premature over-estimation on the part of students of their own potential, and enough of falsely optimistic judgments of students by teachers. On the other hand we are also familiar with the tormenting doubts suffered in their student years as to the scope of their own abilities by men who later became distinguished men of research. Only the further development of the individual can be decisive, and it would be quite meaningless to decree in advance who should be trained as a teacher and who should become a research scholar. If we were asked for an opinion we could only recommend that the goal not be set too high, particularly since that permanent economic independence required for the life of the "private scholar" is granted only to the few. It has thus come about that by and large the men who later became our research scholars and our successors in university chairs, have come up mostly from among the men who had prepared themselves first of all to be secondary school teachers.

If one knows that research is necessary, one recognizes the seriousness of the question as to who is to come after us. Certainly the top talents are not rarer than they used to be. It is only necessary to make sure that they find their true assignment. An understanding of the nature of our profession disseminated among wider circles might lay the groundwork for this. This is the aim in publishing this book, which is based on a series of lectures delivered for students of all faculties at the University of Munich.

We are conscious that in doing so we have ventured upon no very easy task. It is like the mutual understanding—or lack of understanding—between age and youth. Many a great young poet or actor succeeds in portraying the feeling or thought of old age, but many older people no longer succeed in transplanting themselves back into that spirit of youth which they themselves have after all once experienced. Thus it happens that a talented disciple of mathematics is able to see beyond the knowledge which his teacher is imparting to him at the moment. But the teacher whose material has become ever more familiar to him in the course of the years—and often, too, the young instructor who has just completed his own advanced professional training—find it difficult to think themselves into the position of the beginner and to realize what could cause him difficulties. At the same time, individual students vary greatly as to what they find difficult, and only after much experience does a teacher become aware of how many misunderstandings can arise. In lectures given before an audience less familiar with the subject, the opportunity for such misunderstandings increases with every word which is current in the specialty but which is used in a different sense from the ordinary one; it increases also with every fact which has become self-apparent to the specialist and which indeed may also be known to the auditor, but which does not occur immediately to the latter.

To counteract this danger I prepared quite a large number of illustrations and tables. In geometric constructions in particular the sketches were designed to appear step by step in their intermediate stages, not merely in their final form, overburdened by all the lines which were added one after the other.[1]

The last chapter, Ch. XIV, on the curvature of space, lies somewhat outside the framework of the easily understood to which the other questions are confined. It is not so much special preliminary knowledge that is required, as an emancipation from firmly rooted ideas, from ideas, moreover, which an outsider to mathematics usually has not pursued critically enough. If I nevertheless decided to retain this chapter also, it was not from any dread of the number 13, which I have always found ridiculous, but because I simply did not want to evade a subject which was formerly passionately discussed, and about which a great deal has been written, some of it correct, some false, some tenable, some off the track.

Those who have heard me lecture are familiar with my custom of interpolating, on occasion, references to matters which are close to us in time or place, references which serve not only for the enlivenment or illustration of the specialized topics, but are also intended to throw light on general questions of education, the cultivation of science, and culture in general. The elaboration of these lectures in book form, a work which extended over the last war years to about a year after the end of the war, is likewise not free of such interpolations. The proverb, "Out of the abundance of the heart the mouth speaketh," did not of course always enjoy unrestricted validity, and at times intimations had to suffice—and did suffice.

Local coloring and the character of the time have in the meanwhile greatly changed, and from the first outlines for these lectures to the com-

[1] Many works on mathematical amusements and games have been written for a wider circle of readers, but by their nature these touch only exceptionally upon questions of significance for the main stream of science. (See Ch. IV, Note 10 and Ch. XIII, Note 10 for references.) As for the older writings on "mathematica delectans," they mostly contain only a collection of dressed-up exercises in equation-solving, on the following general pattern: The boy Henry comes from school and says to his father: "Father, you are now exactly six times as old as I am. When will you be 25 times as old?" Father: "That was when you were still small, but in $1\frac{3}{4}$ years I will be only five times as old as you." How old are the two? When was the father 25 times as old as his son?

pletion of the manuscript and proof-reading, a decade and a half of world-historic events and catastrophes have rolled by, accompanied by many professional and personal experiences and sufferings. Buildings then standing have collapsed or been cleared away. Young students of that time have become mature men—or never returned home. If allusions had been made here and there in the text to conditions which once were the order of the day, much of this now belongs to the past. In the discussion of the disputes over the priority of discovery of the solution of third-degree equations, a reference to the difference between objective and brachial methods of conflict had a certain timeliness in view of the battles-royal that were then frequently "organized" at political meetings. Or when, in composing the section on Gauss, the war-torn era was described in which the first years of Gauss' activity at Göttingen fell, we were again in the midst of an epoch in which the slogan of creating a "new Europe" by military means was being advanced.

If a work by Albert Einstein can now be quoted without further ado, at that time the book's chances of appearing were endangered by mere mention in it of the theory of relativity, which had the effect of a red flag on many in those days when, blinded by the universal propaganda, some scientists really believed that this theory was pure humbug and when, worse still, one of our greatest theoretical physicists was replaced by a man, foisted upon us from on high, who tossed Planck's quantum theory into the same kettle of damnation with the theory of relativity, so that our theoretical physicists had great difficulty in interceding on behalf of continued use of the theory of relativity in research and in teaching.

If, later on, in the summer of 1945 and the winter of 1945–46, work on this book would probably have come to a halt without medical intervention against symptoms of starvation, then a brief remark alludes to my urgent anticipation, now recurring each year, of the harvest. And if (my) faith that through wise institutions the good in man could be led to prevail, was exposed before and afterward to strong doubts, these too found their precipitate in a few scattered remarks on this problem of squaring the human circle.

The conditions reflected in these interpolations were widely separated from each other in time, and may therefore seem to some readers rather dusty, like yellowed old photographs of strangers who no longer interest the living and could be sorted out of the album. The question was whether a revision of the entire work should be undertaken to remove all non-essentials and restrict the content to factual and professional matters. Some who are personally close to the author have recommended retention of the changing snapshots. It will be found understandable that I have followed these recommendations.

The lectures regularly contain a few biographical data on individual mathematicians who have a special relationship with the problem under discussion, or who discovered its solution. I am indebted to colleagues abroad for a quantity of information. More recent historical studies may have made some biographical details out of date. It could not be my task to pursue all that in detail since my project was only the more modest one of giving to the reader an approximate picture of the research scholars and of their times.

Gratitude is due for the sustained help granted by the Bavarian Academy of Sciences for the preliminary work on the first edition of this book.

It is not possible for me to cite in detail the many kinds of help accorded me in all these years, from near and far, in the form of advice and information, of calculations, of procurement of bibliographical information or of permission to reproduce portraits.

Besides my friend of many years G. Faber, and my colleagues R. Baldus,[2] J. Lense, F. Löbell, J. Heinhold of the Technische Hochschule München, and many not mentioned by name, I should like in particular to express my warmest thanks to Messrs. R. G. Baring, Stephanos Carathéodory, R. Gistl, H. Jantzen, A. Rehm,[2] H. Rüchardt, E. Schoenberg, A. Sommerfeld,[2] G. Stöhr, L. Weigand, J. Zenneck[2] in München; Baron W. v. Freygang formerly in München; A. S. Besicovitch in Cambridge (England); I. A. Barnett in Cincinnati, Ohio; P. J. Heawood[2] in Durham (England); O. Haupt in Erlangen; W. Süss[2] in Freiburg (Breisgau); W. Magnus in Göttingen; Conrad H. Müller[2] in Hannover; E. Dintzl in Kritzendorf (near Vienna); H. Garnir in Liège; H. C. Hammer and E. Hopf in New York, N. Y.; M. Fréchet in Paris; H. Weyl[2] in Princeton, N. J.; O. Neugebauer in Providence, R. I.; K. Herzfeld in Washington, D. C.; K. Mayrhofer in Vienna; K. Clusius, R. Fueter[2] and R. Nevanlinna in Zürich; and not least, to Professor Dr. Kurt Lydtin, my personal physician in a critical time of my life.

The sketches for some of the figures are the work of the painter C. Sturtzkopf, whom I met by chance in 1945, and my hearty thanks go out to him for being so kind as to provide the book with this artistic adornment.

It was of especially valuable assistance to me that a few colleagues and friends of the most varied professional interests have read the proofs, and I should like to express my warmest thanks to my colleague Professor Robert Schmidt, to the business man Mr. Ernst-Johann Horn, to our colleague in History of Law of Antiquity, Professor Mariano San Nicolo,[2] and to Mr. Horst Sund, for the great pains they have all put themselves to, and for their exceedingly valuable advice.

If, however, I dedicate the book to my highly respected colleagues Constantin Carathéodory[2] and Oskar Perron, it is not only in gratitude for the interest which they showed in the preparation of this book, for their reading of individual parts of the manuscript and of proofs, and for numerous items of information and suggestions, whether of a historical, a factual or of a literary nature. Without the atmosphere of their friendship, which I enjoyed for many years and which sustained our common endeavors at the University of München over more than two decades, in good days and bad, this book would probably never have come into being.

For a number of corrections and additions to the first edition in 1949 I owe the deepest debt of gratitude to the Messrs. G. Aumann in München; to Professor Broadbent at the Royal Naval College, Greenwich; to Wilhelm Hardt in Plattenberg; Professor Dr. J. E. Hofmann in Ichenhausen; H. Kneser in Tübingen; B. L. v. d. Waerden in Zürich; Alexander Wilkens in München; and Miss Monika Aumann in München.

HEINRICH TIETZE

Munich, Summer 1959

[2] Deceased.

# INTRODUCTION

The arithmetic and the algebra that we learn in school have been known for centuries,[1] and the geometry taught in the schools is for the most part some thousands of years old. This explains not only why there is scarcely any further change in the content of instruction, but also why the manner of presentation has assumed an established, almost rigid form which conceals the fact that this knowledge had once to be attained by laborious struggle. And this also explains why an outsider to mathematics, in view of the ancient and firm stock of knowledge transmitted to him in school, usually finds it hard to conceive that in mathematics also there are a host of *problems*. But we can only conceive of a science as living if, besides solved problems, it has also unsolved ones, and if the answers to earlier questions lead to new questions and stimulate new research. I should like to make you more aware that mathematics too is such a living science, by telling you something about various solved and unsolved problems.

It is true that only a *narrow selection* is possible here. For many a mathematical problem is of such a nature that it is not possible to discuss it without a preparation, not of a few hours, but of several years. Problems of such depth must naturally be excluded from discussion in these lectures, however important they may be for science and its applications. We will leave out altogether long trains of thought that would extend over many lectures.[2] It will therefore also be necessary, in most cases, to forego proofs of the solutions of the solved problems. Many of these proofs would go far beyond the framework of these lectures and could only be understood on the basis of an exhaustive mathematical training.

Some supplementary material which at times presupposes rather more extensive preliminary knowledge, as well as references to the literature will be found in the notes collected at the end of each chapter. These notes are numbered consecutively for each chapter. *But the reader who wishes to become acquainted with the subject for the first time is advised above all not to hold himself up with referring to these notes.*

According to what has been said above, we will in the main confine ourselves to defining the individual problem according to its essential nature, and to emphasizing, even when dealing with solutions that have long been known, why at one time an unsolved problem existed here before a scholar succeeded in finding a solution. In each chapter we will treat a simple field of inquiry, detached and independent, as far as possible, from the preceding chapters. Problems from the theory of numbers will alternate with problems from geometry.

[1] The same is true of the elements of differential and integral calculus taught in the (German) secondary schools.

[2] At the university level they of course cannot be avoided in more difficult topics and are at the same time indispensable in the training of the future specialist.

## EDITORS' NOTE

The Notes (see the Introduction) follow immediately after each chapter. References to the Notes in the text have been numbered in bold face consecutively in each chapter. The numbers are enclosed in square brackets.

References to the literature, which occur for the most part in the Notes, have also been consecutively numbered in each chapter. These numbers, enclosed in braces, refer to the correspondingly numbered bibliographical notes or items collected by chapters at the end of the book (see References in the Contents).

The references cited in the original text have been reproduced in full (accompanied by references to English translations whenever these exist). However, in many cases, these may not always be available to the general reader. For this reason, a list of books on a variety of topics has been added (see Supplementary References in the Contents). The supplementary list appears after the References and is classified by topic. In addition, a list of papers from the American Mathematical Monthly follows the Supplementary References. Most of the papers are expository and can be used as guides for further reading.

We would like to thank Harvey Swados and Hyman Kamel for reading the first draft of the translation. We are indebted to Douglas M. Scott for the translation of the Preface and Introduction. Thanks are also due to Hyman Kamel for suggesting a number of items included in the supplementary reference list.

*Chapter I*

# PRIME NUMBERS AND PRIME TWINS

The theory of numbers contains two problems which are very simple to state, because their formulation involves only a familiarity with the natural numbers (the positive integers or positive whole numbers). The first of these problems was solved more than 2000 years ago, in classical antiquity, and its solution remains to this day an esthetic model of mathematical proof. The second, a very difficult problem which is still unsolved, is a research problem of present day number theory.

Before stating the first problem, we will write down the beginning of the sequence of natural numbers:

| 1 | 11 | 21 | 31 | 41 | 51 | 61 | 71 | 81 | 91 | 101 | 111 | 121 | 131 | ... |
|---|---|---|---|---|---|---|---|---|---|---|---|---|---|---|
| 2 | 12 | 22 | 32 | 42 | 52 | 62 | 72 | 82 | 92 | 102 | 112 | 122 | 132 | ... |
| 3 | 13 | 23 | 33 | 43 | 53 | 63 | 73 | 83 | 93 | 103 | 113 | 123 | 133 | ... |
| 4 | 14 | 24 | 34 | 44 | 54 | 64 | 74 | 84 | 94 | 104 | 114 | 124 | 134 | ... |
| 5 | 15 | 25 | 35 | 45 | 55 | 65 | 75 | 85 | 95 | 105 | 115 | 125 | 135 | ... |
| 6 | 16 | 26 | 36 | 46 | 56 | 66 | 76 | 86 | 96 | 106 | 116 | 126 | 136 | ... |
| 7 | 17 | 27 | 37 | 47 | 57 | 67 | 77 | 87 | 97 | 107 | 117 | 127 | 137 | ... |
| 8 | 18 | 28 | 38 | 48 | 58 | 68 | 78 | 88 | 98 | 108 | 118 | 128 | 138 | ... |
| 9 | 19 | 29 | 39 | 49 | 59 | 69 | 79 | 89 | 99 | 109 | 119 | 129 | 139 | ... |
| 10 | 20 | 30 | 40 | 50 | 60 | 70 | 80 | 90 | 100 | 110 | 120 | 130 | 140 | ... |

The first column contains the numbers from 1 to 10, the next column, the numbers from 11 to 20, etc. They are written in columns for the sake of convenience.

This table can be used to indicate which are prime numbers, by printing them in bold face type, thus:

| 1 | **11** | 21 | **31** | **41** | 51 | **61** | **71** | 81 | 91 | **101** | 111 | 121 | **131** | ... |
|---|---|---|---|---|---|---|---|---|---|---|---|---|---|---|
| **2** | 12 | 22 | 32 | 42 | 52 | 62 | 72 | 82 | 92 | 102 | 112 | 122 | 132 | ... |
| **3** | **13** | **23** | 33 | **43** | **53** | 63 | **73** | **83** | 93 | **103** | **113** | 123 | 133 | ... |
| 4 | 14 | 24 | 34 | 44 | 54 | 64 | 74 | 84 | 94 | 104 | 114 | 124 | 134 | ... |
| **5** | 15 | 25 | 35 | 45 | 55 | 65 | 75 | 85 | 95 | 105 | 115 | 125 | 135 | ... |
| 6 | 16 | 26 | 36 | 46 | 56 | 66 | 76 | 86 | 96 | 106 | 116 | 126 | 136 | ... |
| **7** | **17** | 27 | **37** | **47** | 57 | **67** | 77 | 87 | **97** | **107** | 117 | **127** | **137** | ... |
| 8 | 18 | 28 | 38 | 48 | 58 | 68 | 78 | 88 | 98 | 108 | 118 | 128 | 138 | ... |
| 9 | **19** | **29** | 39 | 49 | **59** | 69 | **79** | **89** | 99 | **109** | 119 | 129 | **139** | ... |
| 10 | 20 | 30 | 40 | 50 | 60 | 70 | 80 | 90 | 100 | 110 | 120 | 130 | 140 | ... |

We will discuss what happens beyond 140 later in the chapter. First, what is meant by a prime number? To answer this question, we consider the natural numbers from the point of view of multiplication. Given any positive whole number, e.g. 45, it is possible to ask whether it can be expressed as *the product of two smaller positive whole numbers*. The number 45 can in fact be so expressed, indeed in more than one way:

$$45 = 3\cdot 15, \qquad 45 = 5\cdot 9.$$

If, as in the case of 45, a number can be decomposed, in at least one way, into two smaller factors, it is said to be *factorable*, or *composite*. There is of course no difficulty in finding examples of composite numbers:

$$\begin{array}{rclrclrcl} 82 &=& 2\cdot 41, & 91 &=& 7\cdot 13, & 111 &=& 3\cdot 37, \\ 117 &=& 9\cdot 13, & 6 &=& 2\cdot 3, & 4 &=& 2\cdot 2. \end{array}$$

(It does not matter that the decomposition of 4 consists of two equal factors: what is essential is that both factors are smaller than 4.)

Not all numbers, however, can be so decomposed. The number 7, for example, is not a product of two smaller factors. It can be written as the product of two numbers:

$$7 = 1\cdot 7 = 7\cdot 1,$$

but of the two factors, only one is smaller than 7. The other is equal to 7. Thus 7, and other numbers, such as 2, 3, 5, and 11, are unfactorable numbers.

The number 1 is also unfactorable. It can be written as the product of two positive whole numbers in only one way: $1 = 1\cdot 1$. Hence it has no factor smaller than 1, while to satisfy the definition, both factors must be smaller than the number factored.

What, then, is a prime number? *Every unfactorable number, with the sole exception of* 1, *is called a prime number.* Why is the number 1 made an exception? This is a problem that schoolboys often argue about, but since it is a question of definition, it is not arguable. However, it is instructive to try to understand why it has been left out.

The problem centers on the formation of numbers by multiplication. When we factor a number, for example $45 = 3\cdot 15$, into two smaller factors, we must then ask whether either of these factors can again be factored. In the example, 3 is not factorable further, but $15 = 3\cdot 5$ is, so that we obtain

$$45 = 3\cdot 15 = 3\cdot 3\cdot 5.$$

None of the factors 3, 3, 5 is factorable further. With these factors we have reached the end of the process of decomposition. These are the simplest building blocks in the multiplicative formation of the number 45.

Of course, 5 could be replaced by $5 \cdot 1$ or $5 \cdot 1 \cdot 1$; 45 could then be written $45 = 3 \cdot 3 \cdot 5 \cdot 1 = 3 \cdot 3 \cdot 5 \cdot 1 \cdot 1$, and so on. But replacing 5 by $5 \cdot 1$, or $5 \cdot 1 \cdot 1$, does not yield a decomposition into smaller factors; what we are trying to attain by means of successive factorization are the final elements, the atoms, so to speak, in the structuring of the whole numbers by multiplication. The number 1 is not essential to this process, and therefore is not included in the list of primes. To restate the definition of prime number: *Every unfactorable number greater than* 1 *is a prime number* [1].

The importance of the primes is now clear. For, the above discussion indicates that, like 45, *every composite number can be written as a product of primes.* It is simply necessary to factor far enough; for instance, $27 = 3 \cdot 9 = 3 \cdot 3 \cdot 3$. As a consequence, *every composite number is divisible by at least one prime.*

To return to the table of numbers in which the primes are printed in bold face, it can be seen that the primes occur much more frequently at the beginning of the table than further on. Between 1 and 30 we count 10 primes; between 30 and 60, however, only 7; between 60 and 90, again 7; and between 90 and 120 only 6. How are primes distributed in higher ranges? Let us look at Table 7 (at the end of the chapter), where the range of numbers has been extended to 1500, the primes again printed in bold face. (The bracketing of certain primes in pairs is not important at this point.) The number of primes in each interval of 50 numbers is given below in Table 1. Now what can we learn from these prime number statistics?

Certainly as we ascend to higher ranges of numbers, the primes grow fewer. But the decline in the frequency of the primes is by no means regular. While the number of primes between 101 and 150 is 10, between 151 and 200 there are 11. Similar irregularities occur as we go on.

Observing the intervals between consecutive primes, we find that these parallel the distribution of primes. The difference between 3 and 2 is 1; the difference between 5 and 3, as well as between 7 and 5, is 2; then between 7 and 11 there is a larger interval, 4; the interval between 13 and 17 and that between 19 and 23 is also 4. The difference between 29 and 23, larger again, is 6. If we go higher in the table still larger intervals appear, as for example the intervals between 89 and 97 and 113 and 127. But note that the intervals between consecutive primes do not always increase. While the interval from 113 to 127 is 14, the interval between 127 and 131 is only 4; the interval between 131 and 137 is 6; but the interval between 137 and 139 is only 2. Thus there is no steady, uniform growth in the size of the intervals between consecutive primes. On the contrary, the distribution of primes is extremely irregular. It is true that other statistics are also irregular. We are not surprised that the decrease in the incidence of a certain illness, for instance, varies from year to year even while it continues to

TABLE 1

Number of Primes in the Given Intervals

| Interval | Number of primes | Interval | Number of primes |
|---|---|---|---|
| 1–50 | 15 | 751–800 | 7 |
| 51–100 | 10 | 801–850 | 7 |
| 101–150 | 10 | 851–900 | 8 |
| 151–200 | 11 | 901–950 | 7 |
| 201–250 | 7 | 951–1000 | 7 |
| 251–300 | 9 | 1001–1050 | 8 |
| 301–350 | 8 | 1051–1100 | 8 |
| 351–400 | 8 | 1101–1150 | 5 |
| 401–450 | 9 | 1151–1200 | 7 |
| 451–500 | 8 | 1201–1250 | 8 |
| 501–550 | 6 | 1251–1300 | 7 |
| 551–600 | 8 | 1301–1350 | 6 |
| 601–650 | 9 | 1351–1400 | 5 |
| 651–700 | 7 | 1401–1450 | 7 |
| 701–750 | 7 | 1451–1500 | 10 |

decrease. Improvements in treatment, the complicated relationship between the illness and its many causes, and so on, make for an unpredictable statistical picture. But it is remarkable to find so uneven a distribution in so simple a case as the primes.

In addition to this marked irregularity in the distribution of primes, we have noted a decrease in their frequency. Let us investigate further. If we were to extend our observations beyond 1500, would both assertions remain true? The question can be answered by sampling further tables, such as 1501 to 3000, 3001 to 4500, etc. First, however, are the intervals of 50 numbers too small; in larger intervals, might the variations in the frequency of the primes disappear? To check this, we can take a few intervals of 100 numbers from the range we have already considered. In the interval between 1 and 100 we count 25 primes, a prime for every four numbers in this range. In the interval from 101 to 200 there are 21 primes, from 201 to 300 there are 16; and as many between 301 and 400. In the interval between 901 and 1000 there are only 14. Apparently, the decrease is slow. Moreover, it is not without fluctuation: between 501 and 600 there are 14 primes; but between 601 and 700, 16. These fluctuations become even more noticeable if we displace the intervals: in the range 471 to 570 (again an interval of 100 numbers) there are only 13 primes, but between 581 and 680 there are 17.

What happens as we go on into the higher ranges? To answer this ques-

TABLE 2
Primes in the Interval 9991 to 10090

| 9991 | 10001 | 10011 | 10021 | 10031 | 10041 | 10051 | **10061** | 10071 | 10081 |
|---|---|---|---|---|---|---|---|---|---|
| 9992 | 10002 | 10012 | 10022 | 10032 | 10042 | 10052 | 10062 | 10072 | 10082 |
| 9993 | 10003 | 10013 | 10023 | 10033 | 10043 | 10053 | 10063 | 10073 | 10083 |
| 9994 | 10004 | 10014 | 10024 | 10034 | 10044 | 10054 | 10064 | 10074 | 10084 |
| 9995 | 10005 | 10015 | 10025 | 10035 | 10045 | 10055 | 10065 | 10075 | 10085 |
| 9996 | 10006 | 10016 | 10026 | 10036 | 10046 | 10056 | 10066 | 10076 | 10086 |
| 9997 | **10007** | 10017 | 10027 | **10037** | 10047 | 10057 | **10067** | 10077 | 10087 |
| 9998 | 10008 | 10018 | 10028 | 10038 | 10048 | 10058 | 10068 | 10078 | 10088 |
| 9999 | **10009** | 10019 | 10029 | **10039** | 10049 | 10059 | **10069** | **10079** | 10089 |
| 10000 | 10010 | 10020 | 10030 | 10040 | 10050 | 10060 | 10070 | 10080 | 10090 |

TABLE 3
Primes in the Interval 67471 to 67570

| 67471 | **67481** | 67491 | 67501 | **67511** | 67521 | **67531** | 67541 | 67551 | 67561 |
|---|---|---|---|---|---|---|---|---|---|
| 67472 | 67482 | 67492 | 67502 | 67512 | 67522 | 67532 | 67542 | 67552 | 67562 |
| 67473 | 67483 | **67493** | 67503 | 67513 | **67523** | 67533 | 67543 | 67553 | 67563 |
| 67474 | 67484 | 67494 | 67504 | 67514 | 67524 | 67534 | 67544 | 67554 | 67564 |
| 67475 | 67485 | 67495 | 67505 | 67515 | 67525 | 67535 | 67545 | 67555 | 67565 |
| 67476 | 67486 | 67496 | 67506 | 67516 | 67526 | 67536 | 67546 | 67556 | 67566 |
| **67477** | 67487 | 67497 | 67507 | 67517 | 67527 | **67537** | **67547** | 67557 | **67567** |
| 67478 | 67488 | 67498 | 67508 | 67518 | 67528 | 67538 | 67548 | 67558 | 67568 |
| 67479 | **67489** | **67499** | 67509 | 67519 | 67529 | 67539 | 67549 | **67559** | 67569 |
| 67480 | 67490 | 67500 | 67510 | 67520 | 67530 | 67540 | 67550 | 67560 | 67570 |

tion, let us look at Tables 2, 3 and 4 [**2**]. Here again the primes are printed in bold face.

Each of these tables comprises an interval of 100 numbers, in which the number of primes is, in order, 8, 12, 5. There are fewer primes here than in the range 901 to 1000, which had 14. The rate of decrease continues to be irregular.

To continue, let us look at Tables 8, 9 and 10 (at the end of the chapter), which show three intervals of 100 numbers each in the range 200000 to 300000.

In the first interval (Table 8) there are 12 primes; in the next (Table 9) only 1; and in the last (Table 10), 9.

Table 5 gives an over-all picture for several such samples. The intervals, each of 100 numbers, are listed in the first column and the number of primes in each interval is given in the second column (the third column of prime twins will be discussed later). Here again we have the same picture: *A quite irregular decrease in the frequency of the primes as the range increases.*

TABLE 4

Primes in the Interval 112801 to 112900

| | | | | | | | | | |
|---|---|---|---|---|---|---|---|---|---|
| 112801 | 112811 | 112821 | **112831** | 112841 | 112851 | 112861 | 112871 | 112881 | 112891 |
| 112802 | 112812 | 112822 | 112832 | 112842 | 112852 | 112862 | 112872 | 112882 | 112892 |
| 112803 | 112813 | 112823 | 112833 | **112843** | 112853 | 112863 | 112873 | 112883 | 112893 |
| 112804 | 112814 | 112824 | 112834 | 112844 | 112854 | 112864 | 112874 | 112884 | 112894 |
| 112805 | 112815 | 112825 | 112835 | 112845 | 112855 | 112865 | 112875 | 112885 | 112895 |
| 112806 | 112816 | 112826 | 112836 | 112846 | 112856 | 112866 | 112876 | 112886 | 112896 |
| **112807** | 112817 | 112827 | 112837 | 112847 | 112857 | 112867 | **112877** | 112887 | 112897 |
| 112808 | 112818 | 112828 | 112838 | 112848 | 112858 | 112868 | 112878 | 112888 | 112898 |
| 112809 | 112819 | 112829 | 112839 | 112849 | **112859** | 112869 | 112879 | 112889 | 112899 |
| 112810 | 112820 | 112830 | 112840 | 112850 | 112860 | 112870 | 112880 | 112890 | 112900 |

TABLE 5

Number of Primes and Prime Twin Pairs

| Interval | Number of primes | Number of prime twin pairs | Interval | Number of primes | Number of prime twin pairs |
|---|---|---|---|---|---|
| 1–100 | 25 | 8 | 29501–29600 | 10 | 1 |
| 101–200 | 21 | 7 | 29601–29700 | 8 | 1 |
| 201–300 | 16 | 4 | 29701–29800 | 7 | 1 |
| 301–400 | 16 | 2 | 29801–29900 | 10 | 1 |
| 401–500 | 17 | 3 | 29901–30000 | 7 | 0 |
| 501–600 | 14 | 2 | 100001–100100 | 6 | 0 |
| 601–700 | 16 | 4 | 100101–100200 | 9 | 1 |
| 701–800 | 14 | 0 | 100201–100300 | 8 | 0 |
| 801–900 | 15 | 5 | 100301–100400 | 9 | 2 |
| 901–1000 | 14 | 0 | 100401–100500 | 8 | 0 |
| 2501–2600 | 11 | 2 | 299501–299600 | 7 | 1 |
| 2601–2700 | 15 | 2 | 299601–299700 | 8 | 1 |
| 2701–2800 | 14 | 3 | 299701–299800 | 8 | 1 |
| 2801–2900 | 12 | 1 | 299801–299900 | 6 | 0 |
| 2901–3000 | 11 | 1 | 299901–300000 | 9 | 0 |
| 10001–10100 | 11 | 4 | | | |
| 10101–10200 | 12 | 1 | | | |
| 10201–10300 | 10 | 1 | | | |
| 10301–10400 | 12 | 2 | | | |
| 10401–10500 | 10 | 2 | | | |

This apparent decrease in the incidence of the primes leads to a mathematical problem, which was both stated and solved in antiquity.

If the incidence of the primes decreases, there are two possibilities: one, that there is a last and largest prime, after which, of necessity, all the succeeding numbers are composite; two, that despite the apparent decrease in the frequency of the primes and the increase in the size of the intervals between consecutive primes, there is no last prime. The first possibility is equivalent to the assertion that the number of primes is finite; the second, to the assertion that, since every prime is followed by another, there are an infinite number of primes. The problem is, therefore: *Are there a finite or an infinite number of primes?*

As we consider how we are to go about answering this question, we must first understand that tables of primes, no matter how extensive, are of no use to us. We shall not waste time discussing how laborious it can be to decide whether an extremely large number is composite or whether it is a prime. Let us imagine that a computer has succeeded in finding a prime larger than 100 million [**3**]; then, another computer establishes with infinite pains that still another number, greater than a trillion, is a prime [**4**]; and then let us imagine that someone gets the rare notion of setting up a computing laboratory to search for primes with 39 digits, for example. Would this help us answer our question? The answer, of course, is no. Even if all these calculations uncovered primes with 39 digits [**5**], one would still have to go on to primes with 45 digits, 51 digits, etc. Similarly, it is clear that if the computers were to find no primes in a range of very large numbers, nothing would be proved, for there might still be primes in the range just beyond. Further calculations and larger compilations of prime number tables will not solve the problem. No matter how far these calculations are carried, they are always done in a limited range and can never encompass all numbers. Is it then hopeless to seek an answer to our question? Not at all, but the answer cannot be sought in further calculations. A new idea is needed to solve the problem, and such an idea was found by Euclid (about 300 B.C.).

Before discussing Euclid's argument, let us consider an example that will help us to understand it. Let us take a number divisible by 3, say 33, and add 1 to it. The resulting number, $33 + 1 = 34$, is then *not* divisible by 3, since the remainder after division is 1. Moreover, 33 is also divisible by 11, and it is clear that $33 + 1 = 34$ is not divisible by 11, since the remainder is again 1. As another example, consider the number $42 = 2 \cdot 3 \cdot 7$, which is divisible by 2, 3, and 7. Then $42 + 1 = 43$ is certainly not divisible by 2, 3, or 7; for the remainder in each case is 1. These examples and the argument by remainders lead to the following conclusion: If 1 is added to the product of any number of primes, the resulting number is not divisible by any of the original primes. The number is then either itself a prime (like 43 in the above example), or it is the product of primes other than those multiplied together in the beginning; for example, the prime factors of $34 = 2 \cdot 17$ are different from those of $33 = 3 \cdot 11$.

Euclid's proof is by contradiction. Suppose that the number of primes is finite. Then there must be a largest prime $P$ (whose magnitude is, of course, irrelevant). All the primes can then be written in a finite sequence

$$2, 3, 5, \cdots, P.$$

Since $P$ is the largest prime, *all numbers greater than P must be composite*, that is, every number greater than $P$ must be divisible by at least one of the primes in the above sequence (because every composite number is divisible by at least one prime). But now consider the number

$$N = (2 \cdot 3 \cdot 5 \cdot 7 \cdot \ \cdots \ \cdot P) + 1,$$

that is, the number obtained by adding 1 to the product of all the primes. Since $N$ is greater than $P$, it must be a composite number, and therefore divisible by at least one of the primes in the above sequence. But by which? Since $2 \cdot 3 \cdot 5 \cdot \ \cdots \ \cdot P$ is obviously divisible by all the primes $2, 3, 5, \cdots, P$, it is immediately clear, as indicated above, that $N$ is not divisible by any of the primes $2, 3, \cdots, P$. Hence $N$ cannot have any prime factors, which contradicts the fact that $N$ is composite. Therefore, the assumption that the number of primes is finite leads to a contradiction, and we must conclude that there are an infinite number of primes.

There are other proofs of Euclid's theorem [**6**]. At any rate, we now know that, in spite of the fact that the tables show a decrease in the incidence of the primes [**7**], there are an infinite number of primes.

It may be of interest to add a few words about Euclid, a significant portion of whose works has been preserved for twenty-two centuries. Very little is known about his life. Neither the year, nor the place of his birth, nor the circumstances of his death have been established [**8**]. We do know that he lived and worked for most of his life in Alexandria. This city, founded by Alexander the Great, flourished during the fourth century B.C. as the capital of the Nile. In this period it was a center of scientific life. Not much more is known of the life of Euclid, but he is always pictured as a pleasant personality. There is not even a bust of him to give us an idea of his appearance. But his principal work, the *Elements*, which appeared in installments extending over a number of years, and which is based on the works of earlier Greek mathematicians, is a monument of the most profound scientific achievements of the Greek intellect. Eleven centuries after Euclid, in the eighth century, when Arabic scholars began to rework the spiritual treasures of antiquity, the *Elements* was zealously studied. An Arabic edition of Euclid's text appeared at the end of the eighth century. The first printed edition came in 1482.

In the *Elements*, Euclid discussed the theory of numbers as well as geometry, and organized the known results of these fields, results which had long been known but not always rigorously proved, on a systematic axiomatic basis. Whatever earlier works may have been written are lost, so that we have no way of knowing which proofs Euclid simply recorded, and which were discovered by him [9]. It was already known in Plato's time (429–348 B.C.) that there are an infinite number of primes, and the proof found in Euclid may not be his discovery. Nevertheless, our debt to him is beyond dispute [10].

We shall now discuss briefly the second problem mentioned at the beginning of the chapter, a problem which is still unsolved. We noted two characteristics of the distribution of primes indicated by the tables: There was an apparent decrease in the incidence of the primes, and this decrease showed a marked irregularity. The decrease in the frequency of the primes led us to ask whether the number of primes is finite. Euclid proved that this is not so. As to the irregularity in distribution, no matter how large the numbers we considered, we could not be sure of a regular increase in the size of the intervals between consecutive primes. On the contrary, some large intervals were followed by smaller ones, such as the interval between 113 and 127 followed by the interval from 127 to 131. In fact, we note from the tables that despite the decrease in the frequency of the primes, pairs of primes separated by very small intervals do keep recurring. We note especially that there are consecutive primes whose difference is 2, e.g., 3 and 5, 5 and 7, 11 and 13, $\cdots$, 101 and 103, $\cdots$, 881 and 883, etc., even

TABLE 6

Number of Primes and Prime Twin Pairs

| Interval | Number of primes | Number of prime twin pairs | Interval | Number of primes | Number of prime twin pairs |
|---|---|---|---|---|---|
| 1–50 | 15 | 6 | 751–800 | 7 | 0 |
| 51–100 | 10 | 2 | 801–850 | 7 | 3 |
| 101–150 | 10 | 3 | 851–900 | 8 | 2 |
| 151–200 | 11 | 4 | 901–950 | 7 | 0 |
| 201–250 | 7 | 2 | 951–1000 | 7 | 0 |
| 251–300 | 9 | 2 | 1001–1050 | 8 | 2 |
| 301–350 | 8 | 2 | 1051–1100 | 8 | 3 |
| 351–400 | 8 | 0 | 1101–1150 | 5 | 0 |
| 401–450 | 9 | 2 | 1151–1200 | 7 | 1 |
| 451–500 | 8 | 1 | 1201–1250 | 8 | 1 |
| 501–550 | 6 | 1 | 1251–1300 | 7 | 2 |
| 551–600 | 8 | 1 | 1301–1350 | 6 | 2 |
| 601–650 | 9 | 3 | 1351–1400 | 5 | 0 |
| 651–700 | 7 | 1 | 1401–1450 | 7 | 1 |
| 701–750 | 7 | 0 | 1451–1500 | 10 | 3 |

in the very high ranges. Now, except for the case of 2 and 3, the smallest possible difference between two primes is 2. This is obvious because no even number greater than 2 is a prime (since it is divisible by 2). Therefore, all primes greater than 2 must be odd, and the difference between two odd numbers is always at least 2. A pair of primes whose difference is 2 is called a *prime twin pair* [**11**]. In Table 7, such twins are connected by brackets. Because the numbers in the table are not written in a single column, the bracket between prime twins such as 29 and 31 is broken: one number is given the long, and the other the short end of the bracket.

To obtain a picture of the distribution of prime twins, we count the number of twin pairs in each interval of 50 numbers, starting with the interval 1 to 50 (according to Table 7, there are 6 twin pairs in this interval). Table 6 gives the result of this count. Since some twin pairs, such as 149 and 151, extend from one interval into the next, we have added, in all such cases, the pair to the interval containing the larger twin [**12**], i.e., to the interval 151 to 200 in the above case (similarly, the pair 599 and 601 is added to the interval 601 to 650, the pair 1049 and 1051 to the interval 1051 to 1100).

Neglecting noticeable irregularities, there is a decrease in the frequency of prime twins: there are 30 twin pairs from 1 to 750 and only 20 from 751 to 1500. Let us examine intervals of 100 numbers in the higher ranges. In Table 2 we find 3 twin pairs between 9991 and 10090: 10007 and 10009, 10037 and 10039, 10067 and 10069. There are no twins in Tables 3 and 4. Tables 8, 9 and 10 furnish samples in still higher ranges. Twin pairs occur again in the range 209201 to 209300, but not in the intervals covered by Tables 9 and 10. Thus, there are prime twins even in the very high ranges; but their number does decrease. This is to be expected, since the number of all primes decreases. We also conclude from the last column of Table 5 that the decrease in the incidence of prime twins is just as irregular as that of the primes [**13**].

We now pose the same problem for the prime twins as we did for the primes: Is there a last pair of prime twins, that is, is there a finite number of prime twin pairs? Or, is every prime twin pair followed (after an interval) by another pair, that is, are there an infinite number of prime twin pairs? Again, this question cannot be decided by consulting further tables, for the same reason as before. A solution of the problem again requires a new idea. No one has as yet been able to solve this problem. Very likely, it cannot be done with such simple means as Euclid used to prove the infinitude of the primes [**14**].

TABLE 7

Primes and Prime Twins in the Interval 1 to 1500

| 1 | **11** | 21 | **31** | **41** | 51 | **61** | **71** | 81 | 91 |
|---|---|---|---|---|---|---|---|---|---|
| **2** | 12 | 22 | 32 | 42 | 52 | 62 | 72 | 82 | 92 |
| **3** | **13** | **23** | 33 | **43** | **53** | 63 | **73** | **83** | 93 |
| 4 | 14 | 24 | 34 | 44 | 54 | 64 | 74 | 84 | 94 |
| **5** | 15 | 25 | 35 | 45 | 55 | 65 | 75 | 85 | 95 |
| 6 | 16 | 26 | 36 | 46 | 56 | 66 | 76 | 86 | 96 |
| **7** | **17** | 27 | **37** | **47** | 57 | **67** | 77 | 87 | **97** |
| 8 | 18 | 28 | 38 | 48 | 58 | 68 | 78 | 88 | 98 |
| 9 | **19** | **29** | 39 | 49 | **59** | 69 | **79** | **89** | 99 |
| 10 | 20 | 30 | 40 | 50 | 60 | 70 | 80 | 90 | 100 |

| **101** | 111 | 121 | **131** | 141 | **151** | 161 | 171 | **181** | **191** |
|---|---|---|---|---|---|---|---|---|---|
| 102 | 112 | 122 | 132 | 142 | 152 | 162 | 172 | 182 | 192 |
| **103** | **113** | 123 | 133 | 143 | 153 | **163** | **173** | 183 | **193** |
| 104 | 114 | 124 | 134 | 144 | 154 | 164 | 174 | 184 | 194 |
| 105 | 115 | 125 | 135 | 145 | 155 | 165 | 175 | 185 | 195 |
| 106 | 116 | 126 | 136 | 146 | 156 | 166 | 176 | 186 | 196 |
| **107** | 117 | **127** | **137** | 147 | **157** | **167** | 177 | 187 | **197** |
| 108 | 118 | 128 | 138 | 148 | 158 | 168 | 178 | 188 | 198 |
| **109** | 119 | 129 | **139** | **149** | 159 | 169 | **179** | 189 | **199** |
| 110 | 120 | 130 | 140 | 150 | 160 | 170 | 180 | 190 | 200 |

| 201 | **211** | 221 | 231 | **241** | **251** | 261 | **271** | **281** | 291 |
|---|---|---|---|---|---|---|---|---|---|
| 202 | 212 | 222 | 232 | 242 | 252 | 262 | 272 | 282 | 292 |
| 203 | 213 | **223** | **233** | 243 | 253 | **263** | 273 | **283** | **293** |
| 204 | 214 | 224 | 234 | 244 | 254 | 264 | 274 | 284 | 294 |
| 205 | 215 | 225 | 235 | 245 | 255 | 265 | 275 | 285 | 295 |
| 206 | 216 | 226 | 236 | 246 | 256 | 266 | 276 | 286 | 296 |
| 207 | 217 | **227** | 237 | 247 | **257** | 267 | **277** | 287 | 297 |
| 208 | 218 | 228 | 238 | 248 | 258 | 268 | 278 | 288 | 298 |
| 209 | 219 | **229** | **239** | 249 | 259 | **269** | 279 | 289 | 299 |
| 210 | 220 | 230 | 240 | 250 | 260 | 270 | 280 | 290 | 300 |

| 301 | **311** | 321 | **331** | 341 | 351 | 361 | 371 | 381 | 391 |
|---|---|---|---|---|---|---|---|---|---|
| 302 | 312 | 322 | 332 | 342 | 352 | 362 | 372 | 382 | 392 |
| 303 | **313** | 323 | 333 | 343 | **353** | 363 | **373** | **383** | 393 |
| 304 | 314 | 324 | 334 | 344 | 354 | 364 | 374 | 384 | 394 |
| 305 | 315 | 325 | 335 | 345 | 355 | 365 | 375 | 385 | 395 |
| 306 | 316 | 326 | 336 | 346 | 356 | 366 | 376 | 386 | 396 |
| **307** | **317** | 327 | **337** | **347** | 357 | **367** | 377 | 387 | **397** |
| 308 | 318 | 328 | 338 | 348 | 358 | 368 | 378 | 388 | 398 |
| 309 | 319 | 329 | 339 | **349** | **359** | 369 | **379** | **389** | 399 |
| 310 | 320 | 330 | 340 | 350 | 360 | 370 | 380 | 390 | 400 |

Table 7 is continued on the next page

TABLE 7 (Continuation)

| **401** | 411 | **421** | **431** | 441 | 451 | **461** | 471 | 481 | **491** |
|---|---|---|---|---|---|---|---|---|---|
| 402 | 412 | 422 | 432 | 442 | 452 | 462 | 472 | 482 | 492 |
| 403 | 413 | 423 | **433** | **443** | 453 | **463** | 473 | 483 | 493 |
| 404 | 414 | 424 | 434 | 444 | 454 | 464 | 474 | 484 | 494 |
| 405 | 415 | 425 | 435 | 445 | 455 | 465 | 475 | 485 | 495 |
| 406 | 416 | 426 | 436 | 446 | 456 | 466 | 476 | 486 | 496 |
| 407 | 417 | 427 | 437 | 447 | **457** | **467** | 477 | **487** | 497 |
| 408 | 418 | 428 | 438 | 448 | 458 | 468 | 478 | 488 | 498 |
| **409** | **419** | 429 | **439** | **449** | 459 | 469 | **479** | 489 | **499** |
| 410 | 420 | 430 | 440 | 450 | 460 | 470 | 480 | 490 | 500 |

| 501 | 511 | **521** | 531 | **541** | 551 | 561 | **571** | 581 | 591 |
|---|---|---|---|---|---|---|---|---|---|
| 502 | 512 | 522 | 532 | 542 | 552 | 562 | 572 | 582 | 592 |
| **503** | 513 | **523** | 533 | 543 | 553 | **563** | 573 | 583 | **593** |
| 504 | 514 | 524 | 534 | 544 | 554 | 564 | 574 | 584 | 594 |
| 505 | 515 | 525 | 535 | 545 | 555 | 565 | 575 | 585 | 595 |
| 506 | 516 | 526 | 536 | 546 | 556 | 566 | 576 | 586 | 596 |
| 507 | 517 | 527 | 537 | **547** | **557** | 567 | **577** | **587** | 597 |
| 508 | 518 | 528 | 538 | 548 | 558 | 568 | 578 | 588 | 598 |
| **509** | 519 | 529 | 539 | 549 | 559 | **569** | 579 | 589 | **599** |
| 510 | 520 | 530 | 540 | 550 | 560 | 570 | 580 | 590 | 600 |

| **601** | 611 | 621 | **631** | **641** | 651 | **661** | 671 | 681 | **691** |
|---|---|---|---|---|---|---|---|---|---|
| 602 | 612 | 622 | 632 | 642 | 652 | 662 | 672 | 682 | 692 |
| 603 | **613** | 623 | 633 | **643** | **653** | 663 | **673** | **683** | 693 |
| 604 | 614 | 624 | 634 | 644 | 654 | 664 | 674 | 684 | 694 |
| 605 | 615 | 625 | 635 | 645 | 655 | 665 | 675 | 685 | 695 |
| 606 | 616 | 626 | 636 | 646 | 656 | 666 | 676 | 686 | 696 |
| **607** | **617** | 627 | 637 | **647** | 657 | 667 | **677** | 687 | 697 |
| 608 | 618 | 628 | 638 | 648 | 658 | 668 | 678 | 688 | 698 |
| 609 | **619** | 629 | 639 | 649 | **659** | 669 | 679 | 689 | 699 |
| 610 | 620 | 630 | 640 | 650 | 660 | 670 | 680 | 690 | 700 |

| **701** | 711 | 721 | 731 | 741 | **751** | **761** | 771 | 781 | 791 |
|---|---|---|---|---|---|---|---|---|---|
| 702 | 712 | 722 | 732 | 742 | 752 | 762 | 772 | 782 | 792 |
| 703 | 713 | 723 | **733** | **743** | 753 | 763 | **773** | 783 | 793 |
| 704 | 714 | 724 | 734 | 744 | 754 | 764 | 774 | 784 | 794 |
| 705 | 715 | 725 | 735 | 745 | 755 | 765 | 775 | 785 | 795 |
| 706 | 716 | 726 | 736 | 746 | 756 | 766 | 776 | 786 | 796 |
| 707 | 717 | **727** | 737 | 747 | **757** | 767 | 777 | **787** | **797** |
| 708 | 718 | 728 | 738 | 748 | 758 | 768 | 778 | 788 | 798 |
| **709** | **719** | 729 | **739** | 749 | 759 | **769** | 779 | 789 | 799 |
| 710 | 720 | 730 | 740 | 750 | 760 | 770 | 780 | 790 | 800 |

Table 7 is continued on the next page

TABLE 7 (Continuation)

| 801 | **811** | **821** | 831 | 841 | 851 | 861 | 871 | **881** | 891 |
|---|---|---|---|---|---|---|---|---|---|
| 802 | 812 | 822 | 832 | 842 | 852 | 862 | 872 | 882 | 892 |
| 803 | 813 | **823** | 833 | 843 | **853** | **863** | 873 | **883** | 893 |
| 804 | 814 | 824 | 834 | 844 | 854 | 864 | 874 | 884 | 894 |
| 805 | 815 | 825 | 835 | 845 | 855 | 865 | 875 | 885 | 895 |
| 806 | 816 | 826 | 836 | 846 | 856 | 866 | 876 | 886 | 896 |
| 807 | 817 | **827** | 837 | 847 | **857** | 867 | **877** | **887** | 897 |
| 808 | 818 | 828 | 838 | 848 | 858 | 868 | 878 | 888 | 898 |
| **809** | 819 | **829** | **839** | 849 | **859** | 869 | 879 | 889 | 899 |
| 810 | 820 | 830 | 840 | 850 | 860 | 870 | 880 | 890 | 900 |

| 901 | **911** | 921 | 931 | **941** | 951 | 961 | **971** | 981 | **991** |
|---|---|---|---|---|---|---|---|---|---|
| 902 | 912 | 922 | 932 | 942 | 952 | 962 | 972 | 982 | 992 |
| 903 | 913 | 923 | 933 | 943 | **953** | 963 | 973 | **983** | 993 |
| 904 | 914 | 924 | 934 | 944 | 954 | 964 | 974 | 984 | 994 |
| 905 | 915 | 925 | 935 | 945 | 955 | 965 | 975 | 985 | 995 |
| 906 | 916 | 926 | 936 | 946 | 956 | 966 | 976 | 986 | 996 |
| **907** | 917 | 927 | **937** | **947** | 957 | **967** | **977** | 987 | **997** |
| 908 | 918 | 928 | 938 | 948 | 958 | 968 | 978 | 988 | 998 |
| 909 | **919** | **929** | 939 | 949 | 959 | 969 | 979 | 989 | 999 |
| 910 | 920 | 930 | 940 | 950 | 960 | 970 | 980 | 990 | 1000 |

| 1001 | 1011 | **1021** | **1031** | 1041 | **1051** | **1061** | 1071 | 1081 | **1091** |
|---|---|---|---|---|---|---|---|---|---|
| 1002 | 1012 | 1022 | 1032 | 1042 | 1052 | 1062 | 1072 | 1082 | 1092 |
| 1003 | **1013** | 1023 | **1033** | 1043 | 1053 | **1063** | 1073 | 1083 | **1093** |
| 1004 | 1014 | 1024 | 1034 | 1044 | 1054 | 1064 | 1074 | 1084 | 1094 |
| 1005 | 1015 | 1025 | 1035 | 1045 | 1055 | 1065 | 1075 | 1085 | 1095 |
| 1006 | 1016 | 1026 | 1036 | 1046 | 1056 | 1066 | 1076 | 1086 | 1096 |
| 1007 | 1017 | 1027 | 1037 | 1047 | 1057 | 1067 | 1077 | **1087** | **1097** |
| 1008 | 1018 | 1028 | 1038 | 1048 | 1058 | 1068 | 1078 | 1088 | 1098 |
| **1009** | **1019** | 1029 | **1039** | **1049** | 1059 | **1069** | 1979 | 1089 | 1099 |
| 1010 | 1020 | 1030 | 1040 | 1050 | 1060 | 1070 | 1080 | 1090 | 1100 |

| 1101 | 1111 | 1121 | 1131 | 1141 | **1151** | 1161 | **1171** | **1181** | 1191 |
|---|---|---|---|---|---|---|---|---|---|
| 1102 | 1112 | 1122 | 1132 | 1142 | 1152 | 1162 | 1172 | 1182 | 1192 |
| **1103** | 1113 | **1123** | 1133 | 1143 | **1153** | **1163** | 1173 | 1183 | **1193** |
| 1104 | 1114 | 1124 | 1134 | 1144 | 1154 | 1164 | 1174 | 1184 | 1194 |
| 1105 | 1115 | 1125 | 1135 | 1145 | 1155 | 1165 | 1175 | 1185 | 1195 |
| 1106 | 1116 | 1126 | 1136 | 1146 | 1156 | 1166 | 1176 | 1186 | 1196 |
| 1107 | **1117** | 1127 | 1137 | 1147 | 1157 | 1167 | 1177 | **1187** | 1197 |
| 1108 | 1118 | 1128 | 1138 | 1148 | 1158 | 1168 | 1178 | 1188 | 1198 |
| **1109** | 1119 | **1129** | 1139 | 1149 | 1159 | 1169 | 1179 | 1189 | 1199 |
| 1110 | 1120 | 1130 | 1140 | 1150 | 1160 | 1170 | 1180 | 1190 | 1200 |

Table 7 is continued on the next page

TABLE 7 (Continuation)

| **1201** | 1211 | 1221 | **1231** | 1241 | 1251 | 1261 | 1271 | 1281 | **1291** |
|---|---|---|---|---|---|---|---|---|---|
| 1202 | 1212 | 1222 | 1232 | 1242 | 1252 | 1262 | 1272 | 1282 | 1292 |
| 1203 | **1213** | **1223** | 1233 | 1243 | 1253 | 1263 | 1273 | **1283** | 1293 |
| 1204 | 1214 | 1224 | 1234 | 1244 | 1254 | 1264 | 1274 | 1284 | 1294 |
| 1205 | 1215 | 1225 | 1235 | 1245 | 1255 | 1265 | 1275 | 1285 | 1295 |
| 1206 | 1216 | 1226 | 1236 | 1246 | 1256 | 1266 | 1276 | 1286 | 1296 |
| 1207 | **1217** | 1227 | **1237** | 1247 | 1257 | 1267 | **1277** | 1287 | **1297** |
| 1208 | 1218 | 1228 | 1238 | 1248 | 1258 | 1268 | 1278 | 1288 | 1298 |
| 1209 | 1219 | **1229** | 1239 | **1249** | **1259** | 1269 | **1279** | **1289** | 1299 |
| 1210 | 1220 | 1230 | 1240 | 1250 | 1260 | 1270 | 1280 | 1290 | 1300 |

| **1301** | 1311 | **1321** | 1331 | 1341 | 1351 | **1361** | 1371 | **1381** | 1391 |
|---|---|---|---|---|---|---|---|---|---|
| 1302 | 1312 | 1322 | 1332 | 1342 | 1352 | 1362 | 1372 | 1382 | 1392 |
| **1303** | 1313 | 1323 | 1333 | 1343 | 1353 | 1363 | **1373** | 1383 | 1393 |
| 1304 | 1314 | 1324 | 1334 | 1344 | 1354 | 1364 | 1374 | 1384 | 1394 |
| 1305 | 1315 | 1325 | 1335 | 1345 | 1355 | 1365 | 1375 | 1385 | 1395 |
| 1306 | 1316 | 1326 | 1336 | 1346 | 1356 | 1366 | 1376 | 1386 | 1396 |
| **1307** | 1317 | **1327** | 1337 | 1347 | 1357 | **1367** | 1377 | 1387 | 1397 |
| 1308 | 1318 | 1328 | 1338 | 1348 | 1358 | 1368 | 1378 | 1388 | 1398 |
| 1309 | **1319** | 1329 | 1339 | 1349 | 1359 | 1369 | 1379 | 1389 | **1399** |
| 1310 | 1320 | 1330 | 1340 | 1350 | 1360 | 1370 | 1380 | 1390 | 1400 |

| 1401 | 1411 | 1421 | 1431 | 1441 | **1451** | 1461 | **1471** | **1481** | 1491 |
|---|---|---|---|---|---|---|---|---|---|
| 1402 | 1412 | 1422 | 1432 | 1442 | 1452 | 1462 | 1472 | 1482 | 1492 |
| 1403 | 1413 | **1423** | **1433** | 1443 | **1453** | 1463 | 1473 | **1483** | **1493** |
| 1404 | 1414 | 1424 | 1434 | 1444 | 1454 | 1464 | 1474 | 1484 | 1494 |
| 1405 | 1415 | 1425 | 1435 | 1445 | 1455 | 1465 | 1475 | 1485 | 1495 |
| 1406 | 1416 | 1426 | 1436 | 1446 | 1456 | 1466 | 1476 | 1486 | 1496 |
| 1407 | 1417 | **1427** | 1437 | **1447** | 1457 | 1467 | 1477 | **1487** | 1497 |
| 1408 | 1418 | 1428 | 1438 | 1448 | 1458 | 1468 | 1478 | 1488 | 1498 |
| **1409** | 1419 | **1429** | **1439** | 1449 | **1459** | 1469 | 1479 | **1489** | **1499** |
| 1410 | 1420 | 1430 | 1440 | 1450 | 1460 | 1470 | 1480 | 1490 | 1500 |

TABLE 8

Primes and Prime Twins in the Interval 209201 to 209300

| **209201** | 209211 | **209221** | 209231 | 209241 | 209251 | 209261 | 209271 | 209281 | 209291 |
|---|---|---|---|---|---|---|---|---|---|
| 209202 | 209212 | 209222 | 209232 | 209242 | 209252 | 209262 | 209272 | 209282 | 209292 |
| **209203** | **209213** | 209223 | **209233** | 209243 | 209253 | **209263** | 209273 | 209283 | 209293 |
| 209204 | 209214 | 209224 | 209234 | 209244 | 209254 | 209264 | 209274 | 209284 | 209294 |
| 209205 | 209215 | 209225 | 209235 | 209245 | 209255 | 209265 | 209275 | 209285 | 209295 |
| 209206 | 209216 | 209226 | 209236 | 209246 | 209256 | 209266 | 209276 | 209286 | 209296 |
| 209207 | 209217 | **209227** | 209237 | 209247 | **209257** | **209267** | 209277 | 209287 | 209297 |
| 209208 | 209218 | 209228 | 209238 | 209248 | 209258 | 209268 | 209278 | 209288 | 209298 |
| 209209 | 209219 | 209229 | 209239 | **209249** | 209259 | **209269** | 209279 | 209289 | **209299** |
| 209210 | 209220 | 209230 | 209240 | 209250 | 209260 | 209270 | 209280 | 209290 | 209300 |

TABLE 9

Primes in the Interval 268301 to 268400

| 268301 | 268311 | 268321 | 268331 | 268341 | 268351 | 268361 | 268371 | 268381 | 268391 |
|---|---|---|---|---|---|---|---|---|---|
| 268302 | 268312 | 268322 | 268332 | 268342 | 268352 | 268362 | 268372 | 268382 | 268392 |
| 268303 | 268313 | 268323 | 268333 | **268343** | 268353 | 268363 | 268373 | 268383 | 268393 |
| 268304 | 268314 | 268324 | 268334 | 268344 | 268354 | 268364 | 268374 | 268384 | 268394 |
| 268305 | 268315 | 268325 | 268335 | 268345 | 268355 | 268365 | 268375 | 268385 | 268395 |
| 268306 | 268316 | 268326 | 268336 | 268346 | 268356 | 268366 | 268376 | 268386 | 268396 |
| 268307 | 268317 | 268327 | 268337 | 268347 | 268357 | 268367 | 268377 | 268387 | 268397 |
| 268308 | 268318 | 268328 | 268338 | 268348 | 268358 | 268368 | 268378 | 268388 | 268398 |
| 268309 | 268319 | 268329 | 268339 | 268349 | 268359 | 268369 | 268379 | 268389 | 268399 |
| 268310 | 268320 | 268330 | 268340 | 268350 | 268360 | 268370 | 268380 | 268390 | 268400 |

TABLE 10

Primes in the Interval 299901 to 300000

| 299901 | 299911 | 299921 | 299931 | **299941** | **299951** | 299961 | 299971 | 299981 | 299991 |
|---|---|---|---|---|---|---|---|---|---|
| 299902 | 299912 | 299922 | 299932 | 299942 | 299952 | 299962 | 299972 | 299982 | 299992 |
| **299903** | 299913 | 299923 | **299933** | 299943 | 299953 | 299963 | 299973 | **299983** | **299993** |
| 299904 | 299914 | 299924 | 299934 | 299944 | 299954 | 299964 | 299974 | 299984 | 299994 |
| 299905 | 299915 | 299925 | 299935 | 299945 | 299955 | 299965 | 299975 | 299985 | 299995 |
| 299906 | 299916 | 299926 | 299936 | 299946 | 299956 | 299966 | 299976 | 299986 | 299996 |
| 299907 | 299917 | 299927 | 299937 | 299947 | 299957 | 299967 | **299977** | 299987 | 299997 |
| 299908 | 299918 | 299928 | 299938 | 299948 | 299958 | 299968 | 299978 | 299988 | 299998 |
| **299909** | 299919 | 299929 | 299939 | 299949 | 299959 | **299969** | 299979 | 299989 | 299999 |
| 299910 | 299920 | 299930 | 299940 | 299950 | 299960 | 299970 | 299980 | 299990 | 300000 |

TABLE 11

$N(x)$ denotes the number of primes less than or equal to $x$. $Z(x)$ is the number of pairs of prime twins, both of which are less than or equal to $x$. $Li(x)$ is the value of the integral logarithm (see Chapter VII, Notes 16, 17). The last column of the table shows how the ratio of $N(x)$ to $Li(x)$ approaches 1 with increasing $x$.

| $x$ | $N(x)$ | $Z(x)$ | $Li(x)$ | $N(x):Li(x)$ |
|---|---|---|---|---|
| 2 | 1 | 0 | 1,045.. | 0,9568... |
| 3 | 2 | 0 | 2,164.. | 0,9244... |
| 4 | 2 | 0 | 2,968.. | 0,6740... |
| 5 | 3 | 1 | 3,635.. | 0,8254... |
| 6 | 3 | 1 | 4,222.. | 0,7105... |
| 7 | 4 | 2 | 4,757.. | 0,8409... |
| 8 | 4 | 2 | 5,254.. | 0,7614... |
| 9 | 4 | 2 | 5,721.. | 0,6991... |
| 10 | 4 | 2 | 6,166.. | 0,6488... |
| 20 | 8 | 4 | 9,905.. | 0,8076 |
| 30 | 10 | 4 | 13,023.. | 0,7679... |
| 40 | 12 | 5 | 15,840.. | 0,7576... |
| 50 | 15 | 6 | 18,469.. | 0,8122... |
| 60 | 17 | 6 | 20,965.. | 0,8109... |
| 70 | 19 | 7 | 23,362.. | 0,8133... |
| 80 | 22 | 8 | 25,679.. | 0,8567... |
| 90 | 24 | 8 | 27,930.. | 0,8593... |
| 100 | 25 | 8 | 30,126.. | 0,8298... |
| 200 | 46 | 15 | 50,192.. | 0,9165... |
| 300 | 62 | 19 | 68,334.. | 0,9073... |
| 400 | 78 | 21 | 85,418.. | 0,9132... |
| 500 | 95 | 24 | 101,794.. | 0,9333... |
| 600 | 109 | 26 | 117,647.. | 0,9265... |
| 700 | 125 | 30 | 133,089.. | 0,9392... |
| 800 | 139 | 30 | 148,197.. | 0,9379... |
| 900 | 154 | 35 | 163,024.. | 0,9446... |
| 1000 | 168 | 35 | 177,610.. | 0,9459... |
| 2000 | 303 | 61 | 314,809.. | 0,9625... |
| 3000 | 430 | 81 | 442,759.. | 0,9712... |
| 4000 | 550 | 103 | 565,365.. | 0,9728... |
| 5000 | 669 | 126 | 684,281.. | 0,9777... |
| 6000 | 783 | 143 | 800,414.. | 0,9782... |
| 7000 | 900 | 162 | 914,331.. | 0,9843... |
| 8000 | 1007 | 175 | 1026,416.. | 0,9811... |
| 9000 | 1117 | 189 | 1136,949.. | 0,9825... |
| 10000 | 1229 | 205 | 1246,137.. | 0,9862... |

Table 11 is continued on the next page

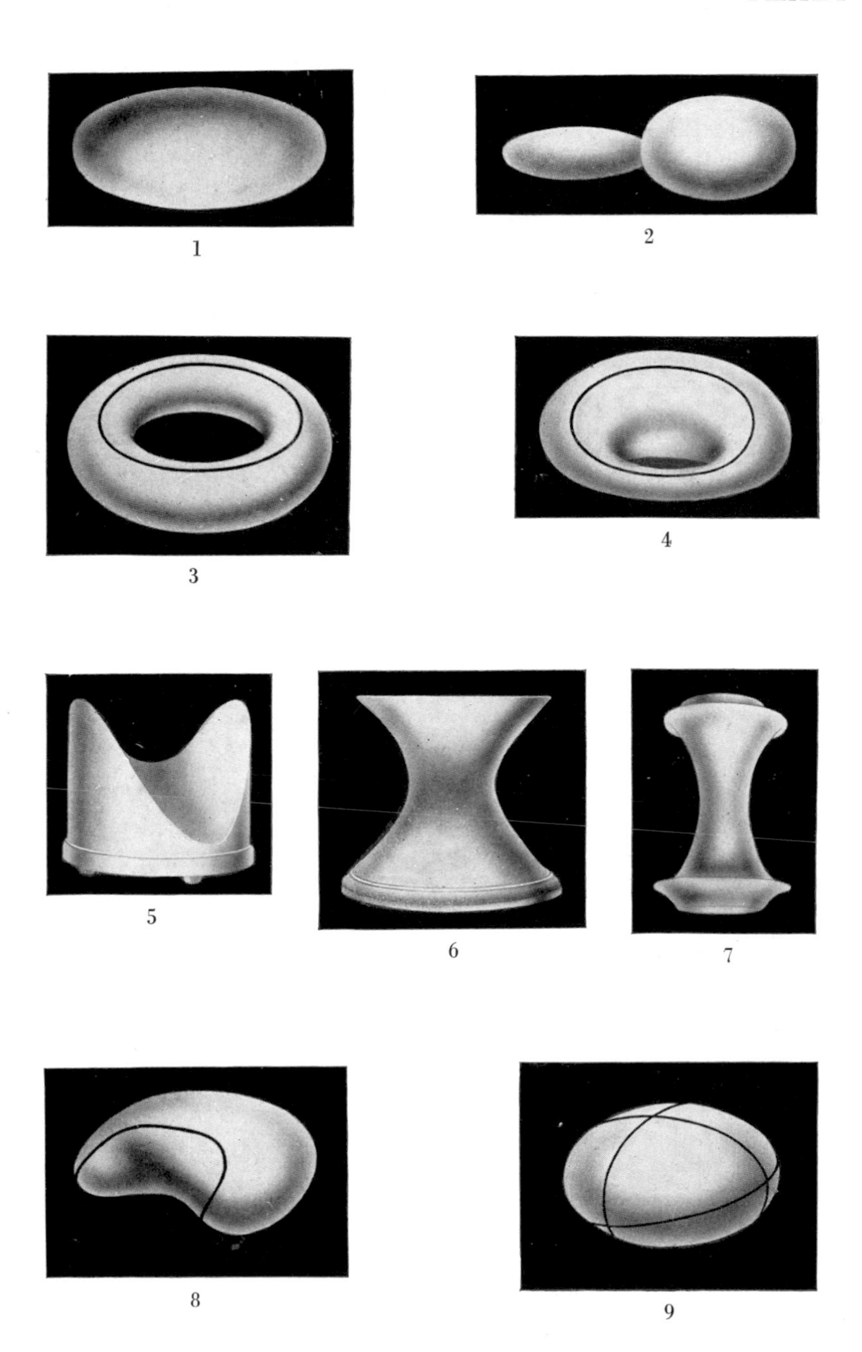
1
2
3
4
5
6
7
8
9

PLATE II

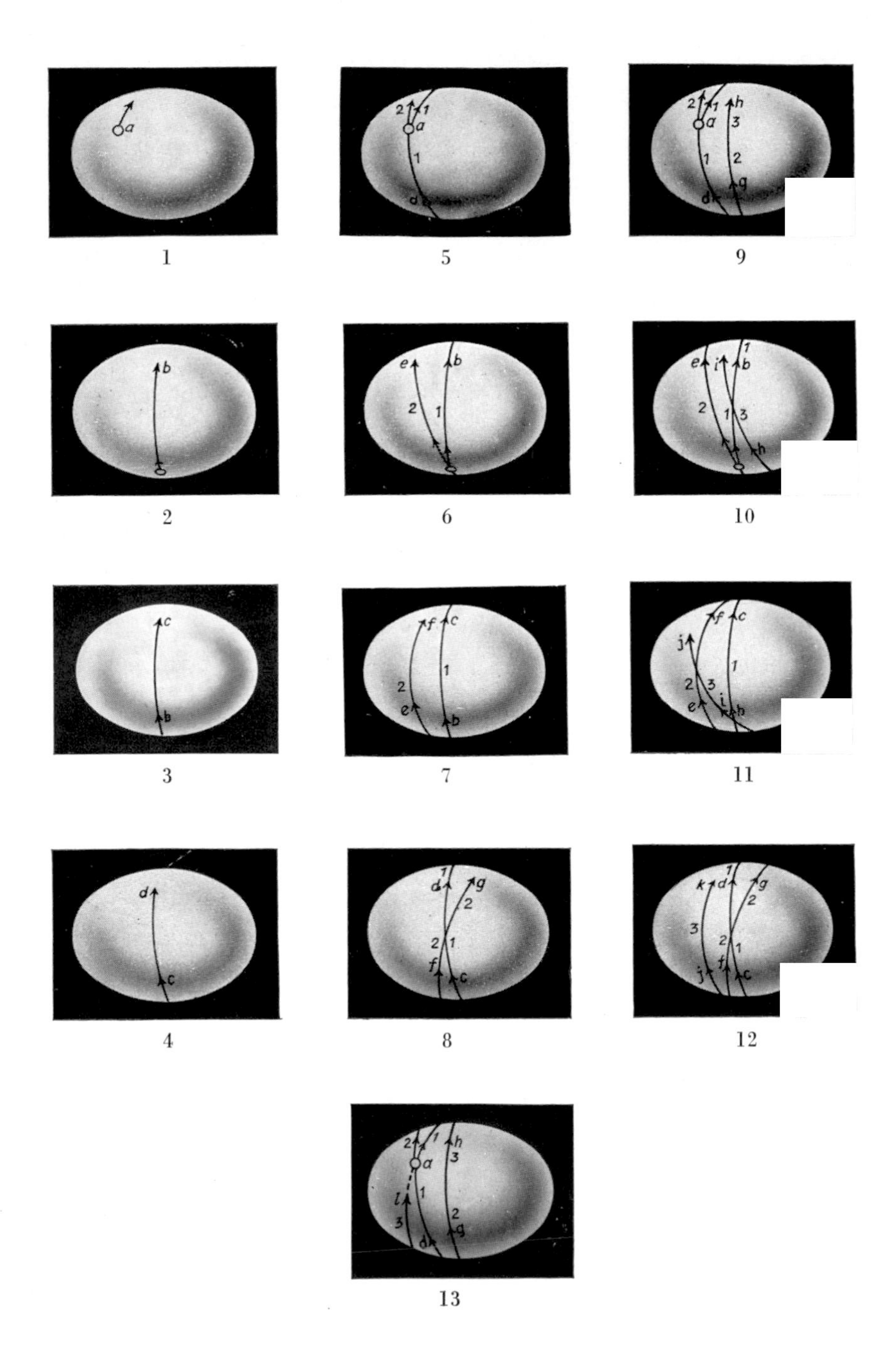

TABLE 11 (Continuation)

| $x$ | $N(x)$ | $Z(x)$ | $Li(x)$ | $N(x): Li(x)$ |
|---|---|---|---|---|
| 20000 | 2262 | 342 | 2288,61... | 0,9884... |
| 30000 | 3245 | 467 | 3276,90... | 0,9903... |
| 40000 | 4203 | 591 | 4233,01... | 0,9929... |
| 50000 | 5133 | 705 | 5166,55... | 0,9935... |
| 60000 | 6057 | 811 | 6082,85... | 0,9958... |
| 70000 | 6935 | 905 | 6985,29... | 0,9928... |
| 80000 | 7837 | 1007 | 7876,21... | 0,9950... |
| 90000 | 8713 | 1116 | 8757,29... | 0,9949... |
| 100000 | 9592 | 1224 | 9629,81... | 0,9961... |

| $x$ | $N(x)$ | $Li(x)$ | $N(x) : Li(x)$ |
|---|---|---|---|
| 100 000 | 9 592 | 9 630,... | 0,9961... |
| 200 000 | 17 984 | 18 037,... | 0,9971... |
| 300 000 | 25 997 | 26 088,... | 0,9965... |
| 400 000 | 33 860 | 33 924,... | 0,9981... |
| 500 000 | 41 538 | 41 607,... | 0,9983... |
| 600 000 | 49 098 | 49 174,... | 0,9985... |
| 700 000 | 56 543 | 56 646,... | 0,9982... |
| 800 000 | 63 951 | 64 038,... | 0,9986... |
| 900 000 | 71 274 | 71 363,... | 0,9988... |
| 1 000 000 | 78 498 | 78 629,... | 0,9983... |
| 2 000 000 | 148 933 | 149 056,... | 0,99917.. |
| 3 000 000 | 216 816 | 216 972,... | 0,99928.. |
| 4 000 000 | 283 146 | 283 353,... | 0,99927.. |
| 5 000 000 | 348 513 | 348 639,... | 0,99964.. |
| 6 000 000 | 412 849 | 413 078,... | 0,99945.. |
| 7 000 000 | 476 648 | 476 828,... | 0,99962.. |
| 8 000 000 | 539 777 | 540 001,... | 0,99959.. |
| 9 000 000 | 602 489 | 602 677,... | 0,99969.. |
| 10 000 000 | 664 579 | 664 919,... | 0,99949.. |

*Notes to Chapter I*

## PRIME NUMBERS AND PRIME TWINS

**1** (p. 3). Historically, this definition was developed gradually. At one time 2 was not considered a prime, so that 3 was the smallest prime {1}. The number 2 is of course as necessary a factor in the multiplicative formation of the integers as any other prime. We shall come back to this formation again in Chapter VII, Note 20.

**2** (p. 5). It might be asked how we know that one number is a prime, while another is not. Theoretically, each number would have to be tested to see whether it is divisible by a smaller number, just as the number 45 was tested. But there are certain systematic devices for shortening the work, and these are used by compilers of prime number tables. (For a table of all primes less than 300000, see {2}. {3} contains a list of all primes less than 10000000. The factors of all numbers up to 3036000 are given in {4}. The British Association, with international cooperation, undertook in 1877 the calculation of factor tables for numbers up to 9000000 {5}.) Left to our own devices, we could first cross out in Table 2 all the even numbers; then all those divisible by 3: $9993 = 3 \cdot 3331$ is divisible by 3; successive addition of 3 yields all the other numbers in this range divisible by 3: 9996, 9999, 10002, 10005, etc. Then the numbers divisible by 5: 9995, 10000, 10005, 10010, etc.; by 7, 11, 13, 17, 19, etc. could be eliminated. For example, 9996 is divisible by 7, 9999 by 11, 9997 by 13, 9996 by 17, and 9994 by 19. A somewhat more detailed test shows that

$$9991 = 97 \cdot 103, \quad 10001 = 73 \cdot 137, \quad 10019 = 43 \cdot 233,$$
$$10027 = 37 \cdot 271, \quad 10033 = 79 \cdot 127, \quad 10057 = 89 \cdot 113,$$
$$10063 = 29 \cdot 347.$$

Without a refinement of this method, it would still require a great deal of work to show that the remaining numbers in bold face in Table 2 are primes. This is analogous to the problem of analyzing the chemical elements of a material, where the experiments can be systematically simplified by utilizing already acquired knowledge.

Moreover, it is possible to treat certain types of numbers, such as $2^n+1$ or $2^n-1$, in special ways. This is how certain isolated results for certain very large numbers are obtained (see Notes 3, 4, 5).

**3** (p. 7). The largest prime known in Euler's time (1772) was $2{,}147{,}483{,}647 = 2^{31} - 1$.

**4** (p. 7). It has indeed been established that $2^{61} - 1 = 2{,}305{,}843{,}009{,}213{,}693{,}951$ is a prime {6}.

**5** (p. 7). One zealous computer actually obtained the following prime: $2^{127} - 1 = 170{,}141183{,}460469{,}231731{,}687303{,}715884{,}105727$ {7}, a number with 39 digits. Édouard Lucas (1842–1891) had already proved in 1876 that $2^{127} - 1$ is a prime {8}.

**6** (p. 8). Euler gave a deeper proof of the infinitude of the primes based on the divergence of the harmonic series

$$1 + \tfrac{1}{2} + \tfrac{1}{3} + \tfrac{1}{4} + \tfrac{1}{5} + \tfrac{1}{6} + \cdots.$$

For a full acount of Euler see Chapter XIII.

**7** (p. 8). In connection with Euclid's proof, the following remark may be useful. If $p$ is a prime, $(2 \cdot 3 \cdot \cdots \cdot p) + 1$ is not divisible by any of the primes $2, 3, \cdots, p$. But it would be an error to believe that

$$Q = (2 \cdot 3 \cdot \cdots \cdot p) + 1$$

is itself a prime; it is true only that the prime factors of $Q$ are all different from $2, 3, \cdots, p$. For example, for

$$\begin{aligned} p &= 3, & Q &= 2 \cdot 3 + 1 = 7, \\ p &= 5, & Q &= 2 \cdot 3 \cdot 5 + 1 = 31, \\ p &= 7, & Q &= 2 \cdot 3 \cdot 5 \cdot 7 + 1 = 211, \\ p &= 11, & Q &= 2 \cdot 3 \cdot 5 \cdot 7 \cdot 11 + 1 = 2311, \\ p &= 13, & Q &= 2 \cdot 3 \cdot 5 \cdot 7 \cdot 11 \cdot 13 + 1 = 30031, \end{aligned}$$

where 7, 31, 211 and 2311 are all primes, but $30031 = 59 \cdot 509$ is not.

**8** (p. 8). Many legends, and many bold guesses as to Euclid's dates have not survived careful historical criticism. There are many intensive historical investigations on this subject, and much has been learned from textual criticism of the various handwritten manuscripts of Euclid's works. In this connection see {9}–{13}. For a survey of the epoch see {14}, {15}. An English edition of the *Elements* is {16}.

**9** (p. 9). The well known proof of the Pythagorean theorem is ascribed to Euclid himself. See {17}.

**10** (p. 9). In the sections of the *Elements* on the divisibility of numbers, Euclid also solved a problem on the decomposition into prime factors (see Chapter VII, Note 20).

**11** (p. 10). This term was first coined by Paul Stäckel (1892–1919) and has since become standard terminology. Stäckel also referred to the occurrence of *prime quadruplets:* four consecutive primes at intervals of 2, 4, and 2, such as 11, 13, 17, 19; or, 101, 103, 107, 109. For this and other related problems see {18}.

**12** (p. 10). This counting procedure is based on the following reasoning: Given a table of primes less than 1500, we see that 1499 is a prime but the table does not tell us whether or not 1501 is also a prime (it is not); similarly, a table of primes up to 3000 will list 2999 as a prime, but will give no information about 3001. In both cases, additional calculations would be necessary to determine whether 1499, 1501, or 2999, 3001, are prime twin pairs. Thus it would not be practical to include a prime twin pair in the interval containing the smaller prime.

**13** (p. 10). An idea of the incidence of prime twins as well as of primes can be obtained from Table 11. According to this table, there are 25 primes and 8 twin pairs less than 100; but only 168 primes and 35 twin pairs less than 1000, rather than 10 times as many.

For a table of prime twin pairs less than 300000 see {19}.

**14** (p. 10). After a lecture on this subject, someone in the audience claimed to have a proof, patterned on Euclid's, of the existence of an infinite number or prime twin pairs. The proof consisted in forming the *pair* of numbers

$$m = (2\cdot 3\cdot \cdots \cdot p) - 1, \qquad n = (2\cdot 3\cdot \cdots \cdot p) + 1$$

for each prime $p$. Each pair then consists of two numbers whose difference is 2, and neither number is divisible by 2, 3, 5, $\cdots$, $p$. This would work, if both $m$ and $n$ were *always* primes, since they would then form a prime twin pair for each $p$. This does happen in special cases, e.g.

$$\begin{aligned} m &= 2\cdot 3 - 1 = 5, & n &= 2\cdot 3 + 1 = 7; \\ m &= 2\cdot 3\cdot 5 - 1 = 29, & n &= 2\cdot 3\cdot 5 + 1 = 31; \\ m &= 2\cdot 3\cdot 5\cdot 7\cdot 11 - 1 = 2309, & n &= 2\cdot 3\cdot 5\cdot 7\cdot 11 + 1 = 2311 \end{aligned}$$

are all prime twin pairs. But in the case of

$$2\cdot 3\cdot 5\cdot 7 - 1 = 209, \qquad 2\cdot 3\cdot 5\cdot 7 + 1 = 211$$

and

$$2\cdot 3\cdot 5\cdot 7\cdot 11\cdot 13 - 1 = 30029, \qquad 2\cdot 3\cdot 5\cdot 7\cdot 11\cdot 13 + 1 = 30031,$$

211 and 30029 are primes, while $209 = 11\cdot 19$, and $30031 = 59\cdot 509$ are not. We must thus reckon with the possibility that beyond a certain point, at least one (and perhaps both) of the numbers $m$, $n$ in each pair is composite and not a prime.

*Chapter II*

# TRAVELING ON SURFACES

## Geodesics—Surface Curvature

In this chapter, we will discuss some problems in geometry which concern straight and curved lines and plane and curved surfaces.

To begin, let us consider the following well known trick problem: "A ship departs from Porto (on the west coast of Portugal) directly for the West. Where on the American coast does it land, assuming it maintains a fixed direction?" A superficial answer would be: "Near New York," since New York has the same latitude as Porto.[1] If the ship moved on a circle of latitude, the answer would be correct. But the answer is wrong: If the ship sails in a fixed direction, it does not move on a circle of latitude; after passing through the Antilles, Cuba and Haiti, it actually[2] lands at Port Antonio in the north-east of Jamaica (see Fig. 1). If Jamaica island were not there, between the ship and the mainland, the ship would touch land at L. de las Perlas on the east coast of Nicaragua, at a northern latitude of about 13°, or about 375 miles from the Panama Canal, and 2000 miles from New York.

Before we return to this problem, let us first clarify what we mean by *maintaining a fixed direction* while traveling on a surface. In the course of our discussion, we shall consider very different types of surfaces. We begin with the simplest of all surfaces, the plane, on which we take a point $A$ as a point of departure. From this point, we wish to travel in a fixed direction, that is, on a straight course, for a certain distance, say to $B$ (see Fig. 2). In order to maintain the initial direction, the path must be straight. To maintain this course on an actual road, we could take a cart with four wheels and fix both wheel axles firmly to the cart so that no turning or steering would be possible. The cart could then only roll straight ahead. Or, we could take an automobile and fix the steering wheel so that no turns are possible and it can ride only straight ahead. Let us think of such a car on a completely flat surface. Its route is of course a straight line. These examples make intuitively clear the fact that, on a plane, maintaining a fixed direction is equivalent to following a straight line path.

[1] The estuary Dóuro at the outlet of the port of Porto (at São João da Foz) has a northern latitude of 41°09′; New York lies between 40°41′ and 40°49′, and the southmost point of Long Island (Long Beach) has a northern latitude of 40°34′. (The relevant longitudes west of Greenwich are 8°40′, 74°, respectively.)

[2] It is to be noted that in the sequel the earth will be regarded as a sphere and that the calculations regarding the route of the ship will not take the flattening of the earth into account.

Fig. 1

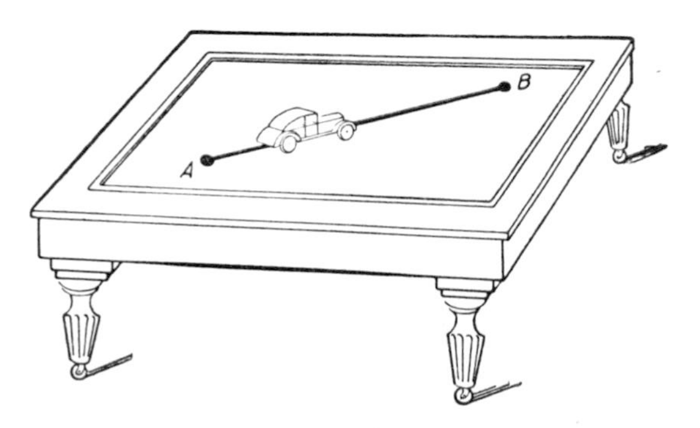


Fig. 2

Now let us consider the straight-line connection between $A$ and $B$ from a different point of view. Consider all possible paths, straight and curved, with and without corners or loops, joining $A$ and $B$ (see Fig. 3, where besides the straight-line connection there are five others numbered 1 to 5). These paths obviously have very different lengths. But the shortest, of course, is the straight line.

While these distinctions are trivial and obvious, one thing should be noted: We have considered the paths joining $A$ and $B$ from two quite different points of view. The first concerned maintenance of direction: If a path that is not a straight line is chosen, the direction is altered, either gradually or suddenly. In Fig. 3, paths 1, 2, 3, 5 change direction gradually; path 4 makes a sudden turn at the points $C$ and $D$. If the point of departure $A$ and the goal $B$ are distant from each other, or if $B$ cannot be seen from $A$, as, say, in a fog, the direction can be maintained by markers at short intervals, like those marking winter paths in the mountains. To be sure one is not deviating from the straight line, from the marker $P$ (see Fig. 4), in principle, it is enough to see the next two markers $Q$ and $R$ and to verify that all three markers coincide along the line of sight from $P$ to $Q$. That is, a direction can be maintained by *sighting;* a change in direction from the straight line could be seen.

The other point of view has to do with the *lengths* of the various paths and here we must use a different approach. By using a measuring rod we need not sight along three markers, but can simply measure the distance

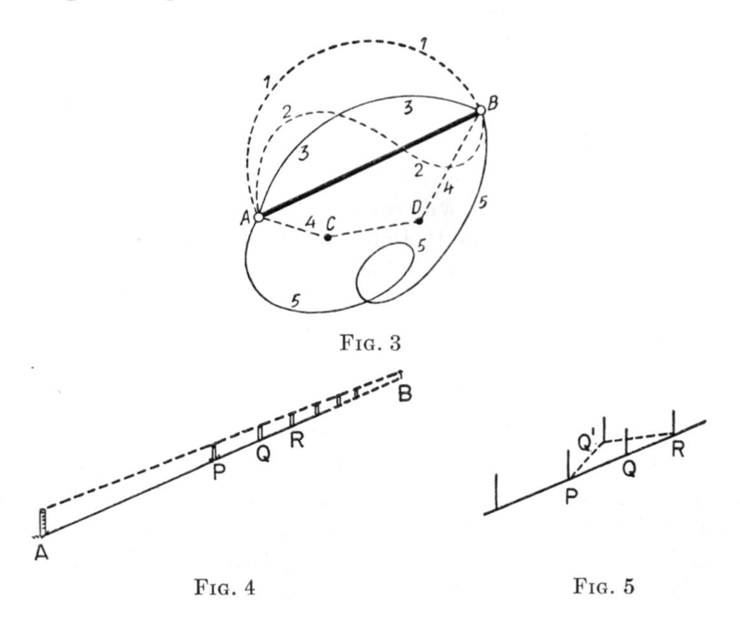


Fig. 3

Fig. 4

Fig. 5

from each marker $P$ to the next $Q$. The fact that the route from $P$ to $R$ through $Q$ is the shortest can be expressed as follows: If the marker $Q$ is displaced in a storm and moved to a different point $Q'$, where it no longer lies on the straight line connecting $P$ to $R$, the sum of the distances $PQ' + Q'R$ will be greater than $PQ + QR$ (see Fig. 5). The distance $PQ + QR$ assumes its smallest possible value only if $Q$ lies on the straight line connecting $P$ to $R$. Thus, from the aspect of distance, the straight line is characterized as the shortest path between the beginning and endpoints.

Comparing the connecting routes between two points from these two different viewpoints, we note: *The definition of a straight line as that connecting path which maintains a fixed direction* (*determined by sighting*) *is equivalent to the definition of a straight line as the connecting path which yields the shortest distance* (*determined by measuring*) *between the initial and endpoints* [**1**]. We also notice that the maintenance of direction, which can be effected by means of markers, can also be achieved by setting a car with a fixed steering wheel upon a smooth road. It might be worthwhile to the owner, to save gas, for example, to take the shortest route. But for the car, a choice of paths based upon cost considerations is completely irrelevant. The car simply rides forth, mechanically preserving its *direction*. The fact that this route is the most economical, because it is the shortest, deserves to be noted.

The discussion up to this point has concerned the plane only. Now let us consider the *surface of a sphere*. Here things become a little more difficult; but the changes are not yet very important. As an example of a large sphere let us take the earth, which is of course not exactly a sphere because of the oblateness at the poles: the diameter of the equator is somewhat larger than the distance from the North to the South Pole. Neglecting this difference [**2**], which is relatively small, let us think of the earth as a smooth, solid sphere, without seas, mountains and valleys. If a wagon starts rolling on this finely polished earth, it will run on a meridian, cut the equator perpendicularly, go on to the South Pole and eventually will reach the North Pole on the opposite meridian semi-circle. This path would cut the sphere into two equal parts. *On a sphere, a path which preserves direction is a circle which cuts the surface of the sphere into two equal halves*. However, not every circle on the surface of a sphere divides it into two equal parts. There are circles on a sphere, such as $b$ in Fig. 6, which do not have this property. To divide the sphere in half, the plane of the circle must pass through the center $M$ of the sphere. If a plane $H$ (Fig. 6) passes through the center $M$ of the sphere, the circle $a$ in which it intersects the sphere divides the sphere in half. But if the plane $N$ of the circle $b$ (Fig. 6) does not pass through $M$, then $b$ divides the surface of the sphere into two unequal parts. Circles of the first kind are called *great circles;* they include the equator and every

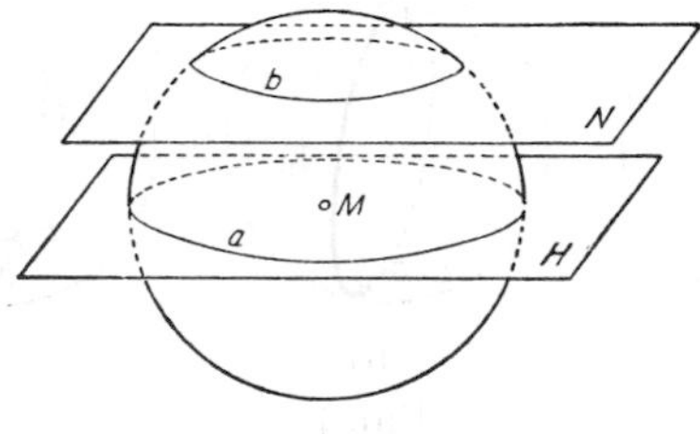


FIG. 6

complete meridian. Circles of the second kind are called *small circles;* they include all the circles of latitude except the equator. The *great circles*, as we said before, *are the paths along which direction is preserved;* these are the paths we would obtain if we proceeded by sighting along markers over the smooth surface of the earth.

To describe a great circle, it is not necessary to choose a Pole as a point of departure for the direction preserving path. Any other point will do as well. On a sphere, the same construction can be carried out, no matter what the starting point. If we start at a point in the vicinity of Munich and proceed from it in a fixed direction the path would be a great circle passing through Munich, assuming that the initial direction is preserved; the particular great circle traversed would depend only on the prescribed direction. All possible great circles which started at Munich would meet at the opposite point, where the *antipode* of Munich is situated [**3**]. Every one of these paths would cut the surface of the earth into two equal parts.

We must remember, however, that of the parallel circles of latitude on the earth's sphere, only the equator is a great circle; it alone divides the surface of the sphere into two equal halves. The hypothetical wagon with the fixed steering wheel may run along the equator, but never on a circle of latitude, *because a circle of latitude changes its direction,* if only gradually. This is very easy to see in the case of a circle of latitude in the vicinity of a Pole. Imagine that the North Pole is in the center of the room you are sitting in. A circle with a radius of 10 yards about this point is then the circle of latitude corresponding to 89°59′59.7″ North, because the .3 of a second short of 90° corresponds to approximately a 10 yard distance from the Pole. As we describe this circle, keeping its center on our right, we move in the high North from East to West. It is obvious that we are continuously changing our direction, for we are always veering towards the right. A wagon with a fixed steering wheel would never roll along this latitude. This path could not be obtained by sighting along markers. And on the open sea, a ship could not sail this course and maintain its direction. What is true for a circle of latitude at a 10 yard distance from the North Pole is true for every other circle of latitude except the equator; the circle

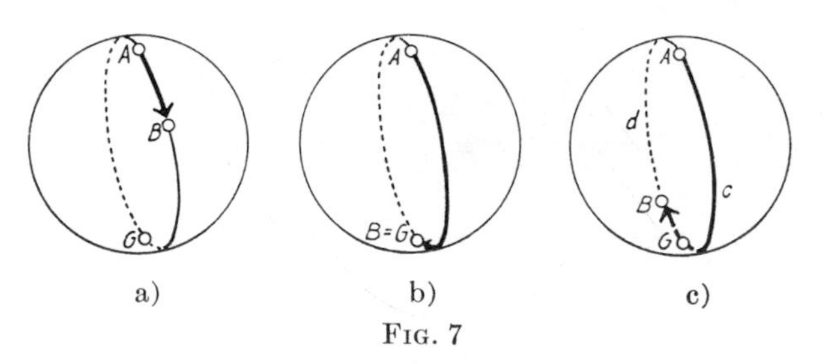


FIG. 7

of northern latitude 89°59′50″ (which is short 10″ of 90° and not .3″) is of course somewhat larger than the latitude just considered, and its radius is not 10 but 332.4 yards. Nevertheless, in traversing this latitude from East to West there is a continuous, even if gradual, change in direction, and a continuous veering towards the right. In the northern hemisphere, as one travels along a circle of latitude from East to West, there is a continuous change in direction, constantly veering towards the right [**4**]; the closer the latitude is to the Pole the stronger is the shift; the closer it is to the equator, the weaker is the shift.[3]

We have now reached the solution to the trick question asked at the beginning of the chapter: If a ship departing from Porto "maintains its course," it will not sail on a latitude (that is, will not stay on an East-West course), but will sail on the great circle passing through Porto, which is tangent to the circle of latitude at Porto.

But let us return to the great circles on a sphere. Consider all the great circles that start from a definite point $A$, say the North Pole; these are called the meridian circles or circles of longitude. All of these circles must pass through the point $G$ opposite $A$, which is of course the South Pole. Now let us proceed from the North Pole along a meridian but stop before we reach the South Pole, that is, we traverse an arc smaller than the semi-circle. Let the endpoint of this meridian arc be $B$ (Fig. 7a). It can be proved that this arc of a great circle [**5**], from $A$ to $B$, is the *shortest path* on the sphere connecting $A$ to $B$.[4] Thus we find that the great circles have a two-fold property: First, they are the paths on a sphere which preserve a direc-

[3] Note the crucial difference between maintaining a constant direction, and moving in the direction from East to West. The latter condition is satisfied by moving on a *latitude;* the former by moving on a *great circle.* Therefore, both conditions can be satisfied only on the equator.

There is a humorous story about people who hear a joke, fail to get the point, and in retelling it manage to lose the point completely. This is analogous to what would happen if at some point in this problem one substituted "steering constantly from East to West," for "maintaining a constant direction."

[4] Obviously, this property is lost as soon as $B$ is moved to the South Pole, the point opposite $A$ (see Fig. 7b): at that point all meridian semi-circles from $A$ to $G$ are equally long and *no one* is shorter than any other. Consider a meridian arc $c = AB$, which includes more than a semi-circle and extends beyond $G$ (see Fig. 7c). It is

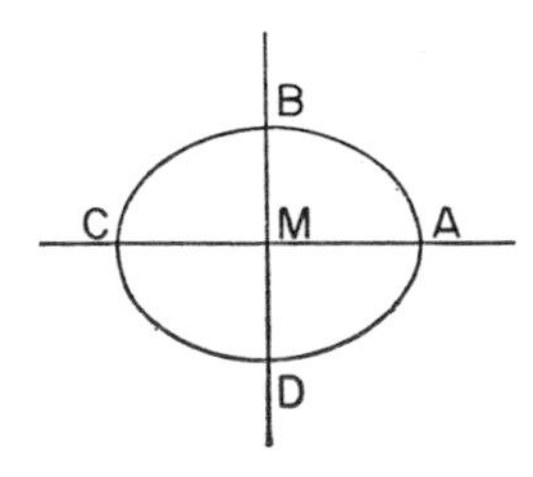


FIG. 8

tion; second, they are—if one does not take an arc longer than a semicircle—the shortest paths between the points they join.

What have we discovered so far? We began with motion on a plane and saw that straight lines have two equivalent properties: They are the only paths which maintain a direction, and they are the paths which yield the shortest connection between two points. Next we saw that the same two-fold property holds for great circles on the surface of a sphere. Curves with this double property are to be found not only in the plane or on the sphere, but on many other surfaces [6]. These curves have a special significance and play a very important role in mathematical considerations of such surfaces. They are called the *geodesics* of the surface [7]. In the plane the geodesics are straight lines; on the sphere, they are great circles.

Let us now investigate the geodesics on some other surfaces. This will also enable us to learn a little about the great variety of types of surfaces.

We shall first examine the *ellipsoids*, a class of surfaces very closely related to the spheres. The simplest of these are the *ellipsoids of rotation*, which are obtained by rotating an ellipse (Fig. 8) about one of its axes, $AC$ or $BD$. If the ellipse is rotated about its minor axis $BD$, the result is an *oblate ellipsoid* (picture 1 of Plate I). If the ellipse is rotated about its major axis $AC$, the result is a *spindle-shaped ellipsoid*, as shown to the left in picture 2 of Plate I. There are ellipses whose axes differ very little from each other in length, as in Fig. 9, where $BD$ is only $1/20$ shorter than $AC$. This ellipse hardly differs from a circle, and the resulting ellipsoid of rotation differs only slightly from a sphere. The earth's surface comes very close to that of an oblate ellipsoid;[5] it deviates only slightly from a sphere, because the oblateness amounts to only $1/299$ of the diameter of the equator.[6]

---

immediately clear that this arc *cannot* be the shortest path between $A$ and $B$. In fact, of the two arcs $c$ and $d$ (in Fig. 7c) on the meridian circle passing through $A$ and $B$, $d$ (which does *not* contain $G$) is the shortest path between $A$ and $B$.

[5] This approximation is of course relative to the size of the earth, so that neglecting the mountains and all other variations in the earth's surface, the major axis (equal to the diameter of the equator) is about 7927 miles, and the minor axis (from the North to the South Pole) is 7900 miles.

[6] The sun, moon and the larger planets too, either show no determinable deviation from a sphere, or, as oblate ellipsoids of rotation, differ very little from a sphere.

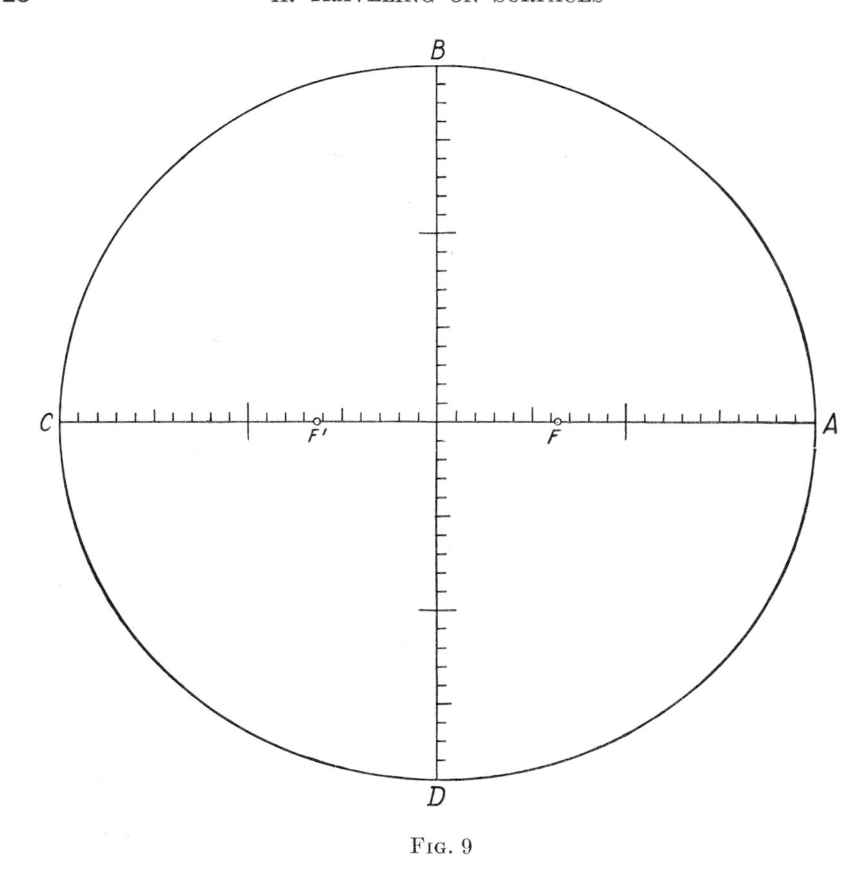


FIG. 9

Just as a sphere is a special case of an ellipsoid of rotation, so the latter is a special case of a general ellipsoid. A general ellipsoid has three *different* axes perpendicular to each other, as shown at the right in picture 2 of Plate I. Such an ellipsoid is called a *tri-axial ellipsoid* [**8**].

Let us now follow the course of a geodesic on an ellipsoid. Picture 1 of Plate II represents an ellipsoid of rotation obtained by rotating an ellipse about its major axis. The initial point $a$ of the trip is marked by a small circle with an arrow pointing in the chosen direction. We shall maintain this fixed direction, that is, we shall travel along a geodesic. Our path will take us far from the point of departure, over to the other side of the ellipsoid, so that we shall have to keep turning it in order to follow the course of our travels. Part of the beginning of the route is drawn in picture 2 of Plate II. The starting point is now down at the bottom, almost at the disappearance point, as we rotate the ellipsoid in order to follow the progress of the journey. The stages of this journey are shown in single steps. A much more impressive and more encompassing view could be obtained from a film portraying the steady progress of the trip. But we shall have to be content with these single photographs of the journey. A continuous turning of the ellipsoid brings us to points $b$, $c$, and $d$, which may be seen in pictures 3 and 4 as encampments, reminiscent of a march in deep snow in which the path behind us is already buried. Picture 5 shows how the geodesic, having circled the body once, finally reaches the starting point $a$.[7] But at this point the path takes a direction different from the one in which the march started. And so the trip continues on this egg-shaped, ellipsoid world, but in another direction. This leads over the stopover points $e$ and $f$ (pictures 6 and 7), crosses the former route and goes on to the point $g$ (picture 8). The point $h$ is reached, not far from the point of departure $a$, on a third world tour; and later (after crossing routes 1 and 2) points $i$ and $j$ (pictures 10 and 11) are reached. Finally after passing through $k$ and $l$ (picture 12), we again return to the starting point $a$ (picture 13), and this time the path continues in exactly the same direction in which the geodesic trip was begun. The journey is ended: we have run through a closed geodesic.

In a similar manner, we may follow a geodesic on a tri-axial ellipsoid in pictures 1–8, Plate III.[8] This geodesic always returns to the starting point $a$, but with another direction, so that it is not a *closed*, but an unending *open* geodesic.

We shall now consider the geodesics on some other surfaces. Picture 3 of Plate I represents a ring surface, also called a *torus;* and picture 4 an asymmetrical ring-like surface.[9] Both of these surfaces, like the sphere and the ellipsoid, are bounded; that is, they are the outer surfaces of bodies having a finite extension. The saddle-surface in picture 5 is an entirely different type of surface; the surface in picture 6 (a *hyperboloid of one sheet*) is of the same type as picture 5. The rotation surface[10] in picture 7 is related

[7] Picture 5 (and also 9 and 13) shows the ellipsoid photographed from the same viewpoint as picture 1, with only the addition of the curve that traces the route just traversed. Similarly, pictures 2, 6, 10, all show the same view of the ellipsoid; as do also 3, 7, 11, as well as 4, 8, 12.

[8] The larger planets, deviating almost unnoticeably from a sphere, are ellipsoids, but oblate ellipsoids, and quite unlike the type considered in Plate III. Small astral bodies, however, often have a different shape. Very soon after the discovery of the planet Eros in 1898, its unusual light nutations led astronomers to suspect that its shape deviates strongly from a sphere. The work of the astronomer Hugo Seeliger stimulated Gustav Herglotz—who will be mentioned again in connection with the general problem of geodesics—to develop a general theory in his dissertation (1902) on the light nutations of arbitrary convex planets [9].

[9] The curve drawn on each of these surfaces is in no sense a geodesic, but—and we shall discuss this later—a demarcation line between domains of positive and negative curvature.

[10] This surface is technically described as having a *constant negative curvature*.

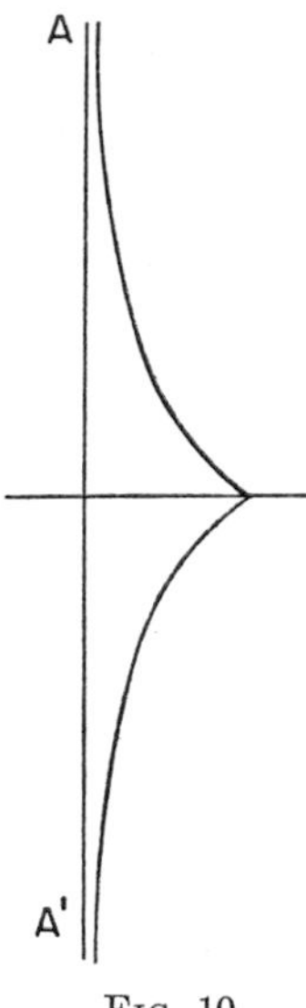


Fig. 10

to the saddle-surfaces. Pictures 1 to 5 of Plate IV show a special geodesic on this surface: a continuously winding path that never again passes through any point reached previously. The winding turns follow one another at ever smaller distances, approaching as a limit the circle which a string wound tight about the surface would make. Here again, we have an open geodesic.

Picture 6, Plate IV, shows another situation. This surface is obtained by rotating a curve, called a *tractrix* (see Fig. 10) about the straight line $AA'$; the resulting surface resembles a pointed harlequin's cap, except that the top of the surface thins out as it approaches infinity.[11] Picture 6 shows a piece of a geodesic on this tractrix-rotation surface; the part of the path shown resembles a small neckerchief held loosely about the throat, the highest point of the curve sitting high on the neck, here hidden by the plaster model. Picture 7 shows the high points of a whole family of geodesics on the reverse side of the model. These, too, are open geodesics.

These examples lead to a distinction between two kinds of geodesics:

---

But it would lead us too far astray to explain the term in greater detail, since this would not only lead us to the difference (to be explained later) between positive and negative curvature of a surface, but furthermore into the problem of how to introduce a numerical value as a measure of the curvature at a point of a surface (see Chapter XIV).

[11] The curve of Fig. 10 has an upper and lower branch. In picture 6 (and 7) of Plate IV, only the part of the surface obtained by rotating the upper branch about $AA'$ is shown. Rotation of the lower branch yields an analogous lower surface.

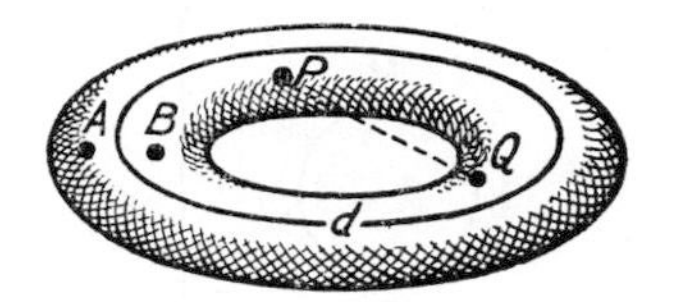


FIG. 11

*closed* geodesics, which return to the initial point with the initial direction; and *open* geodesics, for which this is not the case, no matter how long the path is drawn.

We shall now discuss a problem which has to do with closed geodesics on a special class of surfaces, the *convex* surfaces. These are the outer or bounding surfaces of *convex bodies*. We first discuss convex bodies.

The simplest example of a convex body is a solid sphere. Think of a solid sphere of hard material, and choose any point on its surface. This sphere can be placed on a flat surface such as a table, so that it rests exactly at the chosen point. What is significant is that this contact can be made *no matter where* we choose the point on the surface of the sphere. The same thing is true of some other bodies, but not all. An ellipsoid, for example, has the same property. We may choose an arbitrary point on its surface and turn the ellipsoid so that it touches the table only at the chosen point. (We must, of course, support both the sphere and ellipsoid to keep them from rolling or sliding, but this is irrelevant for our considerations, which are purely geometric, and independent of such physical phenomena as the force of gravity.)

The case of a ring body or solid torus, such as that in picture 3 of Plate I and Fig. 11,[12] differs greatly from that of a sphere. The surface of this solid is a torus. Let us place such a ring on a table top and notice which points on the ring surface form points of contact with the surface of the table. (Again we shall be interested in all possible positions of the ring, even if it means holding it in a slanting position to keep it from falling; and the force of gravity is again irrelevant, since our only concern is with the geometry of the situation.) It is immediately clear that not all the points of the ring surface can be points of contact with the table. For example, points $P$ and $Q$ in Fig. 11 certainly cannot rest on the table. The situation may be more exactly described by saying that the ring can be placed on the table, freely and without support, on one of the circumferences $c$ or $d$ mentioned in

[12] Such a ring is obtained by rotating a circle $k$ about an axis $a$ which does not intersect the circle (see Fig. 12). If $CD$ is the diameter of the circle parallel to $a$, rotation of the points $C$ and $D$ yields two circumferences, $c$ and $d$, on the ring surface; we shall see later that $c$ and $d$ are the boundaries between domains on the surface with entirely different properties. See Fig. 11, where the circumference $d$ is visible, while $c$ (on the other side of the ring) is invisible.

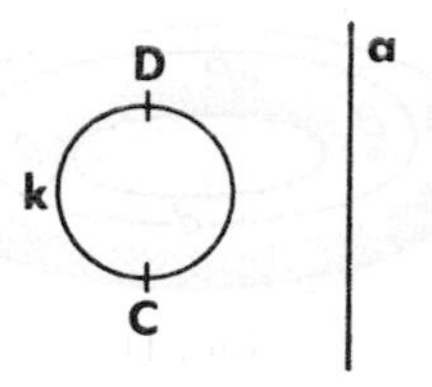


FIG. 12

Footnote 12. Moving from the circumference $d$ outwards (see Fig. 11) we come to points, such as $A$, where the ring can be held in such a position that $A$ touches the plane of the table top. But if we proceed inwards from $d$, we come to points like $B$, which cannot be points of contact with a plane. Therefore, the circumference $d$ separates the points of the surface where contact with a table top is possible from those where it is not; and the same is true for the circumference $c$ (generated by the point $c$ in Fig. 12). Thus the surface of the ring is separated by $c$ and $d$ into two different kinds of regions: the outward part of the surface, all of whose points are possible points of contact with a plane; and the inward part, whose points do not have this property. Now we can distinguish between two kinds of bodies. Those we call *convex* are characterized by the fact that, given any point on the surface of the body, the body can be maneuvered into a position in which it is able to touch a flat table top at precisely the prescribed point. On the other hand, a body is *non-convex* if its surface contains at least one point without the property just described [**10**].

The bounding surfaces of convex bodies are then called *convex surfaces*, more precisely, *closed convex surfaces* [**11**]. In contrast, a torus (see pictures 3 and 4 of Plate I) is an example of a non-convex surface.[13]

We can now state our problem, which has to do with *closed geodesics on a closed convex surface*. Let us take any closed convex surface. We are interested in the closed geodesics on this surface. Are there always such geodesics? We found an infinite number on a sphere, since every great circle was a closed geodesic. We also found a closed geodesic on an ellipsoid of rotation (pictures 1–13 of Plate II). But what about other convex surfaces? Is it possible to make a general statement about the presence of closed geodesics on an aribtrary closed convex surface? It is easy to see that the number of closed convex surfaces is immense. These surfaces can resemble a sphere, an egg, or a bean; others are long and pointy with the points rounded off; still others resemble a flat disk (lenticular shape) with a rounding off of the outer edge, etc. In addition to the examples in pictures 1 and 2 of Plate I, see also Fig. 13, where besides the egg and disk shapes,

[13] Other examples of non-convex surfaces are given in pictures 5 to 8 of Plate I, and in Plate IV.

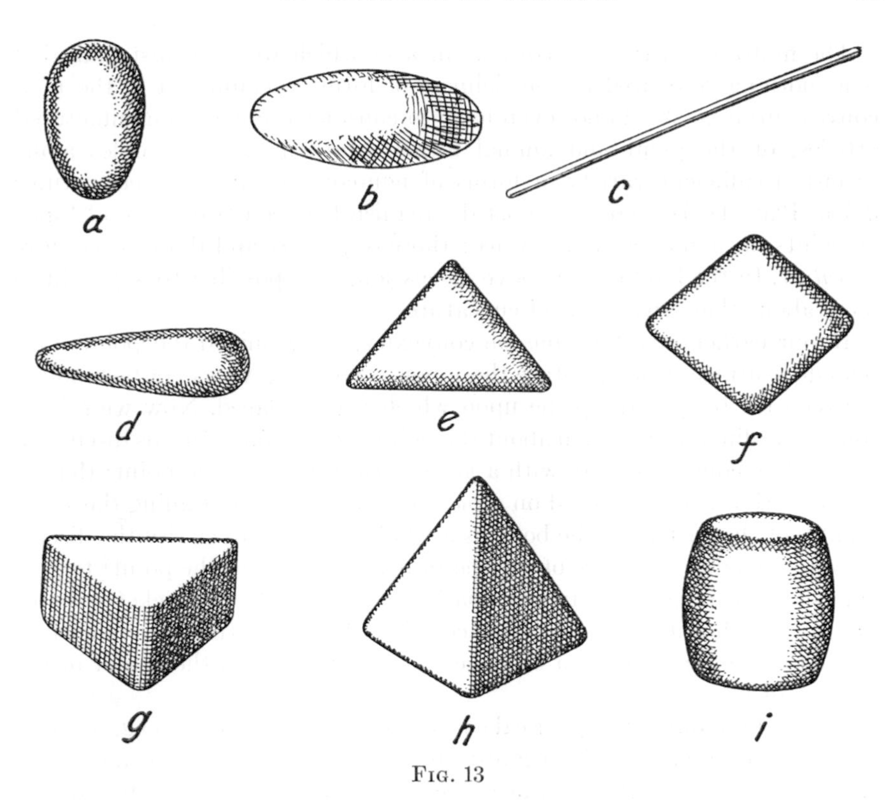


Fig. 13

there are surfaces shaped like a knitting needle, a turnip, a three or four-cornered pillow, a wedge of cheese with rounded edges, a pyramid or a barrel. Our problem is to decide whether the bounding surfaces of all these bodies of very different shape have a closed geodesic. The difficulty of the problem lies precisely in the fact that we cannot just examine one or another of these surfaces; our argument must apply to *all* of them. Nevertheless, mathematicians have arrived at the quite definite result that every closed convex surface not only contains a closed geodesic, but that it contains at least three. The solution to our geometric problem can therefore be stated as follows: *Every closed convex surface contains at least three closed geodesics* [**12**].

We cannot discuss the proof of this result [**13**] in this book, but must be satisfied with confirming the theorem in the case of a particularly simple example, that of a tri-axial ellipsoid. Let us choose two of the three axes (this can be done in three ways). The plane through these two axes cuts the ellipsoid in an ellipse [**14**]. The three ellipses thus obtained (see picture 9, Plate I) are geodesics on the ellipsoid. Thus our general assertion is confirmed in this case.

The multiform nature of convex surfaces which we have just indicated is as nothing compared to the richness of forms encountered in the non-convex surfaces. We do not even have to consider the many manufactured articles, or the plant and animal forms. Mathematical examples alone furnish a sufficient variety of forms of non-convex surfaces (see pictures 3–7 of Plate I). But now we must distinguish between two different kinds of points on a non-convex surface: those of *positive* and those of *negative curvature.* In the light of the above discussion, it is possible to say a little more about these two kinds of curvature.

In our earlier investigations on convexity, we examined the points of a bounded surface to see whether these points could serve as contact points between the body and a plane upon which it was placed. Now we raise a somewhat different question about the points of a surface. In this discussion we shall be concerned only with a *neighborhood* of the given point; that is, our attention will be focused on a piece of the surface containing the given point, not the surface or the body as a whole. In order to clarify the discussion, we imagine this piece of surface (a neighborhood of the point) to be a thin sheet of metal. Now take a small circular disk (like a pocket mirror), and see whether it is possible to place this disk against the piece of surface so that the chosen point on the piece of surface touches the center of the circular disk.

If you think only of a spherical surface, or the surface of an egg, it seems easy to place a circular disk against any chosen spot of these surfaces. But we have only to consider surfaces such as those in pictures 5, 6 and 7 of Plate I to be convinced that this is not always the case. Just imagine applying the test disk to the saddle-surface (picture 5) from above. It is obviously not possible to bring the circular disk into such a position that its center will touch a point of the saddle-surface. Before these two points can meet, the edge of the circular disk will hit against the surface of the saddle and prevent the disk from coming any closer. The example shows that there are indeed surfaces on which the disk test gives a *negative* result.

We must add to these observations in one respect. The saddle-surface in picture 5 of Plate I is shown as the surface of a body, the plaster model in the picture. We must now emphasize that we are henceforth to think of these surfaces, not as surfaces of a body, but as entities free of the body, say as thin sheets of metal divorced from the body. We shall therefore suppose that the plaster model of picture 5 has been covered with a thin sheet of metal fitting the saddle-surface snugly, so that every bit of it is covered. And now we apply the circular disk again. If the disk is applied from above, the test is again negative: it is impossible to touch a point of the surface with the center of the disk. But we can also remove the thin sheet of metal from the plaster model—without changing its shape in any way—and try to place the test disk against the surface from below. Again

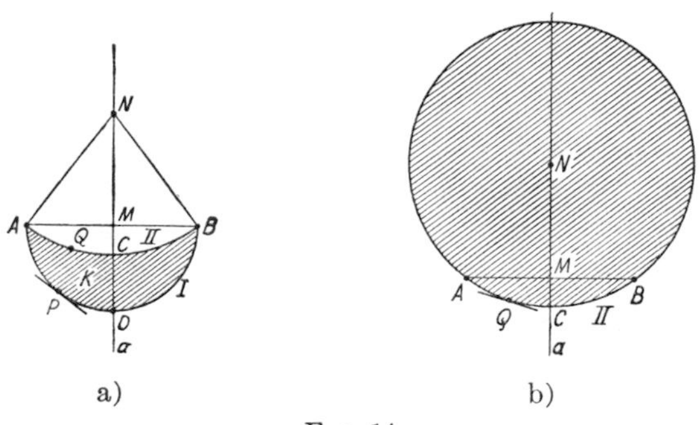


FIG. 14

the test proves negative: the disk cannot be brought close enough to the surface so that a prescribed point of the surface can come into contact with the center of the disk. Again, before contact can be made, the edge of the disk will hit the surface first. (Naturally, the points of the surface hit by the edge of the disk will be different from those in the attempt made from above.)

The failure of the test disk to make contact with the surface from either approach characterizes *negative curvature* of a surface at the prescribed point [**15**].[14] This is obviously a different situation than the one encountered on a sphere (and on many other surfaces). For if $P$ is a point on a sphere, it is at once obvious that we can place the center of the circular disk on the point $P$. And it is to be emphasized that the point $P$ is the only point at which the disk touches the sphere, so that around $P$ the surface falls away from the disk. When a surface behaves in this manner in a neighborhood of a point $P$, we say that the surface has *positive curvature* at $P$ [**16**].

In order to make our point still clearer, we shall give another example. Fig. 14a shows a circular arc $ACB$ with $N$ as center, its chord $AB$ with mid-point $M$, and a semi-circle $ADB$ with $M$ as center and diameter $AB$. The two circular arcs bound a (hatched) sickle-shaped region. If the whole figure is rotated about the straight line $a = NMCD$, the result is a body $K$, shaped like a bowl which can rock on its base. The outer surface of this rocking bowl $K$ consists of two parts (both spherical surfaces) marked I and II in the figure.

If we now test any point $P$ of surface I, it is immediately obvious that the disk can be applied so that its center touches the surface only at $P$ (see Fig. 14a). Every point $P$ of surface I is therefore a point of positive curvature.

But what about any point $Q$ of surface II (Fig. 14a)? In this case the

[14] The disk test, which gave a negative result for the saddle-surface of picture 5, Plate I, gives the same result for the surfaces of pictures 6 and 7 of Plate I; these are also surfaces of negative curvature.

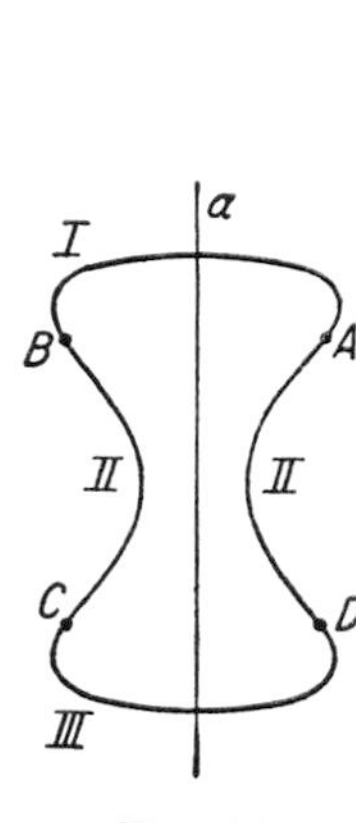


Fig. 15

Fig. 16

center of the circular disk cannot touch $Q$ from above. But we recall that we are not examining the body $K$, but only the surface II itself, and for this purpose we can think of the latter as a piece of a sphere made out of a thin sheet of metal (with $N$ as center). If we think of surface II by itself, removed from $K$, it is clear that the surface may be approached *from below* to give a *positive* test.[15] Hence surface II has a positive curvature at $Q$ (and therefore at all its other points) [**17**].

Now that we have considered examples of surfaces of positive and of negative curvature [**18**], we shall give an example of a surface which has points of positive, as well as points of negative curvature.

Shortly before the first World War, there appeared a game called *diabolo*, which was played by both old and young. The name originated because it seemed *devilishly* difficult even to begin to play the game, yet many children could play it with skill, and even virtuosity. Children who play with balls a good deal seem to acquire a certain confidence with spherical forms, but the game of diabolo used a different body. The toy was made of wood or metal, and its shape was that obtained by rotating the curve of Fig. 15 about the straight line $a$. The two parts swelling outward, formed by the rotation of the arcs $AB$ and $CD$ of the sketch, form the upper (I) and lower (III) boundaries of the body. The part of the outer surface of the body

[15] This can be made clear in another way. Instead of considering surface II as a piece of the outer surface of the bowl $K$, we can think of it as a piece of the surface of a sphere (Fig. 14b) obtained by rotating the hatched circular disk of Fig. 14b about the axis $a = NMC$. Fig. 14b shows how to apply the test disk to surface II to achieve the appropriate contact with the point $Q$.

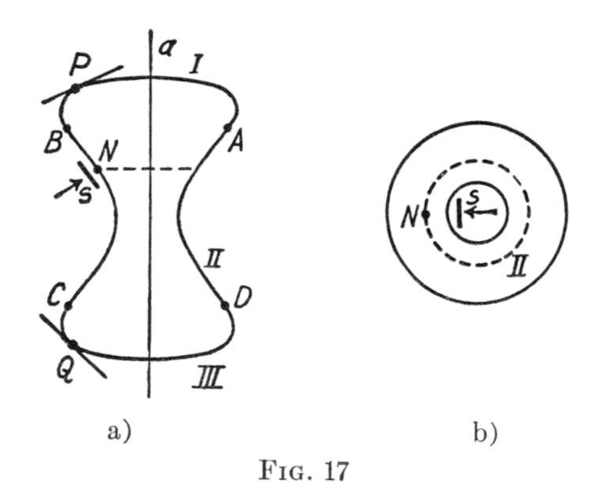


a) b)

Fig. 17

(marked II) lying between I and III is of the same type as a saddle-surface (pictures 6 and 7 of Plate I), and is obtained by rotating the arcs $BC$ and $AD$ in Fig. 15.[16]

It is obvious that the diabolo is a *non-convex* body, for while it is possible to bring many, if not all, points of surfaces I and III into contact with a flat table top, this is not the case for points of the saddle-surface II.

Let us examine the surface of a diabolo for points of positive and negative curvature, again using a circular disk. We see that the disk tests positive at every point $P$ of surface I (see Fig. 17), and at every point $Q$ of surface III. But it tests negative at every point $N$ of surface II, because surface II is of the same type as the surfaces in pictures 5, 6, and 7 of Plate I. We have already seen that the test was negative at all points of these surfaces. All points of I and III are, therefore, points of positive curvature, while all points of II are points of negative curvature.

The surface of a diabolo is not the only example of a surface having points of positive and negative curvature. The same is true of many other surfaces, such as the tori of pictures 3 and 4 of Plate I.[17] The curve on each figure separates the regions of positive and negative curvature.[18]

The organic world contains a large number of surfaces having both negative and positive curvature. However, the world of inorganic nature, of handicraft and industry, is more suitable for the study of mathematics. Innumerable examples of curved surfaces are found in vessels, parts of

[16] To play the game, a string is needed, connected to two rods held in the hand (see Fig. 16). The diabolo is placed on the string, which is manipulated to give the diabolo sufficient initial rotation so that (like a spinning top) it acquires enough stability to prevent it from falling.

[17] The same is true of the surface of the figure in picture 8, Plate I, which resembles a potato.

[18] The curvature is zero at all points [18] of the demarcation curve [19]. On the surface of a diabolo the demarcation lines are the two circles formed by the rotation of the point $A$ (or $B$) and $C$ (or $D$), resp., about the axis $a$ (see Figs. 15 and 17).

buildings, etc. But it is in nature, in the crystalline structures, that we find examples of the *polyhedral* surfaces, that is, surfaces made up of plane pieces, fitted together at the edges. What about the geodesics of the polyhedral surfaces—which include the surface of a cube, a pyramid, a prism? The problem is to find the shortest path between two points on a polyhedral surface. A full treatment of this problem would fill a chapter. We will give a small, but pertinent, example.

In a room 10 feet high, with a ceiling 16 feet long and 8 feet wide, there sits a fly, exactly in the center of the narrow wall, .8 feet below the ceiling. On the opposite wall, also exactly in the center, sits a spider, 2.4 feet above the ground, that is, 7.6 feet from the ceiling. The fly notices that the spider has just awakened, and addresses it: "Honorable spider, would you care to try to come over here and catch me?" The spider answers: "You would not give me enough time to reach you, but would fly away, just in time." "Well, how fast do you intend crawling over here?" the fly asks, and being told that the spider can't make more than 8 feet a minute, answers sorrowfully: "Too bad I can't wait longer than three minutes; I shall sleep for that length of time and then I must get into the sunlight."

Will the spider catch the fly [20]?

*Notes to Chapter II*

# TRAVELING ON SURFACES

**1** (p. 24). The following remark is addressed to those who are interested in the systematic development of mathematics. In order to compare the length of the straight line $AB$ with the lengths of other paths connecting $A$ to $B$, it must first be made clear what the "length" of a path is; i.e. the "length of a curve element" must first be defined. But a general definition of length presupposes a highly developed mathematics (and especially the notion of limit).[1] On the other hand, the concept of "straight line" is one of the fundamental notions of elementary geometry; and the fact that a straight line has a constant direction—in the sense of sighting along markers—is expressed by the axiom of geometry which states that a straight line is determined by any two of its points.[2] After the length of a path is defined, it can then be shown that the straight line of elementary geometry yields the shortest distance between any two of its points.[3] It is thus obvious that this property of straight lines cannot be used as the definition of a straight line in a systematic development of geometry.

**2** (p. 24). The diameter of the equator is 7927 miles, and the distance between the two poles is 7900 miles, which gives a value of $1/299$ for the oblateness, that is, the ratio of the difference to the diameter of the equator.

[1] In the calculus, the length of a curve in the $xy$-plane, whose parametric equations are continuous functions $x = g(t)$, $y = h(t)$, with $a \leq t \leq b$, is given by the integral

$$(1) \qquad \int_a^b [(dg(t)/dt)^2 + (dh(t)/dt)^2]^{1/2}\, dt.$$

(See {1}.)

[2] It is necessary then merely to extend elementary geometry to the beginning of analytic geometry (see Chapter III), that is, to the introduction of coordinates (the location of *geometric* objects by means of numbers) in order to see that the parametric equations of a straight line have the form

$$(2) \qquad x = Ct + D, \qquad y = Et + F,$$

where $C, D, E, F$ are constants which determine for every choice a particular straight line, and where $C$ and $E$ are not both zero. This representation of a straight line expresses in analytic form the property of preservation of direction.

[3] The problem then is to find the minimum of the integral (1) in Footnote 1 over all paths connecting two given points. The solution is, of course, that the integral attains its minimum value when $f(t)$ and $g(t)$ have the form (2) of Footnote 2, that is, when the curve is the straight-line segment joining the two points. The problem of finding the minimum value of an integral over a given set of curves belongs to the branch of mathematics known as the calculus of variations. (See the Postscript.)

Since the distance of a point on the equator from the center of the earth is 13.5 miles more than that of a pole, the heights of the highest mountain peaks (about 5.6 miles) are only a fraction of this difference.

**3** (p. 25). Munich has a longitude of 11°36.5′ east of Greenwich, and a northern latitude of 48°08.8′; its antipode lies to the southeast of New Zealand at an eastern longitude 191°36.5′ = 168°23.5′ western longitude from Greenwich and 48°08.8′ southern latitude, at a distance from the latter of about 745 miles—i.e. double the width of the Chatham Islands—not far from the ice floes of the South Pole at a spot 3 miles below sea level.

**4** (p. 26). In the southern hemisphere the course veers to the left. Traveling along a latitude from East to West would then mean circling the South Pole with the Pole on the left.

**5** (p. 26). This is also a problem in the calculus of variations (see Footnote 3).

**6** (p. 27). These curves (geodesics) are the extremals of the corresponding problem in the calculus of variations. For a more mathematical discussion of the double property of geodesics the interested reader is referred to {2}, where special attention is given to the physical and epistemological aspects of the question. In this connection see also {3}.

**7** (p. 27). This name comes from geodesy, the science of measuring the earth's surface, which includes surveying and the measurement of degrees of latitude and longitude. A small flat area of the earth's surface can be regarded as a plane, and it is then natural that *straight lines* play the most important role in measurements on this restricted area. But on larger areas of the earth's surface, which are spherical, the straight segments are more accurately arcs of *great circles*, and these then become the most important for the measurement of the earth. When dealing with still larger areas, the oblateness of the earth must also be taken into account, and then the great circles of a sphere become the *geodesics* of a flattened ellipsoid of rotation. Finally, if the areas considered are large enough, deviations from an ellipsoid of rotation must be reckoned with, and the geodesics are those of a surface called a "geoid." For measurement of degrees on the earth's surface, see also Chapter IX.

**8** (p. 28). A general ellipsoid cannot be defined by the rotation of an ellipse about an axis, and we must have recourse to the methods of analytic geometry. Introducing rectangular coordinates $x$, $y$ in the plane, we define an ellipse (such as that of Fig. 8) as the set of points $(x, y)$ in the plane which satisfy an equation

$$x^2/a^2 + y^2/b^2 = 1,$$

where $a$ and $b$ are the semi-axes of the ellipse (in Fig. 8, $a = MA$, $b = MB$). By analogy, if $x$, $y$, $z$ are rectangular coordinates in space, an ellipsoid with semi-axes $a$, $b$, $c$ is the set of all points satisfying an equation

$$x^2/a^2 + y^2/b^2 + z^2/c^2 = 1.$$

If $b = c$, the equation represents an ellipsoid of rotation about the $x$-axis; if $a = b = c$, the ellipsoid is a sphere.

**9** (p. 29). See {4}. The notion of convexity is discussed again in Chapter IV. See Chapter IV, Note 16. See also Note 10 below.

**10** (p. 32). There is another way of defining convex bodies. A body $K$, or, more generally, a set of points in space, is said to be *convex* if all the points of the straight-line segment $XY$ joining any two points $X$ and $Y$ of $K$ also belong to $K$. (This is the definition used in present-day mathematics.) It is clear that a solid sphere and a solid ellipsoid have this property. It is also clear that a solid torus does not, since the straight line segment connecting the points $P$ and $Q$ of the solid torus of Fig. 11 contains points which do not belong to the ring body.

That the two definitions of convexity are essentially the same can be proved from the theory of convex bodies and their supporting planes.

**11** (p. 32). A closed convex surface is therefore the outer surface of a bounded convex body. On the other hand, the surface of a paraboloid (obtained by rotating a parabola about its axis) is an example of an open convex surface (the space enclosed by a paraboloid is also convex, but it is unbounded).

**12** (p. 33). In this connection we must mention a sketch of a proof of Gustav Herglotz (1881–1953), who to my knowledge never again returned to the subject. See {5}, where reference is made to the work of Poincaré and G. D. Birkhoff. Birkhoff dealt with the problem of closed geodesics in connection with problems in mechanics. In 1929, Lusternik and Schnirelmann proved a theorem which solved Herglotz's problem as a special case. The proof involves a topological principle which generalizes the work of Birkhoff and Marston Morse. Lusternik and Schnirelmann considered closed geodesics on closed surfaces of genus 0, a more general class than that of closed convex surfaces, and moreover showed that such surfaces contain three closed geodesics *without double points* (that is, without self-intersections). See {6}–{8}.

**13** (p. 33). Besides the differential and integral calculus, this would require a knowledge of differential geometry, since the problem belongs to this branch of mathematics. See Note 9 to Chapter IV.

**14** (p. 33). If the equation of the ellipsoid (see Note 8) relative to a suitably chosen coordinate system is

$$x^2/a^2 + y^2/b^2 + z^2/c^2 = 1,$$

then the equations of the three planes are $z = 0$, $x = 0$ and $y = 0$. In these planes the equations of the ellipses are

$$x^2/a^2 + y^2/b^2 = 1, \qquad y^2/b^2 + z^2/c^2 = 1, \qquad x^2/a^2 + z^2/c^2 = 1,$$

respectively.

**15** (p. 35). The discussion should be supplemented by mentioning the possible existence of points on a surface which yield a negative result when the disk test is applied (from both sides of the surface), but which nevertheless are assigned zero curvature. There are also surfaces (represented by functions which are not twice-differentiable) to which the disk test cannot be applied. We cannot discuss such surfaces here.

**16** (p. 35). Here again a professional mathematician would require certain additions and qualifications in the discussion, similar to those in Note 15. It should especially be noted that certain precisely formulated differentiability conditions enter into a technical exposition of positive and negative curvature of a surface. These are required, for instance, in the study of the tangent plane at a point of the surface, the planes parallel to the tangent plane and their intersections with the surface, as well as in the study of the deviations of these intersections from an ellipse or hyperbola (the Dupin indicatrix). References to the disk test, here applied to the determination of curvature, can be found in papers on convex figures which appeared between 1927 and 1929 {9}. For a related discussion see {10}.

**17** (p. 36). Having noted that each of the two surfaces I and II (see Fig. 14a), which form the outer surface of the bowl $K$, have positive curvature when divorced from the body $K$, it would be well at the same time to distinguish between them as parts of the outer surface of $K$. In this context, it is clear that surface I is curved outwardly, that is, it is *convex*,[4] while surface II is curved inwardly, or is *concave*. This explains why the disk test can be applied to surface I from the exterior of $K$, while in the case of surface II the disk test must be applied from the interior of $K$.

**18** (p. 36). For completeness, we shall say a few words about the points on a surface which have zero curvature. A surface $f$ is said to have zero curvature at a point $P$ if the disk test can be applied at $P$ from either side of $f$ and if an arbitrarily small disk applied at $P$ touches the surface not only at $P$ but also in at least one point distinct from $P$. A simple example of this is a torus (see Fig. 11 and the discussion on p. 31). The torus of Fig. 11 has zero curvature at every point of the circumference $d$ (or the circumference $c$, which is not shown in the figure). This is so because a disk applied at any point of $d$ will touch not only the point in question but other points of $d$ as well, no matter how small the disk is. The cylinder of Fig. 18a and the cone of Fig. 18b are further examples. In both cases a disk will touch the surface not only at the point $P$ but also part of the line $l$ passing through $P$.

[4] This nomenclature agrees with the fact that outwardly curved surfaces occur, in particular, as the outer surfaces of convex bodies.

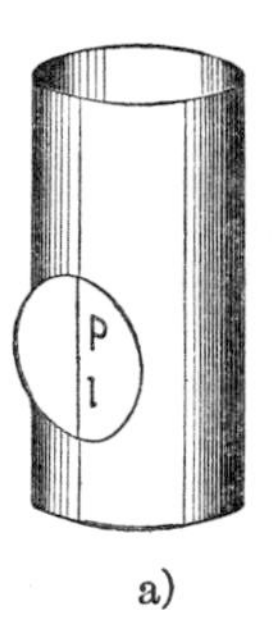


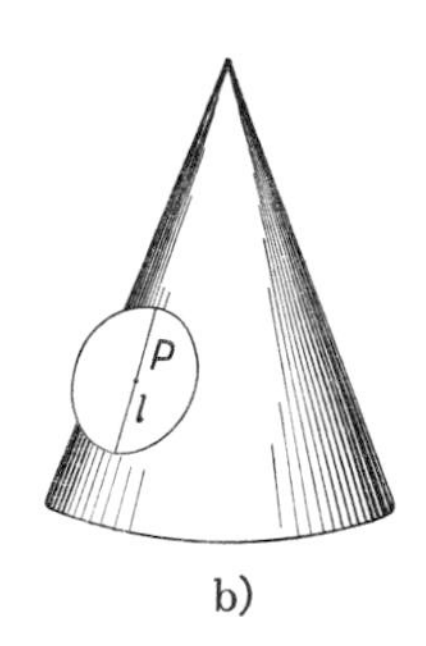


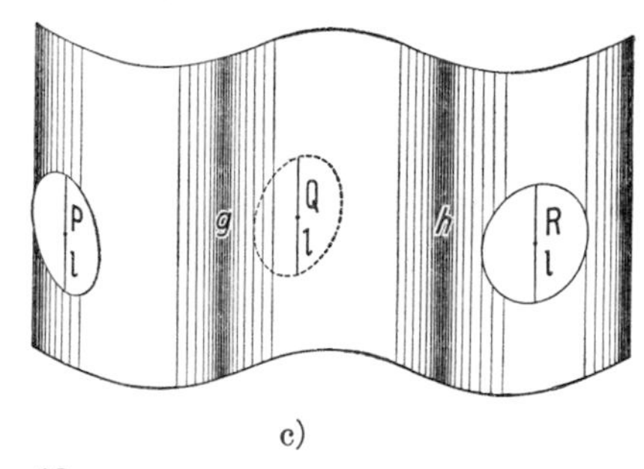


a) b) c)

FIG. 18

Fig. 18c shows the surface of a corrugated sheet which contains points such as $P$ and $R$ at which the disk test can be applied from one side of the surface and other points such as $Q$ at which the disk test can be applied from the other side of the surface; but in both cases every test disk will also touch the surface all along part of the line $l$. These are, therefore, all points of zero curvature. An even simpler example is, of course, a plane, which has zero curvature at all of its points. There are other examples of surfaces with points of zero curvature besides the ones we have already mentioned, but these examples will suffice. The true situation is of course somewhat more complicated than we have indicated here, since zero curvature is also assigned to the corrugated sheet of Fig. 18c at the points of the lines $g$, $h$, etc., even though the disk test cannot be applied at such points. These are the lines of the surface at which it changes from convex to concave.

**19** (p. 37). There are two such lines of demarcation between regions of positive and negative curvature on a torus; these are the circumferences $c$ and $d$ mentioned in Note 18 (see also Figs. 11 and 12). These circumferences were used as examples of curves which separate points such as $A$ in Fig. 11, to which the disk test can be applied, from points such as $B$ at which it is not possible to do so. But the torus is a special case in this respect. On a torus, this separation of the points of the surface at which the disk test can be applied from those at which it cannot agrees with the classification into points of positive and negative curvature. It would, however, be wrong to assume that this is true of all surfaces. For instance, the outer surface of a diabolo contains points of positive curvature at which the disk test *cannot* be applied.[5]

[5] The classification of points on a surface by means of the disk test may be reformulated as follows: Let $H$ be a non-convex body whose surface is $F$. Now form the smallest convex body $K$ which contains $H$ (mathematicians call $K$ the convex hull of $H$). For instance, in order to obtain the convex hull of the solid torus of Fig. 11, one must fill in the space between the circumferences $c$ and $d$ which is missing from the solid torus. Then the part of the surface $F$ of $H$ which also belongs to the surface of the convex hull $K$ consists precisely of those points at which the disk test originally gave a positive result.

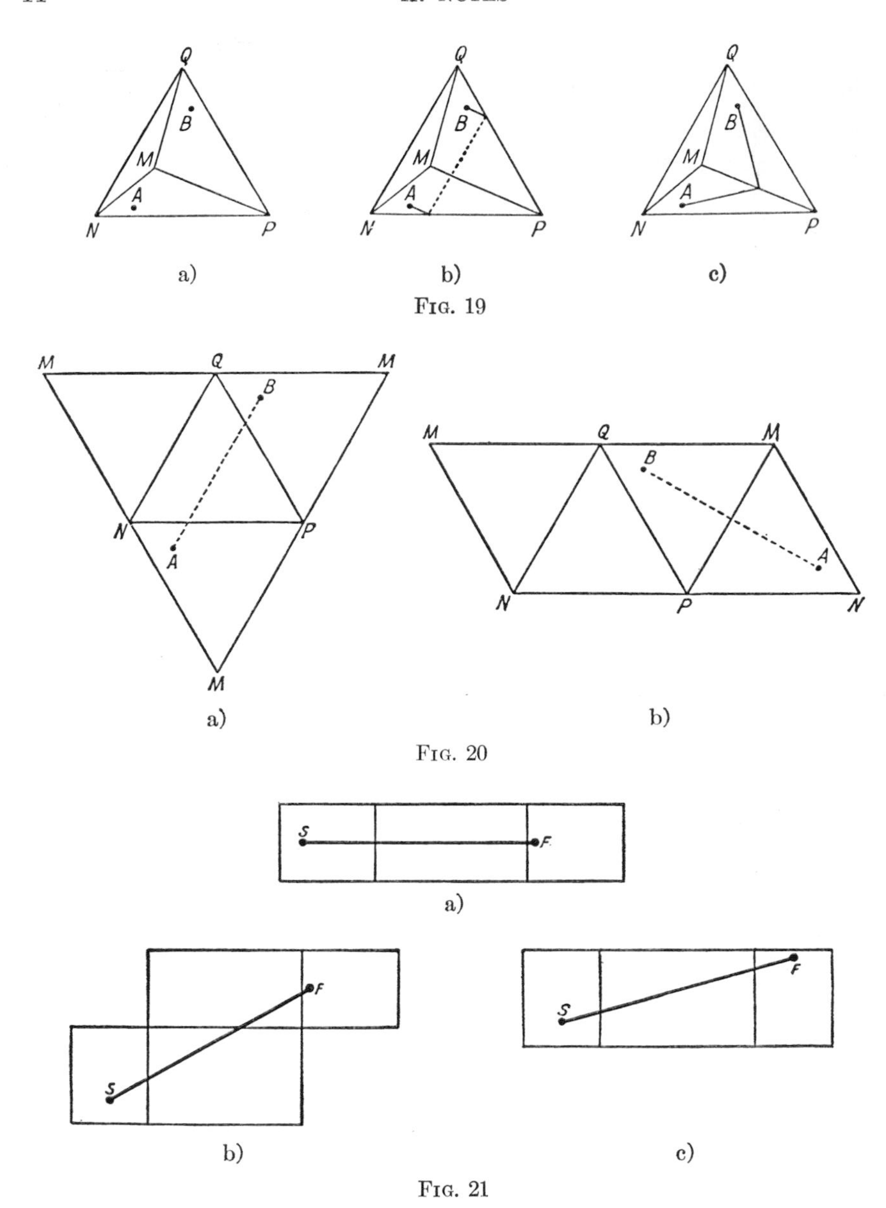


a) b) c)

Fig. 19

a) b)

Fig. 20

a)

b) c)

Fig. 21

**20 (p.** 38). The walls, floor and ceiling of this room can be thought of as the surface of a polyhedron (in fact, a rectangular prism), and the problem is then to find the geodesics on this surface. The problem can be solved by transforming the polyhedron into an equivalent net in the plane (that is, into a figure consisting of simple plane polygons and their interiors).[6] For example, the tetrahedron $MNPQ$ of Fig. 19a can be transformed into the equivalent net of Fig. 20a by cutting the surface of the tetrahedron along the edges $MN$, $MP$ and $MQ$, rotating the triangle $MNP$ about the edge $NP$ until it is in the same plane as the triangle $NPQ$, and then performing the analogous operations on the triangles $MPQ$ and $MQN$.[7] Now in Fig. 19a, let $A$ be the point of triangle $MNP$ which lies one third of the way up from $N$ on the perpendicular from $N$ to $MP$; and let $B$ be the analogous point in triangle $MPQ$. Then we obtain the geodesic (and at the same time the shortest) line connecting $A$ and $B$ on the surface of the tetrahedron (see Fig. 19b) simply by drawing the dotted straight line connecting $A$ and $B$ in Fig. 20a.[8]

Now we can return to our trick problem. The net shown in Fig. 21a is equivalent to part of the surface of the room, the ceiling and the two narrow walls joined to it at either end. Let $S$ be the spider and $F$ the fly. The path from $S$ to $F$ directly over the ceiling is $7.6 + 16 + .8 = 24.4$ feet long, so that the spider would not reach the fly in time along this path. But the spider would catch the fly if it followed the path shown in Fig. 21b, which represents the net equivalent to the narrow wall of the spider, followed by one of the larger walls, then the ceiling and finally the narrow wall of the fly. The length of this path is $(568.2)^{1/2}$ feet, which is less than 24 feet, so that the spider will catch the fly in less than 3 minutes.[9]

[6] These nets first appeared in a book by Albrecht Dürer (see {11}).

[7] Cardboard boxes may be taken apart and flattened out in a similar manner; conversely, they may be bought in flat preformed sheets and assembled.

[8] The length of this geodesic is obviously equal to the length of the edge $NQ$ of the tetrahedron. Fig. 19c (or the equivalent net of Fig. 20b) shows another, but longer geodesic. It is clear from Fig. 20b that the length of this geodesic is $2\sqrt{3}/3$ if the edges of the tetrahedron are set equal to 1. This net, which is somewhat different from the net of Fig. 20a, is obtained by cutting the surface of the tetrahedron along the edges $MQ$, $MN$ and $NP$.

[9] On the other hand, a path avoiding the ceiling and going along one of the larger walls (see Fig. 21c) would be still longer ($= (622.24)^{1/2}$ feet) than the direct path over the ceiling ($= 24.4$ feet).

If we denote the distances of the fly and the spider from the ceiling by $f$ and $s$, and the time which the fly waits by $T$, then we see that if $f = .8$, $s = 7.6$ and $T = 3$ minutes, the spider will reach the fly before it flies off. But what happens if $f = 4$, $s = 4.8$ and $T = 3$ minutes and 3 seconds? Or if $T = 2$ minutes and 50 seconds, $s = 4.8$, and $f = 2.8$, or 2.4?

*Chapter III*

# TRISECTION OF AN ANGLE

In this chapter we shall discuss a famous problem in geometry, which was posed in antiquity, but clarified only in modern times: the problem of dividing an *angle* into three equal parts. At the same time we shall take up the problem of dividing a *line* into three equal parts. The history of the problem of trisecting an angle is very instructive, because it shows how long men can continue to search on the wrong path. It warns us how useless it is to search for something which does not even exist.

To take an example from everyday life, if a stranger in Munich asks: "What is the number of the trolley line which will take me to the Ammersee?", he is posing an unanswerable question, since there is no such line. If, however, the first person he stops is also a stranger, the traveler will have to continue his search until someone familiar with Munich enlightens him. His question was stated incorrectly. He should have asked first whether there is such a trolley line, and only after he receives an affirmative answer should he ask for the number of the line.

The problem of trisecting an angle is a classic example in science of the incorrect formulation of a question. Another example will show how easy it is to formulate a mathematical problem erroneously. Let us take a ruler, on which not only the units, but also the tenths, are marked (see Fig. 22a). Consider the fraction $81/125 = 0.648$. On the ruler, the point $81/125$ distant from zero falls between 0.6 and 0.7; that is, it fails to coincide with any point of division marked on the ruler. The point representing $81/125$ will not be a point of division, even if the units are subdivided into hundredths by fine lines; it will then lie between 0.64 and 0.65 (see Fig. 22b, where the pertinent section of the ruler is enlarged). But if each hundredth is again subdivided into ten equal parts, there will be a new point of division, 0.648, whose distance from zero is exactly $81/125$ (see Fig. 22c, where the relevant portion of the ruler is enlarged to show the new subdivisions). Therefore, the question: "How many times must the original divisions of the ruler be subdivided into ten equal parts to make $81/125$ a point of division?" has an answer: "Two times, until the thousandths are reached."

Now it might seem proper to ask the same question about any other number, e.g. $1/9$. But in the case of $1/9$ the question would be stated incorrectly, because it is easy to see that the point at a distance of $1/9$ from zero is not a point of division in any of the subdivisions into ten equal parts, no matter how far they are carried. If it were possible to find such a point, then the fraction $1/9$ could be represented as a terminating decimal. But

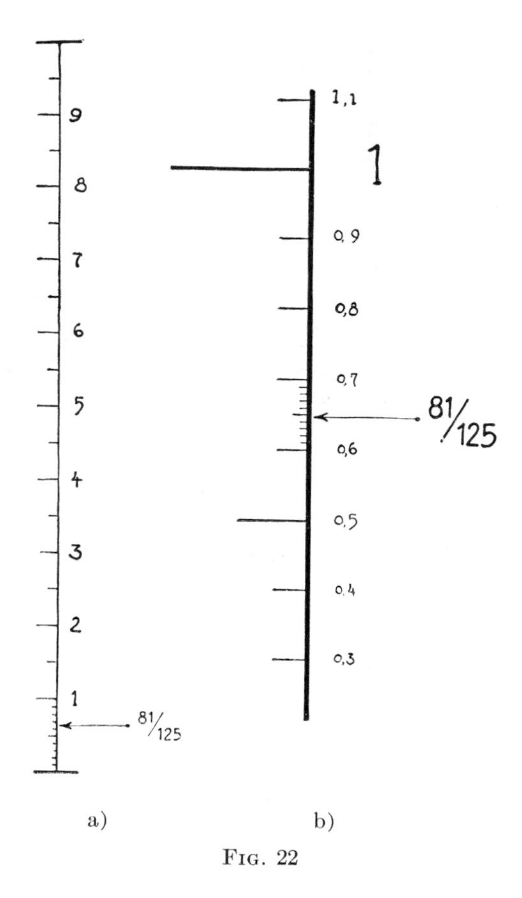


FIG. 22

this is not so, since $1/9 = 0.1111 \cdots$ is a non-terminating decimal [**1**]. Therefore, the question was posed incorrectly. We should have asked first, whether there *is* a point of division of some decimal subdivision of the ruler whose distance from zero is $1/9$. Only if the answer is affirmative can we go on to ask how often the division into tenths must be repeated before we find the required point.

Let us return to the problem of dividing a line or an angle. The problem involves the construction of geometric figures. But, of course, no construction is absolutely exact. No matter how fine the pencil used to draw a straight line, the line will always have a certain width and will always show many irregularities under a magnifying glass or microscope. An actual "point" will appear as an irregular blot. If, for example, the problem is to draw "the" line connecting two such points, we shall never be able, no matter what pains we take to be exact, to surmount the inexactitude of the

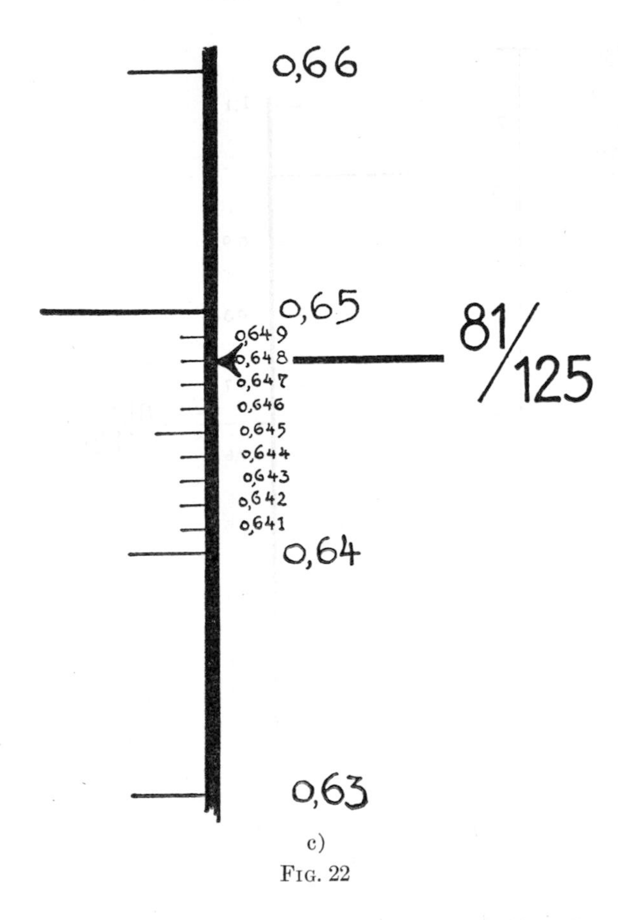


c)

Fig. 22

pair of actual points. In all practical problems of drawing figures in geometry, the question is never one of achieving complete accuracy, but only one of approximation. Bearing this in mind, there are very simple methods of dividing a line or an angle to any practical degree of accuracy. Consider, for instance, the segment $AB$ of Fig. 23. Using as accurate a ruler as possible, I simply measure the segment and read 15.4. If $AB$ is to be divided into two equal parts, I calculate that half of 15.4 is 7.7; and the mid-point of the segment will be the point on the ruler where 7.7 lies (see Fig. 23a). In the same way, Fig. 23b shows the construction of a third of $AB$, based on the computation that a third of 15.4 is 5.13. (The fact that the decimal is nonterminating has no practical significance, since only an approximation is required.) Obviously, the same method can be used to divide a segment into any number of parts. Figure 24 shows the analogous procedure for dividing an angle; instead of a marked ruler we now use a protractor.

PLATE III

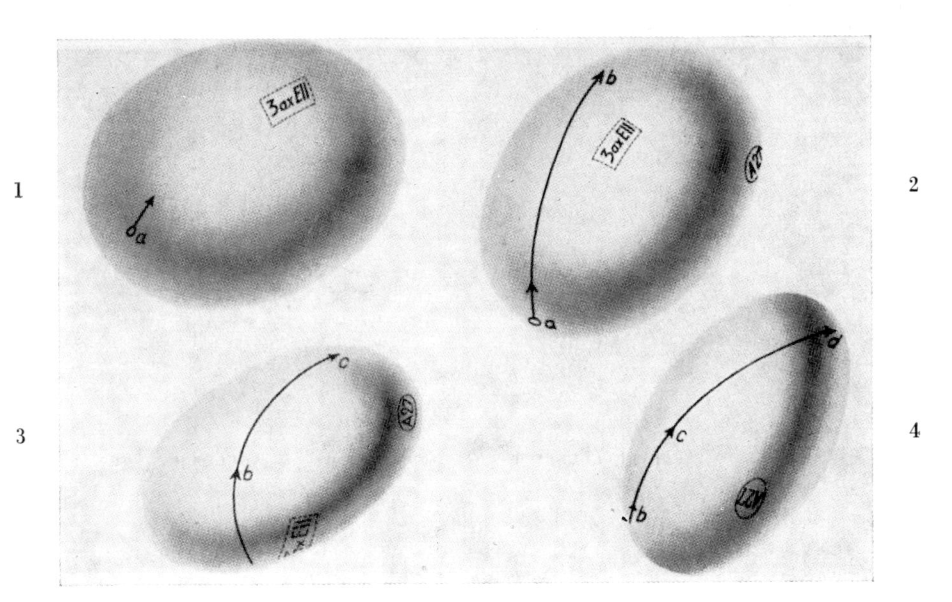


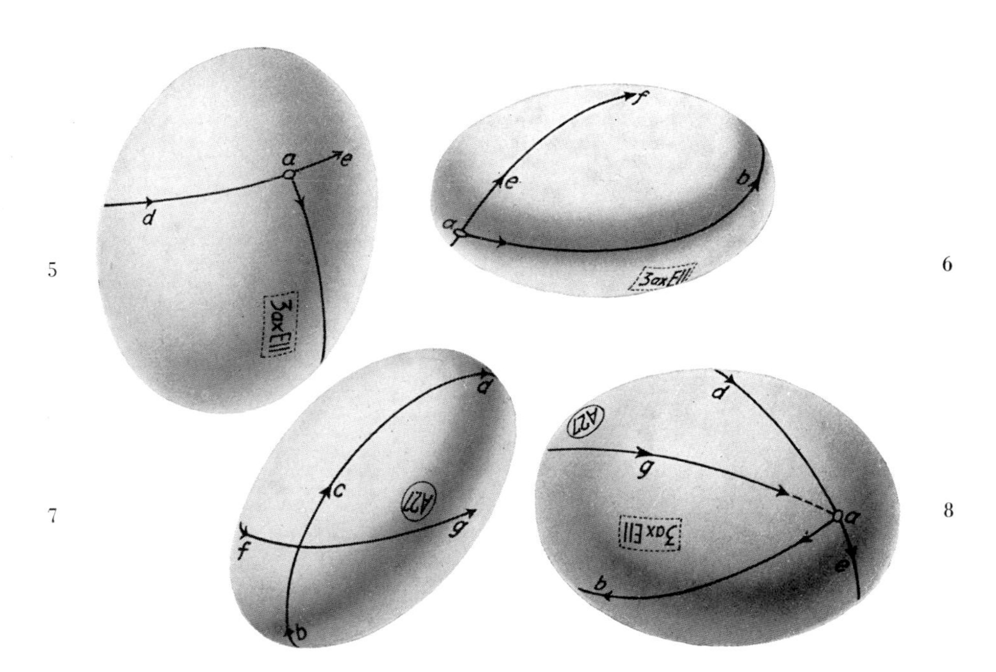

PLATE IV

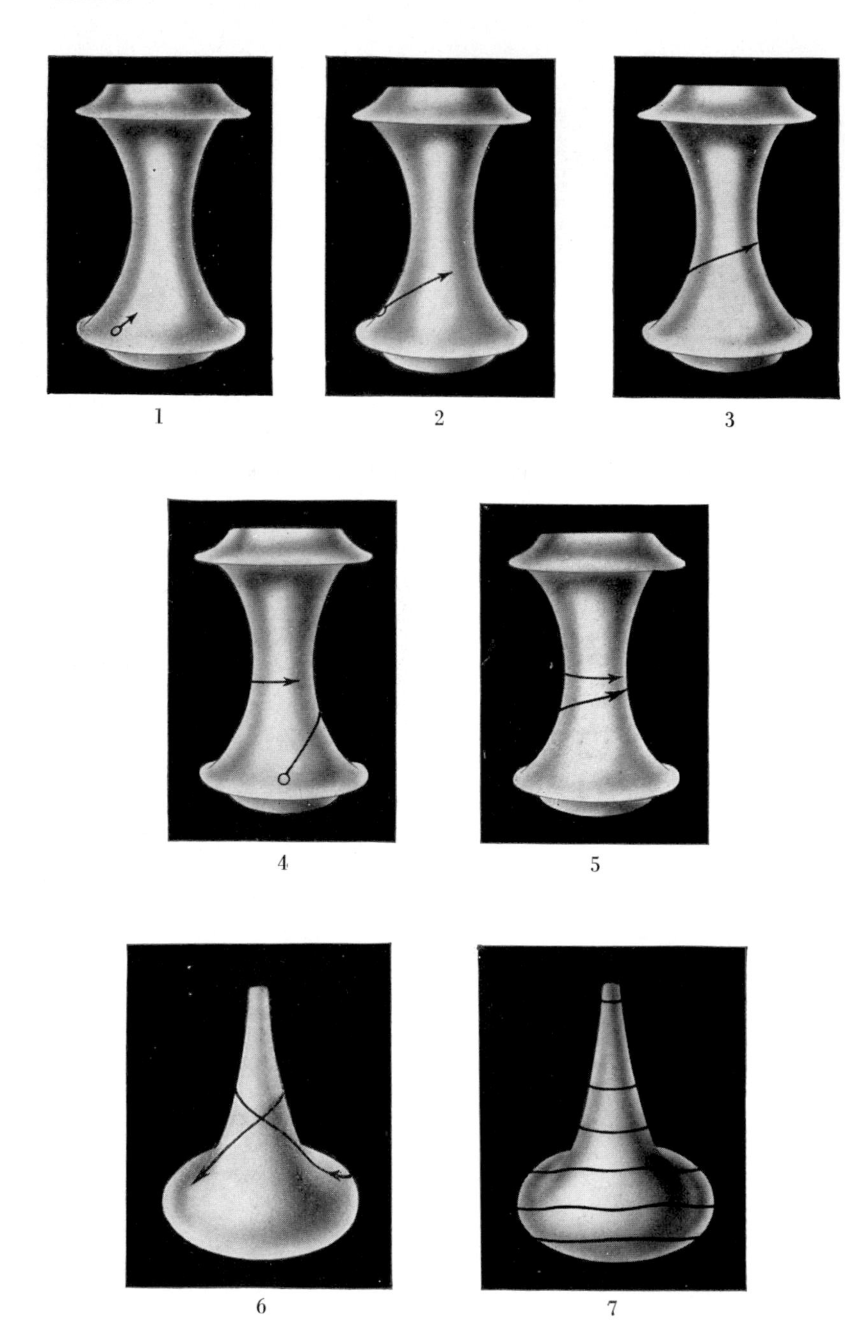

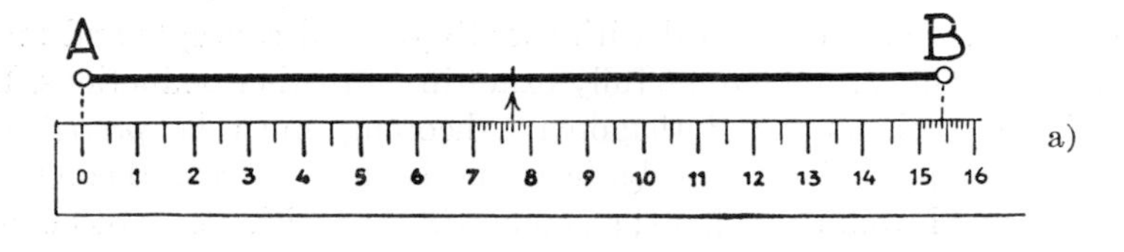


$\frac{1}{2} \cdot 15.4 = 7.7$

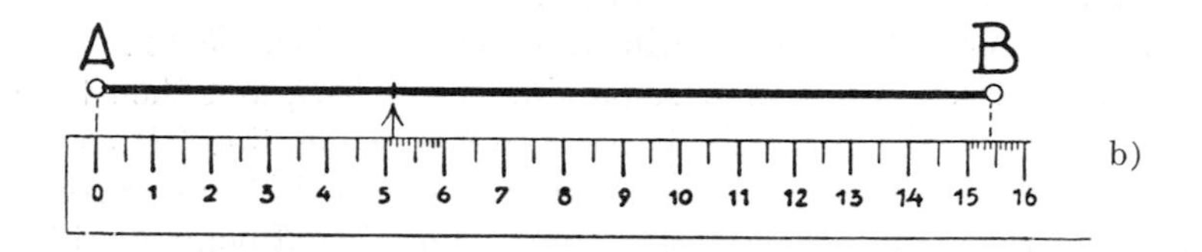


$\frac{1}{3} \cdot 15.4 = 5.13 \cdots$

FIG. 23. *Approximate* bi- and trisection of a segment with a marked ruler.

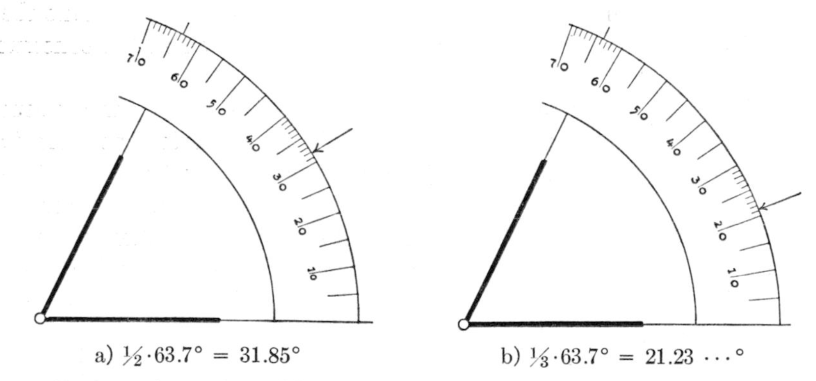


a) $\frac{1}{2} \cdot 63.7° = 31.85°$ b) $\frac{1}{3} \cdot 63.7° = 21.23 \cdots°$

FIG. 24. *Approximate* bi- and trisection of an angle with a protractor.

But the classical problem of trisecting an angle has nothing to do with these purely practical divisions. The science of geometry, as we have inherited it from the Greeks, goes far beyond the practical requirements set by land surveys or the draftsman's art of constructing figures with an approximate degree of accuracy. Rather, geometry is an ideal, rational system; it deals not with the inexactly apprehended objects of experience (actual drawings, actual measurements), but with fundamental propositions and concepts, which are to be understood as being entirely precise. When we assert the proposition that two points determine a straight line, we do not have in mind two blots, and a straight line of a certain thickness. On the contrary, we are concerned with exactly defined concepts and propositions, which will continue to be fully exact in all further deductions. Every proposition (such as the Pythagorean theorem) must be *proved*, either directly from the axioms (the basic propositions) or from theorems previously derived from the axioms; a geometric proposition cannot be proved by measurement. In the science of geometry the problems of *exact construction* are meaningful; therefore our problem will be to seek exact constructions for dividing a segment or an angle.

An exact construction for bisecting a segment $AB$ is indicated in Fig. 25: We draw the circle with center $A$ passing through $B$, and then the circle with center $B$ passing through $A$. Next, we draw the line $CD$ connecting the two points of intersection, $C$ and $D$, of the two circles; then the point of intersection $M$ of $CD$ and $AB$ is the required mid-point of $AB$. This construction requires only a *compass* (to draw the two circles), and a *straight edge* (to draw the line $CD$). It is exact in the sense that we can *prove* that the straight line $CD$ has a point of intersection with the straight line $AB$, and that this point is the exact mid-point of $AB$. The statement that the construction requires only straight edge and compass means that only straight lines and circles, but no other curves, occur in the construction.

The trisection of a segment $AB$ given in Fig. 26 is also exact in the sense described above. On any straight line through $A$, which does not coincide with $AB$, mark off (with a compass) an arbitrary segment $s = AT$ three times in succession (see Fig. 26b, where $s = AT = TU = UC$), and connect the final point $C$ to $B$ by the straight line $g$ (Fig. 26c). Next, draw the circle $k_1$ with center $C$ and radius $s$ (the circle therefore passes through $U$); and also the circles $k_2$ and $k_3$ with centers $U$ and $T$ and the same radius $s$ (Fig.

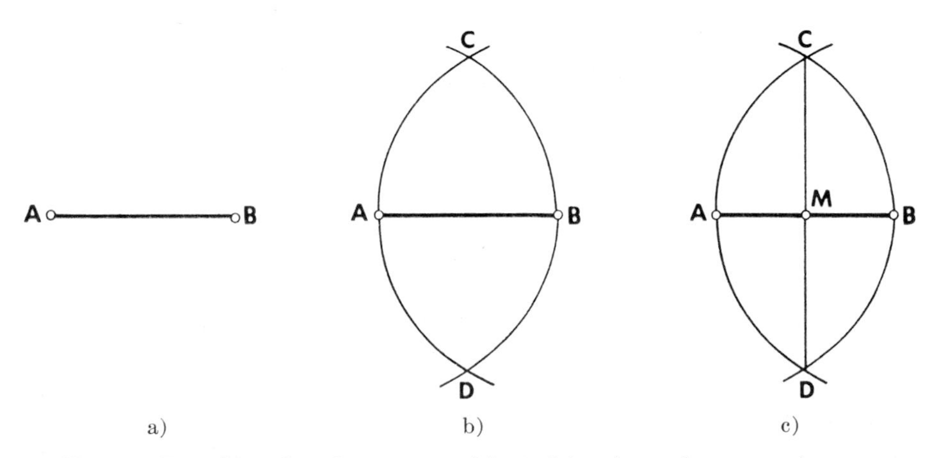


FIG. 25. *Exact* bisection of a segment with straight edge and compass alone.

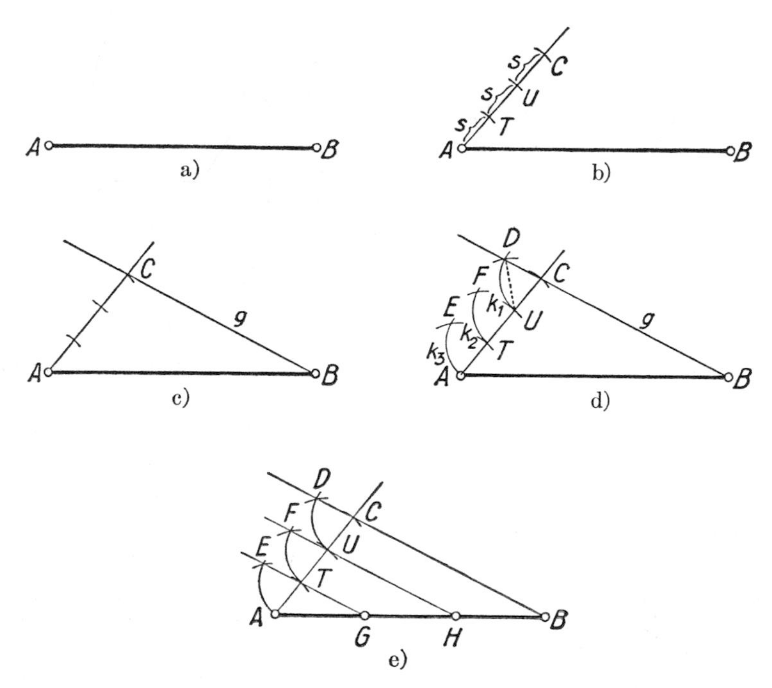


FIG. 26. *Exact* trisection of a segment with straight edge and compass alone.

26d). Now consider the point of intersection $D$ of $k_1$ with the straight line $g = BC$, and the length of the segment $UD$ (the dotted line in Fig. 26d). The point $D$ can be located by drawing an arc with center $U$ and radius $UD$ so that it intersects $k_1$. In the same way, setting the compass to the length $UD$, we draw arcs with centers $T$ and $A$ and radius $UD$ so that they intersect $k_2$ and $k_3$ in the points $F$ and $E$, respectively (Fig. 26d). The lines $FU$ and $ET$ are parallel to $DC$ (i.e. to $g = BC$) by construction. The final step in the construction is to extend the lines $ET$ and $FU$ until they intersect $AB$ in $G$ and $H$ (see Fig. 26e). Since the segment $HC$ is divided, by construction, into three equal parts by the points $T$ and $U$, and the lines $ET$, $FU$, $DC$ are parallel, it follows that $G$ and $H$ trisect [**2**] the segment $AB$.[1]

We now turn to the problem of bisecting and trisecting an *angle*. The bisection is very simple and is given in Fig. 27. Two equal segments, $OA$ and $OB$, are marked off with a compass from the vertex $O$ of the given

[1] In practice, this theoretically exact trisection gives much less accurate results than the approximate construction using a marked ruler. This is no contradiction. The absolute accuracy of a theoretically exact construction depends on the abstract relations of geometry, and not on the imperfections produced by pencil or chalk.

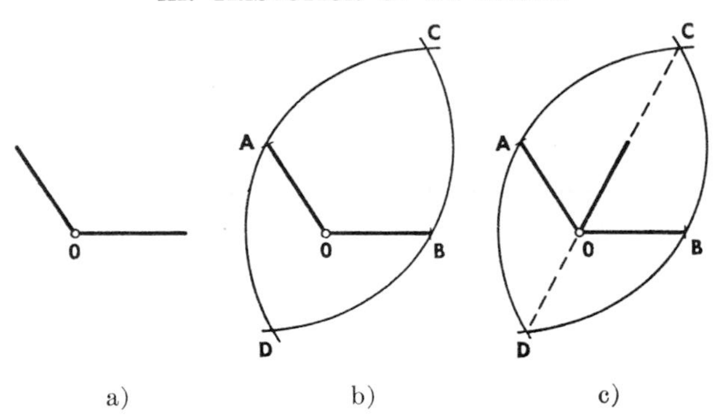


FIG. 27. *Exact* bisection of an angle with straight edge and compass alone.

angle. Setting the compass to the length $AB$, we draw the circle with center $B$ passing through $A$ and then the circle with center $A$ passing through $B$. The two circles intersect at $C$ and $D$. The line determined by $C$ and $D$ (dotted in Fig. 27c) contains $O$ and bisects the angle $AOB$.

This again is an exact construction, with straight edge and compass alone. It would seem to the point to seek such a construction for the trisection of an angle; and thus for two thousand years it was sought for in vain. Every construction that was proposed either used straight edge and compass alone and was inexact; or, if it was exact, it used additional aids. At last the suspicion arose that perhaps the problem itself was stated incorrectly. Instead of asking: "How does one trisect an angle exactly with straight edge and compass alone?" one should first have asked: "Does such a construction exist?" If it does not, one would be like the stranger who asked for the number of the tramline to the Ammersee. The many fruitless attempts to find such a construction tended to strengthen the suspicion of mathematicians that no construction of this sort was possible. Further scientific developments confirmed this suspicion. But it was no simple matter to see why, and to prove rigorously that such a construction is impossible. Elementary geometric arguments alone did not suffice. It was mainly due to the development of algebra during the past century and the existence of an already developed analytic geometry, that a rigorous proof of the impossibility of trisecting an angle with straight edge and compass alone was found.

But long after this impossibility was known, was referred to regularly in lectures on the subject, and had been proved in all the pertinent books [**3**], there were still people who were ignorant of this result and who continued to work on this old problem. Most of them did not have a clear idea of the nature of the problem, or of what an *exact* solution is. When such a treasure hunter is told today that a solution is impossible, he will shake his head unbelievingly. He may even think: Let the professionals talk. They cannot have tested each and every construction, and may it not be my luck, if I keep on digging, to come up with a solution? The man is right in one respect: mathematicians have not tested every construction, as indeed they cannot, for the number of possible constructions, of varying degrees of complexity, is infinite. To try, by this method, to determine the impossibility of trisecting an angle with straight edge and compass alone is fruitless. On the contrary, the essence of progress in mathematics lies precisely in the introduction of appropriate new ideas which lead to deductions encompassing an infinite number of special cases. We met a similar situation in Chapter I, where we saw that the problem of the infinitude of the primes could not be decided by counting primes, but requires a general argument [**4**]. Unfortunately, the proof of the impossibility of trisecting an angle is too technical to reproduce here. We must be content with simply stating that it is possible to prove the proposition: *An exact trisection of an arbitrary angle is not possible with straight edge and compass alone* [**5**].

It is still possible, however, to obtain constructions which are completely exact but are not limited to the use of straight edge and compass; or, constructions with straight edge and compass alone, which are not exact.

An example of the first sort is a construction due to Descartes. It uses a fixed parabola (see Fig. 28b). We denote the axis of the parabola by $PX$ [**6**], and the extension of the axis through the vertex $P$ of the parabola by $PZ$. Bisecting the angle $ZPX$ (180°) with ruler and compass (using the method given above), we obtain $PY$, a perpendicular to the axis; the bisection of the right angle $XPY$ (90°) yields a 45° angle $XPW$, with $PW$ intersecting the parabola at $N$. Dropping the perpendicular from $N$ on the axis $PX$ of the parabola, we denote its point of intersection with the axis by $E$. From $E$ we mark off the segment $PE$ on $PX$ to obtain the point $Q$, and then erect the perpendicular $l$ to the axis at $Q$.

If $UOV$ is the angle (Fig. 28a) to be trisected, we draw the circle with center $O$ and radius $PE$ and denote its points of intersection with the sides of the angle by $A$ and $B$ (Fig. 28c). Using the ruler and compass construction described above, we bisect the chord $AB$, and mark off the half chord $MA$ on the perpendicular $l$ from $Q$, so that $RQ = MA$ (Fig. 28d). With $R$ as center, we draw the circle $k$ passing through $P$. The circle cuts the parabola in three other points, but we shall use only the point $S$ closest to $P$. We then erect the perpendicular $ST$ to the axis, and setting the compass to the length $ST$, determine the point $C$ on the arc $AB$ so that $AC = ST$ (Fig. 28e). It can then be proved that angle $AOC$ is exactly a third of the given angle $AOB$ [**7**]. The point $D$ is obtained by marking off $ST$ once more. This divides the angle into three equal parts, $AOC$, $COD$, and $DOB$.

Here we have shown how an angle may be trisected exactly, but this

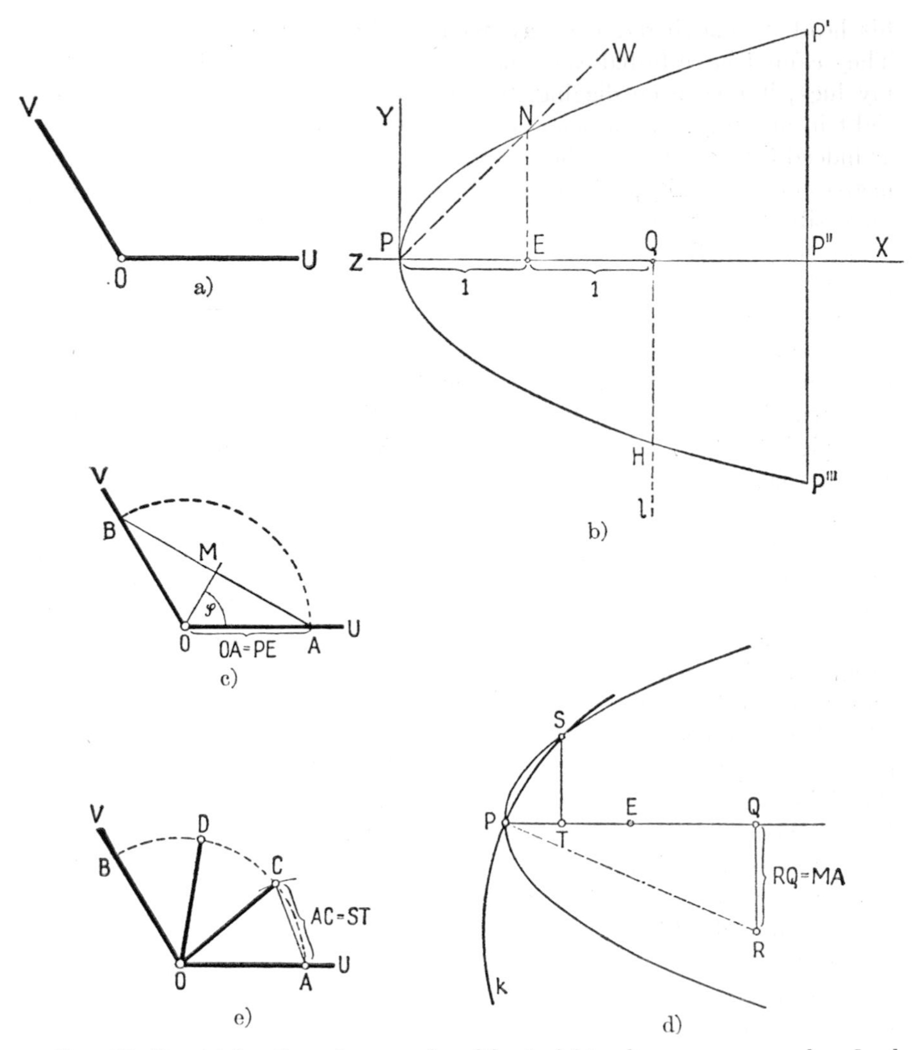


FIG. 28. *Exact* trisection of an angle with straight edge, compass and a fixed parabola (Descartes).

method used a fixed parabola besides straight edge and compass. Many similar methods exist, all of which use an additional aid. We shall now describe a construction which uses only straight edge and compass, but is necessarily not exact. The approximation, however, is quite good. This construction is not very old, and is due to Eugen Kopf, a tailor in Ludwigshafen, who spent his spare time working on this problem. My colleague Perron has shown that the error is always less than (the very small amount)

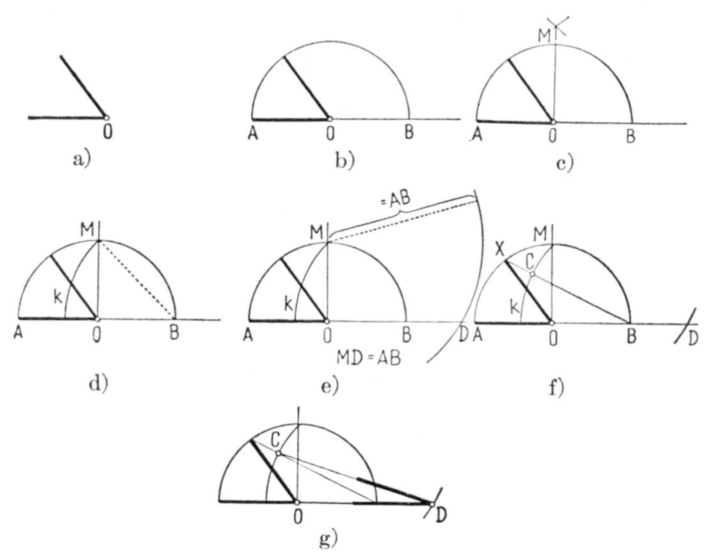


FIG. 29. *Approximate* trisection of an angle with straight edge and compass alone.

8′12″ [**8**]. The construction is pictured in Fig. 29. The first step (Fig. 29b) is to draw the semi-circle with the vertex $O$ of the given angle as center and arbitrary diameter $AB$. The perpendicular to $AB$ at $O$ yields the perpendicular bisector $OM$ of $AB$ (Fig. 29c). Next, we mark off the arc $k$ of the circle with center $B$ and radius $OM$ which lies inside the angle $AOM$ (Fig. 29d). Then we draw the circle with radius $AB$ and center $M$ and denote its intersection with the extension of $AB$ by $D$ (Fig. 29e). If $AOX$ is the given angle, and $C$ the point of intersection of the straight line $BX$ with $k$ (Fig. 29f), then the angle $CDO$ (Fig. 29g) is approximately one third of the angle $AOX$.

We mentioned Descartes as the author of the first of the two constructions discussed above. But Descartes' creation of analytic geometry was a much more important contribution to mathematics. For one thing, the impossibility of trisecting an angle was not demonstrated until the techniques of analytic geometry and the more recent theory of algebraic equations were available.

Descartes is to be numbered among the successful pioneers of mathematics. René Descartes du Perron (his Latin, academic name was Cartesius) was born March 31, 1596, at La Haye in Touraine. From 1604 to 1610 he was a student at the Jesuit College, La Flêche. Between the ages of 18 and 19 he led a dissolute life in Paris, which he suddenly left off to devote himself earnestly to his studies. After a few years he began to travel about Europe, which was then on the eve of the Thirty Years War. It was a

Europe beset with the tensions and strife engendered by religious conflicts, a Europe swarming with wandering adventurers and vagabonds. For ten years, between 1617 and 1627, Descartes traveled in Holland, Germany, Hungary and Italy. Occasionally he stopped to continue his studies, or to visit some of the intellectually eminent men of the area. In 1620, for example, he stayed in Ulm to study algebra with Johann Faulhaber. Of special interest is his acquaintance with Girard Desargues (1593–1662), whose work on conic sections preceded the work of Gaspard Monge (1746–1818), the author of projective or so-called descriptive geometry. There was during this period a group of men with varied intellectual and artistic interests who met regularly in Paris to hear reports on matters of prime interest in their respective fields. Up to our own time men have formed such societies, not oriented to any particular technical field, but joining together a variety of interests, each of whose meetings is centered on the special concern of the lecturer of the moment. This Parisian society proved to be the foundation of the French Academy, officially sanctioned by Richelieu in 1635.

It was in this circle that Descartes met the architect and mathematician Desargues. Desargues was at this time supervising the construction of La Rochelle, the great military fortress, destined to be captured after untold hardships. Descartes went to inspect the great fortifications.

Between 1629–34, he travelled in England, Holland, and Denmark, and later took up his residence once more in Holland. He wrote many scientific works in this period, and after 1640 was involved in many religious-philosophical battles, which made him many enemies who denounced him to the Dutch authorities. However, the French ambassador managed to keep Descartes from being openly attacked. During these years of travel Descartes carried on many long-lived correspondences with his wide acquaintanceship which included both important and interesting personalities. Through his acquaintance with the French ambassador at Stockholm, Descartes began an exchange of letters with Queen Christina of Sweden, the daughter of Gustavus Adolphus. The queen called him to Sweden and Descartes made the trip in 1649. But he became ill in Stockholm, and after a few months died on February 11, 1650.

The work of Descartes which is significant for the problem discussed here appeared in 1637 with the simple title *La Géométrie*. It is not an extensive work, but it marks the beginning of analytic geometry.[2] As we have already noted, analytic geometry, together with the newer developments

[2] Essentially, it locates the position of a point in the plane by means of two numbers (usually denoted by the abscissa $x$ and the ordinate $y$), so that analysis (the theory of the relationships of numbers to one another) is used in the service of geometry.

in algebra [9], made it possible to prove that the classical problem of trisecting an angle with only straight edge and compass had no solution.

Any one acquainted with the practical problems of drafting knows how simple it is to get a satisfactory degree of accuracy when dividing an angle into three, or as many parts as one wishes, by simply using a protractor. He may shake his head over this concern with a classical problem, more than 2000 years old, of an exact trisection with straight edge and compass alone. He may consider the limitation to straight edge and compass wilful, and the exactitude demanded unnecessary, since it has no practical application. As to the demand for exactitude, it accords with the standards the Greeks set for an exact geometry, in opposition to the crude methods of the surveyors of that day. While straight edge and compass are instruments easy to come by, the exclusion of other aids may seem stubborn. The whole problem, in fact, seems a little special. But this problem, like so many other famous problems, stimulated many people to try to solve it just because it would not be solved. Now that we know a solution does not exist, it is tempting to make sport of those generations of mathematicians who expended long years of futile effort on this whimsical problem. What we must realize, however, is that in the end these efforts have broadened our knowledge, and have enriched it with new fields of mathematics of the greatest significance. Only then will this small, special theoretical problem appear in its true significance. Even from a practical point of view it would be foolish to laugh at the long, futile search for a nonexistent solution.

*Notes to Chapter III*

## TRISECTION OF AN ANGLE

**1** (p. 47). We can also show that $1/9$ is not a point of the decimal subdivision of a ruler as follows: Since $1/9$ is greater than $1/10$ but less than $2/10$, it lies (see Fig. 30a) between the subdivision points .1 and .2.

Now $10/9 = 1 + 1/9$ and, therefore, $1/9 = 1/10 \cdot 10/9 = (1/10)(1 + 1/9) = 1/10 + 1/9 \cdot 1/10$. Hence $1/9$ must lie at the endpoint of the first ninth of the segment from .1 to .2. Fig. 30b is a tenfold magnification of the relevant part of Fig. 30a and in this figure the segment from .1 to .2 is subdivided into hundredths. From this figure we see that $1/9$ lies between .11 and .12 and again in the first ninth of this latter segment. By induction we may infer that the same will occur in all further decimal subdivisions of the relevant segments. For example, in Fig. 30c, which is again a tenfold magnification of the part of Fig. 30b in which we are interested, we see that $1/9$ lies between .111 and .112 and again is the endpoint of the first ninth of this segment.

**2** (p. 51). It is not difficult to see that the same construction can be generalized to divide a segment into 4, 5 or in general $n$ equal parts.

This construction uses only lines and circles, so that we may call it a construction using straight edge and compass alone. In addition we note that the two circles whose intersection yields $E$ have another point of intersection on the other side of $AC$. We choose $E$ to be that point of intersection of the two circles which lies on the same side of $AC$ as does $D$. The point $F$ is chosen similarly. It is therefore clear that in order to carry out the construction we must know that a line divides the plane into two parts, and that during the construction we must keep track of the relations between the various parts of the figure. Also, in order to reach the point $C$ by marking off a segment three times, we must be sure to do this always in the same direction. For a more precise account see {1}.

**3** (p. 52). See {2}, {3}.

**4** (p. 53). Here is another example: The Pythagorean theorem is valid for all right triangles, no matter what their size. The theorem is verified, not by proving it for each particular choice of the legs of the triangle, but by proving it simultaneously for all possible cases.

**5** (p. 53). In the same way it is impossible to divide an angle exactly into 5, 7, 11 or in general into $n$ equal parts by straight edge and compass alone if $n$ is divisible by an odd prime. An exact division into $n$ equal parts is possible if $n$ is a power of 2.

**6** (p. 53). Imagine a thin piece of wood covering the area inside the

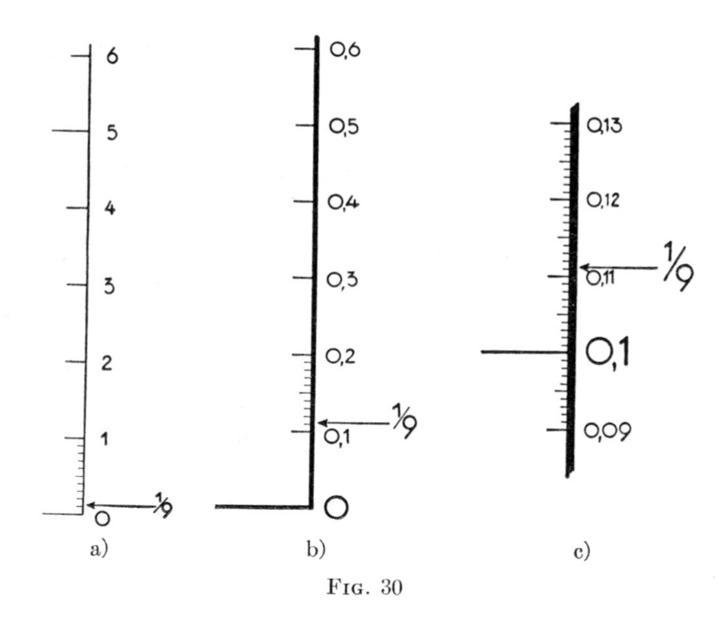


FIG. 30

parabola and bounded by $PP'$, $PP''$ and $P'P''$ (see Fig. 28b). Tracing the outline of the piece of wood we obtain the top half of the parabola; the lower half is obtained by rotating the piece of wood about the axis $PP''$ and again tracing its outline.

**7** (p. 53). The proof is not difficult for a reader with some knowledge of trigonometry and analytic geometry. In the sequel we assume that the unit of length is the length of $OA = PE$ (Figs. 28b and c).

The equation of the parabola of Fig. 28b then assumes a particularly simple form. Now, the equation of a parabola with vertex at the origin and symmetric about the axis is $y^2 = cx = 2px$, where $c$ depends on the particular parabola. In our case, since the angle $XPW$ is 45°, $EN = PE$; and since $PE = 1$, both coordinates $x$ and $y$ of $N$ are equal to 1. Because $N$ is a point on the parabola, the point $x = 1$, $y = 1$ must satisfy the above equation; hence $c = 1$. The equation of the parabola is then

$$y^2 = x.$$

Our assumption about the unit of length also yields a simple expression for the chord $AB$ of Fig. 28c. Let $\varphi$ be the angle $AOM$, which is half the angle $AOB$. Using the right triangle $OAM$ (the right angle is at $M$), we see that $AM = OA \sin \varphi = \sin \varphi$, since $OA = 1$. Then $AB = 2AM = 2 \sin \varphi$. We have therefore proved the following lemma: *In a circle of radius* $OA = 1$, *a chord is twice the* sin *of the central half angle it determines.*

Now set $\varphi/3 = \omega$; then $\omega$ is a third of the angle $AOM$, or a sixth of the angle $AOB$, so that $2\omega$ is a third of the angle $AOB$. *Therefore, $2\omega$ is the required angle.* According to the above lemma, the chord determined by this angle is $2 \sin \omega$, that is, $2 \sin (\varphi/3)$.

In the discussion of the Cartesian construction in the text we asserted that the chord $ST$ determines the required third of the original angle. This assertion rests on the fact that $ST = 2 \sin (\varphi/3) = 2 \sin \omega$; that is, *that the ordinate of the point of intersection $S$ of the circle $k$ with the parabola* is $y = 2 \sin \omega$ (since $ST$ is the ordinate $y$ of the point $S$).

We shall prove this assertion, but, in a certain sense, in reverse order. We shall not concern ourselves at first with determining the ordinate $y$ of $S$. We shall *start rather with that point on the parabola whose ordinate $y = 2 \sin \omega$ and then show that this point is $S$.* To this end we need the equation of the circle $k$ as well as several trigonometric formulas.

Let the coordinates of the center $R$ of the circle $k$ be $x = a$, $y = b$ and let its radius be $r$. Then $a = PQ = 2$ and the ordinate $b$ of $R$ is negative and has the value $RQ = AM = \sin \varphi$; hence, $b = -\sin \varphi$. The equation of the circle is then

$$(x - a)^2 + (y - b)^2 = r^2,$$

or

$$x^2 + y^2 - 2ax - 2by + a^2 + b^2 - r^2 = 0,$$

where $a = 2$, $b = -\sin \varphi$, while $r$ is to be determined in such a way that the circle passes through the origin of coordinates $x = 0$, $y = 0$. The point $x = 0$, $y = 0$ must therefore satisfy the equation of the circle, so that $a^2 + b^2 - r^2 = 0$. This determines $r$:

$$r^2 = a^2 + b^2 = 4 + \sin^2 \varphi.$$

Hence the equation of the circle $k$ becomes

$$x^2 + y^2 - 2ax - 2by = 0;$$

or (substituting $a = 2$, $b = -\sin \varphi$)

$$(K) \qquad x^2 + y^2 - 4x + 2y \sin \varphi = 0.$$

In the sequel we shall refer to this equation as $(K)$.

Now we shall derive the required trigonometric formulas from the formulas

$$\sin (\alpha + \beta) = \sin \alpha \cos \beta + \cos \alpha \sin \beta,$$

$$\cos (\alpha + \beta) = \cos \alpha \cos \beta - \sin \alpha \sin \beta,$$

which we assume as known. First, setting $\beta = \alpha$, we obtain

$$\sin 2\alpha = 2 \sin \alpha \cos \alpha, \quad \cos 2\alpha = \cos^2 \alpha - \sin^2 \alpha.$$

Further, setting $\beta = 2\alpha$ in the formula for $\sin(\alpha + \beta)$ and using the formulas for $\sin 2\alpha$ and $\cos 2\alpha$, we obtain

$$\sin 3\alpha = \sin \alpha \cos 2\alpha + \cos \alpha \sin 2\alpha = 3 \sin \alpha \cos^2 \alpha - \sin^3 \alpha.$$

The latter yields (since $\cos^2 \alpha = 1 - \sin^2 \alpha$)

$$4 \sin^3 \alpha - 3 \sin \alpha + \sin 3\alpha = 0;$$

or, after multiplication by 2,

$$(2 \sin \alpha)^3 - 3(2 \sin \alpha) + 2 \sin 3\alpha = 0.$$

In the last formula substitute $\alpha = \varphi/3 = \omega$, $2 \sin 3\alpha = 2 \sin \varphi = g$, and $2 \sin \alpha = 2 \sin \varphi/3 = 2 \sin \omega = y$. Then we get

$$y^3 - 3y + g = 0,$$

where $g = 2 \sin \varphi$, according to the lemma above, is the chord $AB$ subtending the angle $AOB = 2\varphi$, while $y$ is the chord subtending a third of this angle.

Now to every value of $y$ there corresponds precisely one point of the parabola. For, every parallel to the $x$-axis meets the parabola in exactly one point, and to every $y$-value thus determined the abscissa $x$ of the corresponding point on the parabola is $x = y^2$. Now denote by $F$ that point of the parabola whose ordinate is $y = 2 \sin(\varphi/3) = 2 \sin \omega$ ($F$ is therefore the point $S$, as we shall show). The ordinate $y$ of $F$ therefore satisfies the equation $y^3 - 3y + g = 0$. Multiplying this equation by $y$ we get

$$y^4 - 3y^2 + gy = 0,$$

or

$$y^4 + y^2 - 4y^2 + gy = 0.$$

Since $F$ is on the parabola, we can set $y^2 = x$ and $y^4 = x^2$. Hence, according to the last equation above, the coordinates $x$, $y$ of $F$ satisfy the equation

$$x^2 + y^2 - 4x + gy = 0.$$

But since $g = 2 \sin \varphi$, this reduces to the equation ($K$) of the circle $k$. We have therefore proved: *The point $F$ on the parabola whose ordinate $y = 2 \sin \omega$ is also on the circle $k$; it must therefore be a point of intersection of $k$ with the parabola.*

Our aim was to show that $F = S$, where $S$ is the point of intersection of $k$ with the parabola which is in the upper half plane and is nearest to the vertex $P$. It merely remains to show now that $F$ is this point of intersection. In order to do this, however, we must also consider the other points of intersection of $k$ with the parabola. The only fact we shall use without proof is that a circle and a parabola have at most four points of intersection. As we shall see, in our case there are exactly four points of intersection.

We first note that the given angle $AOB$ is between $0°$ and $180°$, so that $\varphi = AOM$ is between $0°$ and $90°$, and $\omega = \varphi/3$ is between $0°$ and $30°$. Hence $\sin \omega$ is positive and less than $\sin 30°$; since $\sin 30° = 1/2$, $2 \sin \omega < 1$. The ordinate of $F$ is therefore between 0 and 1, and so lies on the arc $PN$ of the parabola (see Fig. 28b) because the ordinate $y$ of $N$ is 1 (since $EN = 1$). We shall now show that $N$ is in the interior of the circle $k$. The coordinates of $N$ are $x = 1$, $y = 1$, while the coordinates of the center $R$ of $k$ are $a = 2$, $b = -\sin \varphi$; the distance $d$ between two points with coordinates $(a, b)$, $(a', b')$ is given by

$$d^2 = (a' - a)^2 + (b' - b)^2;$$

hence for $d = RN$, we obtain

$$\begin{aligned}(RN)^2 &= (1 - a)^2 + (1 - b)^2 = (-1)^2 + (1 + \sin \varphi)^2 \\ &= 2 + 2 \sin \varphi + \sin^2 \varphi.\end{aligned}$$

Since $\sin \varphi < 1$, this yields

$$(RN)^2 < 2 + 2 + \sin^2 \varphi = 4 + \sin^2 \varphi.$$

But, as we have seen above, $4 + \sin^2 \varphi = a^2 + b^2 = r^2$, where $r$ is the radius of $k$. Therefore, $(RN)^2 < r^2$, or $RN < r$, so that the distance of $N$ from the center $R$ is less than $r$. Hence $N$ is in the interior of $k$. If we therefore proceed along the parabola from $N$ in the direction of $P'$ (see Fig. 28b) sufficiently far, we shall finally reach the exterior of $k$. This means that we will have crossed $k$ at least once. There is therefore at least one point of intersection $S'$ of $k$ with the portion of the parabola which starts at $N$ and extends in the direction of $P'$. (The ordinate $y$ of such a point of intersection must be greater than 1.) Similarly, we can show that the point $H$ (whose coordinates are $x = 2$ and $y = 2$), the point of intersection of the perpendicular $l$ (see Fig. 28b) with the parabola, is also *in the interior* of $k$. For obviously,

$$\begin{aligned}(RH)^2 &= (-\sqrt{2} - b)^2 = (-\sqrt{2} + \sin \varphi)^2 \\ &= 2 - 2\sqrt{2} \sin \varphi + \sin^2 \varphi \\ &= 4 + \sin^2 \varphi - 2 - 2\sqrt{2} \sin \varphi.\end{aligned}$$

Therefore $(RH)^2 < 4 + \sin^2 \varphi = r^2$, where $r$ is the radius of $k$. Starting at $H$ and proceeding along the parabola in the direction of $P'''$ sufficiently far we reach the exterior of $k$, and so this portion of the parabola must have at least one point $S''$ of intersection with $k$, whose ordinate $y$ must therefore be negative and less than the ordinate of $H$, i.e., $y < -\sqrt{2}$.

Since there can be at most four points of intersection of $k$ with the parabola, we have found all the points common to the parabola and the circle $k$. The points are: $P$ $(y = 0)$, $S'$ $(y > 1)$, $S''$ $(y < -\sqrt{2})$, and $F$ $(0 < y < 1)$. Since $S$, according to the Cartesian construction, is the point of intersection nearest to $P$, it follows that $S = F$. The ordinate $ST$ of $S$ is therefore equal to the ordinate $2 \sin \omega$ of $F$. But this is what we were to show.[1]

**8** (p. 55). Kopf thought that he had discovered an exact trisection. My colleague Perron examined this construction, as well as some others due to Kopf, and among the latter found one much more accurate than the one discussed in the text. The error in this construction is never more than 15″, that is, the 21,600th part of a right angle! See {4}, {5}.

**9** (p. 57). This has to do with a deeper insight into the existence of solutions of algebraic equations in closed form. See {6}–{9}. The solution of algebraic equations will be discussed in Chapter X.

[1] We can show, moreover, that the ordinates of the other points of intersection, $S'$ and $S''$, satisfy the equation $y^3 - 3y + g = 0$; hence, together with $y = 2 \sin \omega$, they are the three roots of the equation. In fact, the first two roots are $2 \sin (\omega + 120°)$ and $2 \sin (\omega + 240°)$, so that the first is $> 1$ (but $< \sqrt{3}$), while the second is $< -\sqrt{2}$ and indeed lies between $-\sqrt{3}$ and $-\sqrt{2}$.

As the point $R$ moves closer to $Q$ (which occurs as $\varphi$ and $g$ approach zero), the point of intersection $S$ moves toward $P$, while $S'$ and $S''$ approach the two points of the parabola whose coordinates are $x = 3$, $y = \pm\sqrt{3}$. Suppose now that $R$ moves away from $Q$, until $RQ = 1$ (which corresponds to $\varphi = 90°$ and $g = 2$). Then the circle $k$ is tangent to the parabola at $N$ from the interior of the parabola (so that the points $S$ and $S'$ are now identical) and the coordinates of the point $S''$ are $x = 4$ and $y = -2$. What happens to the points of intersection as the point $R$ moves still further away from the axis, so that $RQ$ exceeds 1 (and $g$ exceeds 2)? (Since $RQ = MA = \sin \varphi$, this case no longer has any relation to our problem.) The answer is that then there are no longer any points of intersection of $k$ with the parabola whose ordinates are positive. The only two (real) points of intersection in this case are $P$ and $S''$, and the ordinate of the latter is a negative number $y = -w$ which is less than $-2$, and which approaches $-\infty$ as $RQ$ increases. Now the relation between the ordinate $b = -\frac{1}{2}g$ of $R$ and the ordinate $y$ of $S''$ will no longer be trigonometric but hyperbolic: $g = 2 \cosh t$, $w = 2 \cosh t/3$.

*Chapter IV*

# ON NEIGHBORING DOMAINS

The last two geometric problems we discussed differed greatly from each other. The problems of bi- and trisecting an angle or a segment were *elementary* and originated in classical antiquity. The problems in Chapter II, concerning geodesics on surfaces, however, belong to the domain of *differential geometry* and are barely three hundred years old. The characteristic property of geodesics is that—as curves preserving a direction—they are defined by specifying the behavior of small pieces of the curve. Therefore, the total course of the curve is determined from local properties, that is, from properties in the small. An example of this is the determination of a geodesic by sighting along markers. Each sighting determines only the portion of the curve lying between the first and third marker; for accuracy, the markers should not be too far apart; hence each sighting determines only a small piece of the curve. In order to get the complete geodesic, we have to paste these small portions together. This kind of synthesis of a whole from small pieces is characteristic of the differential and integral calculus. There were forerunners of this calculus in antiquity, but as a systematic branch of mathematics it has existed only since Newton (1643–1727) and Leibniz (1646–1716), each of whom discovered it independently in the second half of the 17th century. Thus, geodesic and related problems are only about 250 years old.

We shall now discuss a geometric problem of much more recent origin. The problem sounds like a game; it is only with difficulty that we discern the very profound geometric questions hidden in the trivial statement. It was first raised about a hundred years ago, in conversations between the famous mathematician and astronomer Ferdinand Möbius, and his friend, Adolph Weiske.

August Ferdinand Möbius (see {1}) was born in Saxony, in 1790, and began to study law but quickly turned to mathematics. In 1813–14, he was a student of Gauss (see Chapter IX), who instructed him in astronomical observations and calculations. In 1815, he was given official recognition as a lecturer at Leipzig, where he was to remain for the rest of his life. In 1816 he became Extraordinary Professor of Astronomy and later Director of the Pleissenburg Observatory. He drew the plans for rebuilding the observatory in 1818. In 1844 he was named Professor of Higher Mathematics and Astronomy at the University of Leipzig. He died in 1868 in Leipzig. His son was a well-known neurologist, whose book, dealing with the "physiologically weaker mind of women," achieved much more notice than the sounder mathematical works of his father. Later in this chapter we shall have occasion to discuss a peculiar discovery Möbius made when he was 68 years old. Here we simply note that Möbius was not only important in the development of analytic geometry [**1**] (see Chapter III), but also made fundamental contributions to the field of statics, which deals with the equilibrium of forces on rigid bodies.[1]

The problem which came up in the discussions between Möbius and Weiske was perhaps originated by Weiske, who was not a mathematician by profession, but had a great interest in mathematical problems. Möbius first presented this problem in the form of a fairy tale in a lecture he gave in 1840 [**2**].

The tale goes like this: *Once upon a time in the Far East there lived a Prince with five sons. These sons were to inherit the kingdom after his death. But in his will, the Prince made the condition that each of the five parts into which the kingdom was to be divided must border on every other.* The Prince was afraid that if the land was divided so that one of the sons could not visit another without crossing the land of a third, the two sons whose lands were thus separated might become estranged. Whether neighbors are always on good terms, and whether friendships, not too firmly grounded to begin with, are not better conserved by distance, are questions which need not detain us here. At any rate, the Prince thought this arrangement the best one. In addition, however, he required that *each of the sons build a road from his residence to that of each of his brothers and that these roads should run separately, without crossings, and without touching the domain of a third brother.* There was thus to be no interference on the part of one of the brothers with the connecting roads of any other two.

Fig. 31a represents a division of the kingdom among the five brothers, $A$, $B$, $C$, $D$, $E$, which fulfills the first but not the second stipulation made by the old Prince. It is easily calculated that this second proviso involves building ten roads.[2] In Fig. 31b, where, for simplicity, simple houses must serve for palaces, the dotted lines mark the paths between houses, but there are only five, not ten, as the will required.

The tale continues. *After the death of the father, the five sons worked hard to find a division of the land which would conform to his wishes; but all their efforts were in vain. After many days had passed in these futile attempts, one of the court scribes informed the brothers that there was a similar condition in an older will of the old Prince. But this will mentioned only four sons, since it had been written long before the much younger, fifth, son was born. And it was found that the conditions of this will could be easily fulfilled.*

[1] Möbius also participated in contemporary efforts—led by von Humboldt—to make the results of technical knowledge available to a broader public.

[2] Namely the paths $AB$, $AC$, $AD$, $AE$, $BC$, $BD$, $BE$, $CD$, $CE$, $DE$.

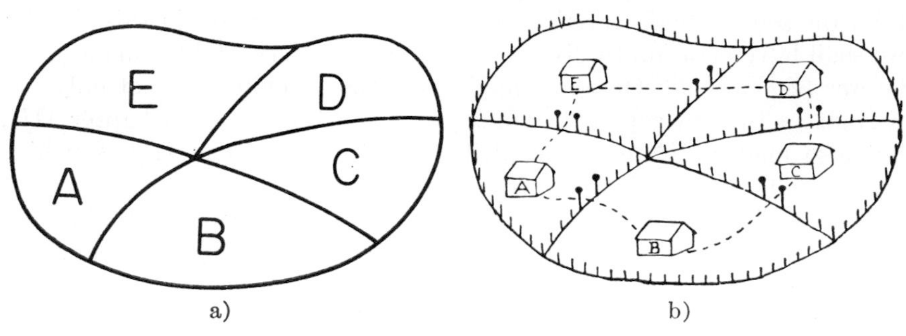


Fig. 31

But the scheme of Fig. 32, where (just as in Fig. 31) each brother is connected with only two others, will not do. The scheme of Fig. 33 does solve this problem. The six dotted paths of Fig. 33b are the non-intersecting roads connecting each of the brothers to all the others. What was to be done? Should the four older brothers divide the land among themselves and let the fifth, their favorite, go empty-handed? Was there any solution

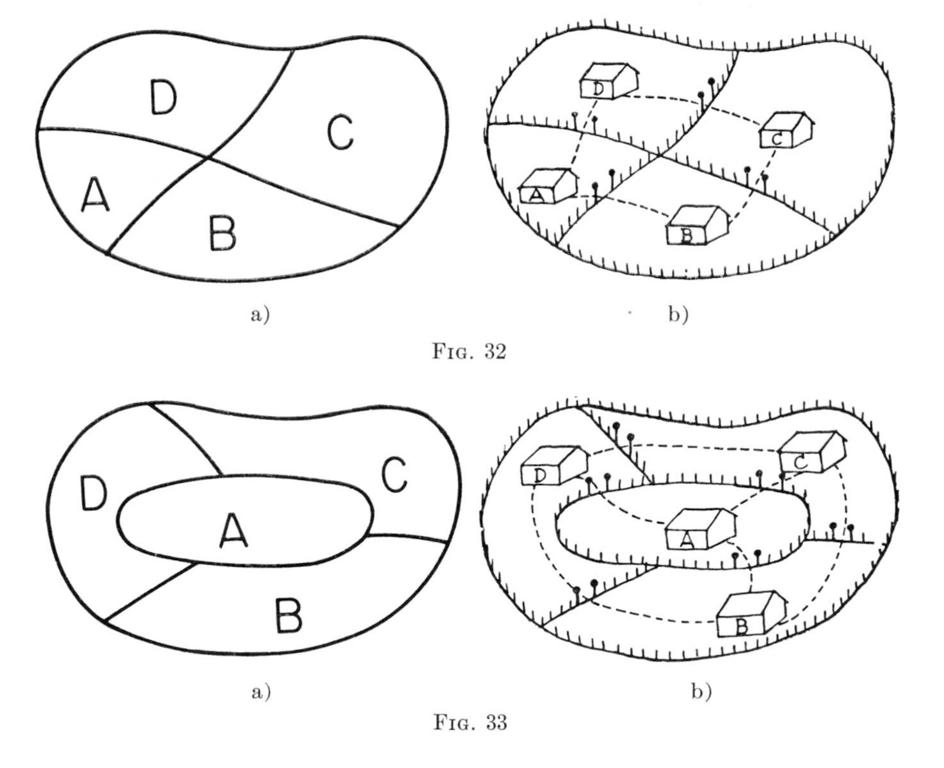


Fig. 32

Fig. 33

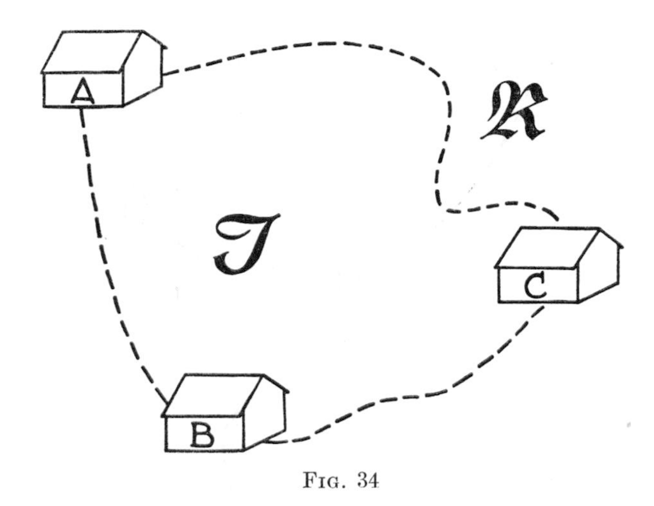


FIG. 34

to the problem of dividing the kingdom into five parts in the required way?

Suppose we attack the problem from another angle, by considering the residences of the brothers and their connecting paths. Consider first the palaces of $A$ and $B$, and connect them with a road (Fig. 34). Then $C$'s palace cannot lie on this road; $C$ can easily be connected (as in the figure) with both $A$ and $B$ by two roads, $AC$ and $BC$, neither of which intersects $AB$. We note—and this is important for the sequel—that these three paths form a closed curve, which divides the kingdom into two regions: the region $\mathfrak{J}$ inside the closed curve and the region $\mathfrak{R}$ outside the closed curve. Since the fourth brother $D$ must also have a residence somewhere, we have to assume that $AB$, $AC$, and $BC$ avoid the domain and residence of $D$. Therefore, $D$'s palace cannot lie on any of these three roads, but must be either in the interior region $\mathfrak{J}$, or in the exterior region $\mathfrak{R}$. Fig. 35a shows the first scheme, and Fig. 35b the second [**3**].

Both schemes are of the same type: the outer boundary is a closed curve on which three of the brothers have their seats;[3] the seat of the fourth brother is in the interior of this closed curve ($D$ in the first case, $B$ in the second). In Fig. 36 the essential features of the situation have been schematized still further by drawing the roads as straight lines (like railroad tracks on maps) and the palaces as rectangles. Either of the Figs. 35a, b may be obtained from Fig. 36 by marking the rectangles with the appropriate letters.

But where will the fifth brother $E$ have his residence? Naturally, he cannot live on any of the six connecting roads. Therefore, $E$ must have his

[3] In case a), these are $A$, $B$, and $C$; in case b), $A$, $C$, and $D$.

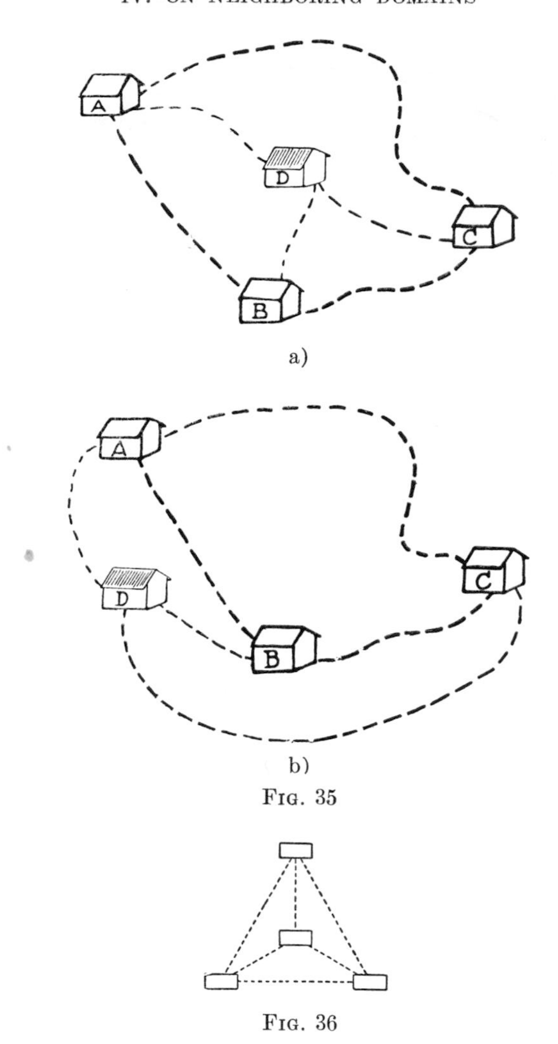


a)

b)

Fig. 35

Fig. 36

palace either in the exterior of the whole road system—but then his house cannot be independently connected to that of $D$ in Fig. 35a or $B$ in Fig. 35b[4]—or $E$ must have his residence in one of the three inner regions. In the last case, he will be denied access to either $A$, $B$, or $C$, depending on the region chosen (if the chosen region is $ABD$ in Fig. 35a, he will not have access to $C$).

Therefore, the conditions of the will can be satisfied for four brothers, but not for five.

[4] This case is shown in Fig. 37: there is no road from $E$ to $D$ but all the other roads are present.

What we have said so far can be stated in purely geometric terms. In mathematical language, the kingdom of the fairy tale is a domain, which is to be divided into a certain number of subdomains. The palaces of the princely sons are points: $A$ is a point in the first subdomain, $B$ a point in the second, etc.; and the roads between the estates are curves between these various points. But what does it mean to require a road from $A$ to $B$ which does not cross (but may touch) any of the other subdomains? It merely means that the subdomain belonging to $A$ must have a piece of its *boundary* in common with that of $B$'s domain; then the connecting path $AB$ can be run across the stretch of common boundary line, without entering any of the other subdomains [**4**].

The last observation penetrates to the root of the problem. We shall say that two subdomains of a domain are *neighboring domains* or *neighbors* if they have a piece of boundary in common. A system of domains will be referred to as a *system of neighboring domains* or simply as *neighboring domains* if *every* two domains of the system are neighbors. *Four* neighboring domains are easily obtained, as in Fig. 33a. The argument above shows that there cannot be *five*. It might seem that there are five in Fig. 31, but, e.g., $A$ and $C$ are not neighbors because they have only a point and not a *piece* of boundary in common.

We have not gone far enough to state the strongest mathematical proposition embodying our results. One essential factor and its meaning have yet to be analyzed. In order to do so, we shall continue with the fairy tale.

*The brothers sank into despair as it became clear that it was not possible to fulfill the last condition of their father's will. Suddenly a wandering wizard, who claimed to possess a solution, was announced.* What was his solution? He began with the partition of Fig. 37, but then proposed to build a bridge connecting $E$ to $D$ as shown in Fig. 38. We can assume that the wizard was richly rewarded.

But what has mathematics to say about this "solution"? On what *assumptions* did we derive the impossibility of obtaining five neighboring domains?

First, we assumed that the question could be settled on a map of the kingdom; that is, that it could be stated and solved in the plane. Thus the complete statement of the mathematical proposition which we proved is: *In the plane, there are four neighboring domains, but never five.*

And four would remain the largest possible number of neighboring domains, even if the kingdom were enlarged to encompass the whole earth, and contained no seas or icy wastes. That is, an analogous argument is valid for a sphere. *On a sphere, too, there are four neighboring domains, but never five* [**5**].

But now we must consider the fundamental changes in the problem due

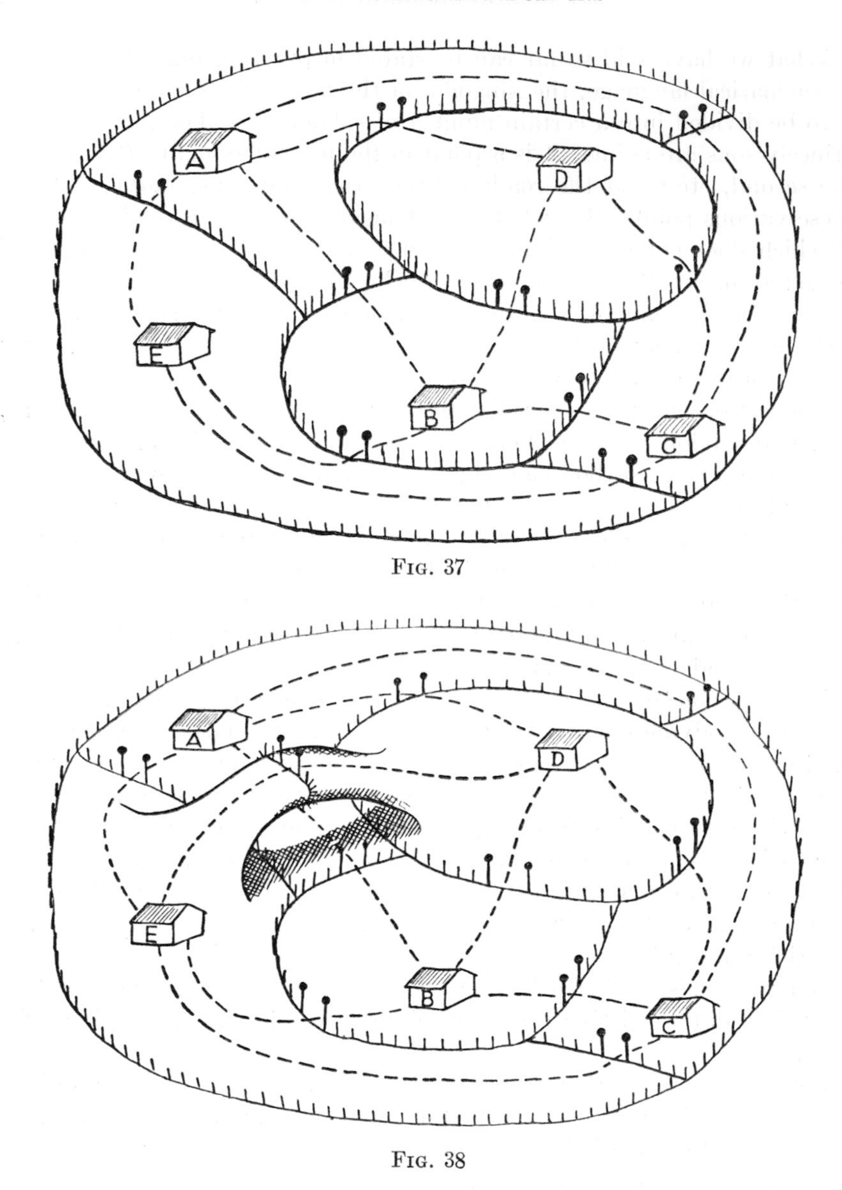


Fig. 37

Fig. 38

to the wizard's proposal that a bridge be built. Think of the bridge as thick and solid, a massive connection bridging a tunnel-like region, as indicated in Fig. 38. In particular, let us imagine that we are standing on the spherical earth and that somewhere on it a massive bridge rises, a structure of the sort pictured. We would then see that the surface of the

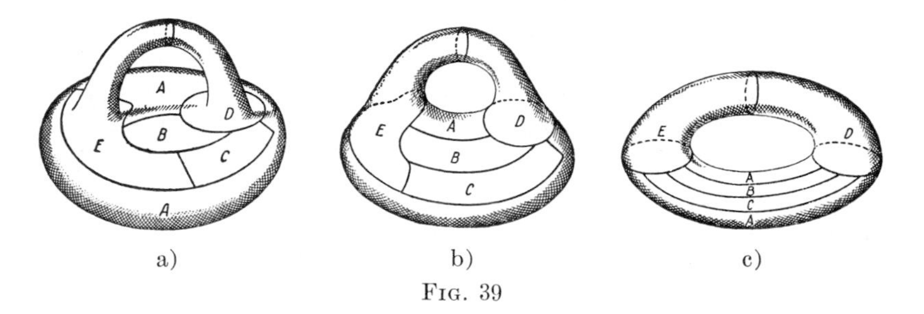


a) b) c)

Fig. 39

total figure is the ring-like surface of picture 4, Plate I. We can think of the thicker part in the background as a bridge connecting the two ends of the part in the foreground. It is easy to see that this ring surface is related to the torus of picture 3, Plate I. The surface of picture 4 can be transformed into the torus of picture 3 by inflating the thinner part and deflating the thicker part of the former surface. A subdivided domain on one surface will be transformed into a similarly subdivided domain on the other surface. It is now clear that the size of the various parts of the ring surface is irrelevant to the problem of determining the number of neighboring domains into which the surface can be divided; the only relevant factor is the ring character of the surface. A ring of this sort was obtained in Fig. 38 by erecting a bridge.

Let us suppose that the original problem was to divide the total surface of the earth, and that in Fig. 37—that is, before the construction of the bridge—as well as in Fig. 38, all the land on the earth's sphere, beyond the outer boundary of these figures, was alloted to $A$ (in addition to the land already assigned to $A$). Then the ring surface obtained by constructing the bridge is partitioned into five neighboring domains $A$, $B$, $C$, $D$, and $E$. Now if we represent this bridged earth sphere (together with the above partition) on the ring surface of picture 4, Plate I, we obtain Fig. 39a. We can then make the transition (as explained above) to a symmetrical ring surface (torus) with a corresponding partition into five neighboring domains (the transition is indicated in Figs. 39b, c). Hence, *there are at least five neighboring domains on a torus*—in contrast to the plane and sphere.

Is this the largest number? No. It is possible to construct six, even seven *neighboring domains* on a torus (picture 1 of Plate V shows seven).[5] Besides

[5] The picture shows the ring surface cut along a closed path leading from $A$ to $B$, from there to $C$, $D$, $E$, over to $F$, and back again to $A$. This makes it possible to see into the (darkly shaded) interior of the surface. On the outer surface the seven domains are distinguished by different colors: green, red, blue, white, yellow, light brown and dark brown. Parts of the light brown, yellow and dark brown regions lie in the back, invisible to the viewer. To get the required partition of the torus, we need merely paste the two edges of the cut together again. This must be done by

the five brothers of the fairy tale, two others could also have been provided for, without violating the condition that the land be divided into neighboring domains. On the other hand, it can be proved that it is not possible to have eight neighboring domains on a torus, but we cannot discuss this here [**6**].

If we are not satisfied with one bridge, we can of course get a different situation. Picture 2 of Plate V shows the case of two bridges; this surface is called a *double torus* or a *sphere with two handles*. It is possible to construct up to eight neighboring domains on a double torus,[6] but no more [**7**]. The number of bridges could of course be increased once more to yield a sphere with three handles, etc. We could again ask for the maximum number of neighboring domains on each surface obtained in this way. Although there are some results (old and new) in this direction, a general solution has yet to be found [**8**].

The problem of finding the maximum number of neighboring domains on a given surface is therefore one which is partially solved and partially unsolved. We have tried to show how to handle the problem mathematically. It is not hard to picture Möbius and his mathematically inclined friend Weiske coming home after a day's work, the one from the observatory, the other from his philological library, to entertain themselves with such a problem. But is the problem no more than a pastime? Does it have scientific significance? We shall try to make clear that this is indeed the case.

The problem we have been considering suggests a more general question: What properties of a surface (or a geometric figure) are the most essential ones; that is, what properties are most intimately connected with the nature of the surface? Let us illustrate with an analogy. We may ask which bodily characteristics distinguish one man from another, or alternatively, men in general from other forms of life. There are such characteristics as bodily height, which increases in youth, and sometimes recedes in old age; or hair color, which—without any artificial aids—undergoes many changes. In contrast to these characteristics, which are subject to change, there are

---

pasting together correspondingly lettered pieces of the cut because the green domain borders each of the other six domains along a piece of the cut: its border with the yellow, dark brown and red domains is unmistakable. But it also borders (after the cut has been repaired) the blue (along $CD$), the white (along $BC$), and the light brown (along $AB$). All the other domains may be checked in the same manner. Noting that along $DE$, yellow and blue, along $EF$, dark brown and blue, along $FA$, dark brown and light brown, adjoin one another, we see that each of the seven domains really does border on every other.

[6] These are shown in picture 2, Plate V, in eight different colors, and are lettered $a, b, c, d, e, f, g, h$. This surface is cut along two curves, $ABCDEA$, and $FGHJKF$. Remarks analogous to those in Footnote 7 are valid here. (Due to an error, the dark brown color was omitted from a small part of domain b.)

stable ones, like the color of the eyes, or fingerprints, which can even be used to identify a corpse. But it is the hereditary characteristics, such as the composition of the blood, or the number of bones and teeth, which are the most significant because they are transmitted without change from one generation to another.

Let us return to geometry and the properties of a surface. Consider a square. If it is enlarged or contracted, the length of its sides will change, but the figure will remain a square. The property of being a square may be, and in *elementary* geometry is (in contrast with the varying lengths of the sides), regarded as an essential property. But, the projection of a square, for example the shadow thrown by a square composed of four rectilinear poles held at an angle above a flat base, is no longer a square, although the shadows of the four poles are still straight lines. The straightness of a line segment is therefore an essential property, not only in elementary geometry, but also in *projective* geometry. But if a straight line (again made by throwing shadows) is projected on a sphere, or an ellipsoid, instead of a plane, the projection will no longer be straight, but curved. Even though the rectilinearity is lost, one important property is retained: a short piece of the projection differs only slightly from a straight piece; accordingly there will be no sudden changes in direction (bends) in the projected line. This property—rectilinearity in the small or local rectilinearity—is thus a deeper property than those discussed up to now. It is an essential property in *differential geometry*, which is concerned with properties in the small (or local properties) [**9**].

To go back to the problem of the maximum number of neighboring domains on a given surface—whether we make the boundary lines in Fig. 33a curved or straight is irrelevant; and it is just as irrelevant, whether the connecting paths in Fig. 34 or 35 are drawn as broken, straight, or curved. Similarly, if four neighboring domains are painted on a sphere composed of thin sheet metal and the sphere is dented (but not torn) with a blow, the dented sphere will still have four neighboring domains; a partition into four neighboring domains is either possible on both surfaces (dented and undented) or on neither. The same will be true on any surface of flexible material which is stretched or bent, but not torn or made to touch at two or more distinct points. The stretching or bending will not introduce new boundaries between domains or remove old boundaries. In other words, the property of being neighboring domains is unchanged or invariant under stretching and bending (without tearing or pasting together). In general, properties such as that of being neighboring, which are invariant under the most radical changes of the sort described are called *topological* properties. The problem of neighboring domains on a surface therefore has to do with the topological properties of the surface.

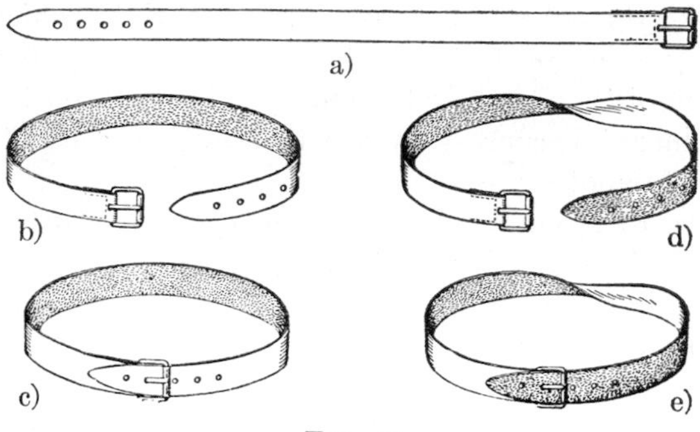


FIG. 40

The branch of mathematics which is systematically concerned with these properties is called *topology*. It is a very young branch of mathematics, developed significantly only within the past few decades. At the time of Möbius it was practically nonexistent. But the problem of neighboring domains in the plane or on the sphere, about which Möbius and Weiske conversed, was a forerunner [**10**] of the modern discipline of topology.

We can supplement our remarks on the problem of neighboring domains by discussing the surprising discovery of entirely new types of surfaces which Möbius made in his old age. The same discovery was made at about the same time (1858) by the mathematician J. B. Listing [**11**] of Göttingen. It is a very simple matter, but someone had to discover it before it could be understood.

Let us take a leather belt (see Fig. 40a) and buckle it in the usual manner (Fig. 40b, c). We can distinguish a smooth, shiny side (the outside of the belt), and the rough inside, which is shaded in Fig. 40b and 40c. We can use the buckling of the belt[7] to illustrate the geometric process shown in Fig. 41a, b, and c, which consists in transforming a rectangle with the vertices 1, 2, 3, 4 into a cylinder by joining side (1, 2) to side (3, 4).[8]

But what do we get when, in our haste to buckle the belt, we twist it before it is buckled (Fig. 40d, e)? Obviously, a surface, which is obtained by the geometric operation shown in Fig. 41a, d, e. But the final result, the surface of Fig. 41f, has a very remarkable property when compared with the original rectangle and with the cylinder of Fig. 41c. The surfaces of Fig. 40a–c, like the leather strap, have two sides, one of which is shaded and the other not. But when the belt is twisted before buckling, as in Fig.

[7] Buttoning a collar around the neck is another illustration of the same mathematical operation.

[8] The cylinder shown in the figure has a relatively small height, because in the rectangle of Fig. 41a the height of the sides (1, 2) and (3, 4) is much smaller than the width, i.e. the length of the sides (1, 3) and (2, 4). Increasing the height of the rectangle will increase the height of the cylinder correspondingly.

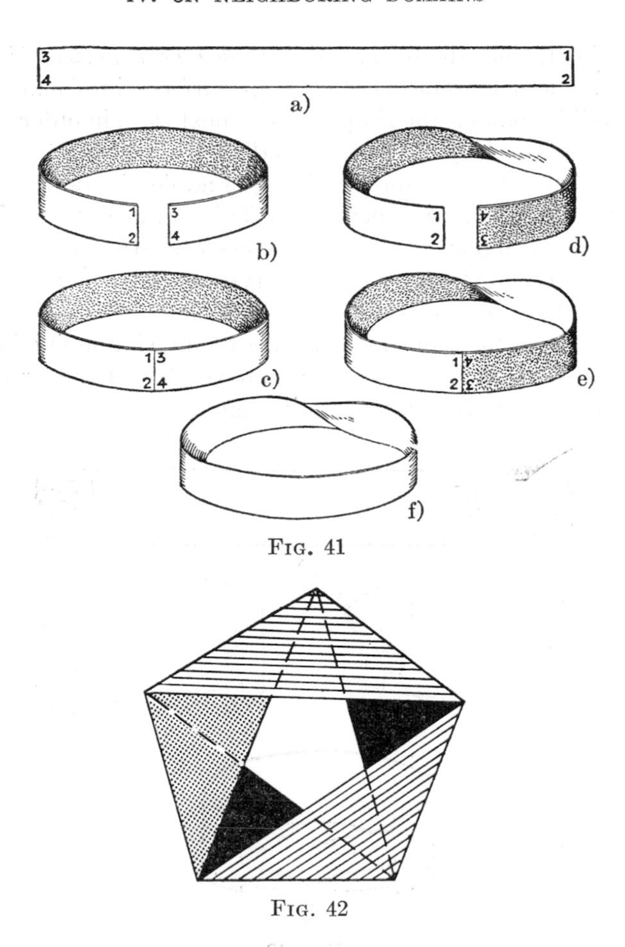


FIG. 41

FIG. 42

40d–e, the smooth side merges with the rough side; similarly, in Fig. 41 d–e, the shaded side merges with the unshaded. It is therefore impossible to distinguish two sides on the surface of Fig. 41f. For this reason, surfaces with this remarkable property are called *one-sided*, while a rectangle (Fig. 41a) and a cylinder (Fig. 41c) are said to be *two-sided* surfaces [**12**]. Now Möbius, in his studies of polyhedral surfaces,[9] included also those with self-intersections, and in this way came upon one-sided surfaces.[10] He himself referred to a twisted band (like the one in Fig. 41f) as a particularly simple example of a one-sided surface. For this reason, it is called a *Möbius band*, or *Möbius strip*.

[9] These are surfaces (such as those of a cube, a prism, a pyramid) composed of plane polygons.

[10] It is perhaps possible by looking at the polyhedral surface of Fig. 42, composed of five triangles, to see that it is a one-sided surface.

The Möbius-Listing discovery of *one-sided or nonorientable* (see [**12**]) surfaces introduced a whole new class of surfaces into mathematics, of which the Möbius band is the simplest. The next case, in order of complication, can be obtained by taking a broad belt with two straps (Fig. 43), and twisting both straps before buckling (Fig. 44 shows how the surface is obtained by a geometric operation). This surface is called a *two-fold one-sided* surface or a one-sided surface of *genus* 2. It is easy to see that the whole class of one-sided surfaces of this type can be generated by using a belt with 1, 2, 3, etc. straps [**13**].

We can now pose the problem of finding the maximum number of neighboring domains on each surface of the above class. For a long time, the solution was known only for the Möbius band.

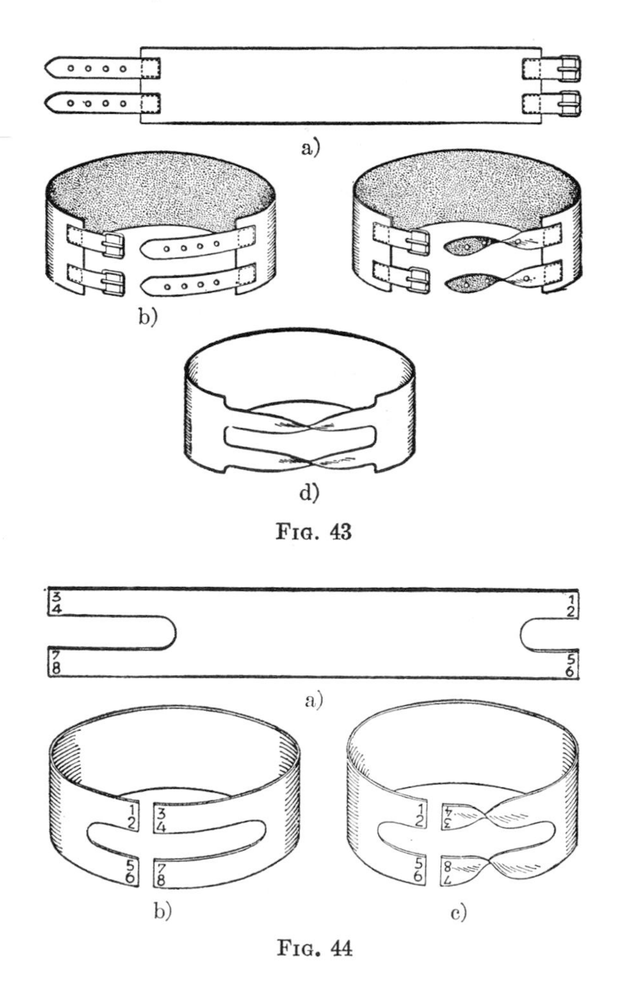


Fig. 43

Fig. 44

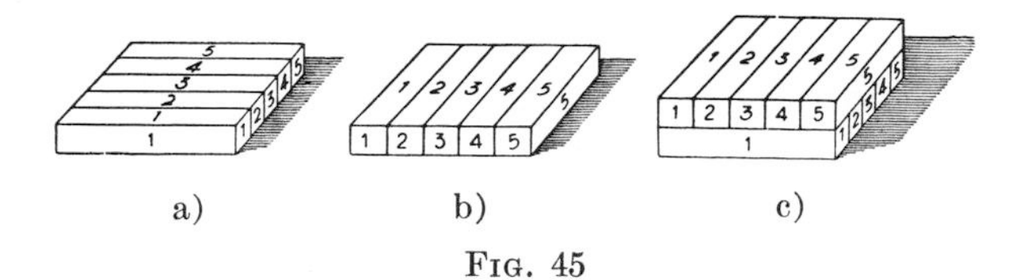


FIG. 45

It is very easy to construct *six* neighboring domains on a Möbius strip (see Plate VI; each of the six neighboring domains is given a distinct color). It can be proved rigorously, although we will not do so here, that the maximum number of neighboring domains on a Möbius strip is six [**14**].

But substantial progress has been made in the last twenty or thirty years. The maximum number of neighboring domains is now known for one-sided surfaces of the type discussed above whose genus is less than or equal to 9 (see [**12**] and [**13**]).

The problem of neighboring domains on surfaces can be, and has been, generalized. Surfaces are two-dimensional domains. The same problem has been posed for three-dimensional, that is spatial, domains. We shall call two three-dimensional domains neighboring domains if their common boundary is a piece of surface, and not merely a curve or a single point.[11]

The question that Möbius and Weiske raised and solved for the plane can now be asked for three-dimensional space. The question was: What is the maximum number of neighboring domains in the plane? The answer was four. Now we ask: What is the maximum number of neighboring domains in space? This question has been answered as often as it has been asked:[12] There is no maximum number of neighboring domains in space; as many as one wishes can be constructed. For example, to construct five neighboring domains, take a thick square board whose thickness is one fifth its length and width. Now cut the board into five prismatic bars, and place them one behind the other (Fig. 45a). Next cut a second board of the same size into five bars, but place these bars side by side, left to right (Fig. 45b). Finally, put the second layer of bars on top of the first (Fig. 45c), and call the region of space filled by these two layers of ten bars $R$. Now bar #1 of the lower layer is screwed to bar #1 of the upper layer (Fig. 46a); similarly bar #2 of the lower layer is screwed to bar #2 of the upper layer (Fig. 46b), etc. (Fig. 46c–e).

[11] Fig. 71 shows a cube divided into $8 \cdot 8 \cdot 8 = 512$ small cubes. Two small cubes, chosen at random, may have no point in common; or they may have a single vertex in common; or one edge; or finally, the side of a square. The two small cubes are neighboring domains only in the last case.

[12] It was a Scotch chemistry student, Frederick Guthrie (who will be mentioned again in Chapter XI in connection with the four color problem), who first posed and solved the problem of the maximum number of neighboring domains in space [**15**].

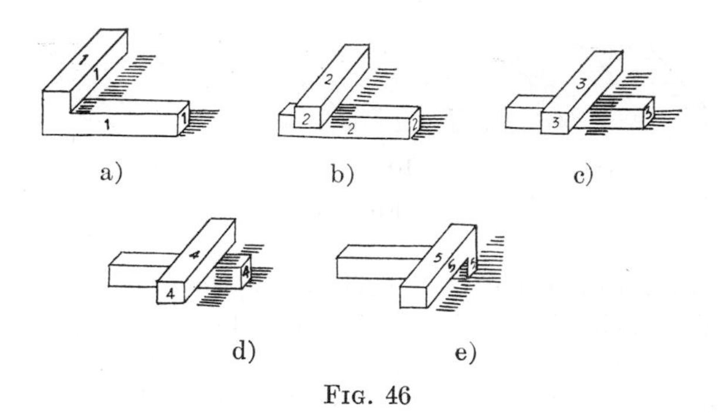


Fig. 46

Let us return to Fig. 45c which shows how the five figures of Fig. 46 are stacked together to fill the region $R$. It is clear that before the correspondingly numbered bars were screwed together pairwise, the upper bar #1 had the surface of a square in common with each bar of the lower layer; the same was true for the upper bars #2–5. Since each of these upper bars is fastened to the corresponding lower bar to give the subdomains of $R$ shown in Fig. 46, it is clear from Figs. 45 and 46, that each of these subdomains will have the surface of a square in common with every other subdomain; that is, the five pieces of Fig. 46 form a partition of $R$ into five neighboring subdomains.

It is also obvious that any number of neighboring domains, instead of five, can be constructed in the same way by repeating the above operations on two boards cut into the appropriate number of bars. This proves that *the number of neighboring domains in space is infinite.*

Paul Stäckel,[13] long a leading mathematician at the University of Heidelberg, who proved (in a somewhat different way; see [**15**]) that there are an infinite number of neighboring domains in space, gave this problem a special twist. Stäckel's problem became famous because it had to do with *convex* figures. The notion of convexity has played an important role in many fields of mathematics in the past few decades, and this is another reason for becoming familiar with the problem (see Chapter II).

Consider the quadrilateral $ABCD$ of Fig. 47a. Because of the re-entrant angle at $B$, the dotted line between $A$ and $C$ has no point in common with the interior of the quadrilateral (shaded in the figure). This is not so in the case of the trapezoid $ABCD$ in Fig. 47b: *The line joining any two boundary*

[13] Paul Stäckel (1862–1919) is one of those highly respected mathematicians, who worked in the German technical schools to prepare the ground for the cultivation of mathematics in Germany. He taught at the Universities of Königsberg and Kiel, at the technical schools of Hannover and Karlsruhe, and finally for many years at the University of Heidelberg. He was distinguished for his broad knowledge of many fields of mathematics, its applications and history, as well as for his rigorous proofs.

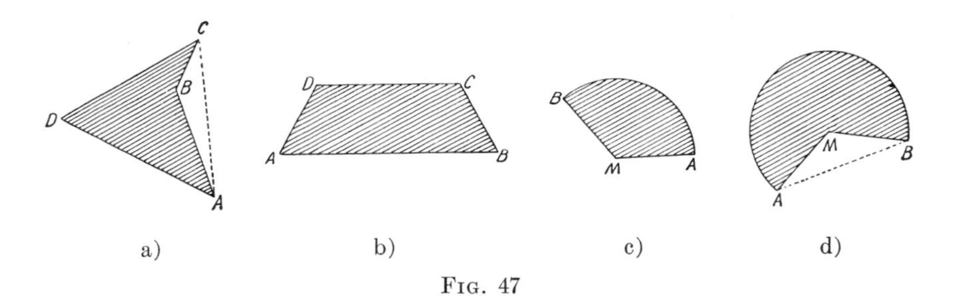


Fig. 47

*points of this figure will always lie either on the boundary, or in the interior of the figure* [**16**]. This property of a trapezoid is expressed by saying that a trapezoid is *convex*, while a quadrilateral with a re-entrant angle is non-convex. Further examples are shown in Figs. 47c and d: a sector of a circle whose angle $AMB$ is less than 180° is a convex figure; on the other hand, a sector whose angle $AMB$ is greater than 180° is non-convex (the line $AB$ connecting the two boundary points $A$ and $B$ is exterior to the sector). The same distinction between convex and non-convex figures may be made in space. A cube and a solid sphere are convex: all the points of the straight line joining two points on the surface of a cube belong to the cube. The same is true for a solid sphere. On the other hand, a ring bounded by a torus (see picture 3, Plate I) is non-convex. It is easy to find two points on the torus such that the line joining them is in the exterior of the ring (e.g. the points $P$ and $Q$ in Fig. 11). Similarly, a hammer, or a fork are examples of non-convex bodies: the lines connecting one tine of the fork with the next lie in the exterior of the fork.

Let us recall Fig. 33, which shows four neighboring domains in the plane. Fig. 48a is a geometric representation of the same example. The way in which these four domains border on one another is also shown in Fig. 48b; but with one difference. In Fig. 48a only the inner circle is convex, while the three ring-sectors are non-convex; while in Fig. 48b all four neighboring domains are convex: the interior triangle as well as the three trapezoids enclosing it. We may therefore assert not only that there are four neighbor-

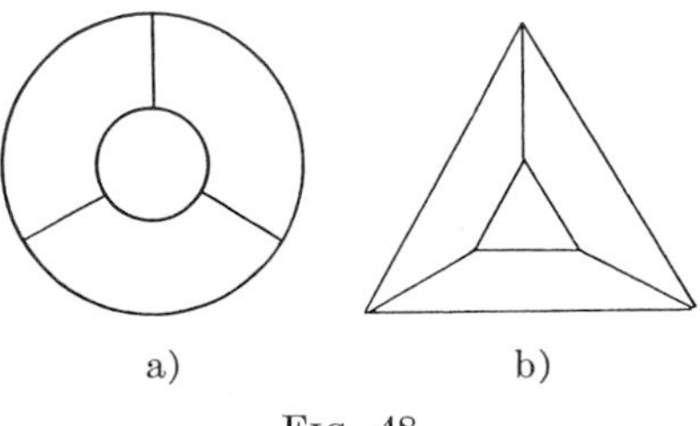


Fig. 48

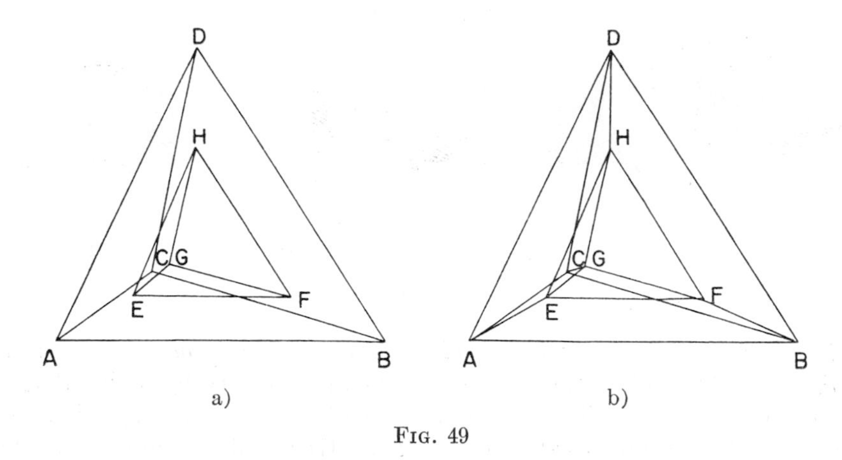


FIG. 49

ing domains in the plane, but that the plane contains four neighboring *convex* domains.

This is the source of Stäckel's problem regarding neighboring domains in space. We have seen that any number of neighboring domains can be constructed in space by the method shown in Fig. 45a, b, and c. But the domains of Fig. 46 are obviously *not* convex. What about neighboring convex domains? Is there a finite or an infinite number of such domains?

Let us consider first the spatial counterpart of the plane figure of Fig. 48b, which shows an equilateral triangle divided into one smaller, inner triangle and three trapezoids. The analogous figure in space is a tetrahedron (i.e. a regular pyramid whose boundary consists of four triangles) divided into a smaller interior tetrahedron and four truncated pyramids surrounding it (Fig. 49b).

With careful study, a more detailed and more exact analysis may be given. Let us start with a tetrahedron having the vertices $A$, $B$, $C$, $D$ (Fig. 49a), and denote by $R$ the region enclosed by the tetrahedron. Consider in the interior of the tetrahedron—and exactly in its center[14]—a smaller tetrahedron $EFGH$ parallel to the large tetrahedron. Each of the six edges of the large tetrahedron corresponds to a parallel edge of the small tetrahedron, e.g. $AB$ to $EF$. The end points $A$, $B$, $E$, $F$ of these two edges form the vertices of a trapezoid (Fig. 49b). Altogether we get six trapezoids: $ABEF$, $ACEG$, $BCFG$, $ADEH$, $BDFH$, $CDGH$. These six trapezoids together with the four faces $EFG$, $EFH$, $EGH$, $FGH$ of the small tetrahedron divide $R$ into five subdomains: one of the domains is the small tetrahedron; the other four are truncated pyramids; e.g. $ABCEFG$, which is bounded by the two triangles $ABC$, $EFG$, and by the three trapezoids $ABEF$, $ACEG$, $BCFG$. Thus each of the triangular faces of the inner tetra-

[14] That is, the centers of the two tetrahedra $ABCD$ and $EFGH$ coincide.

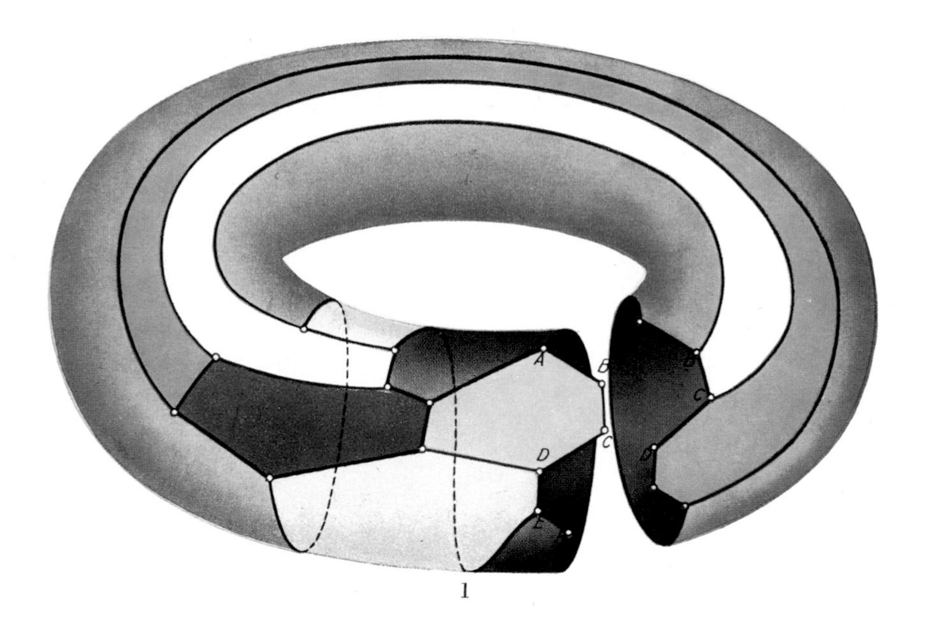
A
B
C
D
E
B
C
D

1

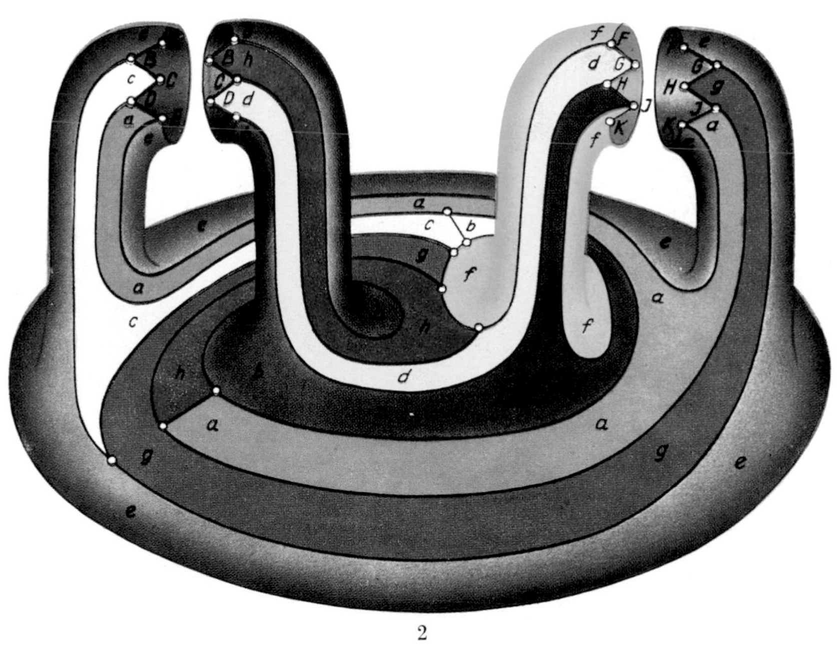
B
C
D
c
a
e
B
h
C
D
d
f
F
d
G
H
J
K
f
e
G
H
g
J
a
K
a
c
b
e
g
f
a
c
h
f
a
e
d
h
a
a
g
g
e
e

2

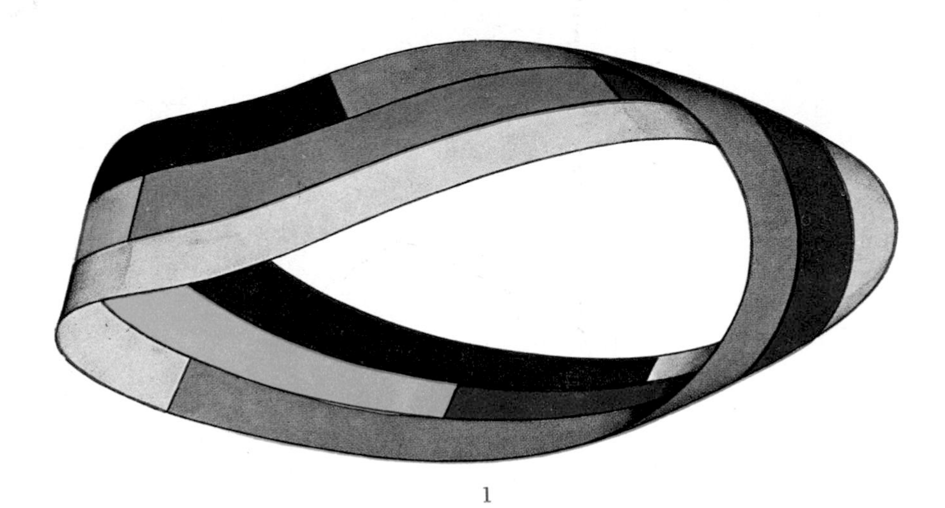

1

2

hedron *EFGH* is a face of one trucated pyramid; so that the interior tetrahedron has each of the four truncated pyramids as a neighbor. It is also easy to see that every two truncated pyramids are neighbors (for example, the trapezoid *ABEF* is the common boundary of *ABCEFG* and *ABDEFH*).

Therefore, the five domains into which the large tetrahedron *R* is divided (according to the scheme of Fig. 49b) are five *neighboring domains*, and they are all obviously *convex*.

Is five—and this was Stäckel's question [**17**]—the maximum number of convex neighboring domains in space? Or can six, or even more, be constructed? The answer is that in space there are not only six, but an *infinite number of convex neighboring domains;* therefore, the additional requirement of convexity does not restrict the maximum number of neighboring domains in space.

Since the proof of this assertion is somewhat complicated [**18**], we shall show instead that the tetrahedron *ABCD* of Fig. 49b can be divided into six neighboring domains. The best way to illustrate the construction is to

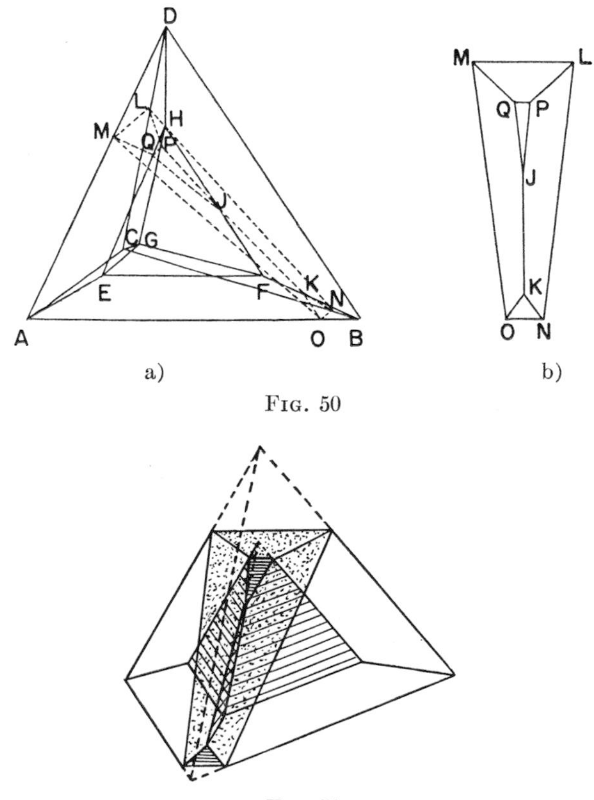


a)

b)

Fig. 50

Fig. 51

use models made of stiff paper, such as drawing paper, and to paint the six subdomains with different colors. The pictures in Plate VII and Fig. 51 show how the six convex pieces can be put together to form a tetrahedron. It is not difficult to prove that these pieces are a system of neighboring domains.

We add the following details of the construction of the subdomains for those who are interested. First, choose a point $J$ on the segment $FH$ and a point $K$ on the segment $BF$ (Fig. 50a); then draw the plane containing $JK$ and parallel to the edges $AC$ and $EG$ of the two tetrahedra. This plane will intersect the large tetrahedron $ABCD$ in a trapezoid $LMNO$, which we denote by $s$; it is easy to prove that $s$ intersects the small tetrahedron $EFGH$ (in the triangle $JPQ$), as well as each of the four truncated pyramids. The trapezoid $s$ is shown in Fig. 50a by dotted lines and in Fig. 50b it is shown by itself, removed from the tetrahedron.

Now we consider the following partition of the tetrahedron $R$. First, we divide $R$ into two parts by means of $s$: part I, which in Fig. 50a is to the left of and below $s$, and which contains $A$ and $C$; and part II, lying to the right of and above $s$, which contains $B$ and $D$. Now we consider in part I the previous division of $R$ into five subdomains. Part I contains a piece of each of these subdomains; we denote these pieces by $R_1$, $R_2$, $R_3$, $R_4$, and $R_5$. For example, let $R_1$ be the piece of the small inner tetrahedron $EFGH$ which, in Fig. 50a, is below $s$.[15] Similarly, let $R_2$ be the piece of the truncated pyramid $ABCEFG$ below $s$, etc. It is immediately seen that the five pieces, $R_1$, $R_2$, $R_3$, $R_4$, $R_5$ are a system of neighboring domains. Finally, to this system of neighboring domains, we add a sixth, $R_6$, consisting of all of part II (which lies to the right of and above $s$ and which is bounded by $s = LMNO$, the triangles $LMD$, $NOB$ and the trapezoids $LNBD$, $MOBD$). Since each of the domains $R_1, \cdots, R_5$ has a two-dimensional piece of its boundary lying on $s$ (see Fig. 50b, which shows each of these pieces), it follows that $R_1, \cdots, R_5, R_6$ is a system of neighboring domains. Furthermore, they are convex and partition $R$.

The pictures in Plate VII and Fig. 51 show the same partition but from another view.

So much for Stäckel's modification of the problem of neighboring domains in space. It must be emphasized here that the modified problem is no longer a *topological* problem. The straightness of a connecting path is not a topological property. Since convexity is defined in terms of straight lines, the classification of figures into convex and non-convex has nothing to do with those deep properties which we have designated as topological. The problem of *convex* neighboring domains is rather a problem of elementary geometry.

[15] To obtain $R_1$, we must be sure to cut off the part of the inner tetrahedron $EFGH$ which is cut by the triangle $QPJ$ near the vertex $H$.

## *Notes to Chapter IV*

# ON NEIGHBORING DOMAINS

**1** (p. 65). Möbius' chief work in this direction is {2}, also reprinted in volume 1 of his collected works {3}. It is characteristic of this work that Möbius consistently paid attention to the orientation of geometric figures (positive or negative sense on a segment, positive or negative measure of an angle, positive or negative circuit of a circle or triangle, etc.), and formulated this notion analytically. Möbius published his investigations in statics in a two volume work {4}, which at first sold badly: the first edition was marked unsaleable after a few years. The first edition of the *Ausdehnungslehre* of H. G. Grassmann (1809–1877) suffered a similar fate; and presumably the same occurred to Desargues' main work, the *Brouillon projet.*[1]

**2** (p. 65). See {6}. The same book, on p. 213 ff., contains many discussions from the older literature of problems related to the map coloring problem (see Chapter XI). For a more recent account see Gerhard Ringel {7}. In this paper, Ringel also solves this and related problems on nonorientable surfaces.

**3** (p. 67). It is clear that in the first case, where $D$ is in the interior of the domain $\mathfrak{J}$, the three paths $DA$, $DB$, $DC$ must be topologically (that is, except for irrelevant bends and turns) related as in Fig. 35a. On the other hand in the second case, when $D$ is in the domain $\mathfrak{R}$, the genesis of Fig. 35b perhaps deserves a more precise account. This might run somewhat as follows: First, draw the path $DA$ (Fig. 52a). There are then essentially two possibilities for the path $DB$: I as in Fig. 52b or II as in Fig. 52c.[2] Now only a path connecting $D$ to $C$ is missing. In Case I (Fig. 52b), $D$ can be connected to $C$ either as in Fig. 35b or as in Fig. 53a by the path 2. In Case II (Fig. 52c), only a path such as 1 in Fig. 53b is possible.

But it is then clear that Figs. 53a and b are of the same type as Fig 35b, and indeed the same as Fig. 35a if the lettering is ignored, as shown in the schematic diagram of Fig. 36.

**4** (p. 69). These remarks lead to a general method of obtaining from a subdivision of a domain a new configuration, which is called the *dual* of the original subdivision. The method is to choose a point in every region

[1] The complete, altogether modest, title is *Brouillon projet d'une atteinte aux événemens des rencontres d'un cone avec un plan*. See {5}. Desargues, who came from Lyon, was mentioned in Chapter III.

[2] The two cases can be distinguished as follows: In Case I the path $AB$ is no longer accessible from the exterior of the simple closed curve $ADBC$, while the paths $AC$ and $BC$ are. In Case II, the reverse is true.

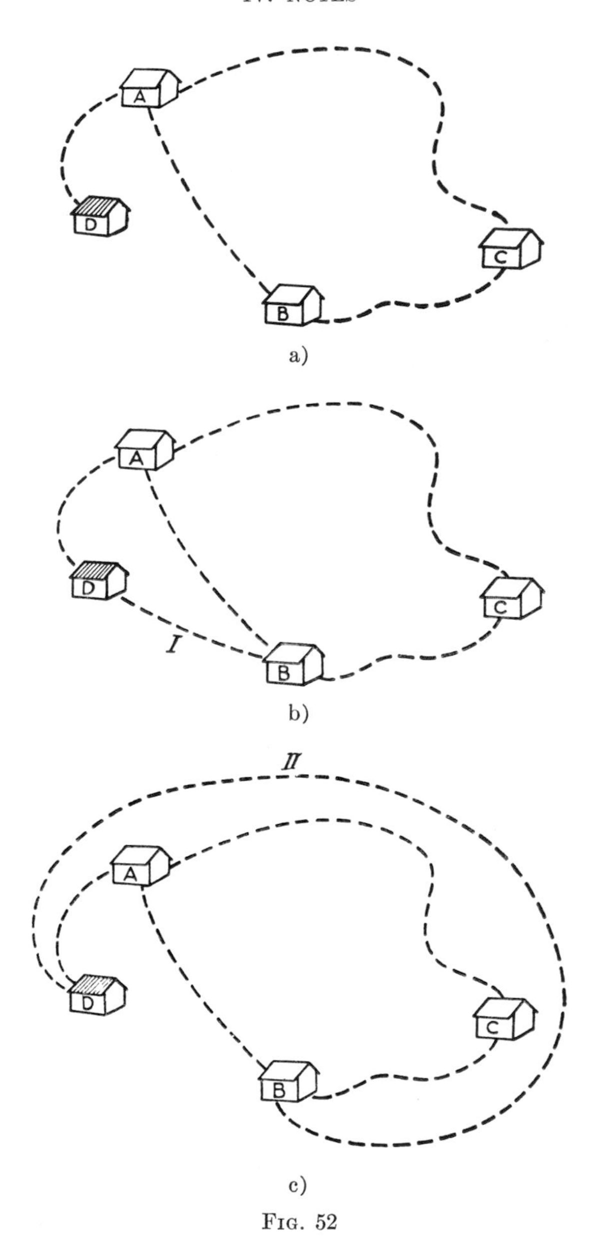


FIG. 52

of the original domain and to connect with a path every two such points which correspond to regions with a common boundary. In this construction the path connecting a pair of chosen points must cross the common boundary of the regions. (See {6; p. 214}.)

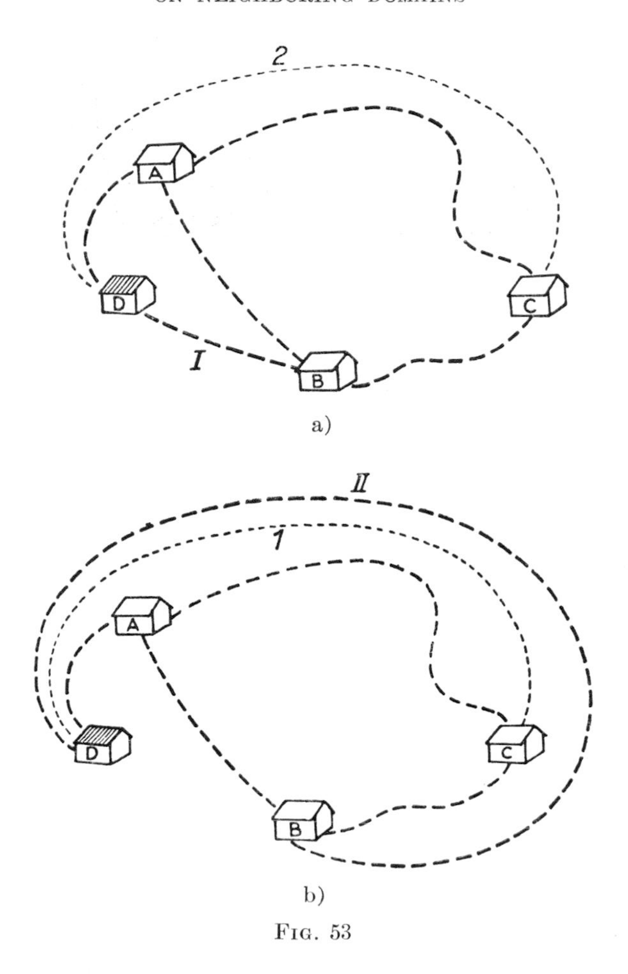


FIG. 53

In our case, we deduce the impossibility of the required subdivision from the impossibility of obtaining its dual.

**5** (p. 69). In carrying over to a sphere the reasoning we used to demonstrate the impossibility of obtaining five neighboring domains in the plane, we must note one difference. The three paths $AB$, $BC$ and $CD$ again, as in Fig. 34, form a closed curve $L$. But, although $L$ separates the plane into an interior region $\mathfrak{J}$ and an exterior region $\mathfrak{R}$[3] (in the plane these regions can be distinguished from each other by the fact that $\mathfrak{J}$ is bounded, while $\mathfrak{R}$ is not), the two regions into which $L$ separates a sphere cannot be distinguished from each other. $D$ must, therefore, lie in the interior of one of these domains.

[3] Those who have a more professional knowledge of mathematics will immediately recognize this as a special case of the celebrated Jordan separation theorem.

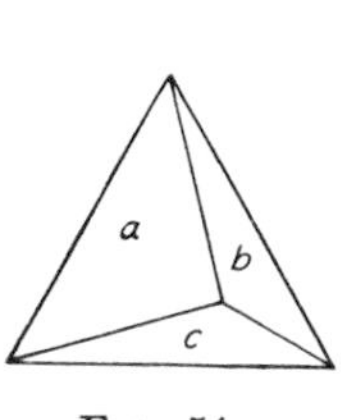

FIG. 54

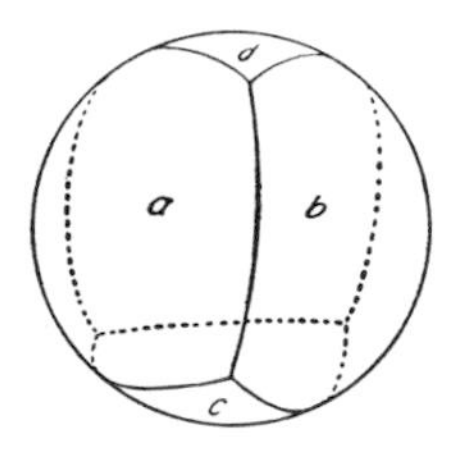


FIG. 55

It is easy to construct four neighboring domains on a sphere by considering instead a tetrahedron (see Fig. 54), which is topologically the same as a sphere. Choose a point $M$ in the interior of the tetrahedron, and draw a sphere with center $M$ and sufficiently large radius so that the sphere contains the tetrahedron in its interior. Now project the edges of the tetrahedron from $M$ onto the sphere. This yields a partition of the sphere into four neighboring domains (Fig. 55), which are the projections onto the sphere of the faces $a$, $b$, $c$, $d$ of the tetrahedron ($d$ is the reverse side of the figure).

**6** (p. 72). This result is due to the English mathematician P. J. Heawood (1861–1955). See Note 7 for the relevant references. Six neighboring domains on a torus had already been constructed by A. B. Kempe in a paper {8}, which contained an erroneous solution of the four color problem. For a discussion of the four color problem see Chapter XI. For Kempe, see Footnote 4 in the Notes to Chapter XI.

**7** (p. 72). See {9}, {10} and also the references cited in Note 14. This and related problems are discussed (without proofs) in {6; pp. 211–225}. For more recent progress see {7}.

**8** (p. 72). These surfaces (the closed orientable two-dimensional surfaces) are characterized by the number of handles which must be attached to a sphere in order to obtain them (the common boundary of each handle with the sphere is of course deleted after the attachment). Denote this number (as usual) by $p$. The problem of finding the maximum number of neighboring domains on a sphere with $p$ handles has been solved for $0 \leq p \leq 9$. For $p > 9$, solutions have been obtained only in special cases, that is, when $p$ satisfies certain additional conditions.[4] It has been conjectured that the maximum number of neighboring domains on a sphere with $p$ handles is the greatest integer in

$$(*) \qquad \tfrac{1}{2}[7 + (1 + 48p)^{1/2}].$$

[4] In addition to the reference {19} cited in Note 14, see {10} and the more recent paper by Ringel {11}.

For $p = 0, 1, 2$ this formula yields the values 4, 7 and 8, which are indeed the right numbers.[5]

The proof of the latter results depends on the Euler polyhedral theorem. This theorem applies to more general figures than the closed surfaces we are considering here, but can be easily stated in this case. First, given a sphere with $p$ handles, let us call the number $2 - 2p$ the Euler characteristic of the surface. Now subdivide the surface into any finite number $A_2$ of regions,[6] denote by $A_1$ the number of common boundaries of the regions, and by $A_0$ the number of vertices of the subdivision, that is, the points at which at least two boundaries meet. Then Euler's theorem states that $A_2 - A_1 + A_0$ is equal to the Euler characteristic of the surface, i.e.,

$$A_2 - A_1 + A_0 = 2 - 2p.$$

For instance, in the tetrahedral subdivision of the sphere in Fig. 55, $A_2 = 4$, $A_1 = 6$, $A_0 = 4$, so that $A_2 - A_1 + A_0 = 2$, in agreement with the fact that $p = 0$ for the sphere. (Actually, Euler obtained the formula only for the sphere. It was later extended to more general figures.) Riemann called a sphere with $p$ handles a surface of genus $p$, and this terminology has been in use since then in those branches of mathematics[7] where this classification is of the greatest importance.

**9** (p. 73). See Hilbert and Cohn-Vossen, *Geometry and the Imagination*, New York, Chelsea, 1952; Ch. IV.

**10** (p. 74). Euler's Königsberg bridge problem and Hamilton's dodecahedron game are in the same vein; see {12}, {13}. Gauss' research on lines in the plane (see {14}) must also be assigned to the beginnings of this field. The most relevant for the origins of this branch of mathematics is the profound research of Listing, Tait, and others on knots in space; see {15}.

**11** (p. 74). See {16}, {17}, {19}.

**12** (p. 75). Two-sidedness and one-sidedness of surfaces are not intrinsic properties of surfaces; that is, someone restricted to the surface would not be able to decide between the two. They are rather imbedding properties;

[5] The same is true for $3 \leq p \leq 7$. The maximum number of neighboring domains has been determined for these values of $p$, and has been found to be in agreement with the value calculated from (*). There are still open problems in this field (apart from those dealing with specific values of $p$). That the maximum number of neighboring domains does not exceed the value given by (*) was shown by Heawood. See Note 6 to Chapter XI.

[6] We must also assume that each of the regions into which the surface is subdivided is topologically equivalent to a disk, so that, in particular, it is simply connected (roughly speaking, it has no holes).

[7] In particular, the theory of algebraic functions of a complex variable and their integrals. For Riemann see Chapter XIV.

that is, they depend on the way in which the surface is situated in a surrounding space. Someone free to move in the space outside the surface will then be able to decide whether the surface is one-sided or two-sided. But it is possible to distinguish the surface of Fig. 41f from a surface such as a cylinder by means of two properties, orientability and nonorientability, which are analogous to two-sidedness and one-sidedness, but are intrinsic properties of the surface, and thus do not depend on the way in which the surface is imbedded in three-dimensional space. These two properties can be defined rigorously, but it is not hard to describe a simple intuitive criterion which will distinguish between them. To this end, consider any simple closed curve on the surface (that is, a closed curve without intersections). Starting at any point on the curve draw a small circle oriented clockwise with this point as center. Now move the circle along the curve. If the circle at the end of the circuit is still oriented clockwise and if this is true for every simple closed curve on the surface, then the surface is orientable. If, on the other hand, for some simple closed curve on the surface, the circle at the end of the circuit is oriented counter-clockwise, then the surface is nonorientable. This test can be easily applied to a cylinder (orientable) and a Möbius band (nonorientable).

The distinction between orientability and nonorientability was already known to Möbius, who expressed it in his Kantengesetz—he confined himself mostly to polyhedral surfaces. For a more general treatment of orientability and nonorientability see {18}.

**13** (p. 76). If $q$ is the number of straps or bands, whose ends are to be identified after the bands are twisted, the resulting surface will have genus $q$.

The problem of neighboring domains we have considered here is closely related to the coloring problem on various surfaces discussed in Chapter XI. For the most general results and a survey of the development of the problem see {11}.

**14** (p. 77). See {19}. The problem of determining the maximum number of neighboring domains on nonorientable surfaces of arbitrary genus has been solved (in a series of papers) during the last twenty or thirty years. See {20}–{26}.

**15** (p. 77). See {27}. Frederick Guthrie's older brother Francis studied mathematics, and Frederick himself attended de Morgan's lectures on mathematics (see Ch. XI). For various proofs of the fact that an arbitrary number of neighboring domains can be constructed in space see {28}, {29}. The proof given in the text is taken from {30}.

**16** (p. 79). A more rigorous definition is: A set of points (in the plane or in space) is *convex* if all the points of the segment joining any two points of the set are also contained in the set.

**17** (p. 81). Frederick Guthrie had already noted this problem—the maximum number of convex neighboring domains in space—in his own work. See {27} and {30; p. 212}.

**18** (p. 81). For the general proof see {30}. An especially simple proof was discovered by Besicovitch, who presented it at a guest lecture in Munich (*Two Problems on Convex Figures*) in 1948. The problem was again raised recently, independently of the sources mentioned here. See {31}.

*Chapter V*

# SQUARING THE CIRCLE

There is a common saying that those who attempt the impossible, who chase after unattainable goals, are trying to "square the circle." The phrase sounds learned, even a little mysterious. Generally, what do we know about this expression? Only that it refers to an utterly insoluble mathematical problem, and has somehow passed into general usage. The phrase is the translation of the Latin "quadratura circuli," where "circulus" means simply circle. We shall explain the meaning of "quadrature" later, since a literal translation of the word will not make the concept any clearer.

The problem of squaring the circle is old and famous, and as worthy of notice as any of the other problems of antiquity we have discussed thus far.[1] At the same time, it signalizes an achievement of modern mathematics; it was only about eighty years ago that it was finally solved.

The statement of the problem is simple enough, but its solution is difficult. The difficulties of discussing the solution with non-mathematicians are analogous to those faced by a chess player reporting a masterful combination on the 64 squares of the chess-board to someone who has never held a chessman in his hand. The chess player would have to begin by explaining the rules of the game, and long before he came to the fine points, probably even before he finished with the fundamentals, his audience would have fled. I must also confess that even the best students feel at home with the solution only after eight semesters of technical courses, and that a few years ago a technical monograph [**1**] of over 100 pages was devoted to describing the original solution. The account given here will therefore necessarily be somewhat hazy.

The ordinary sense of the phrase "squaring the circle," as used at the beginning of the chapter, differs from its mathematical meaning. We shall discuss this meaning, and then relate how the problem was solved by Ferdinand Lindemann.

In considering the nature of this problem, which had already engaged the minds of the ancients, we would like to point out not only *what the problem is*, but also *what it is not;* why it is so easily misunderstood by non-mathematicians, and why year in and year out—even today when the books have long been closed on this problem—so many appear with solutions, appealing to the scientific societies and even importuning mathematicians themselves. We must inquire into the cause of such frequent misunderstandings. The difficulty lies in having to keep in mind several things at the same

[1] The infinitude of the primes (Chapter I) and the trisection of an angle (Chapter III).

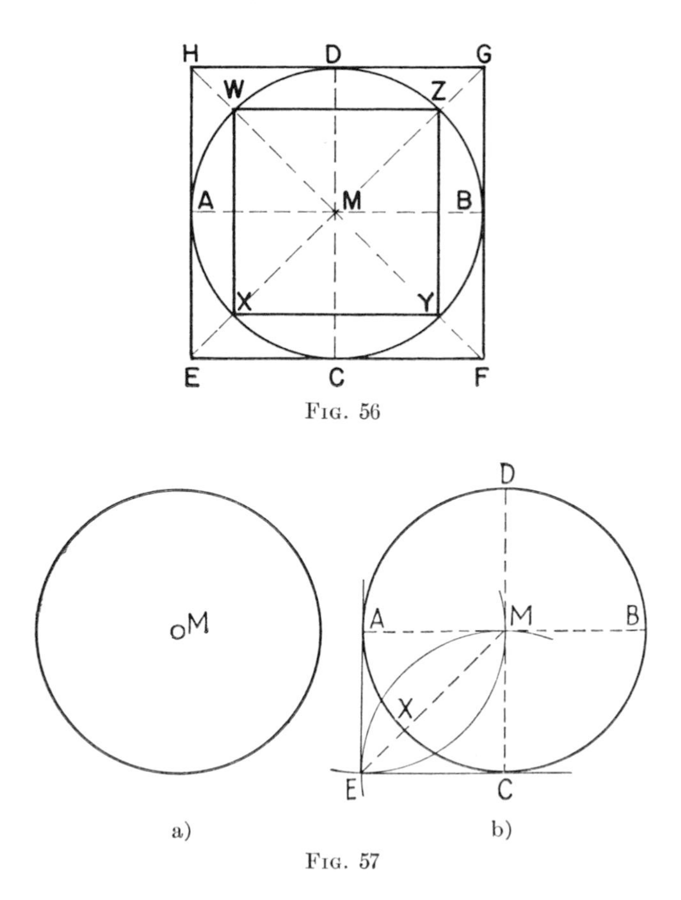


FIG. 56

FIG. 57

time (which in itself requires training), so many that the layman usually neglects some aspect of the problem. The same thing happens to the beginning chess player whose beautiful plan is ruined by a chessman on his opponent's side which he somehow failed to notice.

In its mathematical meaning, the problem of "squaring the circle" is to construct a square having the same area as that of a given circle. But this is not all. On the contrary! The most important factor—one often forgotten—is *how* the square is to be constructed. However, setting this aspect of the problem aside for the moment, it is easy to see that there is certainly a square with the same area as the given circle. We need merely draw a square $EFGH$ circumscribing, and another square $XYZW$ inscribed in, the given circle (Fig. 56).[2] The circumscribed square must have a

[2] Fig. 57a, b shows how these squares can be constructed with straight edge and compass. Draw a diameter $AB$ through the center $M$, and construct the diameter $CD$ perpendicular to it (by constructing the perpendicular bisector; see Fig. 60b).

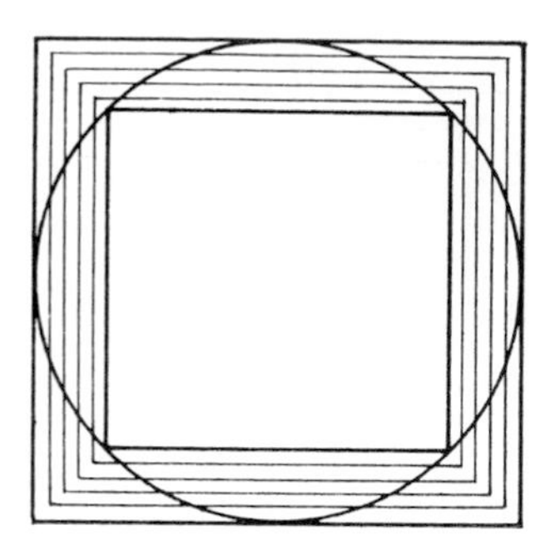

Fig. 58

larger area than the circle, since the circle contains only a part of the total area of the square; and the inscribed square must be smaller. Now (Fig. 58), let the outer square shrink gradually until it becomes the inscribed square. Since we began with a square larger than the circle and ended with a square smaller than the circle, there must be a square between these two with the same area as that of the circle. This is the required square.

We can pose very *different* questions about this square, and an interchange of one question with another may lead to many misunderstandings. A question one might raise first, one which also goes back to antiquity, is: Given the radius of the circle, how long is the side of a square with the same area; how can we *calculate* its length, and hence the area of the square and also of the circle? Everyone who has had some elementary mathematics knows that this question was answered a long time ago (another instance where "pure" science provided for the practical needs of the practical), and that the answer involves the number $\pi = 3.14159\cdots$.

But we can also ask *geometric-constructive* questions about this square, and pose the problem of constructing a square having the same area as a given circle. The question is then not one of calculation, but of geometric construction. Such a construction had already been sought in antiquity. We shall carefully note the precise conditions for such a construction: we must distinguish between a practical drawing with such material aids as real paper and a real pencil, and a theoretical construction, ideally free of errors. For practical purposes, a construction with an error of less than $1/250$ of an inch would be entirely satisfactory. The geometers of ancient Greece did not have such practical constructions in mind. They sought an ideal construction which would yield the exact length of the required

The circle with center $A$ and radius $AM$ intersects the circle with center $C$ and radius $CM$ at $E$, which is therefore a vertex of the circumscribed square. The straight line $EM$ meets the given circle at $X$, a vertex of the inscribed square. The other vertices of these squares are obtained in a similar manner.

square. Therefore, the classical problem of squaring the circle was to find a square equal in area to that of a given circle by means of an ideally *exact* construction [**2**]. Those who are interested only in approximate constructions (of which there are several good ones) have not understood the theoretical, ideal goal of the ancient geometers.

But something else is traditionally required of the construction: no other instruments than a straight edge to draw straight lines and a compass to draw circles are to be used. Hence, a construction using, say an ellipse, or a modern instrument such as an integraph, could *not* be considered a solution, even if it were fully exact.

One might see something wilful in this forced limitation to straight edge and compass; one might even find it interesting to look for constructions using other instruments, and this has of course been done. In any case, this limitation was the preference of the Greeks and speaks for the special role they assigned to the straight line and the circle.

To summarize, the problem requires that we find a square having the same area as a given circle by an *exact* construction using straight edge and compass alone.

Such a construction was not found in antiquity, nor in the Middle Ages, nor in modern times. Gradually the suspicion dawned that it was a chimera. It must be noted that only a limited range of construction problems can be solved with limited aids. After all, the number of constructions with straight edge and compass is greater than the number with straight edge alone. After the futile efforts of so many generations, people began to conjecture that there was an exact construction, but one which required additional instruments. The doubt as to the solvability of the problem with straight edge and compass alone became general in scientific circles—I believe at the beginning of the 19th century—when the Paris Academy declared it would no longer consider solutions to this problem. Whatever their reasons for doing so, they had no proof that the problem could not be solved. But in 1882 Lindemann proved that the construction sought since the days of the Greeks was an impossibility. Although Lindemann finally settled the problem, or rather dismissed it from the world of scientific problems, I dare not prophesy how long it will take before all the circle squarers die out.

Lindemann used very profound methods in his proof. He worked with concepts unknown in antiquity or in the Middle Ages, and his result was based on subtle properties of the number $\pi$. These indications must suffice here.

A non-mathematician always finds one aspect of Lindemann's result difficult to accept. In a straight edge and compass construction one starts, say by connecting two points with the straight edge, then setting the compass opening at the distance between the points and describing one or

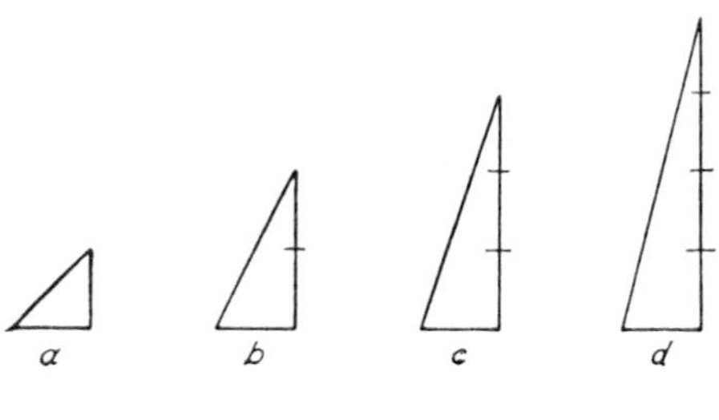


FIG. 59

more circles. This leads to a set of new points of intersection between which straight lines are drawn, which provide new compass openings for describing new circles, etc. This process creates so many possibilities, beginning with simpler figures and progressing to more complicated ones, that certainly no one will ever be able to test every one of these constructions, or to decide whether there is one which yields a square whose area is that of a given circle. Here the non-mathematician is right: there are an infinite number of complicated constructions possible with straight edge and compass alone, and no mathematician will ever be able to study them all, *singly*. But if this is so, how can the mathematicians assert that this infinite set of constructions does not contain one which gives the desired result? Can mathematics assert propositions about an infinite number of cases without testing each *separately?* This is exactly what mathematics can do and this problem is an example. Indeed, almost every mathematical proposition encompasses an infinite number of cases and is not to be doubted just because each case has not been separately tested. A good example is the Pythagorean theorem on right triangles, of which there are an infinite number (see Fig. 59). One of the legs, for example, may be equal to the other, or double its length, or three or four times as large, etc. Nevertheless the Pythagorean theorem, which states that the square of the hypotenuse is equal to the sum of the squares of the other two sides, is valid for all right triangles, and the proof treats all the possible cases simultaneously, without examining each one separately.

This is not an isolated example. It can be stated categorically as an essential property of mathematics that its propositions (not, of course, propositions such as $2 \times 2 = 4$, but general propositions) encompass an infinite number of cases [**3**]. Mathematical certainty is not a result of testing each individual case—this would be impossible whenever there is an infinite number of different cases—but of a general proof which applies to all cases. Such a proof is not always easy to find.

In the halls of the University of Munich, there is a bust of Ferdinand Lindemann (Plate IX). Beneath the engraved name, there appears the letter $\pi$, framed in a circle and a square, as a symbol of the wonderful feat described in this chapter. When he made this discovery, Carl Louis Ferdinand Lindemann was about thirty years old. He was born in Hannover in 1852, and studied in Göttingen, Erlangen, Munich, Paris and London; he then taught for a number of years in several German universities. In 1893, he came to the University of Munich, where he remained until his death in 1939. Both his research and his teaching extended over wide fields of mathematics. In his last years he became an antiquarian, but even then did not give up his mathematical interests.

The classical problem of squaring a circle imposes three essential conditions: 1) The construction must be *geometric;* 2) it must be mathematically exact; 3) it must be carried out with straight edge and compass alone. As we have explained, all three conditions cannot be satisfied simultaneously.

What about geometric constructions which satisfy one of the conditions 2) or 3), but not both? We shall see that there are constructions for squaring a circle, using straight edge and compass alone, which are not exact, but accurate enough for all practical purposes. These constructions satisfy 3) but not 2). There are also exact constructions, which use aids in addition to straight edge and compass, and hence satisfy 2) but not 3).[3]

An example of the first kind of construction—to choose one of many—is an approximate construction due to Kochansky (1685). It is shown in Fig. 60. Given a circle with center $M$ (Fig. 60a), draw a diameter $AB$ through $M$, and construct the perpendicular bisector $CD$ of $AB$. The circles with centers $A$ and $C$ and radius equal to that of the given circle intersect at $E$ (Fig. 60c); the first of these two circles cuts the given circle at $F$. Then $A$, $E$, $C$, $M$ are the vertices of a square and $CE$ is tangent to the circle (Fig. 60d). The straight line $MF$ cuts the tangent $CE$ at $G$ (Fig. 60e); from $G$ the radius $AM$ is marked off three times on the line $CE$ to give the point $H$ (Fig. 60f). Then the length of the segment $HD$ (Fig. 60g) closely approximates half the circumference of the circle [**4**]. Hence, if the length $AM$ of the radius of the circle is taken as the unit of length, so that the circumference is $2\pi$,[4] then the length of $HD$ is approximately $\pi$. If we now construct a rectangle $PQRS$ whose base $PQ = DH$, and whose height $PR = AM$ (Fig. 60h), its area will be approximately equal to $\pi$. Since $\pi$ is the area of the circle,[5] the area of the rectangle is approximately the same as that of the circle. To finish the problem, it is merely necessary to construct a square with the same area as the rectangle. This can be done

[3] A similar situation was encountered in Chapter III in the problem of trisecting an angle: an approximate construction with ruler and compass alone (Kopf); and an exact construction using a parabola (Descartes).

[4] By putting $r = 1$ in the formula $2\pi r$ for the circumference of a circle of radius $r$.

[5] By putting $r = 1$ in the formula $\pi r^2$ for the area of a circle of radius $r$.

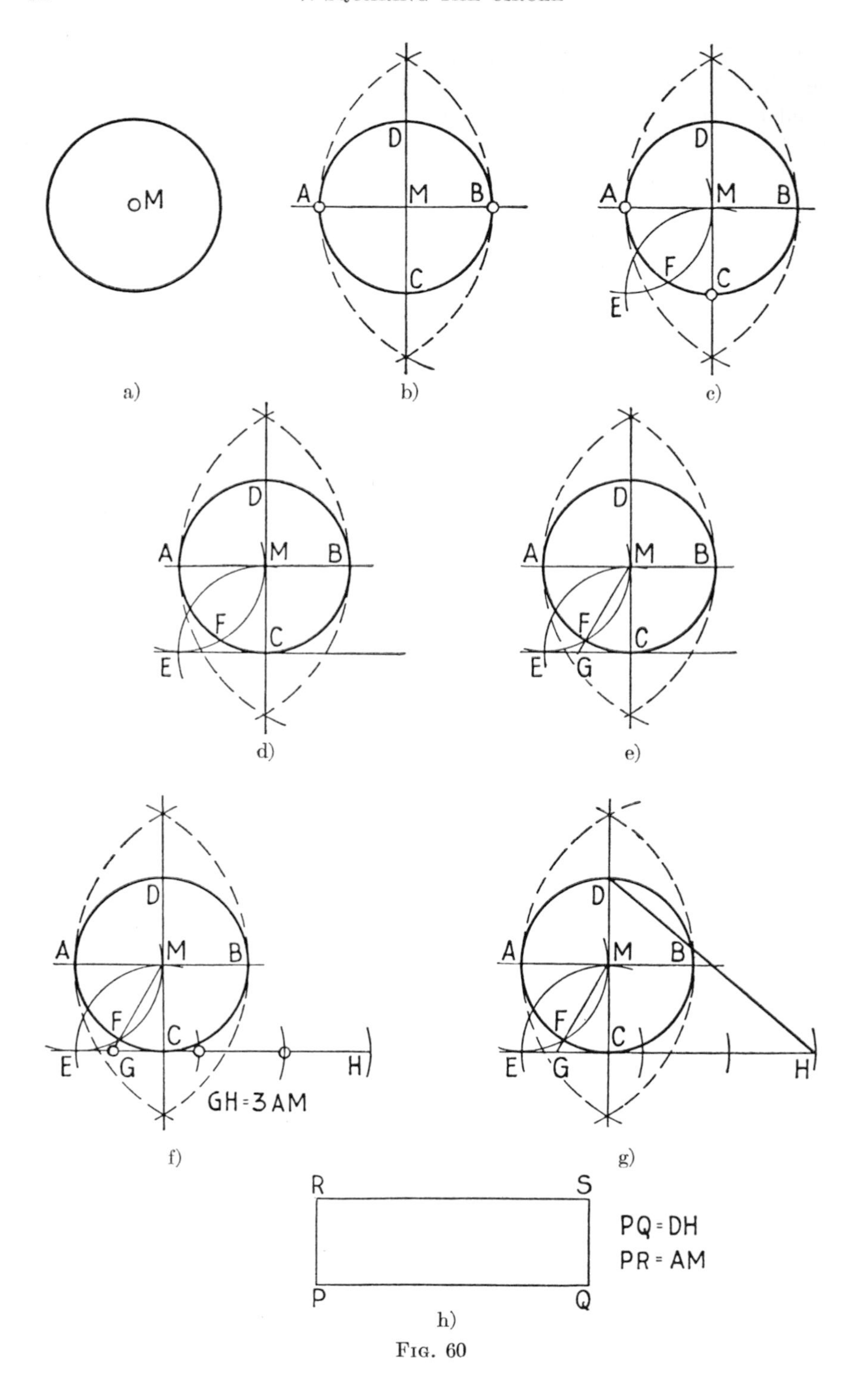


a) b) c) d) e) f) g) h)

FIG. 60

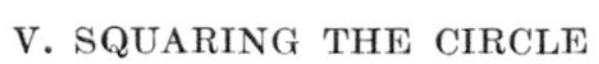


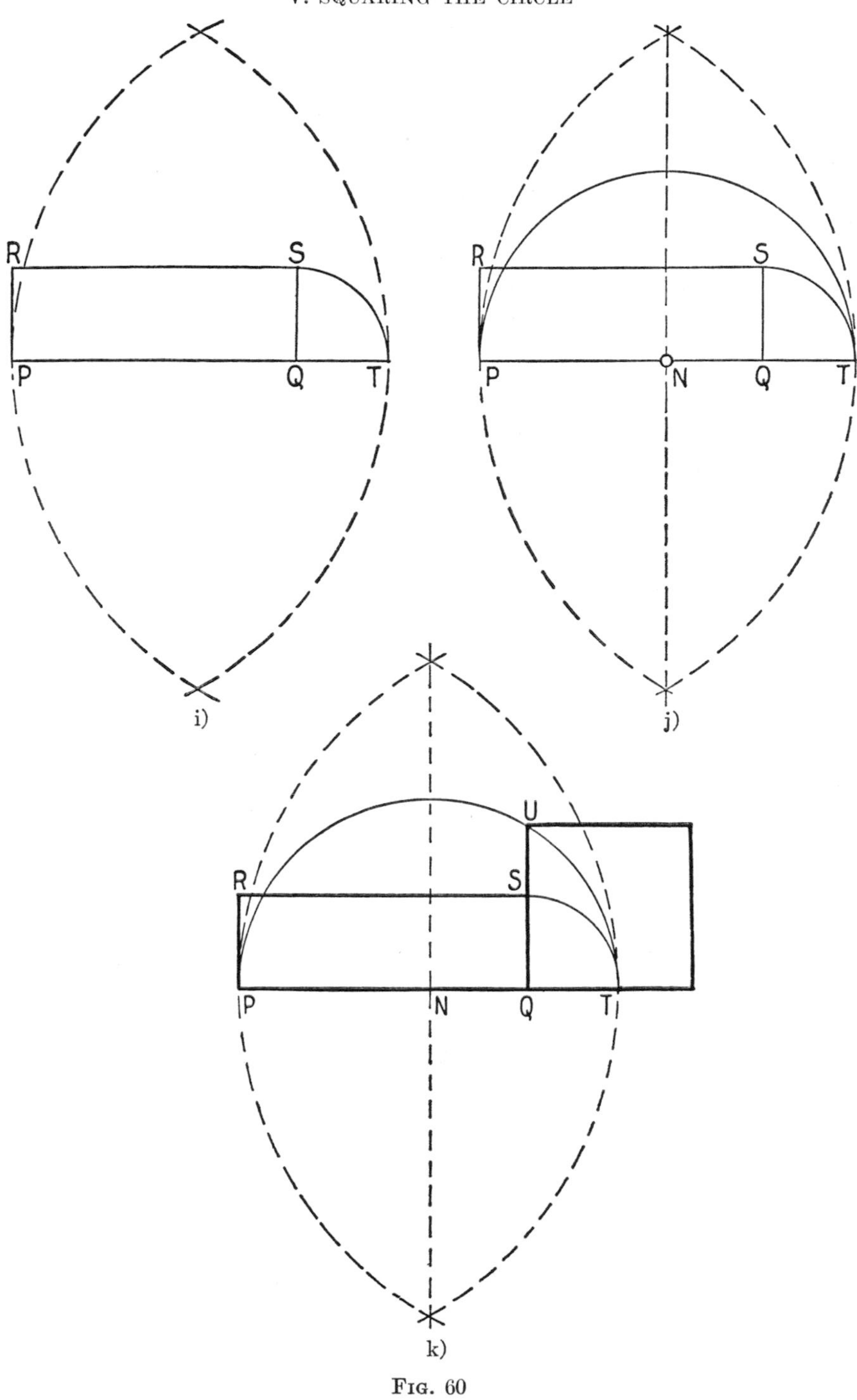


Fig. 60

exactly with straight edge and compass as follows. Mark off $QS$ on the extension of $PQ$ to give the point $T$. Next construct the perpendicular bisector of $PT$ and denote its intersection with $PQT$ by $N$ (Fig. 60j). Finally, draw the circle passing through $P$ and $T$ with $N$ as center. Its point of intersection $U$ with the straight line $QS$ yields the required side $QU$ of a square (Fig. 60k) having the same area as the rectangle $PQRS$, and thus approximately the same area as the given circle.

The following example will illustrate the great accuracy of this construction. If the radius of the given circle is 4 inches, and if we suppose the construction to be carried out with no errors (in drawing), the difference between the side of a square having *exactly* the same area as the given circle and the side $QU$ (which comes out to be a little less) would amount to no more than .00008 of an inch! This is much smaller than the unavoidable inaccuracies involved in the actual construction itself.

Now we shall give an example of an exact construction, which uses an ingenious instrument called an *integraph* (Fig. 61) in addition to straight edge and compass. Given a circle with center $M$ and diameter $AB$, and using only a semi-circle (Fig. 62a), the integraph is placed on the drawing paper so that its frame ($A$) and its rollers ($R$) move in the direction of $AB$. As a pencil $f$ (seen in the foreground of Fig. 61) traces the semi-circle, a pencil ($z$) (on the other side of the frame) describes the "integral curve" $KN$ of Fig. 62b. Since the height of the integral curve at any point is equal to the area under the part of the circumference described up to that point, the length of $LN$ is the area of the semi-circle, or exactly $\frac{1}{2}\pi$. If this segment is doubled with ruler and compass, the result is a segment of length $\pi$, which can be used as the base of a rectangle of height 1 to begin the construction of Fig. 60h–k.

To summarize: The insolubility of this ancient problem is due to the double requirement that the construction be exact and that it be carried

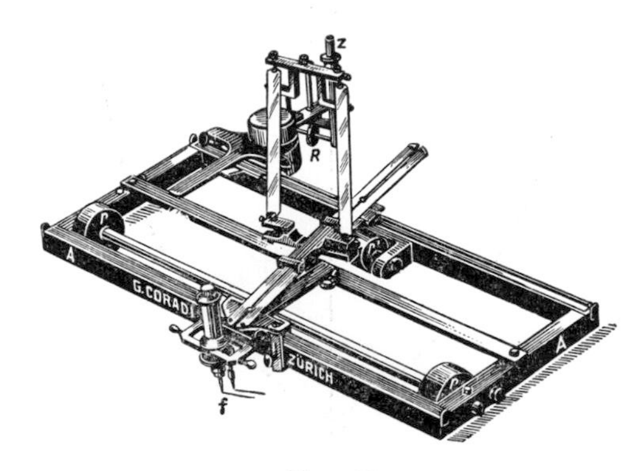


FIG. 61

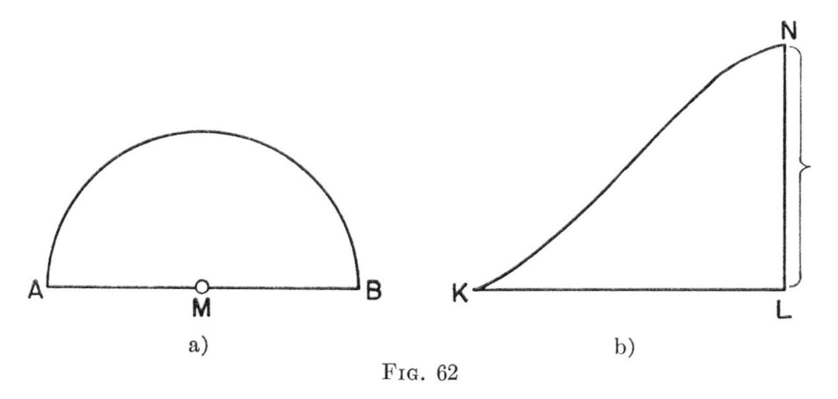


FIG. 62

out with straight edge and compass alone. As soon as one of these demands is sacrificed the problem can be solved.

Let us return to the word "quadrature." It is generally used in mathematics to denote the process of finding, given an area (which need not be a circle), a square with exactly the same area. In other words, we want to know how big the area is. We have already mentioned that the problem of quadrature can be formulated in two different ways: either as a problem in geometric *construction*, or as the problem of *calculating* the area of the surface. The old, celebrated problem of the circle which we have described, involves a geometric construction. But, naturally, mathematicians have also occupied themselves with the problem of calculating the area of a circle. And without the intimate connection between the geometric problem and the analytic calculation, Lindemann's achievement would never have come to pass. Therefore, we must consider the calculation of the area of a circle.

The measurement of a circle—its area as well as its circumference—is connected with the number $\pi$ (called the Ludolph number). (Euler was the first to use the letter $\pi$ (from the Greek *perimetros*), and it has since come into general usage.)

What is known about the number $\pi$, besides the fact that it is the ratio of the area of a circle to the area of a square with side equal to the radius of the circle (and also, of course, the ratio of the circumference of the circle to its diameter)?

At this point, we must distinguish between two questions: the numerical value of $\pi$, and the characteristic properties of $\pi$.

It was known a very long time ago that $\pi$ is approximately equal to 3: a rope placed around a wheel is about three times as long as the diameter of the wheel. Hence $\pi$ is not much different from 3, and can be shown to be somewhat larger. Archimedes'[6] estimate for $\pi$ as lying between $3\frac{10}{71}$ and

[6] Archimedes of Syracuse (287 B.C.?) became acquainted with the scholars of

$3\frac{1}{7}$ was a very considerable achievement for his day. In modern notation, his estimate would be written as:

$$3\tfrac{10}{71} < \pi < 3\tfrac{1}{7}; \quad \text{or,} \quad \tfrac{223}{71} < \pi < \tfrac{22}{7}.$$

Thus, in theory, methods of obtaining more refined estimates for $\pi$ were already known in antiquity. The difficulties at that time were computational, since the ancients lacked our convenient decimal system. In more modern times, industrious computers have obtained more accurate values for $\pi$. Ludolph van Ceulen of Leyden (1540–1610) calculated $\pi$ to 35 decimal places;[7] Zacharias Dase of Hamburg (1824–1861) to 200; and later more than 700 places were calculated. To be sure, the great efforts of these calculators added nothing either to pure or applied science [6]; 5 places at the most are usually sufficient in the applications, in quite special cases 10 to 12 places suffice.[8] The following French verses, where the number of letters in each word is the corresponding digit in $\pi$, have a value far removed from any practical purposes:

Que j'aime à faire apprendre un nombre
utile aux sages!
Immortel Archimède, artiste ingénieur,
Qui de ton jugement peut priser la valeur!
Pour moi ton problème eut de pareils avantages.

This gives 30 decimal places, or even 32, if we know that the next two

Alexandria during his Egyptian travels. He served Syracuse during its two-year siege by Rome with military innovations of a technical nature, and when the city was taken in the year 212 he was killed by a soldier to whom he was unknown. The Roman General Marcellus allowed a gravestone to be erected for him, which Cicero restored in 75 B.C.

[7] Much greater contributions of Ludolph's predecessors [5]—not only Archimedes but many mathematicians who came after him—are ignored by calling $\pi$ the Ludolph number.

[8] Four decimal places will suffice for determining the circumference of a circle to within 1 mm. if the radius is 30 meters or less. If the radius is as large as that of the earth, 10 are sufficient. If the circle has a radius as large as the distance of the earth to the sun, 15 places are enough to determine the circumference to within millimeters.

In order to show the incredible exactitude obtainable with 100 places of $\pi$, consider the following problem [7]: Take a sphere with our earth at its center and extending to Sirius (since the speed of light is 186000 miles per second, it would take 8.75 years to reach the surface of the sphere from the earth); fill this sphere with microbes, so that every cubic millimeter contains a trillion (1,000,000,000,000) microbes. Now if all these microbes are spread out in a straight line, so that the distance between successive microbes is equal to the distance from the earth to Sirius, and the distance from the first to the last is taken as the radius of a circle, then the error in calculating the circumference of this circle using 100 decimal places of $\pi$, will be less than $\frac{1}{10}$ of a millionth of a millimeter.

digits in the decimal expansion of $\pi$ are 5 and 0. We get (Que = 3, j' = 1, aime = 4, $\cdots$):

$$3.14159\ 26535\ 89793\ 23846\ 26433\ 83279\ 50 \cdots .$$

I do not know how these verses originated or whether anyone else has ever composed a similar set in any other language [**8**].

Of far greater significance for mathematics are certain other properties of $\pi$. We shall discuss a few of these briefly.[9]

We write first the following formula:

$$\pi/4 = 2/3 \cdot 4/3 \cdot 4/5 \cdot 6/5 \cdot 6/7 \cdots ,$$

which is ascribed to the English mathematician John Wallis (1616–1703). The formula can be made plausible by the following argument. The first term, $2/3$, is smaller than $\pi/4$; the product of the first two terms, $2/3 \cdot 4/3 = 8/9$, is greater than $\pi/4$; the product of the first three terms, $2/3 \cdot 4/3 \cdot 4/5 = 8/9 \cdot 4/5 = 32/45$, is smaller than $\pi/4$; the product of the first four terms will be greater than $\pi/4$, etc. In other words, the *partial* products

$$2/3,\ 2/3 \cdot 4/3 = 8/9,\ 2/3 \cdot 4/3 \cdot 4/5 = 32/45,\ 2/3 \cdot 4/3 \cdot 4/5 \cdot 6/5 = 192/225, \cdots$$

are alternately less than and greater than $\pi/4$. A rule for writing down the successive factors of the infinite product can easily be obtained by noticing the way in which the even numbers occur in the numerators and the odd in the denominators. The essential point (which we cannot prove here), however, is that the partial products actually approach $\pi/4$.

Another expression for $\pi/4$ is the so-called Leibniz series [**9**]

$$\pi/4 = 1 - 1/3 + 1/5 - 1/7 + 1/9 - 1/11 + \cdots ,$$

in which the successive partial sums: $1,\ 1 - 1/3,\ 1 - 1/3 + 1/5,\ 1 - 1/3 + 1/5 - 1/7$ are alternately greater and less than $\pi/4$.

To illustrate a third noteworthy property [**10**] of $\pi$, we write the following expression, briefly denoted by $S_{10}$ :

$$S_{10} = \frac{1}{10}\left(\frac{1}{2}\cdot\frac{1}{1+0^2} + \frac{1}{1+.1^2} + \frac{1}{1+.2^2} + \frac{1}{1+.3^2} + \cdots + \frac{1}{1+.9^2} + \frac{1}{2}\frac{1}{1+1^2}\right).$$

Except for the first and the last, the terms in the parenthesis are of the form $1/(1 + x^2)$, where $x$ takes the values 0.1, 0.2, 0.3, etc. up to 0.9. The first and last terms are obtained by putting $x = 0$, and $x = 1$ and multi-

[9] The fact that all these formulas give the value of $\pi/4$ (and not $\pi$) is not accidental, because one fourth of the area of a circle of radius 1 occurs in many investigations.

plying by ½. The sum in the parenthesis is 7.84981 to five decimal places and accordingly $S_{10} = 0.784981 \cdots$. We note that this number is not very different from $\pi/4$; of more significance is the fact that this gives another way of approximating $\pi$ as closely as desired. As an illustration, consider the following expression,[10] denoted by $S_{100}$, whose general term (except for the first and last) is again $1/(1 + x^2)$ (but in which $x$ now takes the values 0.01, 0.02, etc. up to 0.99):

$$S_{100} = \frac{1}{100}\left(\frac{1}{2}\cdot\frac{1}{1+0^2} + \frac{1}{1+.01^2} + \frac{1}{1+.02^2} + \frac{1}{1+.03^2} + \cdots + \frac{1}{1+.98^2} + \frac{1}{1+.99^2} + \frac{1}{2}\cdot\frac{1}{1+1^2}\right).$$

This is considerably closer to $\pi/4$ than $S_{10}$ is, but the essential point is that by writing more and more expressions of this sort (dividing the interval from 0 to 1 into thousandths, ten thousandths, etc.) we approach closer and closer to $\pi/4$. Since this can be proved theoretically, we have another algorithm for calculating $\pi/4$ (and hence $\pi$ itself) to arbitrary accuracy.

The expressions for $\pi$ which we have written down are derived in the so-called higher mathematics (the last expression, for example, is a formula from calculus). Lindemann's result of 1882, achieved by methods which go beyond the usual differential and integral calculus, yields a still deeper property of $\pi$.

We cannot go into Lindemann's result here [**11**], except to say that it implies the impossibility of squaring a circle with straight edge and compass alone. Anyone not acquainted with the development of the various branches of mathematics in the past few hundred years will regard this as very surprising. All the more so, since the calculus was first developed to study curves, terrestrial and celestial motion, to express physical laws, and to put all these at the disposal of applied mathematics and science. Now we see that a purely theoretical problem of geometric construction, significant only for the 2000 years of futile effort to solve it, was finally solved by methods developed for quite other reasons.

There could be no more remarkable proof of the inner unity of mathematics.

[10] The first and last terms in the sum are again distinguished from the others by the factor ½.

*Notes to Chapter V*

# SQUARING THE CIRCLE

**1** (p. 90). See {1}.

**2** (p. 93). By this we mean a finite number of steps, each consisting of the construction of a straight line or circle, with the last step yielding a definite segment whose length is exactly equal to the side of the square with the same area as that of the prescribed circle. We exclude constructions requiring an infinite number of approximations to the required side.

**3** (p. 94). We give two more examples of general propositions which subsume an infinite number of special cases, but which are of course proved at one stroke and not case by case.

Example 1. Everyone acquainted with elementary algebra knows that

$$(a + 1)(a - 1) = a^2 - 1,$$

so that, in particular,

$$(3 + 1)(3 - 1) = 3^2 - 1,$$

$$(4 + 1)(4 - 1) = 4^2 - 1,$$

etc. But the proof of course proceeds by using the rules of algebra (or by induction) and not by examining each case separately.

Example 2. A theorem of elementary geometry states that the bisectors of the angles of a triangle meet in one point. The proof proceeds by considering a general triangle, and not by verifying the truth of the theorem for each of a host of special triangles (see Fig. 63).

**4** (p. 95). By means of elementary calculations (and the Pythagorean theorem), we find, if we set $AM = 1$, that the length of $DH$ is

$$[40/3 - (12)^{1/2}]^{1/2} = 3.141533 \cdots ;$$

hence, very near the value of $\pi = 3.14159265 \cdots$. To prove this, note that $AFM$ is an equilateral triangle with side 1. If $F_1$, $F_2$ are the feet of the perpendiculars from $F$ to $MA$, $MC$, resp., then $MF_1 = F_2F = \frac{1}{2}$ is half the length of a side of the triangle, and $F_1F = MF_2 = \frac{1}{2}\sqrt{3}$ is the altitude. Since triangles $GCM$ and $FF_2M$ are similar, it follows that $GC:CM = FF_2:F_2M$, or $GC:1 = \frac{1}{2}:\frac{1}{2}\sqrt{3}$; hence $GC = \frac{1}{3}\sqrt{3}$. Noting that the legs of the right triangle $CDH$ are $CH = GH - GC = 3 - \frac{1}{3}\sqrt{3}$ and $CD = 2$, we obtain the hypotenuse $DH$.

**5** (p. 100). The most important name in this connection is that of François Viète (1540–1603), who made contributions to the theory of the number $\pi$ and not only, as was the case with Ludolph, to its calculation. Ludolph's

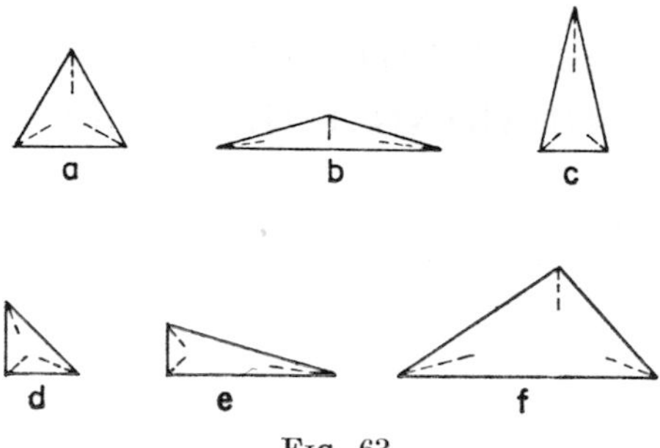


FIG. 63

and Viète's method for calculating approximations to $\pi$ was the same as that of Archimedes: they approximated a circle by inscribed or circumscribed polygons. More recent computers (like Dase and others) have used other algorithms, which have become available through the development of more powerful methods in analysis. See {2}.

**6** (p. 100). Perhaps many people thought that there was a pattern in the decimal expansion of $\pi$; but this of course is not the case. The reason is that $\pi$ is an irrational number (see Chapter VIII), a fact which was proved by Johann Heinrich Lambert (1728–1777).

**7** (p. 100). See {3}.

**8** (p. 101). My friend and colleague Klaus Clusius, who has a lively interest in mathematics, has called my attention to some German verses which yield 23 digits of $\pi$:

> Wie, o dies
> Macht ernstlich so vielen viele Müh'!
> Lernt immerhin, Jünglinge, leichte Verselein,
> Wie so zum Beispiel dies dürfte zu merken sein!

An English verse of the same kind is:

> Now I know a spell unfailing
> An artful charm for tasks availing
> Intricate results entailing
> Not in too exacting mood.
> (Poetry is pretty good). Try the talisman.
> Let be adverse ingenuity.

This is one of three English $\pi$-poems which Professor A. S. Besicovitch of Cambridge found for me. He also found a longer poem by W. Hope Jones, which was published in the Mathematical Gazette of October 1921 (p. 328), and which gives 67 digits of the logarithm to the base 10 of the number $e$, the base of the natural logarithms. For the number $e$ see Note 13 to Chapter VII. Here is a one line verse for $e$ itself:

Tu aideras à rappeler ta quantité à beaucoup de docteurs amis.

**9** (p. 101). There is no doubt that Leibniz independently discovered the series named after him. But James Gregory (1638–1675) had previously discovered a more general series, of which Leibniz's is a special case.

**10** (p. 101). Anyone acquainted with the definite integral will see at once that

$$\pi/4 = \lim S_n = \int_0^1 (1/1 + x^2)\, dx.$$

**11** (p. 102). To describe the connection between Lindemann's achievement and the impossibility of squaring a circle would first require a discussion of the relation between geometric constructions and algebraic equations (see Note 3 to Chapter III). Lindemann's achievement was to prove that $\pi$ is a transcendental number, that is, $\pi$ is not a root of any algebraic equation with integral coefficients. Perhaps the following will make this a little clearer. Consider the successive powers of $\pi$:

$$\begin{aligned} \pi^0 &= 1, \\ \pi^1 &= \pi = 3.14159 \cdots, \\ \pi^2 &= 9.8696 \cdots, \\ \pi^3 &= 31.00628 \cdots, \text{ etc.} \end{aligned}$$

Now form any polynomial in powers of $\pi$ with integral coefficients, that is, a sum of a finite number of powers of $\pi$ each multiplied by an integer, e.g.,

$$\pi^5 + 6\pi^4 + 4\pi^2 + 3\pi + 27.$$

The value of this polynomial is approximately 966.377427. Now Lindemann proved that no two polynomials in $\pi$ (with integral coefficients) can have the same value. This is another way of saying that $\pi$ is transcendental. We note in passing that a number which is a zero of a polynomial with integral coefficients is called an algebraic number. For instance, the number $1 + [2 - (5)^{1/3}]^{1/2}$ is algebraic because it is a zero of the polynomial $x^6 - 6x^5 + 9x^4 + 4x^3 - 9x^2 - 6x + 4$ (that is, the value of the polynomial is 0 if $x = 1 + [2 - (5)^{1/3}]^{1/2}$); or, equivalently, the polynomial $x^6 + 9x^4 + 4x^3 + 4$ has the same value as the polynomial $6x^5 + 9x^2 + 6x$ for the above value of $x$.

*Chapter VI*

# THREE DIMENSIONS—HIGHER DIMENSIONS

"A line has *one dimension*—length; a surface, such as a sheet of paper, has *two dimensions*—length and width; space, and everything with a spatial extension, such as a cupboard, a box, a paving stone, has *three dimensions*—length, width, and height."

This is the popular explanation of the concept of dimension. It seems simple, clear, and hardly in need of further elaboration. But is the concept of dimension as simple and free of problems as this uncomplicated explanation would indicate? Not at all. Recently, the problem of dimension has become increasingly important in several branches of mathematics, and has occasioned much penetrating research. Although we cannot discuss this research here, we can clarify the essential problem, and show that the *properties of dimension listed above are completely inadequate.*

I can remember my dissatisfaction, even as a student, with these definitions. Of course, a piece of line has only length, and not width or height, since it has extension only in the direction of its length, that is, it has only one dimension. It is equally clear that a rectangle, say a table-top, which has two extensions, length and width, should be assigned two dimensions. But what about a circle? In this case there is only *one* measurement of size, the length of the diameter, which is the same in all directions. Yet a circle, like every other surface, is said to have not *one* but *two* dimensions. But what does this mean? It must of course be granted that, starting from the center, we can move not only along a single diameter, say the horizontal one, but also along a vertical diameter. But there are an infinite number of possible directions of motion, since there are an infinite number of different diameters. Why then is a circle assigned *two* dimensions? According to the same argument, why is an oval, such as an ellipse, also assigned two dimensions? It has not only length and width, but a different size along each of an infinite number of directions.

One could make similar objections to the treatment of spatial figures. We agree that box-like objects with length, width, and height have three dimensions; the same applies to a region of space, such as that enclosed by a room, whose spatial extent is determined by its measurements in the three directions of length, width, and height. But for a spatial figure, such as a solid sphere, the statement that *three* measurements determine its extent is no longer true.

Therefore, it is clear that the old vague definitions of dimension are inadequate even for the lower dimensions, and that we must try to make the concept more precise before venturing into higher dimensions. We will

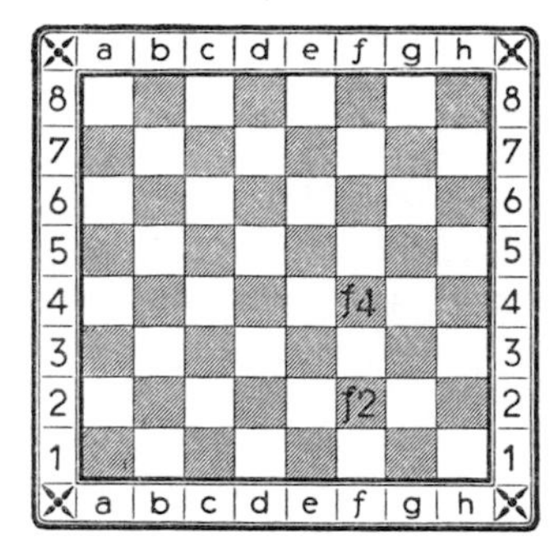


FIG. 64

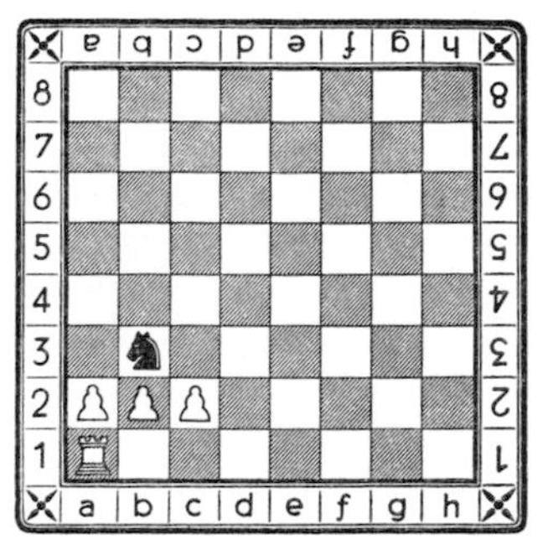


FIG. 65

try to do so without going into difficult technical explanations. To begin, let us look at a chessboard with its 64 squares (Fig. 64), on which two chess players alternately move their men from one square to another in accordance with certain rules.

Actually chess can be played *without a chessboard*. In order to do this, the two players must have the ability to visualize the board and to keep the position of the pieces in their minds. They are then faced with the problem of communicating their moves to each other. Each player must describe his mental move by indicating which square his piece has occupied and to which square it is being moved. That is, a game without a board requires an unambiguous designation of each of the 64 squares. There are various ways of doing this. We shall employ the system used in city maps, on which the city is divided by horizontal and vertical lines into squares. The vertical strips can be designated from left to right by the letters $a$, $b$, $c$, $d$, $\cdots$ ; the horizontal strips by the numbers 1, 2, 3, $\cdots$ from bottom to top.[1] Each square can then be unambiguously located by giving the letter and number of the vertical and horizontal strips in which it occurs. A stranger, using such a map and a guide keyed to it, can easily find whatever place he is looking for by finding the square in which it is located.

The same system can be used for designating the squares of a chessboard. It is not at all difficult to understand what is meant by, say, moving the pawn from square $f2$ to square $f4$ [**1**]. We may, however, ask whether it would not be more convenient simply to number the squares of a chessboard from 1 to 64. Certainly, it is possible to do so (Fig. 66), but it would not serve our purpose. To understand why, let us look at the map of Munich (Plate VIII). Suppose a tourist lives in a hotel on the spot designated by * in square $e4$. He wants to attend a play at the theater marked $S$ on the map in the square $e3$. He knows from the designations of the two squares that he does not have far to go, since $e4$ and $e3$ are adjoining squares.

[1] See the map of pre-war Munich in Plate VIII.

| 64 | 63 | 62 | 61 | 60 | 59 | 58 | 57 |
|---|---|---|---|---|---|---|---|
| 49 | 50 | 51 | 52 | 53 | 54 | 55 | 56 |
| 48 | 47 | 46 | 45 | 44 | 43 | 42 | 41 |
| 33 | 34 | 35 | 36 | 37 | 38 | 39 | 40 |
| 32 | 31 | 30 | 29 | 28 | 27 | 26 | 25 |
| 17 | 18 | 19 | 20 | 21 | 22 | 23 | 24 |
| 16 | 15 | 14 | 13 | 12 | 11 | 10 | 9 |
| 1 | 2 | 3 | 4 | 5 | 6 | 7 | 8 |

FIG. 66

They are both in the same vertical strip *e*, and in adjoining horizontal strips. It is also clear from their designations that the squares *d*3 and *e*4 are also near each other—they have a vertex in common—because *d* and *e* are neighboring vertical strips, and 3 and 4 are neighboring horizontal strips. Even a visit to the old St. Peter's Church (*Pt*), or the City Hall (*Rt*), would not take him too far afield, since both lie in the square *d*3. On the other hand, the same tourist is at some distance from the art collections of the picture galleries (*AP* and *NP*) in square *c*6, since the strips *c* and *e* are farther apart, as are also strips 4 and 6. Furthermore the hotel * is not near the railway station (*Bh* in square *a*4), even though the two buildings are in the same horizontal strip 4, since the vertical strips *a* and *e* are far apart. The hotel is also at some distance from the Siegestor (*ST*): *e*4 and *e*7 are in the same vertical column, but in widely separated horizontal strips. The assignment of two symbols (a letter and a number in this case) to each square is therefore useful both in locating squares and in indicating whether two squares are near each other or far apart. In order that two squares be close to one another, it is necessary (and sufficient) that both symbols be near each other (in the sense both of alphabetical order and of numerical magnitude). In the sequel, we shall refer to this as the *neighborhood principle*. We can then say that the usual system used for identifying squares in a city map (or the analogous system for identifying the squares on a chessboard) accords with the neighborhood principle: Small changes in position correspond to small changes in both symbols.

By way of contrast, consider the numbering of the squares in Fig. 66. In this scheme the representation of nearby squares such as 9 and 24 by widely separated numbers cannot be avoided. This would be true for some adjoining squares in any scheme which assigns only one number to each square [**2**]. Hence an indexing such as that of Fig. 66 would not indicate the neighborhood relationships of squares, and would not therefore be useful either for a city map or a chessboard. But there are cases in which simple enumeration is suitable, e.g. the numbering of years; the years do follow one another in a series, like beads on a string, with years not too

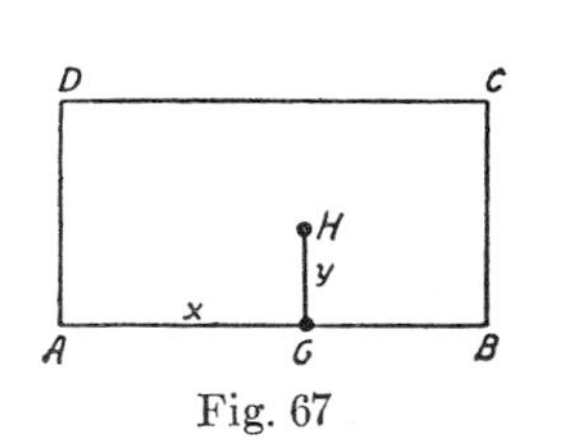


Fig. 67

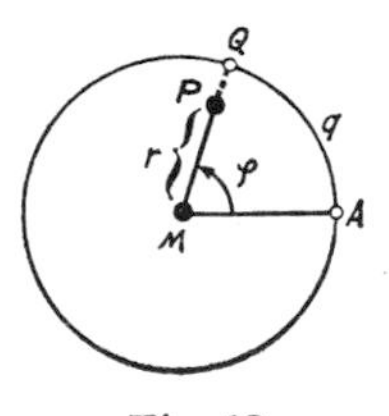


Fig. 68

far apart being assigned numbers having the same relationship. Degrees of temperature can also be suitably designated by a single number. Both schemes (the enumeration of years and the assignment of degrees) are in accord with the neighborhood principle. The same is true for milestones on a road.

We have now penetrated to the mathematical essence of the concept of dimension. Indexing with single numbers, or simple enumeration is applicable only to those cases in which the order of the objects has the character of a sequence, that is, if simple enumeration does accord with the neighborhood principle. These cases are *one-dimensional.*

The grounds of a town and the surface of a chessboard, however, are two-dimensional. It would of course be possible simply to enumerate the squares[2] in these cases also, but any enumeration would not be in accord with the neighborhood principle. In order to take this principle into account, *two* indices are necessary for each square.[3] This requirement expresses the *two-dimensional* character of a city or a chessboard.

In order to illustrate the neighborhood principle, we have divided a surface into squares. But a different procedure must be followed to locate *specific points* on a surface. Suppose that a hook for suspending a lamp is to be attached to a certain spot of the ceiling of a room. It is then not enough to divide the ceiling into squares, and then to indicate in which square the hook is to be placed. A more exact indication is needed. If $ABCD$ (Fig. 67) is the ceiling and $H$ is the spot for the hook, the distance $GH$ from this point to one of the walls of the room, and the distance from $G$ to the corner $A$ must be measured. This would give two numbers $x = AG$ and $y = GH$, say $x = 3.15$ yards, and $y = 1.28$ yards, which would suffice to locate the hook precisely. In accordance with the neighborhood principle, points close to $H$ would be assigned numerical values $x$ and $y$

[2] The districts of a town, such as postal and tax districts, are numbered sequentially, for the sake of simplicity. Of course, such an enumeration does not have to take the relative positions of the districts into account and there is therefore no need to satisfy the neighborhood principle.

[3] Two numbers, instead of a letter and a number, would serve just as well. The square *a*1 would then be (1, 1), the square *f*2 (6, 2), etc.

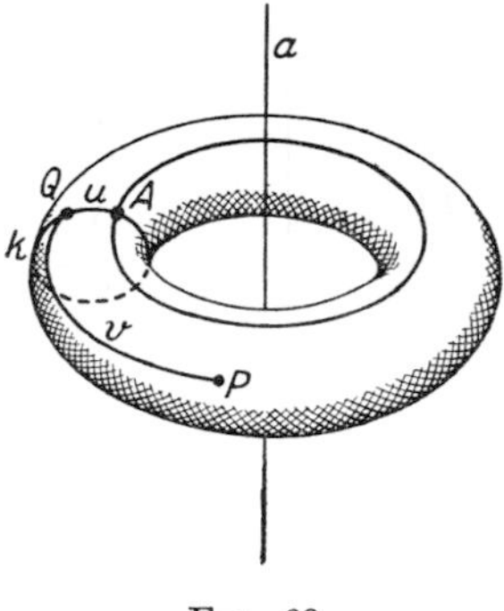


FIG. 69

which differ very little from 3.15 or 1.28. Hence the surface of a ceiling is two-dimensional because precisely two numbers are needed to specify properly the location of each point of the surface.

An analogous situation prevails in the case of other surfaces, for example, the circle, whose two-dimensional character perplexed us at the beginning of this chapter. Let $M$ be the center of the circle (Fig. 68). Choose a fixed point $A$ on the circumference and let $P$ be an arbitrary point of the circle. Then the radius $MP$ meets the circumference at $Q$, and $P$ can be located by specifying its distance $MP = r$ from the center $M$ and the length $q$ of the arc $AQ$. This assigns *two* numbers, $r$ and $q$, to every point $P$ of the circle, and the assignment satisfies the neighborhood principle [**3**]; hence the circle is two-dimensional.[4] In a similar way we verify that the surface of a sphere is two-dimensional by showing that exactly *two* numbers, geographic longitude and latitude, determine any spot on the earth's surface. The same is true of all other surfaces, including all the surfaces considered in Chapter II.[5] There are still other examples of two-dimensional domains. For instance, the temperature in Munich during a single day can be denoted numerically. If $t$ is the time in hours beginning with midnight, so that $t$ is a number between 0 and 24, and $T$ is the temperature in Centigrade, then, for example, $t = 23.1$, $T = -2.5$ means that at 6 minutes after 11 PM the temperature was 2.5 degrees Centigrade below zero. Two numbers are enough to fix the time and temperature in agree-

[4] The angle $\varphi = AMQ$ could be used as the second number, instead of the length of the arc $q$. For fixed radius, an angle and the corresponding arc determine each other uniquely [**4**].

[5] The same thing can be done on a torus (Fig. 69). If $A$ is a fixed point on the circle $k$, and $P$ is an arbitrary point on the surface, let $Q$ be the point of $k$ which is carried into $P$ by the rotation of $k$ about the axis $a$. Then the position of $P$ can be defined by the lengths $u$ and $v$ of the arcs $AQ$ and $QP$.

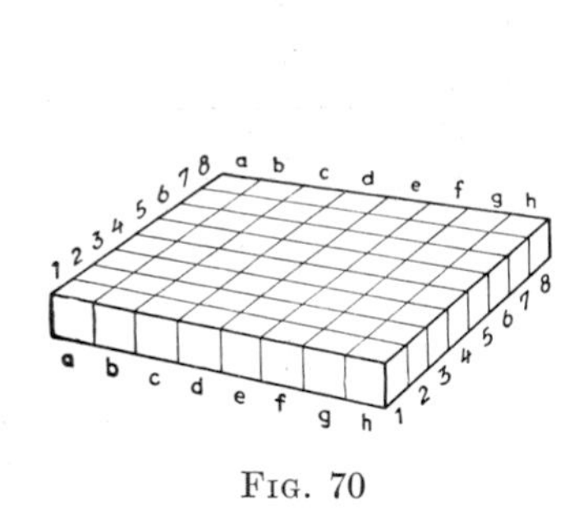


FIG. 70

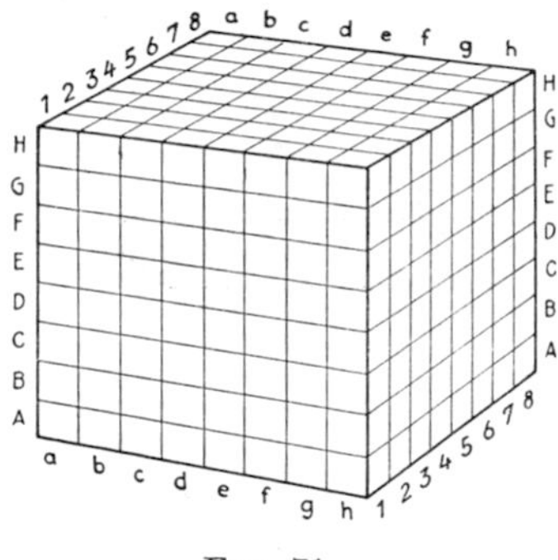


FIG. 71

ment with the neighborhood principle. Hence, the domain of temperature change with time is two-dimensional.[6]

The next step in understanding our problem leads to the third dimension. We shall start with an example obtained by generalizing the usual two-dimensional chess game. Imagine a small cubical box. Arrange eight of these small cubes in a column, and place eight such columns side by side. The result is 64 cubical boxes, arranged exactly like the squares of the conventional chessboard. These 64 boxes form one layer (Fig. 70). A second identical layer of 64 boxes is placed on the first, then a third, etc., up to eight; so that there are altogether $8 \cdot 64 = 512$ small cubes which fill a large cube (see Fig. 71, where of course the small cubes lying in back of the surface rows are hidden). In this three-dimensional chess game some boxes will contain a white chessman, others a black chessman, and the rest will be empty. A move in this game is made by taking the box containing the selected chesspiece, removing the piece, returning the empty box to its correct place, and placing the piece in another box. Clearly, this process is very clumsy: to get to the inside boxes, one must move aside a large number of other boxes and then replace them. Even more grotesque and annoying than this awkward procedure is the inability of the players to survey the positions of all the pieces before making their moves, since it is impossible to see where the chessmen are placed. The boxes could be made of glass, but in fact this is not necessary. All that is really needed is a scheme for describing the moves unambiguously, which will thereby do away with the necessity of moving the boxes. The problem is again one of assigning symbols to a set of objects, this time 512 cubes; and, just as in the case of the chessboard, it will not do simply to number them. Here *three* symbols are required. One procedure would be to assign the same letters and num-

[6] According to the chromatic theory of Maxwell and Helmholtz, the totality of all colors is also a two-dimensional domain [**5**].

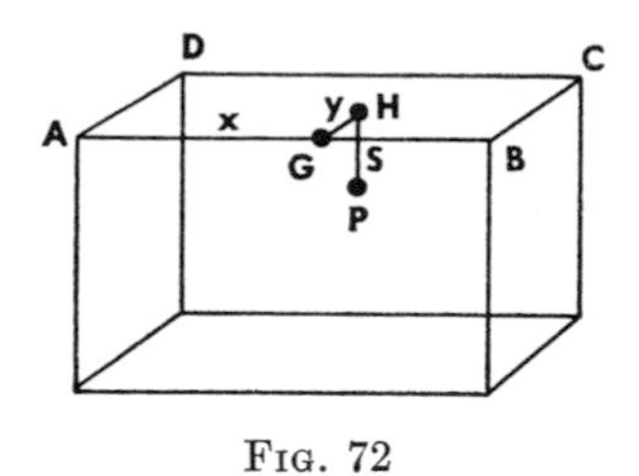


FIG. 72

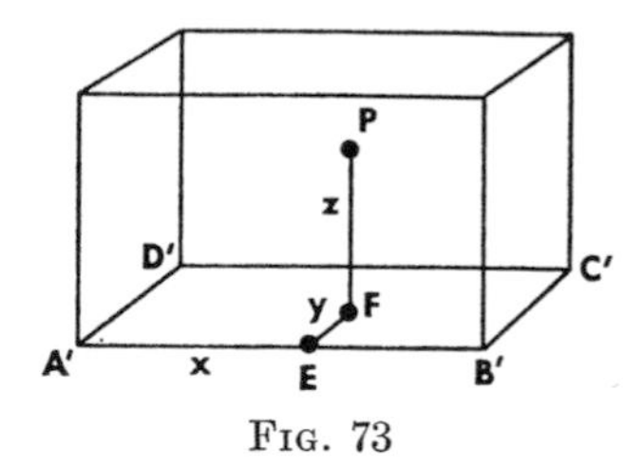


FIG. 73

bers to the cells of the lowest layer (Fig. 70) as were given to the squares of a chessboard, e.g. *f*2, *d*4, etc., and then to add to these a third symbol, say $A$, to indicate the lowest layer. The cells of the next layer can likewise be assigned the symbols used on the conventional chessboard, with an additional symbol $B$ for the new layer. Thus, cube *Bf*2 is exactly on top of cube *Af*2. Continuing in this way, we use $C$ for the third layer, etc., and $H$ for the eighth layer. The game can now be played simply by communicating the moves. No physical boxes or chessmen are needed.

We have chosen an indexing system for the 512 small cubes in which *three* symbols are assigned to each cube. It is easily seen that this scheme again agrees with the neighborhood principle: Neighboring cubes are represented by triplets of symbols which do not vary markedly from each other. Hence this chess game is *three-dimensional.*

As in the two-dimensional case, we must now consider the problem of locating specific points in the cube. Let us again consider the example of a lamp suspended from a hook in the ceiling of a room. Suppose now that a taut cord of length $s = 1.16$ yards is hung from this hook (see Fig. 72). The point $H$ from which the cord was to hang, in the earlier example, was given by the two numbers $x = 3.15$, and $y = 1.28$. The three numbers

$$x = 3.15, \qquad y = 1.28, \qquad s = 1.16$$

determine a point $P$ in the room. This expresses the three-dimensional nature of the space enclosed by the room; small displacements of $P$ correspond to small changes in the three numbers $x$, $y$, $s$, and thus this assignment of three numbers to each point satisfies the neighborhood principle. It is often more convenient to measure the height $z = FP$ of $P$ from the floor rather than its distance from the ceiling (see Fig. 73). Then $x$ and $y$ can also be measured on the floor $A'B'C'D'$, instead of on the ceiling $ABCD$:

$$AG = x = A'E, \qquad GH = y = EF.$$

Since $z + s$ is the total height of the room, say 3.5 yards, it follows that $z = 3.5 - s = 3.5 - 1.16 = 2.34$. $P$'s position is then [6],

$$x = 3.15, \qquad y = 1.28, \qquad z = 2.34.$$

PLATE VII

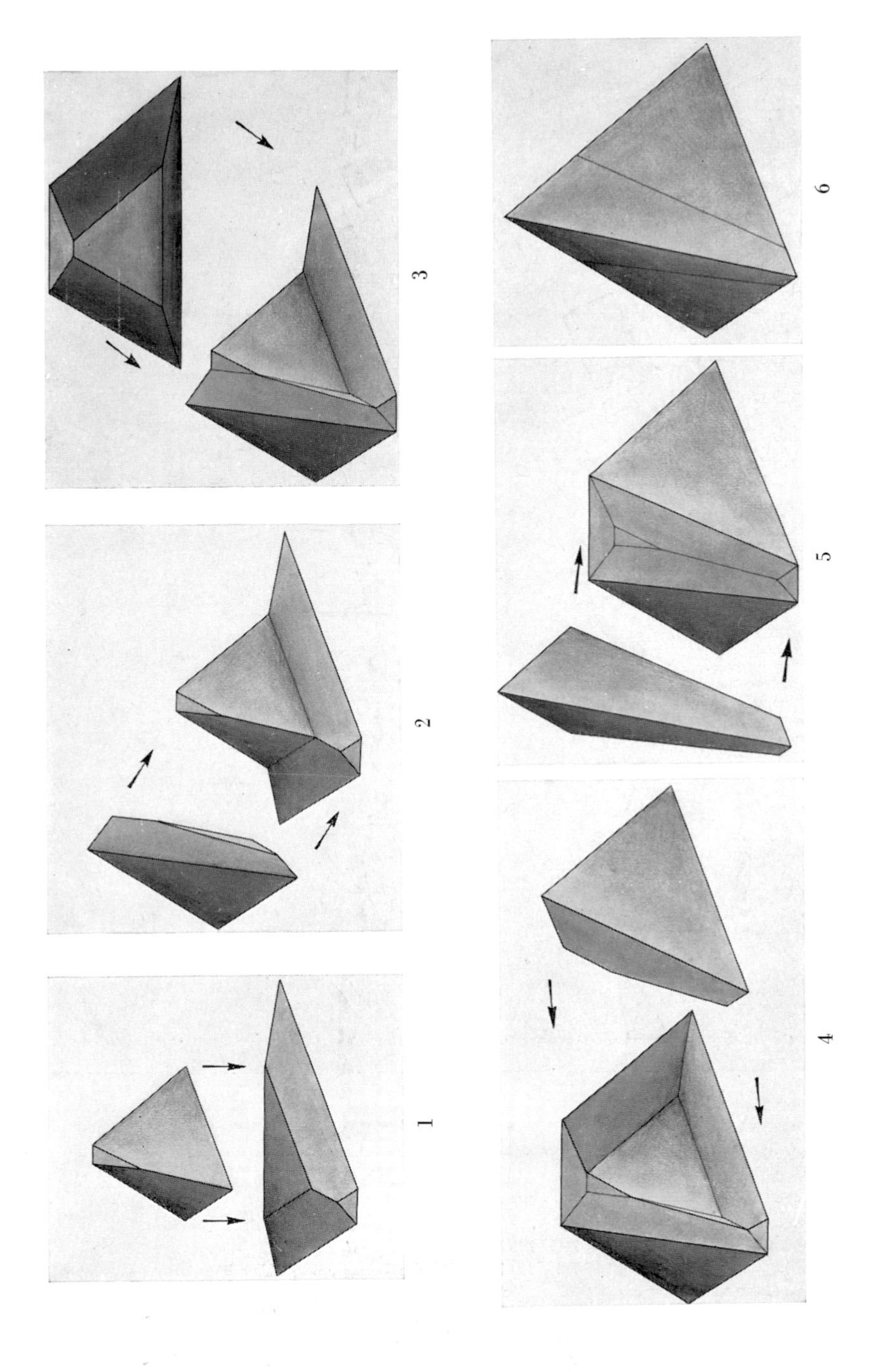

PLATE VIII

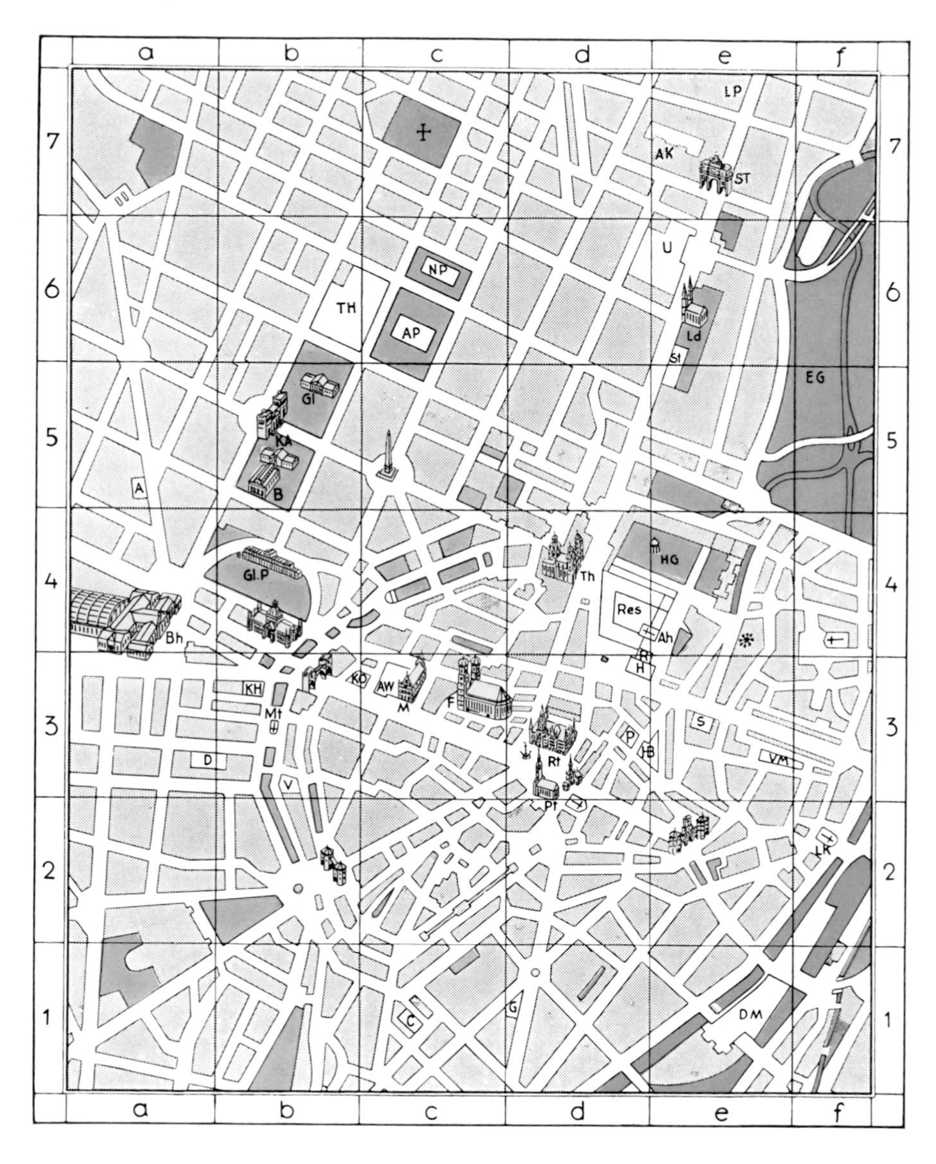


MUNICH

| | | |
|---|---|---|
| AK | Akademie der bildenden Künste | *d*, *e* 7 |
| AP | Alte Pinakothek | *c* 6 |
| AW | Akademie der Wissenschaften | *c* 3 |
| B | Basilika | *b* 5 |
| Bh | Haupt-Bahnhof | *a* 4 |
| DM | Deutsches Museum | *e* 1 |
| EG | Englischer Garten | *e*, *f* 4-7 |
| F | Frauenkirche | *c* 3 |
| Gl | Glyptothek | *b* 5 |
| GlP | Glas-Palast | *b* 4 |
| H | Hof- und National-Theater | *d*, *e* 3 |
| HB | Hofbräuhaus | *d*, *e* 3 |
| HG | Hofgarten | *d*, *e* 4 |
| Ld | Ludwigs-Kirche | *e* 6 |
| M | Michaels-Hofkirche | *c* 3 |
| Mt | Matthäus-Kirche | *b* 3 |
| NP | Neue Pinakothek | *c* 6 |
| P | Platzl | *d* 3 |
| Pt | Peterskirche | *d* 3 |
| Res | Residenz | *d* 4 |
| Rt | Rathaus | *d* 3 |
| S | Schauspielhaus | *e* 3 |
| ST | Siegestor | *e* 7 |
| St | Staats-Bibliothek | *e* 5, 6 |
| TH | Technische Hochschule | *b*, *c* 6 |
| Th | Theatiner-Kirche | *d* 4 |
| U | Universität | *d*, *e* 6 |
| VM | Völkerkunde-Museum | *e*, *f* 3 |

The three-dimensional chess game described above has often been played, and years ago in Hamburg there was a club which published a magazine devoted to three-dimensional chess. But occasionally people have gone even further. From our discussion of two- and three-dimensional chess, it is clear that physical equipment—chessboard, pieces, cubes, etc.—can be replaced by symbols. We need merely designate the squares of the two-dimensional game by *two* symbols, for example:

$$f2,\ d4,\ a1,\ h8;$$

and the cubes of three-dimensional game by *three* symbols, such as

$$Bf2 \quad \text{or} \quad Fd3.$$

Equally, it is possible to go beyond three dimensions. One need only take *four* symbols, e.g.

$$\text{I}\ Bf2, \qquad \text{II}\ Bf2, \qquad \text{VIII}\ Fh8.$$

This would give all $512 \times 8 = 4096$ positions of a four-dimensional chess game. Two positions would be near each other if all their corresponding symbols were near each other, e.g. II *Bf*2 and III *Ag*1. A move would then consist of (mentally) moving a piece from one position to another.

The game is four-dimensional because four symbols are required to designate each position. It is of course impossible to make an actual physical representation of such a game. A few decades ago, the students of the Göttingen Mathematical Club amused themselves by trying to play a four-dimensional game, but no actual match was ever finished.

From these examples it is clear that we need not restrict ourselves to four dimensions, but may go further. We used two- and three-dimensional chess to clarify the concept of dimension: i.e. to point out that *dimension is the number of symbols required to characterize the elements of a domain suitably*. It should now be clear that a purely mathematical concept of more than three dimensions, that is of four, five, or more, is not mysterious. We say, for example, that a domain is four-dimensional if four symbols are needed to index its elements in accord with the neighborhood principle. Consider motion in space, such as the flight of an airplane: to describe its position we need its longitude, latitude and height above the ground; and to these three numbers we must add a fourth, the time. This is an example of what we mean when we speak of a four-dimensional space-time world.

We have now reached the following conclusion about the dimension number of a domain: It depends on how many numbers (or equivalent symbols) are needed to give a suitable characterization of the elements of the domain. The number of these numbers (symbols) will then give the dimension of the domain. Accordingly a line $AB$ (see Fig. 74) has *one* dimension: a point $P$ on the line is characterized by its distance $x = AP$

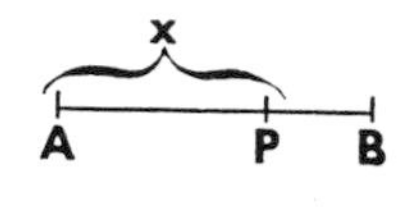


FIG. 74

from the origin $A$, thus by a single number. A rectangle $ABCD$ (Fig. 67) has *two* dimensions, because an arbitrary point $H$ of $ABCD$ is characterized by two numbers, such as $x = 3.15$, $y = 1.28$. A domain in space, such as the room pictured in Fig. 73, has *three* dimensions, since the position of its points is suitably characterized (in agreement with the neighborhood principle) by three numbers $x$, $y$, $z$.

The nature of dimension as we have discussed it was not always recognized, and for a long time many erroneous ideas about it were prevalent.[7] But after these errors were corrected one problem still remained. We can explain this problem by using the rectangle in Fig. 67. We know that we can locate the points of a rectangle by using two numbers $x$, $y$, in accord with the neighborhood principle. Is it possible—perhaps in a very complicated way—to characterize the points of a rectangle by a single number $t$, and still observe the neighborhood principle? This would seem highly improbable. But there have been many surprises in the history of mathematics,[8] and it would be foolish to consider any statement as certain before it is proved. What would it mean if, in keeping with the neighborhood principle, all the points of a rectangle could be characterized by a single number $t$ (say between 0 and 1)? Suppose that $t$ denotes the time, and that there is a one-to-one correspondence between the points $P$ of the rectangle and the values of $t$ in the interval from 0 to 1. Then if we think of a point moving on the interval from 0 to 1, the corresponding point of the rectangle will pass through every point of the rectangle exactly once. In addition we require adherence to the neighborhood principle, which means here that for any two moments of time which are close to each other [**7**], the corresponding points of the rectangle will be near each other, and conversely [**8**]. Is such a motion impossible? We are justified in distinguishing between one-dimensional and two-dimensional domains only if we have a rigorous

[7] It was, for instance, thought at one time that a rectangle contained more points than a straight line and a domain in space, such as a room, more points than a rectangle. But since a line contains an infinite number of points, just as a rectangle and a cube do, the question is, What does "more" or "less" mean as applied to infinite collections? When a meaningful definition of these terms was finally obtained (see Chapter XII), it was proved that a line, a rectangle and a cube all have the same number of points. It follows that the definition of dimension cannot be based on a comparison of the number of points in two domains.

[8] The discovery that a line, a rectangle and a cube have the same number of points (see Footnote 7) is one of these.

proof of this impossibility. Otherwise there would be no essential difference, and the same domain could equally well be called one-dimensional as two-dimensional.

The same problem can be raised about the distinction between one and three dimensions, or two and three dimensions, etc. The general problem, then, is the following: A space is $m$-dimensional if its elements can be suitably characterized by $m$ numbers, $x_1, x_2, \cdots, x_m$. Is it also possible to suitably characterize these elements with $n$ numbers, $t_1, t_2, \cdots, t_n$, where $n$ is different from $m$? This problem, which in its day was quite difficult, was finally solved in 1913 by the Dutch mathematician L. E. J. Brouwer (1881–) when he proved that it is *not* possible to assign two different dimension numbers to the same domain. This means that, using the definition of dimension discussed above, every figure has *one completely determined dimension number.*[9]

This achievement of modern mathematics not only put a shaky concept—the concept of dimension—on solid ground, but led to the development of dimension theory, which has been extended since that time and has proved to be rich in further problems and results. As the concept of dimension has been developed, it has been fruitfully applied to the most various and apparently unrelated branches of mathematics.

[9] We shall have to forego a discussion of Brouwer's deep proof. We merely mention that some of Brouwer's methods had already been anticipated by the great French mathematician, Henri Poincaré (1854–1912) [9]. We shall say more about Poincaré in the Postscript.

*Notes to Chapter VI*

## THREE DIMENSIONS—HIGHER DIMENSIONS

**1** (p. 107). Fig. 65 shows a white castle on *a*1, a black knight on *b*3, and three white pawns on *a*2, *b*2 and *c*2. On many chessboards the files *a* to *h*, and 1 to 8, are marked in duplicate, as shown in Fig. 65, so that each player may read them on his own side of the board.

**2** (p. 108). Figs. 75 and 76 show two enumerations of the squares of a chessboard different from that of Fig. 66. These also contain neighboring squares whose numbers are widely separated. For the problem of finding an enumeration in which it is impossible to express all the differences of the numbers of neighboring domains see {1}.

**3** (p. 110). In Fig. 67, the numbers $x$, $y$ are the rectangular or Cartesian coordinates of a point; in Fig. 68, $r$, $\varphi$ are the polar coordinates of a point.

**4** (p. 110). $q$ is indeterminate if and only if $r = 0$, and this occurs only if $P$ coincides with the center $M$. But the neighborhood principle is still satisfied, since all points $P$ near $M$ have values of $r$ near zero.

**5** (p. 111). This is true only if all possible colors are included (e.g., brown and all mixed colors), and not only the pure colors of the spectrum. For, each of the latter can be characterized by one number (its wavelength), and therefore the spectrum is one-dimensional.

**6** (p. 112). The numbers $x$, $y$, $z$ (or $x$, $y$, $s$) are the spatial Cartesian coordinates of a point.

**7** (p. 114). The fact that nearby points are traversed in correspondingly short time intervals is expressed mathematically by the concept of continuity; the position coordinates $x$, $y$ are said to be continuous functions of the time $t$. The other conditions on the motion can then be phrased in more technical language by saying that precisely one point $t$ corresponds to each point $(x, y)$ of the rectangle, and that $t$ is a continuous function of $(x, y)$. The proof that such a motion, i.e., the existence of functions satisfying these conditions, is impossible (and that this is true not just for the one- and two-dimensional case, but also for any two different dimensions) was not found until the concept of dimension itself was finally clarified. We must supplement the discussion in the text by remarking that the real dimension problem has to do with continuous variables $x$, $y$, $t$, etc. (for example, with *all* the points in a square and *all* the values of $t$ in a full number interval), and not merely with discrete variables such as the squares of a chessboard. We used a chessboard because it is a simple illustration of the relevance and use of the neighborhood principle.

**8** (p. 114). The motion is required to satisfy three conditions, which can be expressed in more technical language as follows (see Note 7):

| 57 | 58 | 59 | 60 | 61 | 62 | 63 | 64 |
|---|---|---|---|---|---|---|---|
| 49 | 50 | 51 | 52 | 53 | 54 | 55 | 56 |
| 41 | 42 | 43 | 44 | 45 | 46 | 47 | 48 |
| 33 | 34 | 35 | 36 | 37 | 38 | 39 | 40 |
| 25 | 26 | 27 | 28 | 29 | 30 | 31 | 32 |
| 17 | 18 | 19 | 20 | 21 | 22 | 23 | 24 |
| 9 | 10 | 11 | 12 | 13 | 14 | 15 | 16 |
| 1 | 2 | 3 | 4 | 5 | 6 | 7 | 8 |

FIG. 75

| 36 | 43 | 49 | 54 | 58 | 61 | 63 | 64 |
|---|---|---|---|---|---|---|---|
| 28 | 35 | 42 | 48 | 53 | 57 | 60 | 62 |
| 21 | 27 | 34 | 41 | 47 | 52 | 56 | 59 |
| 15 | 20 | 26 | 33 | 40 | 46 | 51 | 55 |
| 10 | 14 | 19 | 25 | 32 | 39 | 45 | 50 |
| 6 | 9 | 13 | 18 | 24 | 31 | 38 | 44 |
| 3 | 5 | 8 | 12 | 17 | 23 | 30 | 37 |
| 1 | 2 | 4 | 7 | 11 | 16 | 22 | 29 |

FIG. 76

(a) The points $(x, y)$ of the rectangle must be expressed as continuous functions $x = g(t)$, $y = h(t)$ of $t$, where $t$ takes all values between (and including) 0 and 1.

(b) Each point $(x = g(t),\ y = h(t))$ of the rectangle must correspond to precisely one value of $t$, that is, $t$ must be a single-valued function of $(x, y)$: $t = f(x, y)$.

(c) The function $t = f(x, y)$ must be continuous.

It was long suspected and later (as we shall see) proved that all three conditions (a)–(c) cannot be satisfied at the same time. It is interesting to note, however, that it is possible to define a motion in a rectangle which passes through *each point* of the rectangle *at least once*, but which of course passes through some points more than once. The condition (a) is satisfied, but conditions (b) and (c) are replaced by the weaker condition:

(d) Each point $(x, y)$ of the rectangle corresponds to at least one value of $t$.

Both Peano {2} and Hilbert[1] {3} proved that there are continuous functions satisfying (a) and (d). Hilbert's method is especially intuitive and is illustrated in Figs. 77–81. To make the discussion more concrete, let us imagine that the given rectangle is a square garden and that a person is required to walk through the garden in such a way that his path satisfies conditions (a) and (d). Let us further suppose that the walk is to last an hour. If we represent the person by a point, Fig. 77 indicates schematically that the moving point remains in the subsquare (1) at the lower left of the large square during the first quarter of an hour, in the subsquare (2) during the next quarter hour, in the subsquare (3) during the third quarter hour, and in the subsquare (4) during the last quarter hour. Fig. 78 gives a more detailed picture of the position of the moving point during each quarter hour. This picture is obtained by dividing each of the subsquares (1)–(4) into four equal smaller squares and then indicating the location of the moving point during the first $1/16$ hour, during the second $1/16$ hour, etc.

[1] David Hilbert (1862–1943) was the great mathematician and leading exponent of international scientific cooperation. For an account of his life and work see {4}.

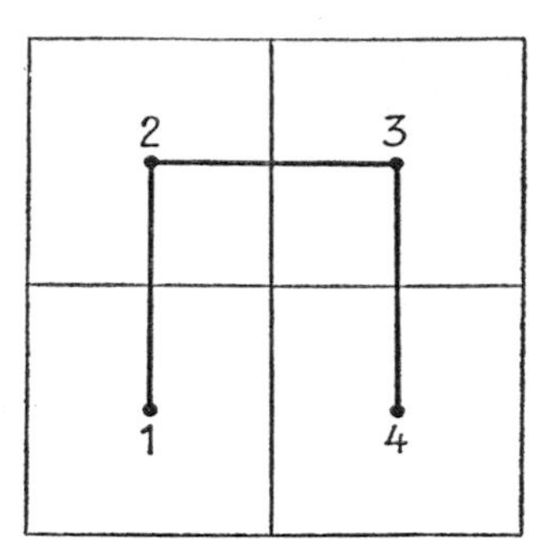


Fig. 77

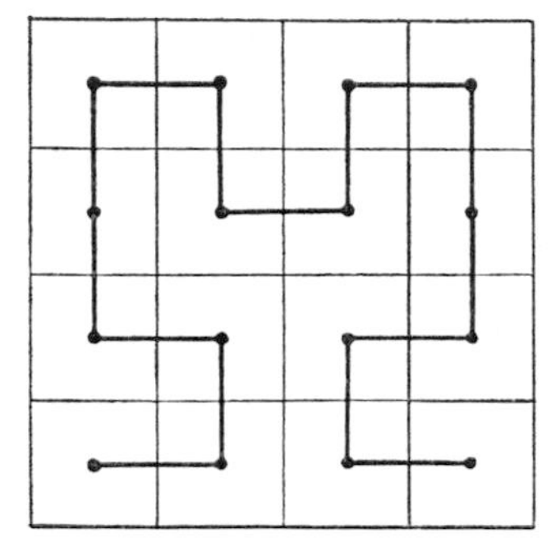

Fig. 78

| | | | |
|---|---|---|---|
| 6 | 7 | 10 | 11 |
| 5 | 8 | 9 | 12 |
| 4 | 3 | 14 | 13 |
| 1 | 2 | 15 | 16 |

Fig. 79

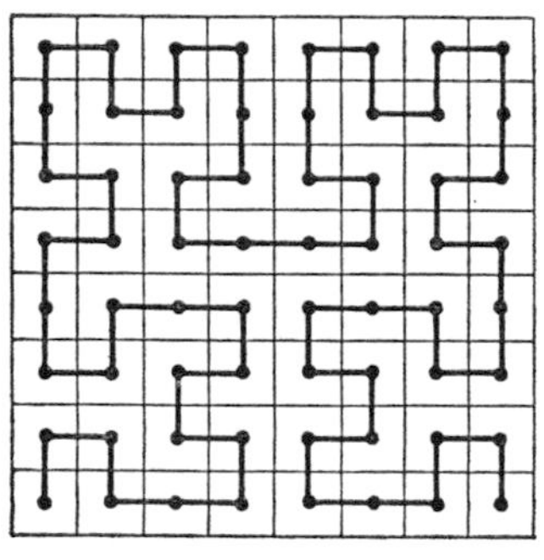

Fig. 80

| | | | | | | | |
|---|---|---|---|---|---|---|---|
| 22 | 23 | 26 | 27 | 38 | 39 | 42 | 43 |
| 21 | 24 | 25 | 28 | 37 | 40 | 41 | 44 |
| 20 | 19 | 30 | 29 | 36 | 35 | 46 | 45 |
| 17 | 18 | 31 | 32 | 33 | 34 | 47 | 48 |
| 16 | 13 | 12 | 11 | 54 | 53 | 52 | 49 |
| 15 | 14 | 9 | 10 | 55 | 56 | 51 | 50 |
| 2 | 3 | 8 | 7 | 58 | 57 | 62 | 63 |
| 1 | 4 | 5 | 6 | 59 | 60 | 61 | 64 |

Fig. 81

The successive small squares in which the moving point is to be found during the first, second, etc. $\frac{1}{16}$ hours can be determined by starting at the lower left of the figure and following the straight line segments continuously. It should be emphasized that the straight line segments do not represent the actual path of the point; they merely indicate the order in which the point traverses the small subsquares of the large square. In fact, the straight line segments can be dispensed with by using Fig. 79, where the numbers in the small squares mean that the moving point is *somewhere* in square (1) during the first $1/16$ hour, *somewhere* in square (2) during the second $1/16$ hour, etc. Figs. 80 and 81 indicate in still further detail the location of the moving point during the first $1/64$ hour, second $1/64$ hour, etc. By continuing the process of subdividing and renumbering the squares, we would obtain a sequence of figures, which would give at each successive stage a more and more detailed picture of the motion. Such a sequence of figures would therefore give a complete description of the walk proposed by Hilbert, and which satisfies conditions (a) and (d). However, it will not satisfy (b), since the moving point passes through the center of the square three times, and not once as condition (b) requires.

**9** (p. 115). The barest sketch of the basic ideas of the proof would run as follows. An interior point $P$ of a segment $AB$ (see Fig. 82) disconnects the segment, that is, the deletion of $P$ breaks the segment into two pieces $AP$ and $PB$. Similarly, two distinct points $P$ and $Q$ disconnect a circumference (see Fig. 83): the deletion of $P$ and $Q$ separates the circumference into two pieces $PAQ$ and $PBQ$. There are, therefore, figures which are disconnected by a finite set of points. Let us call any finite set of points a

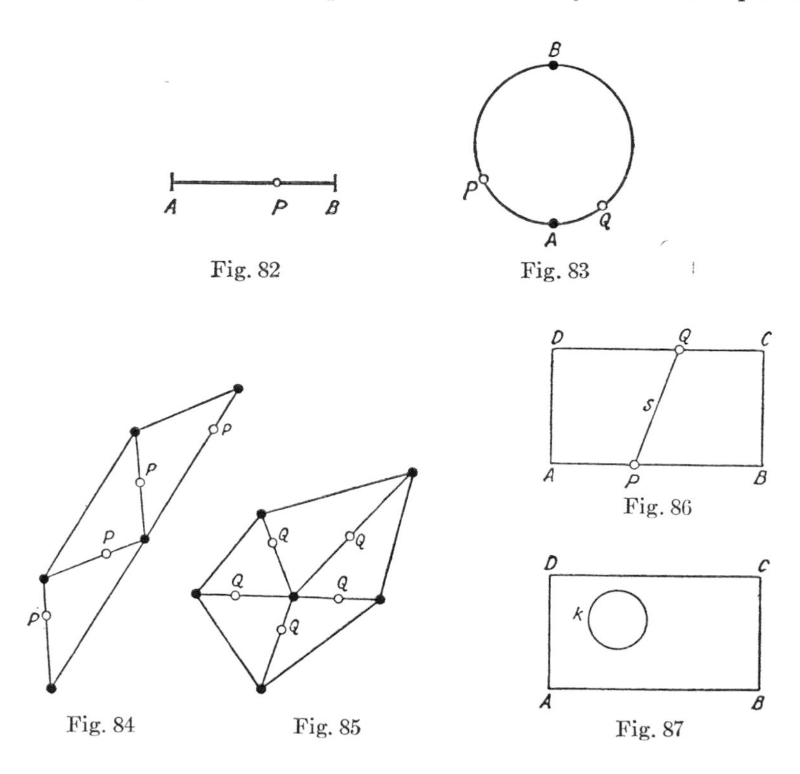


Fig. 82 Fig. 83 Fig. 84 Fig. 85 Fig. 86 Fig. 87

figure of rank 0, and let us refer to any figure which is disconnected by some finite set of points (that is, disconnected by some figure of rank 0) as a figure of rank 1. Other examples of figures of rank 1 are shown in Figs. 84 and 85. In Fig. 84, the set of straight line segments is disconnected by the set of four points marked $P$ (the omission of these four points breaks the figure into more than one piece). Similarly, the set of straight line segments in Fig. 85 is disconnected by the set of five points marked $Q$.

Let us now define a figure of rank 2 as a figure which can be disconnected by some figure of rank 1, but cannot be disconnected by any figure of rank 0. For instance, the rectangle of Fig. 86 is disconnected by the segment $s = PQ$ or by a circumference $k$ (Fig. 87), but cannot be disconnected by any finite set of points. Another example is the surface of a sphere (which is disconnected by, say, its equator). Therefore, a rectangle and the surface of a sphere are figures of rank 2.

In the same way, we can define a figure of rank 3 as one which can be disconnected by some figure of rank 2, but cannot be disconnected by any figure of rank 0 or 1. The space enclosed by a room is of rank 3: it is not disconnected by finite sets of points or by figures of rank 1, but it can be disconnected by an interior wall, that is, by a rectangle (a figure of rank 2). The same room can be disconnected by the surface of a sphere; we can then refer to the space of the room inside the sphere and outside the sphere.

In general, then, we can define a figure of rank $n$ as one which can be disconnected by some figure of rank $n - 1$, but cannot be disconnected by any figure of rank less than $n - 1$. It is clear from the definition of rank that every figure has a unique rank.

The following proposition can then be demonstrated: An $n$-dimensional figure, that is, a figure whose points require $n$ numbers for their characterization (in accordance with the neighborhood principle) has rank $n$, for $n = 1, 2, 3, \cdots$. Since every figure has a unique rank, it follows that an $n$-dimensional figure cannot be $m$-dimensional, unless $m = n$. This is Brouwer's theorem. In the technical literature, it is referred to as: *The theorem on the invariance of the dimension number*.

For Brouwer's proof see {5}. A very beautiful, but different, proof was given by Sperner {6} and also by Hurewicz {7}. Among the principal contributors to the dimension theory mentioned at the end of the chapter were P. S. Alexandroff, Menger, Urysohn and Fréchet. For references to the literature see {8}.

*Chapter VII*

# PRIME NUMBERS AGAIN—MORE ON THEIR DISTRIBUTION

In our previous discussion of prime numbers (Chapter I), we learned that these are the numbers 2, 3, 5, 7, 11, 13, $\cdots$ which cannot be expressed as the product of two smaller factors. In the following table the primes are printed in bold-face:

| 1 | **11** | 21 | **31** | **41** | 51 | **61** | **71** | 81 | 91 | **101** | 111 | 121 | **131** | .... |
|---|---|---|---|---|---|---|---|---|---|---|---|---|---|---|
| **2** | 12 | 22 | 32 | 42 | 52 | 62 | 72 | 82 | 92 | 102 | 112 | 122 | 132 | .... |
| **3** | **13** | **23** | 33 | **43** | **53** | 63 | **73** | **83** | 93 | **103** | **113** | 123 | 133 | .... |
| 4 | 14 | 24 | 34 | 44 | 54 | 64 | 74 | 84 | 94 | 104 | 114 | 124 | 134 | .... |
| **5** | 15 | 25 | 35 | 45 | 55 | 65 | 75 | 85 | 95 | 105 | 115 | 125 | 135 | .... |
| 6 | 16 | 26 | 36 | 46 | 56 | 66 | 76 | 86 | 96 | 106 | 116 | 126 | 136 | .... |
| **7** | **17** | 27 | **37** | **47** | 57 | **67** | 77 | 87 | **97** | **107** | 117 | **127** | **137** | .... |
| 8 | 18 | 28 | 38 | 48 | 58 | 68 | 78 | 88 | 98 | 108 | 118 | 128 | 138 | .... |
| 9 | **19** | **29** | 39 | 49 | **59** | 69 | **79** | **89** | 99 | **109** | 119 | 129 | **139** | .... |
| 10 | 20 | 30 | 40 | 50 | 60 | 70 | 80 | 90 | 100 | 110 | 120 | 130 | 140 | .... |

Various tables showing the occurrence of primes beyond this range were given in Chapter I. These demonstrated that the primes, as far as could be seen from the tables, apparently became rarer and rarer. We also saw that although they become rarer, the primes do not die out: There is no largest prime.

We shall now discuss two problems having to do with a more precise analysis of the distribution of the primes. The first problem is this: Can the increasing rarity of the primes be expressed more precisely, i.e. can we formulate a general law governing the decreasing occurrence of the primes, in spite of the irregularity of their distribution? In other words, *how* does the number of primes decrease?

Before investigating this problem, however, let us raise a second problem. This problem has to do with the arrangement of the natural numbers in columns of ten in the table above [1]. Looking at the table, we see that the first row consists of the numbers 1, 11, 21, $\cdots$ , that is, all numbers whose last digit is 1; the next row consists of all numbers ending in 2. In the ninth row all the numbers end in 9, and in the last row the last digit is 0. And now we ask: *Which rows contain primes?* With this question, we can define our problem more precisely: What is the distribution of primes in each of the ten rows? We then notice the following:

The first row certainly contains *more than one prime:* 11, 31, 41, 61 are primes and there are others. The first row would seem to be a rich source of primes.

The second row consists of numbers divisible by 2; the only prime divisible by two is 2 itself; all the others are composite. Except for the number 2, no other prime will ever appear in this row. We shall call it a *dead row;* in contrast, the first row will be referred to as a *living row.*

The third row contains the primes 3, 13, 23, hence certainly more than one prime; it is therefore a living row.

The fourth row is a dead row, since it contains no primes at all. All the numbers in this row are divisible by 2 and are greater than 2.

The only prime in the fifth row is 5; all the other numbers in this row are divisible by 5 and at the same time greater than 5; this row is similar to the second row, and we call it a dead row.

The sixth row contains no primes (all the numbers are divisible by 2 and also greater than 2). It is a dead row.

The seventh row contains the primes 7, 17, 37. Since it has more than one prime, it is a living row.

The eighth row (like the fourth and sixth) has no prime numbers and is a dead row.

The ninth row contains 19, 29, thus more than one prime; hence it is a living row.

Row ten is dead, since it contains no primes.

Since the 2nd, 4th, 5th, 6th, 8th, and 10th are dead rows (they contain at most one prime) and the 1st, 3rd, 7th, and 9th are living rows, *all the primes greater than 10 occur only in these four rows*, i.e., their last digit must be 1, 3, 7 or 9.

In Chapter I we proved that there are an *infinite number of primes.* What does this imply about the rows into which the numbers have been divided? Obviously, *at least* one row must contain an infinite number of primes. It is therefore impossible for *every* row to have a last prime. We have just seen that every prime greater than 10 must occur in one of the four living rows, that is, in the 1st, 3rd, 7th or 9th. Therefore, *at least* one of these rows must contain an infinite number of primes. The question immediately arises as to which of these four rows contains an infinite number of primes. Does only one living row contain an infinite number of primes? Or do several? Or do *all* living rows contain an infinite number of primes? This question was only answered about 100 years ago, in a famous paper by Dirichlet which appeared in 1837.

Before discussing his solution, let us reexamine the tables given earlier, keeping in mind our present problem: the row distribution of primes. In particular, let us look at Table 7 (Chapter I) which covers the range of numbers 1 to 1500. We see at a glance that in this range, primes keep occurring in the four living rows—the 1st, 3rd, 7th and 9th.[1] We are therefore led to conjecture that *every one* of these rows contains an infinite number of primes. The conjecture cannot, of course, be proved by reference to tables. The first row, for instance, might contain only a finite number of primes, and yet the last prime in this row might be larger than all the numbers in any given table. Here is another example of a problem which *cannot* be solved by the preparation of extensive tables or the calculation of a large number of primes, and Dirichlet needed new ideas to solve it.

Dirichlet proved that *each of the four living rows does indeed contain an infinite number of primes*, that is, there are an infinite number of primes whose last digit is 1, 3, 7, and 9, respectively. In other words, *none* of the four living rows contains a greatest prime.

Unfortunately, the methods Dirichlet used in the proof are too difficult to present here. To indicate the extent of the difficulty, we may mention that, even before Dirichlet, the French mathematician Adrien-Marie Legendre (1752–1833) believed he had a proof of the same result. To be sure, one must credit Legendre (who was nineteen years old at the time [**2**]) with being the first to have made the correct conjecture and, therefore, with having raised the problem. But his proof, published in 1808, contains a gap, so that in spite of all his research the problem was unsolved until Dirichlet devised entirely new methods of proof [**3**].

I must also say that Legendre conjectured and Dirichlet proved a much more general result than the one I have indicated. To give you an idea of what I mean, I shall write the sequence of numbers a little differently. We again arrange the numbers in columns, but this time in columns of 12 numbers each:

| | | | | | | | | | | | | |
|---|---|---|---|---|---|---|---|---|---|---|---|---|
| 1 | **13** | 25 | **37** | 49 | **61** | **73** | 85 | **97** | **109** | 121 | 133 | .... |
| **2** | 14 | 26 | 38 | 50 | 62 | 74 | 86 | 98 | 110 | 122 | 134 | .... |
| **3** | 15 | 27 | 39 | 51 | 63 | 75 | 87 | 99 | 111 | 123 | 135 | .... |
| 4 | 16 | 28 | 40 | 52 | 64 | 76 | 88 | 100 | 112 | 124 | 136 | .... |
| **5** | **17** | **29** | **41** | **53** | 65 | 77 | **89** | **101** | **113** | 125 | **137** | .... |
| 6 | 18 | 30 | 42 | 54 | 66 | 78 | 90 | 102 | 114 | 126 | 138 | .... |
| **7** | **19** | **31** | **43** | 55 | **67** | **79** | 91 | **103** | 115 | **127** | **139** | .... |
| 8 | 20 | 32 | 44 | 56 | 68 | 80 | 92 | 104 | 116 | 128 | 140 | .... |
| 9 | 21 | 33 | 45 | 57 | 69 | 81 | 93 | 105 | 117 | 129 | 141 | .... |
| 10 | 22 | 34 | 46 | 58 | 70 | 82 | 94 | 106 | 118 | 130 | 142 | .... |
| **11** | **23** | 35 | **47** | **59** | **71** | **83** | 95 | **107** | 119 | **131** | 143 | .... |
| 12 | 24 | 36 | 48 | 60 | 72 | 84 | 96 | 108 | 120 | 132 | 144 | .... |

[1] Tables 2, 3, 4 (Chapter I), as well as 8, 9, 10 (Chapter I), which give samples of the higher ranges arouse the same suspicion.

Again we ask which rows contain primes, and especially which rows have more than one prime. We must first characterize the numbers in each row. The characterization is simple: The numbers of the first row are obtained by first writing 1 and then adding 12 to each successive number: $1 + 12 = 13$; $13 + 12 = 25$; etc.[2] We obtain the numbers in the second row by first writing 2 and then adding 12 successively: 2, 14, 26, $\cdots$ ;[3] similarly, the numbers of the 3rd row are obtained by adding successive multiples of 12 to 3: 3, 15, 27, $\cdots$ ; and all the other rows are similarly characterized.

It is immediately obvious that no prime can appear in the 4th row; since the first number is 4, successive additions of 12 can only give rise to numbers divisible by 4.[4] As before, the 4th row will be called dead. The same can be said of the 8th and 12th rows, and also of the 6th and 9th (whose numbers are all divisible by 3), as well as of the 10th row (whose numbers are divisible by 2). Finally, all the numbers of the 2nd row are divisible by 2, and those of the 3rd by 3, so that these rows contain no primes other than 2 and 3. All these rows are therefore dead.

Therefore, except for the primes 2 and 3, which occur in the first column, there are no primes in the 2nd, 3rd, 4th, 6th, 8th, 9th, 10th, and 12th rows (the dead rows). *More than one prime* can then occur only in the remaining rows (the living rows), i.e. the 1st, 5th, 7th, and 11th [4]. It is also clear that each of these living rows contains more than one prime: 13, 37, 61, $\cdots$ in the 1st; 5, 17, 29, 41, $\cdots$ in the 5th; 7, 19, 31, 43, $\cdots$ in the 7th; 11, 23, 47, $\cdots$ in the 11th.

Table 12 (at the end of this chapter) would indicate that primes continue to appear in each of the living rows even in the higher ranges. We may therefore ask once more whether each of the living rows contains an infinite number of primes.

It was Legendre's conjecture, proved by Dirichlet, that this is the case. Actually, Dirichlet's result was stronger. He proved that if the natural numbers are arranged in columns of arbitrary finite length (each column having the same length), then each of the living rows (those having more than one prime) contains an infinite number of primes. Another example will make this clearer.

In this example, let each column consist of 9 numbers (see Table 13 at the end of this chapter). Reasoning as before, we see that no prime can occur in the 6th and 9th rows, and that 3 is the only prime in the 3rd row. Thus the 3rd, 6th and 9th rows are now the dead rows. We can then expect to find more than one prime only in the remaining rows, which we

[2] In mathematical notation, the numbers of the first row are of the form $1 + 12n$, $n = 0, 1, 2, 3, \cdots$ .

[3] The numbers of the second row are of the form $2 + 12n$, $n = 0, 1, 2, \cdots$ .

[4] The numbers of this row can all be written as $4 + 12n = 4(1 + 3n)$, $n = 0, 1, 2, \cdots$ .

again call the living rows, i.e. in the 1st, 2nd, 4th, 5th, 7th and 8th rows [5]. Primes do occur in each of these six rows in the range of Table 13, so that here too Legendre's conjecture seems likely. Dirichlet's theorem [6] confirms the conjecture in this case also.

In the Introduction we mentioned that most new developments in mathematics follow the solution of old problems. In this case, the very penetrating and original methods which Dirichlet used to solve this problem were particularly significant for the development of mathematics, and brought him lasting fame [7].

In 1837, when Dirichlet presented this solution to the Prussian Academy of Sciences, he was 32 years old and a Professor of Mathematics at the War College in Berlin, where he had taught for nine years. During this time he had often been invited to lecture at the University. He had been brought to Berlin originally through the efforts of Alexander von Humboldt (1769–1859), who had met Dirichlet in Paris in 1825. Dirichlet, who was then 20, had already published important papers which had given him a reputation as a promising young mathematician.

Gustav Lejeune Dirichlet was born February 13, 1805, in Düren—between Aix and Cologne—the son of a postmaster. At an early age he had shown a decided preference for mathematics, much to the disappointment of his parents, who had hoped he would become a merchant. In 1821, when he finished his secondary education,[5] he decided to continue his studies in Paris, both because of its many eminent teachers of mathematics, and because he had family connections there. He became a tutor in the cultivated and hospitable household of General Foy, where he gave German lessons and acquired fluency in French. In this household, he had the opportunity to meet men distinguished in both intellectual and political fields, and also had enough time to continue his studies. More important to him than the lectures he attended was a little book by Gauss, *Disquisitiones Arithmeticae*, published in 1801. The profound significance of this book was as yet understood by only a few, but it contained this great master's fundamental research on number theory. Many years later the story was told that young Dirichlet had as a constant companion on all his travels, like a devout man with his prayer book, an old, worn copy of the *Disquisitiones*. It was not surprising that the young mathematician's first paper, presented to the Paris Academy,[6] dealt with problems in number theory.[7]

[5] It will interest those acquainted with Ohm's Law that Georg Simon Ohm (1787–1854) had been Dirichlet's mathematics instructor at the gymnasium in Cologne. In Munich, where he worked after 1849, Ohm was honored by a statue and a street bearing his name.

[6] Legendre, who was 73 years old at the time, was one of the referees whose favorable opinion was responsible for publication of the paper by the Academy. Legendre of course had no way of knowing that 12 years later the author of this paper would

Fourier (1768–1830), a stimulating teacher who is still remembered for his research on the theory of heat, also had a great influence on Dirichlet's scientific development. Fourier was responsible for Dirichlet's interest in mathematical physics, an interest which later culminated in a number of outstanding papers.

In 1827, Alexander von Humboldt had an annual stipend established for Dirichlet at the University of Breslau, and soon afterwards secured for him an appointment at Berlin, where he was to remain for 27 years. In 1855, he was offered the Professorship at Göttingen as the mathematician most worthy to succeed the great Gauss. But Dirichlet lived only a few years longer. In 1859 he died of a heart ailment. Professional friends testified that he had obtained some valuable results, which he had not yet published, but they were not found among his papers, probably because it was Dirichlet's habit to think a problem through completely before writing anything down. Even without the lost results, however, Dirichlet's contribution to mathematics was very great. The theory of numbers alone includes three of his greatest achievements: the one discussed in this chapter, and two others which are too technical to state here [**8**]. In the history of mathematics at the University of Göttingen, Dirichlet stands between his predecessor, Gauss, and his successor, Riemann, both of whom we shall discuss later.

Dirichlet's theorem on the distribution of primes is now more than a century old. In sciences like chemistry or the theory of electricity, which developed much later than mathematics, a century old discovery is an ancient achievement. But a hundred years ago, mathematics had already reached a stage where the differential and integral calculus and many other modern theories had been developed long before. The science had extended so far beyond the realm of the ancients, that although there have been new results since his time, Dirichlet's achievement can hardly be regarded as ancient. We shall now discuss some of the later results.

We have already seen that the number of primes appears to decrease in the higher ranges, but that the primes never die out entirely. Therefore, the number of primes less than or equal to $x$, where $x$ is a positive integer, increases with $x$: there are 25 primes less than 100 (see Table 5, Chapter I); there are another 21 primes between 100 and 200, so that there are 46 primes less than 200, etc. We may then ask: How many primes are there less than or equal to $x$, where $x$ is an arbitrary positive integer? Denoting the number of primes less than or equal to $x$ by $N(x)$ [**9**], we have

---

prove Legendre's own conjecture. He died at 81 in 1833 and did not live to see his conjecture confirmed.

[7] These concerned a problem of Fermat's. We shall discuss Fermat's work in Chapter XIII.

$$N(100) = 25,$$

$$N(200) = 46.$$

Other values of $N(x)$ are listed in Table 11 (Chapter I). For example,

$$N(1000) = 168,$$

that is, there are 168 primes less than 1000. The observed gradual decrease in the incidence of the primes expresses itself in the tables by the fact that, for example, the number of primes between 200 and 300, i.e. $N(300) - N(200) = 62 - 46 = 16$, while $N(100100) - N(100000) = 9598 - 9592 = 6$.[8] Hence $N(x)$ increases because primes continue to occur; but, as far as can be observed, the rate of increase—which is quite irregular—gradually diminishes.

Many people had wondered whether $N(x)$ could be expressed, at least approximately, by a simple formula. Such a formula should enable one to state at least the approximate number of primes between, say 1 and 1000[9] without counting each prime in that range. One would simply put $x = 1000$ in the formula and get either the exact value 168 or a value not too different from it. The formula should also work for even very large numbers, larger than those given in any of the prime number tables at our disposal, e.g. 1,000,000,000,000. Naturally, the correctness of the formula must rest on theoretical considerations, particularly since we cannot always compare the answer—lacking a table extending into the trillions—with the exact figure.

Is there such a formula, and, moreover one whose validity can be established? This question was answered only 70 years ago. It was suspected for a long time that this formula (in various essentially equivalent forms) was probably related to the primes. We shall return to this point later. But that it actually gives the desired results for arbitrarily large numbers was first proved at the end of the last century independently by the French mathematician Jacques Hadamard (1865–1963) and the Belgian mathematician Charles de la Vallée Poussin (1866–).

The formula appears simple to the professional, but is difficult for the layman. Many expressions in it are highly technical and would need elaborate clarification.[10] Actually, it is not a simple formula, but a *functional*

[8] Table 11, which is meant to give only a brief summary of the variation of $N(x)$ with $x$, does not give the value of $N(x)$ for $x = 100100$. A table giving the values of $N(x)$ at intervals of 100 for all $x$ up to 10 million would take up too much space in this book.

[9] That is, $N(1000) = 168$. This exact value can of course be found simply by counting, once all the primes up to 1000 have been found; or even more simply by consulting a prime number table.

[10] See Note 17, formulas (5) and (6).

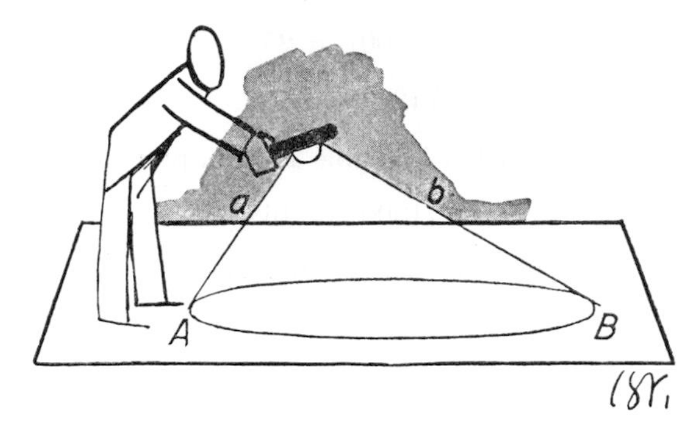


FIG. 88

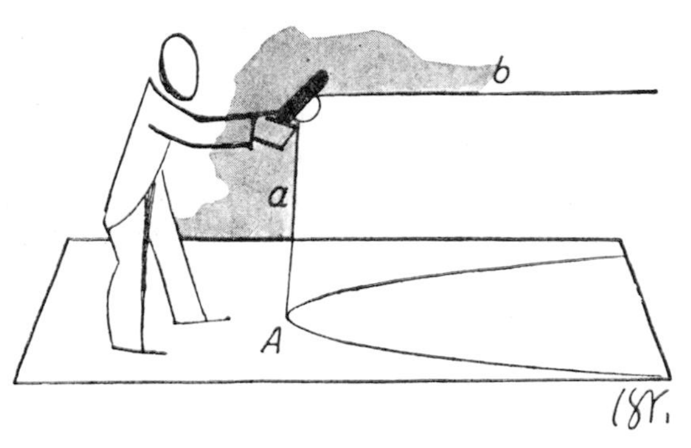


FIG. 89

*relation*. Although it is not possible to describe this relation in all its details, I can give a rough description of it. To do so, surprisingly enough, it is most convenient to use geometric language.

First, let us see how a physical picture of a hyperbola may be obtained by using a flashlight. If a flashlight is held perpendicular to the floor, it will light up a circular area on the floor; the border of this area will be clearly seen as a circumference.[11] If the flashlight is moved so it is held at an angle (Fig. 88), the result is an ellipse; one of the light rays on the boundary of the cone of light ($b$ in the figure) ends in the most distant point $B$ of the

[11] Another way of putting this is that the surface of the floor cuts the light cone in a circle; from this point of view, the circle (and later the ellipse, the parabola and the hyperbola) is the intersection of a cone with a plane, that is, a conic section. Did classical Greece foresee the significance that conic sections would have in astronomy? Since Kepler (1571–1630) and Newton (1643–1727), we know that the paths of the planets and the comets around the sun are conic sections.

For the best results, shine the flashlight on a wall instead of the floor; the wall should not be too dark in color and the light should be held not too far away from the wall.

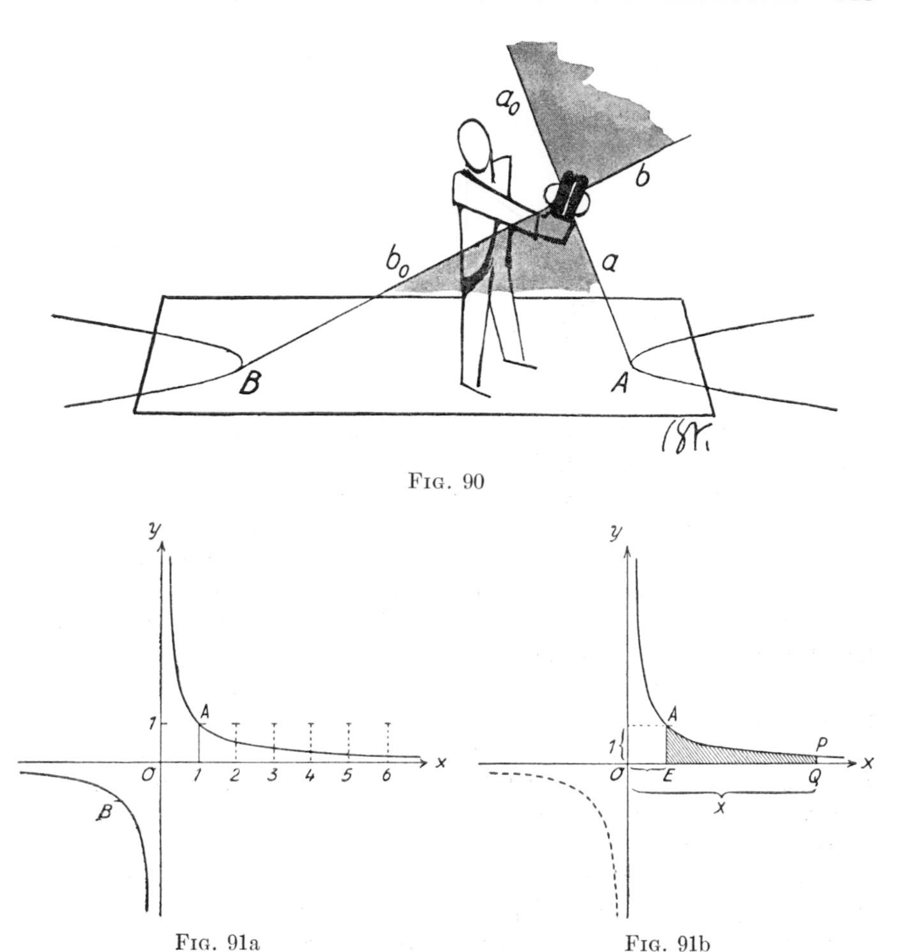


FIG. 90

FIG. 91a

FIG. 91b

ellipse, which is most weakly lit here.[12] As the light is inclined, the ellipse lengthens; when the upper boundary $b$ of the cone of light (Fig. 89) is parallel to the surface of the floor, the boundary of the lit surface becomes a parabola extending to infinity.[13] If the lamp is inclined still further (Fig. 90), so that the upper boundary $b$ of the light cone is no longer parallel to the floor, but is directed upwards, a section of the light cone will not meet the floor at all. The part of the floor that is lit up will then have as its boundary one branch of a hyperbola.[14]

[12] Let $a$ be the ray of light on the boundary of the light cone opposite the light ray $b$. If $A$ is the point at which this light ray meets the floor, the line $AB$ is the major axis of the ellipse; the points $A$ and $B$ are two vertices of the ellipse.

[13] The ray $a$ opposite the ray $b$ on the boundary of the light cone meets the floor at a point $A$, the vertex of the parabola.

[14] Fig. 90 shows how to obtain the second branch of the hyperbola. A second light

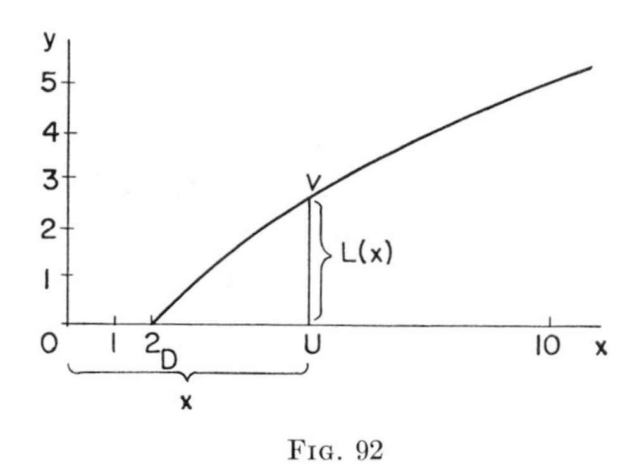


FIG. 92

Figs. 91a and b show a definite hyperbola, which can be made by further manipulations of a flashlight [**11**].

Notice in the figures that there are two perpendicular lines, the $x$- and $y$-axes, which are approached by the different parts of the hyperbola.[15] We need only one branch of the hyperbola here (the unnecessary branch is dotted in Fig. 91b). We shall take the segment $OE = EA$ as the unit of length.[16] If $x$ is any number greater than 1, mark off the segment $OQ$ of length $x$ on the $x$-axis. The perpendicular to the $x$-axis at $Q$ meets the hyperbola at $P$. Now consider the region (hatched in Fig. 91b) bounded by the three straight lines $PQ$, $QE$, and $EA$, and by the piece $AP$ of the hyperbola. It is clear that the area of this region depends on $x$. As $x$ increases, $P$ and $Q$ move to the right and the area increases. As $x$ decreases, $Q$ and $P$ move to the left and the area decreases. If $x$ is only a little greater than 1, the point $Q$ on the $x$-axis will be very close to $E$, and the corresponding point $P$ on the hyperbola will be very close to $A$. The hatched region will then be only a small strip lying to the right of the line $EA$, and the area of this small strip will not be much greater than zero. The variation of this area with $x$ is a functional relation between two quantities [**13**]. A few simple geometric considerations are enough to derive a second functional relation (shown in Fig. 92) from the first. For an explanation of the transition from the hyperbola of Fig. 91 to the curve of Fig. 92, see Fig. 99a–g (Notes to Chapter VII) and [**14**].

The remarkable thing about the curve of Fig. 92 is *its significance for the theory of prime numbers.* This is due to the following property of the

$L_0$ is held so that its light cone is the other nappe of the first light cone. If $a_0$ and $b_0$ are the light rays of $L_0$ which are the continuations of the light rays $a$ and $b$ of the first light $L$, $b_0$ and part of the light cone of the second light will meet the surface of the floor and there form the second branch of the hyperbola. The points $A$ and $B$ at which $a$ and $b_0$ meet the floor are the vertices of the hyperbola [**10**].

[15] This hyperbola is the graph of the function given by the equation $xy = 1$ or $y = 1/x$.

[16] $O$ is the center of the hyperbola and $A$ and $B$ are its two vertices [**12**].

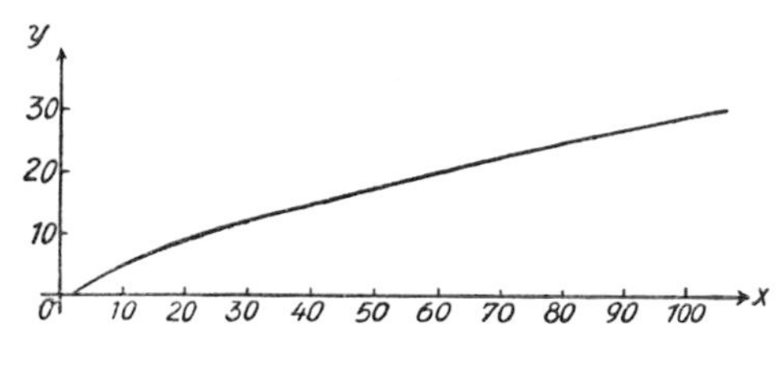


FIG. 93

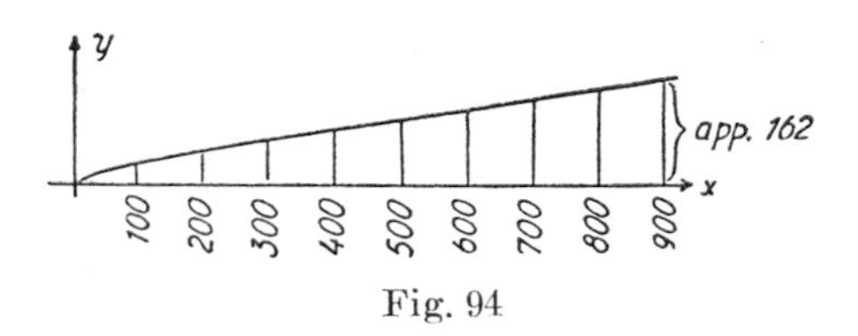


Fig. 94

curve. Let $D$ be the point on the $x$-axis at a distance 2 from $O$, the point of intersection of the two axes, so that $OD = 2$. The curve begins at $D$ and gradually draws away from the $x$-axis. Let $x$ be any number greater than 2, and let $U$ be the point on the $x$-axis such that $OU = x$. Erect a perpendicular to the $x$-axis at $U$ and denote its point of intersection with the curve by $V$. The point $V$ varies with $x$, and the length $UV$ increases with $x$. For instance,[17] for

$$\begin{array}{llll} x = 5, & UV = & 2.5894\cdots \\ x = 6, & UV = & 3.1771\cdots \\ x = 10, & UV = & 5.1204\cdots \\ x = 20, & UV = & 8.8601\cdots \\ x = 100, & UV = & 29.0810\cdots \\ x = 900, & UV = & 161.9737\cdots \\ x = 5000, & UV = & 683.23\cdots \\ x = 50000, & UV = & 5165.5\cdots \quad . \end{array}$$

Hence, for each value of $x$ there is a definite value of $UV$, the increasing distance of the curve from the $x$-axis. Fig. 92 extends only to $x = 10$, and since we shall be especially interested in the part of the curve corresponding to larger values of $x$, we shall have to draw it on a greatly diminished scale. In Fig. 93 the scale is reduced by $1/10$; in Fig. 94[18] it is reduced by $1/100$.

[17] These values of $UV$ are calculated by using the geometric relations between the hyperbola of Fig. 91 and the curve of Fig. 92. See [**14**].

[18] The unit of length is so small here that a very small segment will have a length

Denoting $OU$ by $x$ and $UV$ by $L(x)$, we get

$$\begin{aligned} L(5) &= 2.5894\cdots \\ L(6) &= 3.1771\cdots \\ L(10) &= 5.1204\cdots \\ L(20) &= 8.8601\cdots \\ L(100) &= 29.0810\cdots \\ L(900) &= 161.9757\cdots \\ L(5000) &= 683.23\cdots \\ L(50000) &= 5165.5\cdots . \end{aligned}$$

We are now in a position to make a surprising discovery. If we write down the number $N(x)$ of primes less than or equal to $x$, for the above values of $x$, we find that

$$\begin{aligned} N(5) &= 3, \\ N(6) &= 3, \\ N(10) &= 4, \\ N(20) &= 8, \\ N(100) &= 25, \\ N(900) &= 154, \\ N(5000) &= 669, \\ N(50000) &= 5133. \end{aligned}$$

We write the two lists side by side for comparison:

$$\begin{aligned} N(5) &= 3, & L(5) &= 2.5894\cdots \\ N(6) &= 3, & L(6) &= 3.1771\cdots \\ N(10) &= 4, & L(10) &= 5.1204\cdots \\ N(20) &= 8, & L(20) &= 8.8601\cdots \\ N(100) &= 25, & L(100) &= 29.0810\cdots \\ N(900) &= 154, & L(900) &= 161.9757\cdots \\ N(5000) &= 669, & L(5000) &= 683.23\cdots \\ N(50000) &= 5133, & L(50000) &= 5165.5\cdots . \end{aligned}$$

We then see that for large values of $x$, $L(x)$ (the length of $UV$) is approximately equal to $N(x)$ (the number of primes less than or equal to $x$). The expression "approximately equal to" can be made more precise by computing the ratio $N(x)/L(x) = M(x)$. For example,

$$\begin{aligned} M(10) &= 4/5.1204 &&= 0.78119, \\ M(100) &= 25/29.0810 &&= 0.859668, \\ M(900) &= 154/161.9757 &&= 0.95076, \end{aligned}$$

---

of 100. For this reason the curve seems to start at the origin and not at the point two units away from the origin, as it actually does.

$$M(5000) = 669/683.23 = 0.97917,$$
$$M(50000) = 5133/5165.5 = 0.99371.$$

The remarkable thing is that *this ratio approaches* 1 as $x$ increases!

This result is all the more surprising if we remember that the curve of Fig. 92 was derived from a hyperbola using certain geometric relations which have nothing to do with prime numbers [**15**]. The function represented by the curve of Fig. 92 is called the integral logarithm [**16**], an unfortunate name[19] whose only purpose seems to be to arouse a shudder in the nonmathematician [**17**].

Gauss was the first to observe that $M(x) = N(x)/L(x)$ seems to approach 1 as $x$ approaches infinity. He was fifteen years old when he noticed the apparent connection between the integral logarithm and the number of primes. But Gauss never published this result during his life and it became known only in 1849, when he was 72, through a letter which he wrote to the astronomer Encke,[20] who was also interested in the distribution of the primes. Before the publication of Gauss' letter, others had made the same observation, notably Legendre (1752–1833), who published his results in 1798 and 1808.

Comparison of the number of primes (obtained from prime number tables) with the integral logarithm[21] and some very important results obtained by the Russian mathematician Tschebyschef (1821–1894) in 1851–1852 all tended to point to the validity of Gauss' conjecture. But it took another 40 years to find a rigorous proof; it was not until 1896 that Hadamard and de la Vallée Poussin independently at last solved the problem by proving that $N(x)$ is approximately equal to $L(x)$ and that the approximation improves (in a precise sense) with increasing $x$.

In the Introduction, I said that problems are the life blood of a living science, and that the solution of a problem leads to the posing of new questions. This is borne out by the problem we have just discussed. Instead of considering *all* the primes, as we did above, we can restrict our attention to those ending in 7: 7, 17, 37, 47, 67, 97, 107, 127, 137, $\cdots$ . There are an infinite number of these, as Dirichlet proved. If $x$ is any number, say 100, we may now ask: How many primes ending in 7 are less than 100? A count shows that there are six. Can we again find a simple expression which gives the approximate number of primes ending in 7 less than or equal to any

[19] For the curve represents neither the logarithm of an integral, nor the integral of the logarithmic function, although both integrals and logarithms occur in the relevant formulas (see Note 17, formulas (5) and (6)).

[20] J. F. Encke (1791–1865) is known especially for his calculation of the periodic return of the comets named after him (discovered in 1818 by Pons in Marseille).

[21] Compare with Table 11, Chapter I. Notes 16 and 17 explain the relation between $L(x)$ and $Li(x)$.

number $x$, and such that the approximation improves (in a precise sense) with increasing $x$?

This problem was also solved by de la Vallée Poussin and Hadamard as a byproduct of their work on the prime number theorem. They proved that approximately one quarter of all the primes less than or equal to $x$ end in 7; and that the same [18] is true for the primes ending in 1, 3, and 9. This is not obvious, since it could easily happen that the primes of one class occur more frequently than those of another. Moreover, certain deviations (already studied by Tschebyschef [19]) can still be observed. These lead to further problems which have not yet been completely solved [20].

TABLE 12

Sequence of Integers 1–1440 in Columns of 12. Primes in Bold Face.

| 1 | **13** | 25 | **37** | 49 | **61** | **73** | 85 | **97** | **109** |
|---|---|---|---|---|---|---|---|---|---|
| **2** | 14 | 26 | 38 | 50 | 62 | 74 | 86 | 98 | 110 |
| **3** | 15 | 27 | 39 | 51 | 63 | 75 | 87 | 99 | 111 |
| 4 | 16 | 28 | 40 | 52 | 64 | 76 | 88 | 100 | 112 |
| **5** | **17** | **29** | **41** | **53** | 65 | 77 | **89** | **101** | **113** |
| 6 | 18 | 30 | 42 | 54 | 66 | 78 | 90 | 102 | 114 |
| **7** | **19** | **31** | **43** | 55 | **67** | **79** | 91 | **103** | 115 |
| 8 | 20 | 32 | 44 | 56 | 68 | 80 | 92 | 104 | 116 |
| 9 | 21 | 33 | 45 | 57 | 69 | 81 | 93 | 105 | 117 |
| 10 | 22 | 34 | 46 | 58 | 70 | 82 | 94 | 106 | 118 |
| **11** | **23** | 35 | **47** | **59** | **71** | **83** | 95 | **107** | 119 |
| 12 | 24 | 36 | 48 | 60 | 72 | 84 | 96 | 108 | 120 |

| 121 | 133 | 145 | **157** | 169 | **181** | **193** | 205 | 217 | **229** |
|---|---|---|---|---|---|---|---|---|---|
| 122 | 134 | 146 | 158 | 170 | 182 | 194 | 206 | 218 | 230 |
| 123 | 135 | 147 | 159 | 171 | 183 | 195 | 207 | 219 | 231 |
| 124 | 136 | 148 | 160 | 172 | 184 | 196 | 208 | 220 | 232 |
| 125 | **137** | **149** | 161 | **173** | 185 | **197** | 209 | 221 | **233** |
| 126 | 138 | 150 | 162 | 174 | 186 | 198 | 210 | 222 | 234 |
| **127** | **139** | **151** | **163** | 175 | 187 | **199** | **211** | **223** | 235 |
| 128 | 140 | 152 | 164 | 176 | 188 | 200 | 212 | 224 | 236 |
| 129 | 141 | 153 | 165 | 177 | 189 | 201 | 213 | 225 | 237 |
| 130 | 142 | 154 | 166 | 178 | 190 | 202 | 214 | 226 | 238 |
| **131** | 143 | 155 | **167** | **179** | **191** | 203 | 215 | **227** | **239** |
| 132 | 144 | 156 | 168 | 180 | 192 | 204 | 216 | 228 | 240 |

| **241** | 253 | 265 | **277** | 289 | 301 | **313** | 325 | **337** | **349** |
|---|---|---|---|---|---|---|---|---|---|
| 242 | 254 | 266 | 278 | 290 | 302 | 314 | 326 | 338 | 350 |
| 243 | 255 | 267 | 279 | 291 | 303 | 315 | 327 | 339 | 351 |
| 244 | 256 | 268 | 280 | 292 | 304 | 316 | 328 | 340 | 352 |
| 245 | **257** | **269** | **281** | **293** | 305 | **317** | 329 | 341 | **353** |
| 246 | 258 | 270 | 282 | 294 | 306 | 318 | 330 | 342 | 354 |
| 247 | 259 | **271** | **283** | 295 | **307** | 319 | **331** | 343 | 355 |
| 248 | 260 | 272 | 284 | 296 | 308 | 320 | 332 | 344 | 356 |
| 249 | 261 | 273 | 285 | 297 | 309 | 321 | 333 | 345 | 357 |
| 250 | 262 | 274 | 286 | 298 | 310 | 322 | 334 | 346 | 358 |
| **251** | **263** | 275 | 287 | 299 | **311** | 323 | 335 | **347** | **359** |
| 252 | 264 | 276 | 288 | 300 | 312 | 324 | 336 | 348 | 360 |

Table 12 is continued on the next page

TABLE 12 (continuation)

| | | | | | | | | | |
|---|---|---|---|---|---|---|---|---|---|
| 361 | **373** | 385 | **397** | **409** | **421** | **433** | 445 | **457** | 469 |
| 362 | 374 | 386 | 398 | 410 | 422 | 434 | 446 | 458 | 470 |
| 363 | 375 | 387 | 399 | 411 | 423 | 435 | 447 | 459 | 471 |
| 364 | 376 | 388 | 400 | 412 | 424 | 436 | 448 | 460 | 472 |
| 365 | 377 | **389** | **401** | 413 | 425 | 437 | **449** | **461** | 473 |
| 366 | 378 | 390 | 402 | 414 | 426 | 438 | 450 | 462 | 474 |
| **367** | **379** | 391 | 403 | 415 | 427 | **439** | 451 | **463** | 475 |
| 368 | 380 | 392 | 404 | 416 | 428 | 440 | 452 | 464 | 476 |
| 369 | 381 | 393 | 405 | 417 | 429 | 441 | 453 | 465 | 477 |
| 370 | 382 | 394 | 406 | 418 | 430 | 442 | 454 | 466 | 478 |
| 371 | **383** | 395 | 407 | **419** | **431** | **443** | 455 | **467** | **479** |
| 372 | 384 | 396 | 408 | 420 | 432 | 444 | 456 | 468 | 480 |

| | | | | | | | | | |
|---|---|---|---|---|---|---|---|---|---|
| 481 | 493 | 505 | 517 | 529 | **541** | 553 | 565 | **577** | 589 |
| 482 | 494 | 506 | 518 | 530 | 542 | 554 | 566 | 578 | 590 |
| 483 | 495 | 507 | 519 | 531 | 543 | 555 | 567 | 579 | 591 |
| 484 | 496 | 508 | 520 | 532 | 544 | 556 | 568 | 580 | 592 |
| 485 | 497 | **509** | **521** | 533 | 545 | **557** | **569** | 581 | **593** |
| 486 | 498 | 510 | 522 | 534 | 546 | 558 | 570 | 582 | 594 |
| **487** | **499** | 511 | **523** | 535 | **547** | 559 | **571** | 583 | 595 |
| 488 | 500 | 512 | 524 | 536 | 548 | 560 | 572 | 584 | 596 |
| 489 | 501 | 513 | 525 | 537 | 549 | 561 | 573 | 585 | 597 |
| 490 | 502 | 514 | 526 | 538 | 550 | 562 | 574 | 586 | 598 |
| **491** | **503** | 515 | 527 | 539 | 551 | **563** | 575 | **587** | **599** |
| 492 | 504 | 516 | 528 | 540 | 552 | 564 | 576 | 588 | 600 |

| | | | | | | | | | |
|---|---|---|---|---|---|---|---|---|---|
| **601** | **613** | 625 | 637 | 649 | **661** | **673** | 685 | 697 | **709** |
| 602 | 614 | 626 | 638 | 650 | 662 | 674 | 686 | 698 | 710 |
| 603 | 615 | 627 | 639 | 651 | 663 | 675 | 687 | 699 | 711 |
| 604 | 616 | 628 | 640 | 652 | 664 | 676 | 688 | 700 | 712 |
| 605 | **617** | 629 | **641** | **653** | 665 | **677** | 689 | **701** | 713 |
| 606 | 618 | 630 | 642 | 654 | 666 | 678 | 690 | 702 | 714 |
| **607** | **619** | **631** | **643** | 655 | 667 | 679 | **691** | 703 | 715 |
| 608 | 620 | 632 | 644 | 656 | 668 | 680 | 692 | 704 | 716 |
| 609 | 621 | 633 | 645 | 657 | 669 | 681 | 693 | 705 | 717 |
| 610 | 622 | 634 | 646 | 658 | 670 | 682 | 694 | 706 | 718 |
| 611 | 623 | 635 | **647** | **659** | 671 | **683** | 695 | 707 | **719** |
| 612 | 624 | 636 | 648 | 660 | 672 | 684 | 696 | 708 | 720 |

Table 12 is continued on the next page

TABLE 12 (continuation)

| 721 | **733** | 745 | **757** | **769** | 781 | 793 | 805 | 817 | **829** |
|---|---|---|---|---|---|---|---|---|---|
| 722 | 734 | 746 | 758 | 770 | 782 | 794 | 806 | 818 | 830 |
| 723 | 735 | 747 | 759 | 771 | 783 | 795 | 807 | 819 | 831 |
| 724 | 736 | 748 | 760 | 772 | 784 | 796 | 808 | 820 | 832 |
| 725 | 737 | 749 | **761** | **773** | 785 | **797** | **809** | **821** | 833 |
| 726 | 738 | 750 | 762 | 774 | 786 | 798 | 810 | 822 | 834 |
| **727** | **739** | **751** | 763 | 775 | **787** | 799 | **811** | **823** | 835 |
| 728 | 740 | 752 | 764 | 776 | 788 | 800 | 812 | 824 | 836 |
| 729 | 741 | 753 | 765 | 777 | 789 | 801 | 813 | 825 | 837 |
| 730 | 742 | 754 | 766 | 778 | 790 | 802 | 814 | 826 | 838 |
| 731 | **743** | 755 | 767 | 779 | 791 | 803 | 815 | **827** | **839** |
| 732 | 744 | 756 | 768 | 780 | 792 | 804 | 816 | 828 | 840 |

| 841 | **853** | 865 | **877** | 889 | 901 | 913 | 925 | **937** | 949 |
|---|---|---|---|---|---|---|---|---|---|
| 842 | 854 | 866 | 878 | 890 | 902 | 914 | 926 | 938 | 950 |
| 843 | 855 | 867 | 879 | 891 | 903 | 915 | 927 | 939 | 951 |
| 844 | 856 | 868 | 880 | 892 | 904 | 916 | 928 | 940 | 952 |
| 845 | **857** | 869 | **881** | 893 | 905 | 917 | **929** | **941** | **953** |
| 846 | 858 | 870 | 882 | 894 | 906 | 918 | 930 | 942 | 954 |
| 847 | **859** | 871 | **883** | 895 | **907** | **919** | 931 | 943 | 955 |
| 848 | 860 | 872 | 884 | 896 | 908 | 920 | 932 | 944 | 956 |
| 849 | 861 | 873 | 885 | 897 | 909 | 921 | 933 | 945 | 957 |
| 850 | 862 | 874 | 886 | 898 | 910 | 922 | 934 | 946 | 958 |
| 851 | **863** | 875 | **887** | 899 | **911** | 923 | 935 | **947** | 959 |
| 852 | 864 | 876 | 888 | 900 | 912 | 924 | 936 | 948 | 960 |

| 961 | 973 | 985 | **997** | **1009** | **1021** | **1033** | 1045 | 1057 | **1069** |
|---|---|---|---|---|---|---|---|---|---|
| 962 | 974 | 986 | 998 | 1010 | 1022 | 1034 | 1046 | 1058 | 1070 |
| 963 | 975 | 987 | 999 | 1011 | 1023 | 1035 | 1047 | 1059 | 1071 |
| 964 | 976 | 988 | 1000 | 1012 | 1024 | 1036 | 1048 | 1060 | 1072 |
| 965 | **977** | 989 | 1001 | **1013** | 1025 | 1037 | **1049** | **1061** | 1073 |
| 966 | 978 | 990 | 1002 | 1014 | 1026 | 1038 | 1050 | 1062 | 1074 |
| **967** | 979 | **991** | 1003 | 1015 | 1027 | **1039** | **1051** | **1063** | 1075 |
| 968 | 980 | 992 | 1004 | 1016 | 1028 | 1040 | 1052 | 1064 | 1076 |
| 969 | 981 | 993 | 1005 | 1017 | 1029 | 1041 | 1053 | 1065 | 1077 |
| 970 | 982 | 994 | 1006 | 1018 | 1030 | 1042 | 1054 | 1066 | 1078 |
| **971** | **983** | 995 | 1007 | **1019** | **1031** | 1043 | 1055 | 1067 | 1079 |
| 972 | 984 | 996 | 1008 | 1020 | 1032 | 1044 | 1056 | 1068 | 1080 |

Table 12 is continued on the next page

TABLE 12 (continuation)

| | | | | | | | | | |
|---|---|---|---|---|---|---|---|---|---|
| 1081 | **1093** | 1105 | **1117** | **1129** | 1141 | **1153** | 1165 | 1177 | 1189 |
| 1082 | 1094 | 1106 | 1118 | 1130 | 1142 | 1154 | 1166 | 1178 | 1190 |
| 1083 | 1095 | 1107 | 1119 | 1131 | 1143 | 1155 | 1167 | 1179 | 1191 |
| 1084 | 1096 | 1108 | 1120 | 1132 | 1144 | 1156 | 1168 | 1180 | 1192 |
| 1085 | **1097** | **1109** | 1121 | 1133 | 1145 | 1157 | 1169 | **1181** | **1193** |
| 1086 | 1098 | 1110 | 1122 | 1134 | 1146 | 1158 | 1170 | 1182 | 1194 |
| **1087** | 1099 | 1111 | **1123** | 1135 | 1147 | 1159 | **1171** | 1183 | 1195 |
| 1088 | 1100 | 1112 | 1124 | 1136 | 1148 | 1160 | 1172 | 1184 | 1196 |
| 1089 | 1101 | 1113 | 1125 | 1137 | 1149 | 1161 | 1173 | 1185 | 1197 |
| 1090 | 1102 | 1114 | 1126 | 1138 | 1150 | 1162 | 1174 | 1186 | 1198 |
| **1091** | **1103** | 1115 | 1127 | 1139 | **1151** | **1163** | 1175 | **1187** | 1199 |
| 1092 | 1104 | 1116 | 1128 | 1140 | 1152 | 1164 | 1176 | 1188 | 1200 |

| | | | | | | | | | |
|---|---|---|---|---|---|---|---|---|---|
| **1201** | **1213** | 1225 | **1237** | **1249** | 1261 | 1273 | 1285 | **1297** | 1309 |
| 1202 | 1214 | 1226 | 1238 | 1250 | 1262 | 1274 | 1286 | 1298 | 1310 |
| 1203 | 1215 | 1227 | 1239 | 1251 | 1263 | 1275 | 1287 | 1299 | 1311 |
| 1204 | 1216 | 1228 | 1240 | 1252 | 1264 | 1276 | 1288 | 1300 | 1312 |
| 1205 | **1217** | **1229** | 1241 | 1253 | 1265 | **1277** | **1289** | **1301** | 1313 |
| 1206 | 1218 | 1230 | 1242 | 1254 | 1266 | 1278 | 1290 | 1302 | 1314 |
| 1207 | 1219 | **1231** | 1243 | 1255 | 1267 | **1279** | **1291** | **1303** | 1315 |
| 1208 | 1220 | 1232 | 1244 | 1256 | 1268 | 1280 | 1292 | 1304 | 1316 |
| 1209 | 1221 | 1233 | 1245 | 1257 | 1269 | 1281 | 1293 | 1305 | 1317 |
| 1210 | 1222 | 1234 | 1246 | 1258 | 1270 | 1282 | 1294 | 1306 | 1318 |
| 1211 | **1223** | 1235 | 1247 | **1259** | 1271 | **1283** | 1295 | **1307** | **1319** |
| 1212 | 1224 | 1236 | 1248 | 1260 | 1272 | 1284 | 1296 | 1308 | 1320 |

| | | | | | | | | | |
|---|---|---|---|---|---|---|---|---|---|
| **1321** | 1333 | 1345 | 1357 | 1369 | **1381** | 1393 | 1405 | 1417 | **1429** |
| 1322 | 1334 | 1346 | 1358 | 1370 | 1382 | 1394 | 1406 | 1418 | 1430 |
| 1323 | 1335 | 1347 | 1359 | 1371 | 1383 | 1395 | 1407 | 1419 | 1431 |
| 1324 | 1336 | 1348 | 1360 | 1372 | 1384 | 1396 | 1408 | 1420 | 1432 |
| 1325 | 1337 | 1349 | **1361** | **1373** | 1385 | 1397 | **1409** | 1421 | **1433** |
| 1326 | 1338 | 1350 | 1362 | 1374 | 1386 | 1398 | 1410 | 1422 | 1434 |
| **1327** | 1339 | 1351 | 1363 | 1375 | 1387 | **1399** | 1411 | **1423** | 1435 |
| 1328 | 1340 | 1352 | 1364 | 1376 | 1388 | 1400 | 1412 | 1424 | 1436 |
| 1329 | 1341 | 1353 | 1365 | 1377 | 1389 | 1401 | 1413 | 1425 | 1437 |
| 1330 | 1342 | 1354 | 1366 | 1378 | 1390 | 1402 | 1414 | 1426 | 1438 |
| 1331 | 1343 | 1355 | **1367** | 1379 | 1391 | 1403 | 1415 | **1427** | **1439** |
| 1332 | 1344 | 1356 | 1368 | 1380 | 1392 | 1404 | 1416 | 1428 | 1440 |

TABLE 13

Sequence of Integers 1–1440 in Columns of 9. Primes in Bold Face.

| | | | | | | | | | |
|---|---|---|---|---|---|---|---|---|---|
| 1 | 10 | **19** | 28 | **37** | 46 | 55 | 64 | **73** | 82 |
| **2** | **11** | 20 | **29** | 38 | **47** | 56 | 65 | 74 | **83** |
| **3** | 12 | 21 | 30 | 39 | 48 | 57 | 66 | 75 | 84 |
| 4 | **13** | 22 | **31** | 40 | 49 | 58 | **67** | 76 | 85 |
| **5** | 14 | **23** | 32 | **41** | 50 | **59** | 68 | 77 | 86 |
| 6 | 15 | 24 | 33 | 42 | 51 | 60 | 69 | 78 | 87 |
| **7** | 16 | 25 | 34 | **43** | 52 | **61** | 70 | **79** | 88 |
| 8 | **17** | 26 | 35 | 44 | **53** | 62 | **71** | 80 | **89** |
| 9 | 18 | 27 | 36 | 45 | 54 | 63 | 72 | 81 | 90 |

| | | | | | | | | | |
|---|---|---|---|---|---|---|---|---|---|
| 91 | 100 | **109** | 118 | **127** | 136 | 145 | 154 | **163** | 172 |
| 92 | **101** | 110 | 119 | 128 | **137** | 146 | 155 | 164 | **173** |
| 93 | 102 | 111 | 120 | 129 | 138 | 147 | 156 | 165 | 174 |
| 94 | **103** | 112 | 121 | 130 | **139** | 148 | **157** | 166 | 175 |
| 95 | 104 | **113** | 122 | **131** | 140 | **149** | 158 | **167** | 176 |
| 96 | 105 | 114 | 123 | 132 | 141 | 150 | 159 | 168 | 177 |
| **97** | 106 | 115 | 124 | 133 | 142 | **151** | 160 | 169 | 178 |
| 98 | **107** | 116 | 125 | 134 | 143 | 152 | 161 | 170 | **179** |
| 99 | 108 | 117 | 126 | 135 | 144 | 153 | 162 | 171 | 180 |

| | | | | | | | | | |
|---|---|---|---|---|---|---|---|---|---|
| **181** | 190 | **199** | 208 | 217 | 226 | 235 | 244 | 253 | 262 |
| 182 | **191** | 200 | 209 | 218 | **227** | 236 | 245 | 254 | **263** |
| 183 | 192 | 201 | 210 | 219 | 228 | 237 | 246 | 255 | 264 |
| 184 | **193** | 202 | **211** | 220 | **229** | 238 | 247 | 256 | 265 |
| 185 | 194 | 203 | 212 | 221 | 230 | **239** | 248 | **257** | 266 |
| 186 | 195 | 204 | 213 | 222 | 231 | 240 | 249 | 258 | 267 |
| 187 | 196 | 205 | 214 | **223** | 232 | **241** | 250 | 259 | 268 |
| 188 | **197** | 206 | 215 | 224 | **233** | 242 | **251** | 260 | **269** |
| 189 | 198 | 207 | 216 | 225 | 234 | 243 | 252 | 261 | 270 |

| | | | | | | | | | |
|---|---|---|---|---|---|---|---|---|---|
| **271** | 280 | 289 | 298 | **307** | 316 | 325 | 334 | 343 | 352 |
| 272 | **281** | 290 | 299 | 308 | **317** | 326 | 335 | 344 | **353** |
| 273 | 282 | 291 | 300 | 309 | 318 | 327 | 336 | 345 | 354 |
| 274 | **283** | 292 | 301 | 310 | 319 | 328 | **337** | 346 | 355 |
| 275 | 284 | **293** | 302 | **311** | 320 | 329 | 338 | **347** | 356 |
| 276 | 285 | 294 | 303 | 312 | 321 | 330 | 339 | 348 | 357 |
| **277** | 286 | 295 | 304 | **313** | 322 | **331** | 340 | **349** | 358 |
| 278 | 287 | 296 | 305 | 314 | 323 | 332 | 341 | 350 | **359** |
| 279 | 288 | 297 | 306 | 315 | 324 | 333 | 342 | 351 | 360 |

Table 13 is continued on the next page

TABLE 13 (continuation)

| 361 | 370 | **379** | 388 | **397** | 406 | 415 | 424 | **433** | 442 |
|---|---|---|---|---|---|---|---|---|---|
| 362 | 371 | 380 | **389** | 398 | 407 | 416 | 425 | 434 | **443** |
| 363 | 372 | 381 | 390 | 399 | 408 | 417 | 426 | 435 | 444 |
| 364 | **373** | 382 | 391 | 400 | **409** | 418 | 427 | 436 | 445 |
| 365 | 374 | **383** | 392 | **401** | 410 | **419** | 428 | 437 | 446 |
| 366 | 375 | 384 | 393 | 402 | 411 | 420 | 429 | 438 | 447 |
| **367** | 376 | 385 | 394 | 403 | 412 | **421** | 430 | **439** | 448 |
| 368 | 377 | 386 | 395 | 404 | 413 | 422 | **431** | 440 | **449** |
| 369 | 378 | 387 | 396 | 405 | 414 | 423 | 432 | 441 | 450 |

| 451 | 460 | 469 | 478 | **487** | 496 | 505 | 514 | **523** | 532 |
|---|---|---|---|---|---|---|---|---|---|
| 452 | **461** | 470 | **479** | 488 | 497 | 506 | 515 | 524 | 533 |
| 453 | 462 | 471 | 480 | 489 | 498 | 507 | 516 | 525 | 534 |
| 454 | **463** | 472 | 481 | 490 | **499** | 508 | 517 | 526 | 535 |
| 455 | 464 | 473 | 482 | **491** | 500 | **509** | 518 | 527 | 536 |
| 456 | 465 | 474 | 483 | 492 | 501 | 510 | 519 | 528 | 537 |
| **457** | 466 | 475 | 484 | 493 | 502 | 511 | 520 | 529 | 538 |
| 458 | **467** | 476 | 485 | 494 | **503** | 512 | **521** | 530 | 539 |
| 459 | 468 | 477 | 486 | 495 | 504 | 513 | 522 | 531 | 540 |

| **541** | 550 | 559 | 568 | **577** | 586 | 595 | 604 | **613** | 622 |
|---|---|---|---|---|---|---|---|---|---|
| 542 | 551 | 560 | **569** | 578 | **587** | 596 | 605 | 614 | 623 |
| 543 | 552 | 561 | 570 | 579 | 588 | 597 | 606 | 615 | 624 |
| 544 | 553 | 562 | **571** | 580 | 589 | 598 | **607** | 616 | 625 |
| 545 | 554 | **563** | 572 | 581 | 590 | **599** | 608 | **617** | 626 |
| 546 | 555 | 564 | 573 | 582 | 591 | 600 | 609 | 618 | 627 |
| **547** | 556 | 565 | 574 | 583 | 592 | **601** | 610 | **619** | 628 |
| 548 | **557** | 566 | 575 | 584 | **593** | 602 | 611 | 620 | 629 |
| 549 | 558 | 567 | 576 | 585 | 594 | 603 | 612 | 621 | 630 |

| **631** | 640 | 649 | 658 | 667 | 676 | 685 | 694 | 703 | 712 |
|---|---|---|---|---|---|---|---|---|---|
| 632 | **641** | 650 | **659** | 668 | **677** | 686 | 695 | 704 | 713 |
| 633 | 642 | 651 | 660 | 669 | 678 | 687 | 696 | 705 | 714 |
| 634 | **643** | 652 | **661** | 670 | 679 | 688 | 697 | 706 | 715 |
| 635 | 644 | **653** | 662 | 671 | 680 | 689 | 698 | 707 | 716 |
| 636 | 645 | 654 | 663 | 672 | 681 | 690 | 699 | 708 | 717 |
| 637 | 646 | 655 | 664 | **673** | 682 | **691** | 700 | **709** | 718 |
| 638 | **647** | 656 | 665 | 674 | **683** | 692 | **701** | 710 | **719** |
| 639 | 648 | 657 | 666 | 675 | 684 | 693 | 702 | 711 | 720 |

Table 13 is continued on the next page

TABLE 13 (continuation)

| 721 | 730 | **739** | 748 | **757** | 766 | 775 | 784 | 793 | 802 |
|---|---|---|---|---|---|---|---|---|---|
| 722 | 731 | 740 | 749 | 758 | 767 | 776 | 785 | 794 | 803 |
| 723 | 732 | 741 | 750 | 759 | 768 | 777 | 786 | 795 | 804 |
| 724 | **733** | 742 | **751** | 760 | **769** | 778 | **787** | 796 | 805 |
| 725 | 734 | **743** | 752 | **761** | 770 | 779 | 788 | **797** | 806 |
| 726 | 735 | 744 | 753 | 762 | 771 | 780 | 789 | 798 | 807 |
| **727** | 736 | 745 | 754 | 763 | 772 | 781 | 790 | 799 | 808 |
| 728 | 737 | 746 | 755 | 764 | **773** | 782 | 791 | 800 | **809** |
| 729 | 738 | 747 | 756 | 765 | 774 | 783 | 792 | 801 | 810 |

| **811** | 820 | **829** | 838 | 847 | 856 | 865 | 874 | **883** | 892 |
|---|---|---|---|---|---|---|---|---|---|
| 812 | **821** | 830 | **839** | 848 | **857** | 866 | 875 | 884 | 893 |
| 813 | 822 | 831 | 840 | 849 | 858 | 867 | 876 | 885 | 894 |
| 814 | **823** | 832 | 841 | 850 | **859** | 868 | **877** | 886 | 895 |
| 815 | 824 | 833 | 842 | 851 | 860 | 869 | 878 | **887** | 896 |
| 816 | 825 | 834 | 843 | 852 | 861 | 870 | 879 | 888 | 897 |
| 817 | 826 | 835 | 844 | **853** | 862 | 871 | 880 | 889 | 898 |
| 818 | **827** | 836 | 845 | 854 | **863** | 872 | **881** | 890 | 899 |
| 819 | 828 | 837 | 846 | 855 | 864 | 873 | 882 | 891 | 900 |

| 901 | 910 | **919** | 928 | **937** | 946 | 955 | 964 | 973 | 982 |
|---|---|---|---|---|---|---|---|---|---|
| 902 | **911** | 920 | **929** | 938 | **947** | 956 | 965 | 974 | **983** |
| 903 | 912 | 921 | 930 | 939 | 948 | 957 | 966 | 975 | 984 |
| 904 | 913 | 922 | 931 | 940 | 949 | 958 | **967** | 976 | 985 |
| 905 | 914 | 923 | 932 | **941** | 950 | 959 | 968 | **977** | 986 |
| 906 | 915 | 924 | 933 | 942 | 951 | 960 | 969 | 978 | 987 |
| **907** | 916 | 925 | 934 | 943 | 952 | 961 | 970 | 979 | 988 |
| 908 | 917 | 926 | 935 | 944 | **953** | 962 | **971** | 980 | 989 |
| 909 | 918 | 927 | 936 | 945 | 954 | 963 | 972 | 981 | 990 |

| **991** | 1000 | **1009** | 1018 | 1027 | 1036 | 1045 | 1054 | **1063** | 1072 |
|---|---|---|---|---|---|---|---|---|---|
| 992 | 1001 | 1010 | **1019** | 1028 | 1037 | 1046 | 1055 | 1064 | 1073 |
| 993 | 1002 | 1011 | 1020 | 1029 | 1038 | 1047 | 1056 | 1065 | 1074 |
| 994 | 1003 | 1012 | **1021** | 1030 | **1039** | 1048 | 1057 | 1066 | 1075 |
| 995 | 1004 | **1013** | 1022 | **1031** | 1040 | **1049** | 1058 | 1067 | 1076 |
| 996 | 1005 | 1014 | 1023 | 1032 | 1041 | 1050 | 1059 | 1068 | 1077 |
| **997** | 1006 | 1015 | 1024 | **1033** | 1042 | **1051** | 1060 | **1069** | 1078 |
| 998 | 1007 | 1016 | 1025 | 1034 | 1043 | 1052 | **1061** | 1070 | 1079 |
| 999 | 1008 | 1017 | 1026 | 1035 | 1044 | 1053 | 1062 | 1071 | 1080 |

Table 13 is continued on the next page

TABLE 13 (continuation)

| 1081 | 1090 | 1099 | 1108 | **1117** | 1126 | 1135 | 1144 | **1153** | 1162 |
|---|---|---|---|---|---|---|---|---|---|
| 1082 | **1091** | 1100 | **1109** | 1118 | 1127 | 1136 | 1145 | 1154 | **1163** |
| 1083 | 1092 | 1101 | 1110 | 1119 | 1128 | 1137 | 1146 | 1155 | 1164 |
| 1084 | **1093** | 1102 | 1111 | 1120 | **1129** | 1138 | 1147 | 1156 | 1165 |
| 1085 | 1094 | **1103** | 1112 | 1121 | 1130 | 1139 | 1148 | 1157 | 1166 |
| 1086 | 1095 | 1104 | 1113 | 1122 | 1131 | 1140 | 1149 | 1158 | 1167 |
| **1087** | 1096 | 1105 | 1114 | **1123** | 1132 | 1141 | 1150 | 1159 | 1168 |
| 1088 | **1097** | 1106 | 1115 | 1124 | 1133 | 1142 | **1151** | 1160 | 1169 |
| 1089 | 1098 | 1107 | 1116 | 1125 | 1134 | 1143 | 1152 | 1161 | 1170 |
| | | | | | | | | | |
| **1171** | 1180 | 1189 | 1198 | 1207 | 1216 | 1225 | 1234 | 1243 | 1252 |
| 1172 | **1181** | 1190 | 1199 | 1208 | **1217** | 1226 | 1235 | 1244 | 1253 |
| 1173 | 1182 | 1191 | 1200 | 1209 | 1218 | 1227 | 1236 | 1245 | 1254 |
| 1174 | 1183 | 1192 | **1201** | 1210 | 1219 | 1228 | **1237** | 1246 | 1255 |
| 1175 | 1184 | **1193** | 1202 | 1211 | 1220 | **1229** | 1238 | 1247 | 1256 |
| 1176 | 1185 | 1194 | 1203 | 1212 | 1221 | 1230 | 1239 | 1248 | 1257 |
| 1177 | 1186 | 1195 | 1204 | **1213** | 1222 | **1231** | 1240 | **1249** | 1258 |
| 1178 | **1187** | 1196 | 1205 | 1214 | **1223** | 1232 | 1241 | 1250 | **1259** |
| 1179 | 1188 | 1197 | 1206 | 1215 | 1224 | 1233 | 1242 | 1251 | 1260 |
| | | | | | | | | | |
| 1261 | 1270 | **1279** | 1288 | **1297** | 1306 | 1315 | 1324 | 1333 | 1342 |
| 1262 | 1271 | 1280 | **1289** | 1298 | **1307** | 1316 | 1325 | 1334 | 1343 |
| 1263 | 1272 | 1281 | 1290 | 1299 | 1308 | 1317 | 1326 | 1335 | 1344 |
| 1264 | 1273 | 1282 | **1291** | 1300 | 1309 | 1318 | **1327** | 1336 | 1345 |
| 1265 | 1274 | **1283** | 1292 | **1301** | 1310 | **1319** | 1328 | 1337 | 1346 |
| 1266 | 1275 | 1284 | 1293 | 1302 | 1311 | 1320 | 1329 | 1338 | 1347 |
| 1267 | 1276 | 1285 | 1294 | **1303** | 1312 | **1321** | 1330 | 1339 | 1348 |
| 1268 | **1277** | 1286 | 1295 | 1304 | 1313 | 1322 | 1331 | 1340 | 1349 |
| 1269 | 1278 | 1287 | 1296 | 1305 | 1314 | 1323 | 1332 | 1341 | 1350 |
| | | | | | | | | | |
| 1351 | 1360 | 1369 | 1378 | 1387 | 1396 | 1405 | 1414 | **1423** | 1432 |
| 1352 | **1361** | 1370 | 1379 | 1388 | 1397 | 1406 | 1415 | 1424 | **1433** |
| 1353 | 1362 | 1371 | 1380 | 1389 | 1398 | 1407 | 1416 | 1425 | 1434 |
| 1354 | 1363 | 1372 | **1381** | 1390 | **1399** | 1408 | 1417 | 1426 | 1435 |
| 1355 | 1364 | **1373** | 1382 | 1391 | 1400 | **1409** | 1418 | **1427** | 1436 |
| 1356 | 1365 | 1374 | 1383 | 1392 | 1401 | 1410 | 1419 | 1428 | 1437 |
| 1357 | 1366 | 1375 | 1384 | 1393 | 1402 | 1411 | 1420 | **1429** | 1438 |
| 1358 | **1367** | 1376 | 1385 | 1394 | 1403 | 1412 | 1421 | 1430 | **1439** |
| 1359 | 1368 | 1377 | 1386 | 1395 | 1404 | 1413 | 1422 | 1431 | 1440 |

*Notes to Chapter VII*

# PRIME NUMBERS AGAIN—MORE ON THEIR DISTRIBUTION

**1** (p. 121). In Chapter I the natural numbers were arranged in columns of 10 for convenience. In this case, however, the arrangement has a meaning, which will become clear later.

**2** (p. 123). See {1}.

**3** (p. 123). For Dirichlet's original paper see {2}. For a preliminary announcement see {3}. The prerequisites for understanding Dirichlet's paper are an acquaintance with algebra, the integral calculus, and the meaning of convergence in the theory of infinite series.

Since then a great many mathematicians have tried to find a simpler proof. A few years ago a former student sent me a proof. His proof, however, was essentially the same as Legendre's and contained a gap in the very same place. Dirichlet also first tried Legendre's method without success.

For Legendre's attempt at a proof see {4}.

**4** (p. 124). The numbers 1, 5, 7, 11 of the living rows are characterized by the fact that each one of them is relatively prime to 12, that is, the greatest common divisor of each of these numbers and 12 is 1. This is not true of the dead rows: the greatest common divisor of each of 2, 3, 4, etc. and 12 is greater than 1.

The numbers of the $a$th row are of the form $a + 12n$; if $t$ is the greatest common divisor of $a$ and 12, $a + 12n$ is divisible by $t$ for every $n$, and is therefore not a prime if $t$ is greater than 1, i.e., if $a$ and 12 are not relatively prime.

**5** (p. 125). The numbers in the $a$th row now have the form $a + 9n$. The values of $a$ relatively prime to 9 are $a = 1, 2, 4, 5, 7$, and 8.

**6** (p. 125). Suppose there are $k$ numbers in each column; the natural numbers are then partitioned into $k$ rows. The numbers of the $a$th row, where $1 \leq a \leq k$, are of the form $a + kn$. Let $t$ be the greatest common divisor of $a$ and $k$, and suppose $t > 1$. If $a = tb$, $k = th$, then the numbers of the $a$th row are:

$$a = tb,\ a + k = t(b + h),\ a + 2k = t(b + 2h),\ \cdots .$$

The only possible prime in this row is $a = tb$, and this is a prime only if $b = 1$ and $t$ is a prime, that is, if the first number of row $a = t$ is a prime;[1] all other numbers in this row are divisible by $t$ and greater than $t$, and hence are not primes. Therefore, if $t > 1$, the corresponding row is a dead row.

[1] This is the case, for example, if $k = 10$ and $a = t = 2$.

If $t = 1$, i.e., $a$ and $k$ are relatively prime, the corresponding row is a living row. Dirichlet's theorem then states that every living row contains an infinite number of primes.

A sequence of numbers

$$a, a + k, a + 2k, a + 3k, \cdots, a + nk, \cdots$$

is called an arithmetic progression. An arithmetic progression is said to be relatively prime if $a$ and $k$ are relatively prime. Dirichlet's theorem may then be restated as: *A relatively prime arithmetic progression contains an infinite number of primes.*[2]

Dirichlet's theorem can be stated in a more elegant form by introducing another definition. Two numbers, $a$ and $b$, are said to be in the same residue class modulo $k$ (or $a \equiv b \bmod k$) if $a - b$ is divisible by $k$. Thus, the numbers 1, 11, 21, 31, $\cdots$ are all in the same residue class modulo 10, since the difference of any two of these numbers is divisible by 10. Further, if the natural numbers are divided into $k$ rows, as in the preceding examples, all the numbers of a given row are in the same residue class modulo $k$. Let us say that a row with initial number $a$, i.e., a residue class whose least number is $a$, is relatively prime if $a$ and $k$ are relatively prime. Then Dirichlet's theorem is: *A relatively prime residue class modulo $k$ contains an infinite number of primes.*

**7** (p. 125). See Kummer's memorial speech {5}, and Minkowski's speech on the occasion of the centennial of Dirichlet's birth {6}. See also {7}.

**8** (p. 126). The professional mathematician will know that we are referring to the class number of quadratic forms (1838), and the theory of units in a finite algebraic number field (1846).

**9** (p. 126). Number theoreticians denote this number by $\pi(x)$. But this number has nothing to do with the number $\pi$ which appears in the formulas $2\pi r$ and $\pi r^2$ for the circumference and area of a circle. Since we have already used this symbol in Chapter V, we do not wish to use it here with an entirely different meaning.

**10** (p. 130). We shall add a few remarks on conic sections for those acquainted with geometric constructions. We begin with the ellipse. The plane $\zeta$ of Fig. 95 is the plane perpendicular to the plane of the floor $\epsilon$ and containing the light source $L$ and the light rays $a$ and $b$. The perpendicular from $L$ to the floor intersects the plane $\epsilon$ in the point $K$; the straight line $e$ is the intersection of the plane $\zeta$ with the plane $\epsilon$. The angle $ALB$ formed by the light rays $a$ and $b$ is called the opening angle of the light cone. It is easy to see that the bisector $m$ of the angle $ALB$ is the axis or line of symmetry of the light cone. The point $M$ is the point of interesection of $m$ with

[2] In an arithmetic progression whose general term is $a + pn$, $a$ is called the first term and $k$ is called the difference. See the title of Dirichlet's paper in {2}.

René Descartes (1596-1650) · August Ferdinand Möbius (1790-1868)
Ferdinand Lindemann (1852-1939) · Henri Poincaré (1854-1912)

PLATE X

Pafnutij Liwowitsch Tschebyschef (1821-1894) · Gustav Lejeune Dirichlet (1805-1859)
Emmy Noether (1882-1935) · Richard Dedekind (1831-1916)

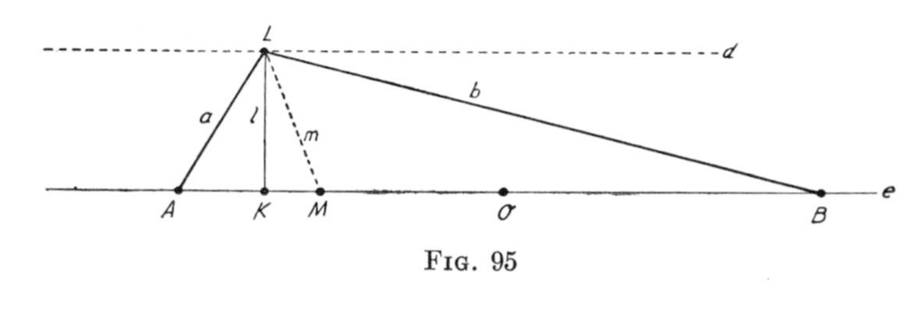


FIG. 95

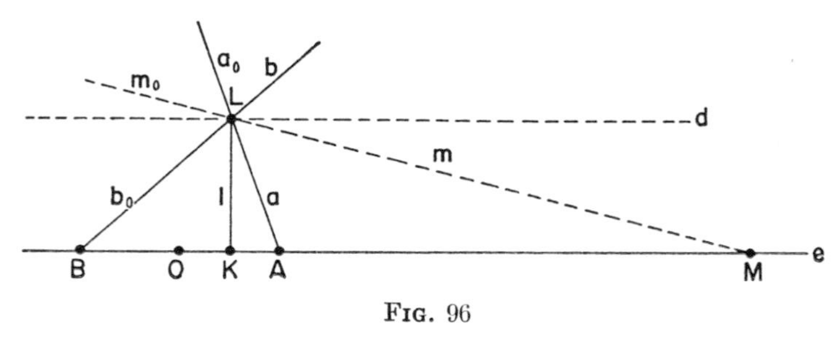


FIG. 96

the plane of the floor $\epsilon$. If the light were directed perpendicularly to the floor (making the ellipse a circle), $m$ would coincide with $l$, and $M$ with $K$; the rays $a$, $b$ would then meet the floor at the two points $A$, $B$ equidistant from $K$. But in the case illustrated in Fig. 95, $AM$ is of course shorter than $MB$. Hence, if $O$ is the midpoint of $AB$, $O$ must lie between $M$ and $B$. (Since $AB$ is the major axis of the ellipse, $O$ is the center of the ellipse.)

Fig. 96 illustrates the analogous situation for the case when the conic section is a hyperbola. In Fig. 96, $L$, $l$, $K$, $e$, $a$, $b$, $m$, $M$ have the same meaning as before; $A$ is again the point of intersection of the light ray $a$ with the floor; but $B$ is now the point of intersection of the floor with the extension $b_0$ of the ray $b$. The rays $a_0$, $b_0$ have the same meaning for the light cone emanating from the point $L$, but in the reverse direction, as do $a$, $b$ for the first light cone; $m_0$ is the axis of the second light cone. $A$ and $B$ are the two vertices of the hyperbola; the midpoint $O$ of $AB$ is now the center of the hyperbola.

The two straight lines passing through the center $O$ of the hyperbola, called its asymptotes, are now of interest. To obtain these lines, let us imagine the whole room in addition to the plane $\zeta$ of Fig. 96. We denote by $\delta$ the plane through the light source $L$ parallel to the floor $\epsilon$. The plane $\delta$ intersects the plane $\zeta$ in a straight line $d$ (Fig. 96). The plane $\delta$ intersects the boundary of the two light cones in two straight lines passing through $L$ (one of these straight lines runs to the right of $L$ in front of the plane $\zeta$ and to the left of $L$ behind the plane $\zeta$; the other straight line runs to the right of $L$ behind the plane $\zeta$, and to the left of $L$ in front of $\zeta$). The asymptotes of the hyperbola are then the two lines in the floor $\epsilon$ which pass through $O$ and are parallel to the lines through $L$ in the plane $\delta$ described above. It can easily be shown that the asymptotes are limiting curves for the branches of the hyperbola, in the sense that as one goes farther along a branch, one approaches nearer and nearer to the corresponding asymptote.

**11** (p. 130). This can be done easily by holding a lamp whose opening angle is exactly 90° directly over the point $O$ at a distance $OA = \sqrt{2}$ from the plane of Fig. 91a, and setting the axis of the light cone parallel to the line $OA$. The hyperbola of Fig. 91 can be obtained only with a lamp whose opening angle is at least 90°.

**12** (p. 130). By the Pythagorean theorem, $OA = \sqrt{2}$, and therefore $AB$, the axis of the hyperbola, is $2\sqrt{2}$.

**13** (p. 130). This area has certain properties, which will be needed in the sequel. This is, therefore, a good place to point them out. If $x = OQ$, denote by $F(x)$ the shaded area in Fig. 91b. For instance, if $x = 5$ in Fig. 91b, the appropriate calculations (see Note 17) show that the shaded area is $1.61\cdots$; hence

$$F(5) = 1.61.\cdots.$$

First, we examine what happens to $F(x)$ as $x$ increases. It is clear that the shaded area increases as $x$ moves to the right; however, does it increase without bound? In other words, is the shaded area always less than some fixed number no matter how large $x$ is (in that case, we would say that $F(x)$ is bounded), or does it exceed any prescribed value for sufficiently large $x$ (in this case we would say that $F(x)$ is without bound or unbounded)? For instance, is it possible to find a value of $x$ for which $F(x) > 1000$? We shall show that $F(x)$ does indeed increase without bound as $x$ increases,[3] in spite of the fact that the hyperbola itself approaches the $x$-axis with increasing $x$. To this end, we consider in Fig. 97 various positions of the point $Q$ and the point $P$ on the curve corresponding to $Q$. The points $Q$ we have chosen and the corresponding values of $x$ are: $Q_2$, $x = 2$; $Q_4$, $x = 2^2 = 4$; $Q_8$, $x = 2^3 = 8$; and, in general, $Q_{2^n}$, $x = 2^n$ (this point is not shown in the figure). The corresponding points $P$ on the curve have heights: $Q_2P_2 = 1/2$, $Q_4P_4 = 1/4$, $Q_8P_8 = 1/8$, $\cdots$, $Q_{2^n}P_{2^n} = 1/2^n$. We now calculate the areas of the rectangles below the curve—the areas of the *lower* rectangles. The area of the rectangle with base $Q_2Q_4$ is $Q_2Q_4 \cdot Q_4P_4 = 2(1/2^2) = 1/2$; the area of the rectangle with base $Q_4Q_8$ is $Q_4Q_8 \cdot Q_8P_8 = (2^3 - 2^2)(1/2^3) = 1/2$; in general, the rectangle with base $Q_{2^{n-1}}Q_{2^n}$ is $Q_{2^{n-1}}Q_{2^n} \cdot Q_{2^n}P_{2^n} = (2^n - 2^{n-1})(1/2^n) = 2^{n-1}(1/2^n) = 1/2$. Hence all the lower rectangles have the same area, $1/2$.

[3] An example of a similar curve for which the corresponding area is always less than a fixed number is given in Footnote 4.

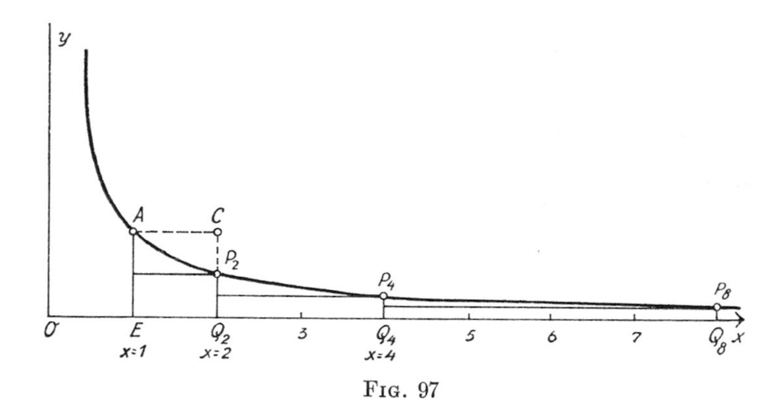


FIG. 97

It is also clear that the area under the curve bounded by $EA$, the $x$-axis, and any of the lines $QP$ is greater than the sum of the areas of the lower rectangles up to the line $QP$. Thus,

$$F(2) > \tfrac{1}{2},$$
$$F(2^2) = F(4) > \tfrac{1}{2} + \tfrac{1}{2},$$
$$F(2^3) = F(8) > \tfrac{1}{2} + \tfrac{1}{2} + \tfrac{1}{2} = \tfrac{3}{2},$$

and, in general,

$$F(2^n) > n(\tfrac{1}{2}).$$

From this it is clear that $F(x)$ will exceed any arbitrarily chosen number for sufficiently large $x$. Hence $F(x)$ increases without bound as $x$ increases.[4] For example, $F(x) > 1000$, if $n = 2000$, i.e. if $x = 2^n = 2^{2000}$.[5]

From Fig. 97 we see that the shaded area whose value is $F(2)$ is contained in the square $EQ_2CA$. Since the side of this square has length 1, its area is also 1; therefore,

$$F(2) < 1.$$

The *second* assertion concerns the value of $F(3)$. We assert that $F(3) > 1$. In Fig. 98, the interval from $x = 1$ to $x = 3$ is divided into 8 equal subintervals; since $EQ_3 = 2$, the length of each subinterval is $\tfrac{1}{4}$. Hence if the points of division are $H_1, H_2, \cdots, H_7$, we have

$$EH_1 = H_1H_2 = \cdots = H_6H_7 = H_7Q_3 = \tfrac{1}{4}.$$

[4] In the case of the curve whose equation is $x^2y = 1$ or $y = 1/x^2$, the corresponding shaded areas would always be less than 1.

[5] $2^{2000}$ (the 2000th power of 2) is a number with 603 digits, of which the first four are 1148; it may be written as $1.148 \cdots \times 10^{602}$. Actually, it can be shown that $F(x) > 1000$ if $x = 1.971 \times 10^{434}$.

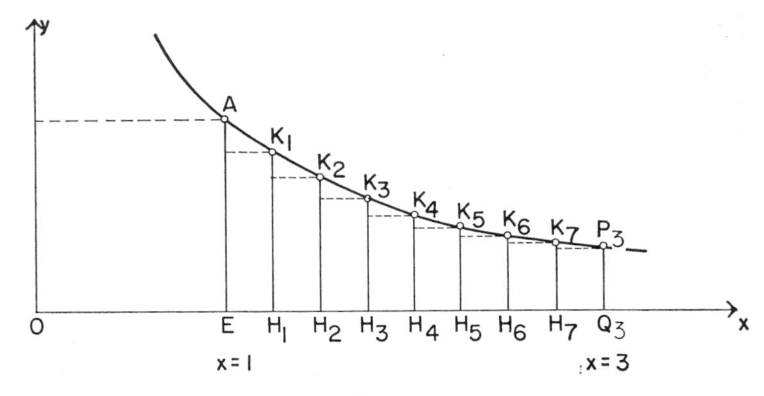


FIG. 98

It is then clear from Fig. 98 that the sum of the areas of the lower rectangles erected on the bases $EH_1$, $H_1H_2$, etc. with heights $H_1K_1$, $H_2K_2$, etc. is less than the area under the hyperbola bounded by the $x$-axis and the lines $EA$ and $Q_3P_3$, that is, this sum is less than $F(3)$. Since

$$OE_1 = 1, OH_1 = 1 + 1/4 = 5/4, OH_2 = 1 + 2/4 = 6/4, \cdots,$$
$$OH_7 = 1 + 7/4 = 11/4, OH_8 = 1 + 8/4 = 12/4 = 3,$$

we have

$$H_1K_1 = 4/5, H_2K_2 = 4/6, H_3K_3 = 4/7, \cdots, H_7K_7 = 4/11, Q_3P_3 = 4/12.$$

Therefore, the sum of the areas of the lower rectangles in question is

$$(1/4)(4/5 + 4/6 + \cdots + 4/11 + 4/12) = 28271/27720.$$

Hence $F(3) > 28271/27720 > 1$.

Since $F(2) < 1$ and $F(3) > 1$, it follows that there is a value of $x$ between 2 and 3 for which $F(x) = 1$. This value of $x$ is a very important number; in 1731 Euler denoted this number by $e$, and this notation has been in common use since then.[6] The number $e$ to the first thirteen decimal places is:

$$e = 2.7182818284590 \cdots.$$

The numer $e$ is no less important in analysis than the number $\pi$. (See Chapter V, end of Note 8.)

**14** (p. 130). The transition from Fig. 91 to Fig. 92 is most simply explained by using Fig. 99a–g. Fig. 99a shows the graph of the curve $y = 1/x$ (the same curve as that in Fig. 91). Curve II in Fig. 99b is the graph of $y = F(x)$, that is, at each value of $x$ it shows the value of the shaded

[6] The number $e$ is the base of the natural logarithms. The function $F(x)$ defined above is actually the logarithm of $x$ to the base $e$: $F(x) = \log_e x$.

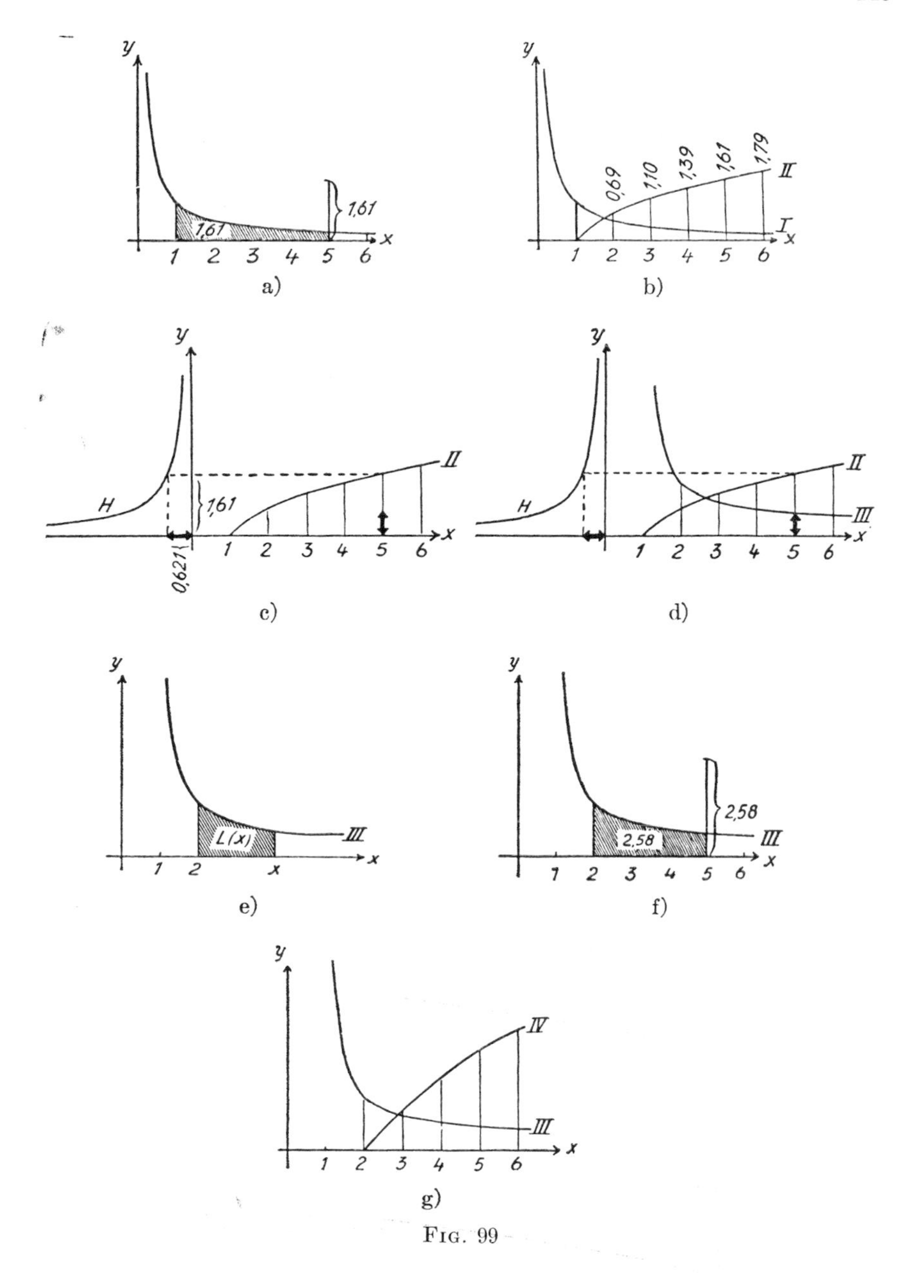


FIG. 99

area in Fig. 99a from 1 to $x$. Curve I in Fig. 99b is merely the curve of Fig. 99a redrawn. Thus, in Fig. 99b, $F(1) = 0$, $F(5) = 1.61 \cdots$, etc.

The next step is shown in Fig. 99c, where the curve $H$ is the branch of the hyperbola of Fig. 99a reflected about the $y$-axis. The other curve

(curve II) of Fig. 99c is the same as curve II of Fig. 99b. Now, for every $x$, find the corresponding point on curve II, project this point onto the curve $H$ (by means of the horizontal dotted line), and finally project the last point onto the $x$-axis (by means of the vertical dotted line; Fig. 99c shows the process for $x = 5$). This procedure defines another function of $x$, and the graph of this function is shown as curve III in Fig. 99d. It is clear from the procedure used to obtain curve III that it is the graph of the function $y = 1/F(x)$ for $x > 1$.

We now consider for $x > 2$ the area under the curve III (reproduced in Fig. 99e) and above the $x$-axis from 2 to $x$. This area is denoted by $L(x)$, and from Fig. 99f we see that, for instance, $L(5) = 2.58$ (the value of $L(x)$ at this point is the height of the vertical line at $x = 5$ in Fig. 99f). The graph of the function $y = L(x)$ is shown by curve IV in Fig. 99g. The same curve is shown in Fig. 92.

In order to show the values of $L(x)$ for large values of $x$, the graph of $L(x)$ is drawn in Fig. 93 on a smaller scale; and in Fig. 94 on a still smaller scale. Thus, for example, we see from Fig. 94 that $L(900)$ is approximately 162. For convenience, Figs. 93 and 94 are reproduced in Figs. 100 and 101. We shall return to these figures in Note 18.

**15** (p. 133). We have used the phrase *geometric relations* in describing the transition from the hyperbola of Fig. 91 to the curve of Fig. 92 (curve of the integral logarithm). A technical mathematical explanation would use different language. Above all, the connection between two very different fields of mathematics, which is what we are dealing with here, would be described in quite other terms. The prime number problems we are discussing are concerned only with whole numbers (in fact, positive whole numbers or natural numbers). Both the definition of prime number and

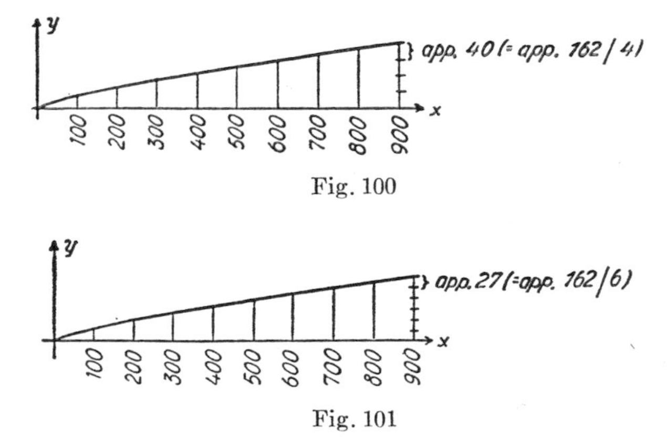


Fig. 100



Fig. 101

the question of how many primes are less than or equal to a given natural number involves only the natural numbers. However, the case of the hyperbola is another matter. In the functional relation $y = 1/x$, both $x$ and $y$ take on values which are not always whole numbers: $x$ and $y$ take on all real values (such as $e$, $\pi$, $\sqrt{2}$, etc.) and $y$ varies continuously with $x$. Whole numbers, on the other hand change by jumps, from 1 to 2, 2 to 3, etc. In other words, prime number problems deal with discrete variables; curves such as the hyperbola are defined for variables which are continuous.[7] It is of course also true that the domains and ranges of the other functions we have just considered (such as $F(x)$ and $L(x)$) consist of continuous variables.

The branch of mathematics which has to do with continuous variables and functions defined on them is called *analysis;* the study of the properties of the natural numbers, in particular the primes, is called *number theory.* The remarkable thing is then that a problem in number theory, that is, a discrete problem, seems to be intimately connected with analysis. This, however, is the case with the relation between the discrete function $N(x)$ and the continuous function $L(x)$.[8]

See Note 17 for a more technical discussion of the functions treated descriptively in this note.

**16** (p. 133). The actual integral logarithm curve, which we shall denote by $Li(x)$, is a slight modification of the curve $L(x)$ of Figs. 92, 93, 94. It is defined by the equation

$$\text{(A)} \qquad L(x) = Li(x) - Li(2)$$

(see Note 17). That is, $Li(x)$ is obtained from $L(x)$ by translating the curve $L(x)$ a distance of $Li(2) = 1.045$ in the vertical direction (see (6) at the end of Note 17).

However, since $L(x)$ and $Li(x)$ differ by a constant, there is no essential difference between the relation of $L(x)$ to $N(x)$ and that of $Li(x)$ to $N(x)$: both quotients $N(x){:}L(x)$ and $N(x){:}Li(X)$ approach 1 as $x$ increases (as can be surmised from Table 11, Chapter I). To see this, we note that, since $N(x)$ increases without bound as $x$ increases, the quotient $Li(2)/N(x) = 1.045/N(x)$ can be made arbitrarily small by choosing $x$ and hence $N(x)$ sufficiently large. From formula (A) we have

[7] The domain of the variables in the continuous case is the set of real numbers; in the discrete case, either the whole or the natural numbers. For a discussion of the real numbers see the last half of Chapter VIII.

[8] Such number theoretic problems, whose methods of solution require analytic methods, belong to the branch of mathematics called *analytic number theory*. Due to the work of Dirichlet (1837), Tschebyschef (1851–1852), Riemann (1860) and their successors, analytic number theory is now a very extensive field of research.

(B) $$N(x)/Li(x) = N(x)/(L(x) + Li(2)) = 1/[(L(x)/N(x)) + (Li(2)/N(x))],$$

and

(C) $$N(x)/L(x) = N(x)/(Li(x) - Li(2)) = 1/[(Li(x)/N(x)) - (Li(2)/N(x))].$$

It is possible to prove rigorously that $N(x)/L(x)$ approaches 1 as $x$ increases; the same sort of proof would show that the same is true for $L(x)/N(x)$. Since $Li(2)/N(x)$ approaches 0 as $x$ increases, $L(x)/N(x) + Li(2)/N(x)$ also approaches 1 as $x$ increases. Hence $N(x)/Li(x)$ approaches 1 as $x$ increases. But an analogous examination of (C) shows that the same is true for $N(x)/L(x)$ if $N(x)/Li(x)$ approaches 1 as $x$ increases.

**17** (p. 133). In this note we shall give a slightly more technical explanation of the steps leading up to the derivation of the integral logarithm function. We start with the hyperbola of Fig. 91, whose equation is

(1) $$xy = 1, \quad \text{or} \quad y = 1/x.$$

The shaded area of Fig. 91b or Fig. 99a, according to the integral calculus, is

(2) $$F(x) = \int_1^x dt/t.$$

Evaluating the integral, we obtain

(3) $$F(x) = \log_e x.$$

The heights or ordinates of the points of curve III are defined as the reciprocals of those of curve II. Hence the equation of curve III is

(4) $$y = 1/\log_e x.$$

Since the ordinate of each point of curve IV is defined as the value of the area under curve III above the $x$-axis from 2 to $x$, it again follows from the integral calculus that

(5) $$L(x) = \int_2^x dt/\log_e t.$$

The integral logarithm $Li(x)$ is defined in analysis as:

(6) $$Li(x) = \lim_{r\to 0^+} \left( \int_0^{1-r} (dt/\log_e t) + \int_{1+r}^x (dt/\log_e t) \right).$$

We have, therefore,

$$Li(x) - Li(2) = \lim_{r \to 0^+} \left( \int_0^{1-r} (dt/\log_e t) + \int_{1+r}^{x} (dt/\log_e t) \right)$$

$$- \lim_{r \to 0^+} \left( \int_0^{1-r} (dt/\log_e t) + \int_{1+r}^{2} (dt/\log_e t) \right)$$

$$= \int_2^x dt/\log_e t = L(x),$$

as we indicated in Note 16.

**18** (p. 134). We recall that, except for 2 and 5, all primes end with 1, 3, 7, or 9, and that each of these four classes of primes contains an infinite number of primes. Now, for large values of $x$, $N(x)$, the number of primes less than or equal to $x$, is approximated by $L(x)$. Let us denote by $N_i(x)$ (where $i = 1, 3, 7, 9$) the number of primes $\leq x$ in each of the classes of primes which end with the digits $i = 1, 3, 7$ or 9. The new proposition then asserts that $N_i(x)/(L(x)/4)$ approaches 1 as $x$ increases, i.e., $N_i(x)$ is approximately $L(x)/4$. For example, $L(900)$ is about 162 (see Fig. 100); hence $L(900)/4$ is about 40. By actual count, $N_1(900) = 36$, $N_3(900) = 40$, $N_7(900) = 40$, $N_9(900) = 36$.

In fact, a more general theorem is true. The classes of primes of the preceding paragraph are the residue classes of primes modulo 10 (see Note 6). The theorem is true also for the residue classes of primes with respect to an arbitrary modulus, if we take care to divide $L(x)$ by the number of such classes. For example, the residue classes of primes modulo 9 are the classes of primes which on division by 9 leave a remainder of 1, 2, 4, 5, 7, 8. There are thus 6 residue classes of primes modulo 9. If we denote by $M_i(x)$ (where $i = 1, 2, 4, 5, 7, 8$) the number of primes in each class $\leq x$, then the theorem asserts that $M_i(x){:}L(x)/6$ approaches 1 as $x$ increases. For instance, by actual count, $M_1(900) = 24$, $M_2(900) = 26$, $M_4(900) = 26$, $M_5(900) = 26$, $M_7(900) = 24$, $M_9(900) = 27$; and each of $M_i(x)$ is approximately $L(900)/6 = 162/6$ or approximately 27 (see Fig. 101).

**19** (p. 134). A nontechnical statement of the deviation is that for every natural number $m$ there is a natural number $x > m$ such that the number of primes of the form $4n + 3$ less than or equal to $x$ is greater than the number of primes of the form $4n + 1$ less than or equal to $x$; and that this deviation exceeds a certain expected deviation. In 1853 Tschebyschef asserted, and in 1891 E. Phragmen (1863–) proved, a theorem to this effect (see {8}). More recent research by J. E. Littlewood (1885–) indicates that in problems such as these, conjectures based on even a great deal of empirical evidence (for empirical evidence in support of such conjectures see {9}) may prove to be quite wrong (see {10}).

**20** (p. 134). Before leaving prime number theory, we would like to say a few words about one of Euclid's results, which was mentioned in Chapter I. In Chapter I we discussed the decomposition of natural numbers into prime factors. Thus, we can write

$$90 = 2 \cdot 45 = 2 \cdot 3 \cdot 15 = 2 \cdot 3 \cdot 3 \cdot 5.$$

But we can also write

$$90 = 9 \cdot 10 = 3 \cdot 3 \cdot 2 \cdot 5,$$

and

$$90 = 15 \cdot 6 = 3 \cdot 5 \cdot 2 \cdot 3.$$

We note that the same primes occur in all these decompositions, and that at most the order of writing the prime factors changes. Since the same is true for every particular number we examine, we have come to take the *uniqueness of prime factor decomposition* for granted and to regard it as self evident. But we have learned from considering other problems that a proposition which makes an assertion about an infinite number of cases cannot be proved by testing each case singly. It stands to reason, therefore, that we cannot test all numbers to see whether there is perhaps one which admits two essentially different prime factor decompositions, that is, two decompositions which differ not merely in the order in which the prime factors are written, but in the prime factors. For instance, the product of the primes 97 and 101 is 9797, and the product of the primes 41 and 239 is 9799, which differs very little from 9797.[9] It is then relevant to ask whether it is possible to obtain the same number as the product of different primes.

Is then the proposition which asserts the uniqueness (except for order) of prime factor decomposition valid? The problem of its validity rightly belongs at the very beginning of prime number theory, and its solution is already to be found in Book VII of Euclid's *Elements*.

In §24 of Book VII, in connection with the greatest common divisor of two numbers, [10] Euclid proves the following lemma: *If two numbers $a$ and $b$ are relatively prime to a number $c$, then $ab$ is relatively prime to $c$.* Since a prime is by definition a natural number which has no divisors except itself and 1, it is clear, furthermore, that two distinct primes are relatively prime.

[9] Another example: The product $17 \cdot 23 \cdot 947 = 370277$ differs very little from the product $43 \cdot 79 \cdot 109 = 370273$, and still less from the product $7 \cdot 13 \cdot 13 \cdot 313 = 370279$.

[10] Of importance in this connection is the Euclidean algorithm for determining the greatest common divisor of two numbers. Unfortunately, many presentations of elementary number theory, while recognizing the significance of the Euclidean algorithm for computing greatest common divisors, ignore the fact that the prime factorization theorem needs to be proved.

If we ask, for instance, whether the number

$$370279 = 7 \cdot 13^2 \cdot 313$$

is divisible by any prime $p$ different from 7, 13, or 313, we can see that the answer is negative by means of the following argument. For brevity, set

$$7 = q,\ 13 = r,\ 313 = s,\ 370279 = Z,$$

so that $Z = qr^2s$. Since $q$, $r$, $s$ are primes, they are relatively prime to $p$. Now, in the lemma, set $a = q$, $b = r$, $c = p$; then $qr$ is relatively prime to $p$. If in the lemma we set $a = qr$, $b = r$, and $c = p$, then $ab = qr^2$ is relatively prime to $p$. Finally, setting $a = qr^2$, $b = s$, and $c = p$, it follows that $(qr^2)s = Z$ is relatively prime to $p$. Hence $p$ cannot be a divisor of $Z$, and $Z$ cannot be divisible by any prime which differs from $q$, $r$ and $s$. Further, it is easy to see that $Z = qr^2s$ is not divisible by any power of $q$ and $s$ greater than 1[11] or by any power of $r$ greater than 2. This proves the uniqueness of the prime factor decomposition for $Z$, and in the same way for an arbitrary natural number.

[11] If, for instance, $Z = q(r^2s)$ were divisible by $q^2$, then $r^2s$ would be divisible by $q$; this is impossible since application of the lemma shows that $r^2s$ is relatively prime to $q$.

*Chapter VIII*

# COUNTING AND CALCULATING

In how many ways would our culture be different than it is, if man had six fingers on each hand instead of five? Manufacturing and handicraft, of course, are fields which are strongly influenced by the number of fingers, and other fields whose historical development has been critically or marginally influenced by the number of our fingers come to mind. But nowhere has the influence of our ten fingers been so primary, as on the first beginnings of mathematics, that is, on the theory of numbers. In primitive societies the ten fingers of man comprised a counting and calculating apparatus he carried with him wherever he went. Because of this counting machine, the numbers from one to ten each received a special name. But the usefulness of this machine was limited. If the number of objects to be counted, such as the sheep in a herd, exceeded ten, the fingers of both hands were soon used up. The solution to this problem is clearly reflected in the nomenclature of numbers. The name fourteen, for example, means that there are four objects more than the number of all the fingers.

It may of course happen that all the fingers are used twice but objects to be counted still remain. Thus, twice the total count of fingers and six objects more is called *twenty-six*, twenty signifying twice ten, twice the full count of all the fingers.

The names of the numbers: one, two, three, ···, ten, twenty, thirty, ··· are different, of course, in the various languages. Number symbols (see Fig. 102) have also differed widely. Those we are accustomed to, which we call Arabic numerals, came into use relatively late in history.[1] In primitive ages, before the invention of writing, there were *names* for numbers but no *number symbols*. *Without referring to any particular number symbols, or any particular language*, let us see how an extended counting process can be carried out using only the ten fingers of man. In one South African tribe, it goes along smoothly in the following manner [**2**].

Let us suppose that a chieftain wishes to count a large number of men. As they pass before him, an aide raises one finger for the first, another for the next, and so on, so long as he has a finger available. This purely mechanical process does not require speaking a word or making a mark. But when ten people have passed, the counting capacity of this aide is gone. In order to continue the count—as before, without uttering a sound or making a mark—a second aide must take up the job. To show that the first aide—who counted the units—is finished with the range of numbers

[1] Fig. 102 is taken from {1}. See also {2}, and Figs. 113a, b in the Notes to Chapter VIII. A great deal of material is to be found in historical works [**1**].

## *THE ORIGIN OF OUR NUMBERS*

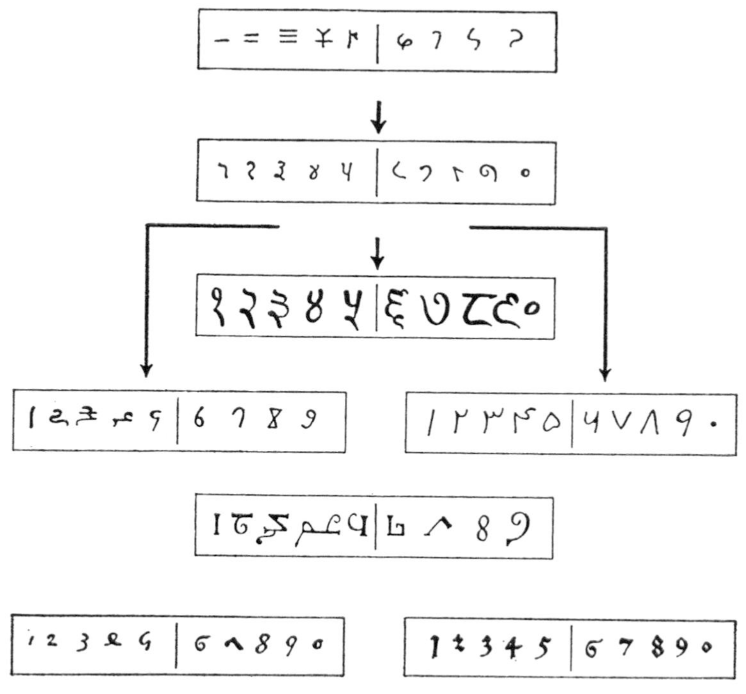

Fig. 102

represented by his fingers, the second aide raises a finger while the first lowers both hands. One finger of the second aide is equivalent to all ten of the first aide. In our words, the second aide counts the tens. Now when another man of the group to be counted comes along—we would say the eleventh—the first aide begins again, raising one finger for each man who passes. After fourteen men have passed, the second aide has one finger raised, while the first holds up four. Because this process is carried out without speaking or writing, but only with the counting apparatus which man carries with him on his two hands, we see that our system of units and tens derives from our own bodies. After twenty—that is after ten and again ten—men have filed past, the first aide will again have all his fingers raised, and his counting capacity will again be exhausted. This will cause the second aide to raise his second finger as the first lowers his hands. The two raised fingers of the second aide represent as many counted men as twice the full finger count of the first aide. After ten times ten—in our words a hundred—have passed, the first aide will have exhausted his fingers for the tenth time, and the second aide will have raised his tenth finger, thus reaching the end of his counting capacity. A third aide will now be required. He will raise one finger to signify that the second aide has exhausted his counting capacity, while the second aide lowers all his. The fact that a hundred persons have passed before the Chief is symbolized by the picture of the first two aides standing with lowered hands, while the third—who counts the hundreds—has one finger raised. Now the first and second aide can start counting all over again, and only when they have reached the end of their counting capacity, i.e., when two hundred persons have passed, does the third aide raise his second finger. The three aides are sufficient for a count up to 1000; a fourth is needed to count between 1000 and 10000, etc. With each additional aide the range of numbers that can be counted is multiplied by ten. With seven aides one can count up to 10 million, with 8 up to 100 million. A population of 60 million, for instance, can be counted with 8 aides; 10 aides are sufficient to count all mankind.

In addition to the need for a counting procedure, there is the need for communicating it, either in writing or orally [**3**]. *Oral* communication requires a word for each unit represented by a raised finger; in our language, there are special words for one, two, three, four, five, six, seven, eight, nine, ten, for ten times ten, or hundred, and for the numbers which result from multiplication by ten: thousand, million and billion.

To communicate by writing, we need symbols only for the numbers one to nine, in the form conventional to us:

1, 2, 3, 4, 5, 6, 7, 8, 9,

and one more symbol, zero:

0.

The symbol 10 signifies that the second aide has one finger raised, while the first has his hands lowered;[2] 14, that the second aide has one finger up and the first one four; and 472, that the third aide has four, the second seven and the first two fingers raised. In short, this manner of writing numbers, which has come down to us from India [**4**] through the Arabs, known as the decimal system, is the exact systematic representation of the primitive South African counting process.

The pre-historic and historical development of this system was not uniform, but rather irregular. There are numerous examples of early deficiencies in the system: In written symbols, a deficiency is most marked in the case of the Romans, who, lacking a zero,[3] could not discover any

[2] This shows how our written symbols were decisively influenced by the number of our fingers: 10 signifies that the counting capacity of the first aide has been exhausted once.

[3] Through habitual usage, a special symbol for zero is taken as a matter of course, although the young child may still view it as something special. But in the develop-

position system. They required not only new *words* for 100 or 1000, but also new symbols: C, M (in addition to the ten-fold multiples of 5: V = 5, L = 50, D = 500).

Various modern languages still show evidences of such deficiencies. In French, quatre-vingt and quatre-vingt-dix are deviations from the decimal constructions; quatre-vingt means 4 times 20, not 8 times 10. In many languages the count above ten does not proceed with formations such as *ten and one*, *ten and two*, but with special words:

elf, onze, eleven;
zwölf, douze, twelve;

as if ten was not yet considered a separate and larger unit than the first nine digits; it is only with dreizehn in German or thirteen in English that the decimal construction becomes manifest [**5**].

How, then, would the number system have developed if men had 12 rather than 10 fingers? Our African chieftain would have needed a new aide only after 12 men had been counted; and a third, only when the counting capacity of the second had been exhausted, which would now be a little later, because of the 12-fingered hands of the first two aides; a third aide would now be needed only after the second had held up all of his 12 fingers, that is after the first had raised all of his 12 fingers 12 times. The third aide would be needed beginning with the number which *we* call *one-hundred fourty-four* and write 144. Three aides would be enough to count up to twelve times twelve times twelve (1728, using our designation), and only after this would a fourth aide be needed.

The names and symbols for numbers would of course also be quite different from those in present use. For example, consider the number for which we write 15 and say *fifteen*. Using the twelve-fingered aides in the counting process detailed above, the second aide will have one finger raised, and the first, three. To name this number we would not then say *ten and five* or *fifteen*, but perhaps *twelve-three*. The written system would differ correspondingly. Since the first aide has three fingers raised and the second aide one, we would now write **13** in the twelve-fingered system instead of 15, as in the decimal system. We shall use bold face for the duodecimal notation to distinguish it from the decimal system.

The duodecimal system may seem strange at first, but more detailed examination will make it more familiar. To begin with, we need a word for each of the finger patterns exhibited by the first aide (the units from

ment of mathematics, it took a special insight to understand that a positional notation was impossible without a symbol for the unoccupied positions. The Indian mathematician *Brahmagupta* (b. 598) developed rules for computing with zero, whose significance for the positional system seems to have been known at the time. See {4; p. 16 ff.} and [**4**].

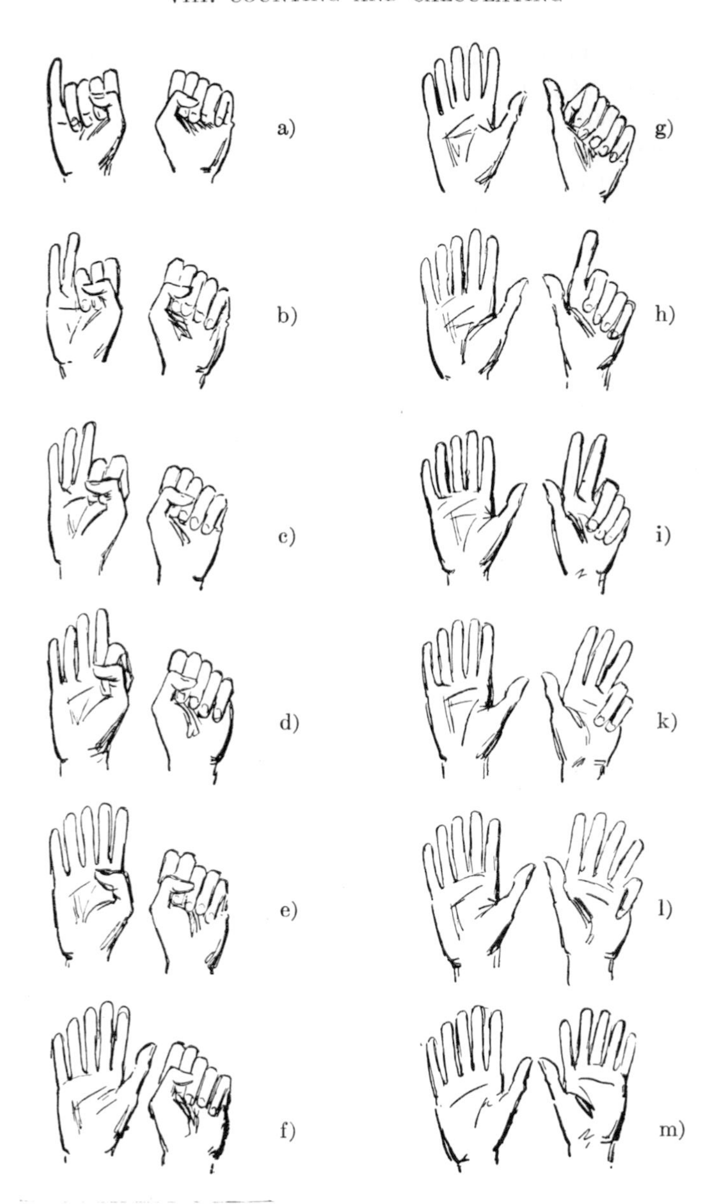


FIG. 103a–m

one to twelve; see Fig. 103a–m). We can use the usual words *one* to *nine* for the patterns in Fig. 103a–i; but, in order to avoid confusion with the decimal system, we shall introduce new names for the patterns in Fig. 103 k–m in place of the customary *ten*, *eleven* and *twelve*. Our choice of names for these last three can be made arbitrarily, since the origin of the customary number names: one, two, · · · , nine, ten is so old [6] that it is lost, and therefore we cannot know what the words would have been, had man been born with twelve fingers.[4] For convenience, we shall use the word *year* for twelve and shall borrow the tenth and eleventh letters of the Greek alphabet, *kappa* ($\kappa$) and *lambda* ($\lambda$), for the patterns in Fig. 103k, l. In this way, we shall later be able to use $\kappa$ and $\lambda$ as number symbols instead of 11 and 12. However, to avoid awkwardness, we will sometimes use the familiar words: ten, eleven, and twelve [7].

We can now assign names to the numbers greater than twelve (= year) in the duodecimal system. Thirteen is now twelve plus one and we will refer to it as *twelve-one* or *year-one*. Continuing in this way, we would have

twelve-two = year-two (fourteen),
twelve-three = year three (fifteen),
twelve-four = year-four (sixteen),

. . . . . . . . . . . . . . . . . . . . . . . . . . . . . . . . . .

twelve-nine = year-nine (twenty-one),
twelve-ten = year-kappa (twenty-two),
twelve-eleven = year-lambda (twenty-three).

The next number would be two times twelve = two times year (twenty-four), the number of months in two years. Continuing, we get two times twelve and one (twenty-five) up to eleven times twelve = lambda times year (one hundred and thirty-two), and then eleven times twelve and one, eleven times twelve and two, etc. until finally we reach eleven times twelve and eleven = lambda times year and lambda (one hundred forty-three). We would now need a new word for *year times year* or *twelve times twelve* (hundred fourty-four). We might use *year-squared* or *twelve-squared*, just as we use the word *hundred* for *ten times ten* in the decimal system. This corresponds to the point in the counting process at which the first twelve-fingered aide has raised and lowered all his fingers twelve times, the second aide has raised his twelve fingers in order and has lowered them, and the third aide has raised his first finger.

But the symbolic representation of numbers would also change. For the numbers one through nine we will use the usual symbols, but now these will be printed in bold face to emphasize the fact that the duodecimal system is meant (bold face type will be used in this chapter for all symbols, except $\kappa$ and $\lambda$, referring to the duodecimal system). In addition, we introduce special symbols **T** and **E**, or $\kappa$ and $\lambda$, for ten and eleven. The first two are meant to be reminiscent of the words ten and eleven, the last two

[4] One would have to consider how the consequent change in manual skill would have influenced the whole history of tools and weapons and the division of peoples according to their linguistic roots; if not indeed a whole new world.

of the words kappa and lambda, which we have chosen as names for these numbers. We would then have the following symbols (besides the symbol **0** for zero):

$$\mathbf{1, 2, 3, 4, 5, 6, 7, 8, 9, T}\ (\text{or } \kappa),\ \mathbf{E}\ (\text{or } \lambda).$$

What shall we write for twelve = year? Since this is the number at which the first aide (who counts the units) lowers all his fingers, while the second (who counts the years) raises one, it would be logical to write **10** (= a full year and no months) (see Footnote 2). We would then have the following new notation:

| | |
|---|---|
| twelve = year | (12) is now **10** |
| twelve-one = year-one | (13) is now **11** |
| twelve-two | (14) is now **12** |
| twelve-three | (15) is now **13** |
| . . . . . . . . . . . . . . . . . . . . | . . . . . . . . . . . . . . . . |
| twelve-nine | (21) is now **19** |
| twelve-ten = year-kappa | (22) is now **1T** (or **1**$\kappa$) |
| twelve-eleven = year-lambda | (23) is now **1E** (or **1**$\lambda$) |
| two times twelve | (24) is now **20** |
| two times twelve and one | (25) is now **21** |
| etc. | |

Continuing, we reach:

| | |
|---|---|
| nine times twelve and nine | (117) now **99** |
| nine times twelve and ten = nine times year and kappa | (118) now **9T** (or **9**$\kappa$) |
| nine times twelve and eleven = nine times year and lambda | (119) now **9E** (or **9**$\lambda$) |
| ten times twelve = kappa times year | (120) now **T0** (or $\kappa$**0**) |
| ten times twelve and one | (121) now **T1** (or $\kappa$**1**) |
| . . . . . . . . . . . . . . . . . . . . | . . . . . . . . . . . . . . . . |
| ten times twelve and nine = kappa times year and nine | (129) now **T9** (or $\kappa$**9**) |
| ten times twelve and ten = kappa times year and kappa | (130) now **TT** (or $\kappa\kappa$) |
| ten times twelve and eleven = kappa times year and lambda | (131) now **TE** (or $\kappa\lambda$) |
| eleven times twelve = lambda times year | (132) now **E0** (or $\lambda$**0**) |

eleven times twelve and one = lambda times year and one (133) now **E1** (or **λ1**)

. . . . . . . . . . . . . . . . . . . . . . . . . . . . . . . . . . . . . . . . . . . . . . . .

eleven times twelve and nine = lambda times year and nine (141) now **E9** (or **λ9**)
eleven times twelve and ten = lambda times year and kappa (142) now **ET** (or **λκ**)
eleven times twelve and eleven = lambda times year and lambda (143) now **EE** (or **λλ**),

and finally twelve times twelve = twelve squared:

twelve squared = year squared (144) now **100.**

This corresponds to the case in which both the first and second twelve-fingered aides drop their hands while the third raises one finger.

Force of habit, and our own hands, make us think that the decimal

FIG. 104 FIG. 105

system is simple, compared to the strange and complicated duodecimal system [**8**]. But the number ten—that is, the number itself (Fig. 104) and not the name or symbol representing it—has no intrinsic quality (except the anatomical one) to make it mathematically preferable to the number twelve (Fig. 105) [**9**].

It should now be clear that any number could be substituted for 10 as a base in counting. We could, for instance, use the number nine. Our symbols would then be[5]

*1, 2, 3, 4, 5, 6, 7, 8,* and *0.*

The number nine would now be written as *10.* Our ten would be understood as *nine plus one, nine-one,* and would be written *11,* etc.;

our seventeen = nine + eight would be written *18,*
our eighteen = twice nine would be written *20,*
etc.
our eighty = eight times nine plus eight would be written *88,*
our eighty-one = nine times nine would be written *100.*

The latter is obvious because nine times nine (*nine squared*) is a new higher

[5] We shall use italics for numbers written in the nonary system.

unit and thus plays the same role as ten times ten in the decimal system, or twelve times twelve in the duodecimal system.

The preceding discussion has nothing to do with the whole numbers themselves, but rather with their spoken and written symbols, that is, with the base 10 as a convention created by anatomy, an extra-mathematical consideration. There are essential mathematical properties of whole numbers, such as their relation to each other, which are independent of these formal conventions. Numbers have a meaning independent of their representation. The number shown in Fig. 104, for example, whether it is written as 10 in the decimal system, or as **T** in the duodecimal system or as *11* in the nonary system, is the number of the Commandments of the God of the Old Testament, the number of members (feet and wings) of a butterfly, a bee or a fly, and the number (responsible for our present numerical system) of fingers or toes of a man.

In the same way, the number in Fig. 105 is the number of disciples of Jesus, the number of months into which the year is divided, etc. It is the *same number* whether it is written as 12, or as **10**, or as *13*.

The arithmetical relations between numbers are also independent of their symbolic representations. The sum of the numbers shown in Figs. 104 and 105 is the number in Fig. 106. In the decimal system, the sum is called twenty-two (22); in the duodecimal system, it is called twelve-ten or year-kappa (**1T** or **1**$\kappa$); in the nonary system, it is called twice nine plus four (*24*). The fact that the number of Fig. 106 is the sum of the numbers of Figs. 104 and 105 is independent of the particular representation chosen, but the symbols used to describe the addition depend on the choice of a base. Thus,

in the decimal system: $10 + 12 = 22$,
in the duodecimal system: $\mathbf{T} + \mathbf{10} = \mathbf{1T}$ (or $\kappa + \mathbf{10} = \mathbf{1}\kappa$),
in the nonary system: $\mathit{11} + \mathit{13} = \mathit{24}$.

In Roman numerals, the addition would be written [**10**]

$$\mathrm{X} + \mathrm{XII} = \mathrm{XXII}.$$

Another essential property of a number, independent of its designation, is that of being a square, that is the product of a number by itself: e.g. twenty-five = five times five = five squared. The reason is that the statement "$N$ is a square" merely means that there is a square which can be partitioned into $N$ subsquares in the way shown in Figs. 107, 108, and 109

Fig. 106

Partition of a Square Into Twenty-five Subsquares
Numbered Relative to Various Bases

Base Ten

| 1 | 6 | 11 | 16 | 21 |
|---|---|---|---|---|
| 2 | 7 | 12 | 17 | 22 |
| 3 | 8 | 13 | 18 | 23 |
| 4 | 9 | 14 | 19 | 24 |
| 5 | 10 | 15 | 20 | 25 |

Fig. 107

Base Twelve

| 1 | 6 | E | 14 | 19 |
|---|---|---|---|---|
| 2 | 7 | 10 | 15 | 1T |
| 3 | 8 | 11 | 16 | 1E |
| 4 | 9 | 12 | 17 | 20 |
| 5 | T | 13 | 18 | 21 |

Fig. 108

Base Nine

| 1 | 6 | 12 | 17 | 23 |
|---|---|---|---|---|
| 2 | 7 | 13 | 18 | 24 |
| 3 | 8 | 14 | 20 | 25 |
| 4 | 10 | 15 | 21 | 26 |
| 5 | 11 | 16 | 22 | 27 |

Fig. 109

for $N$ = twenty-five.[6] Whether the subsquares are numbered relative to the decimal system (Fig. 107), or the duodecimal system (Fig. 108), or the nonary system (Fig. 109) has no bearing on the fact that the number of subsquares is a square number.

The property of being either a composite number or a prime (see Chapter I) is also an essential property [**11**]. On the other hand, a "round" number, a number which ends in one or more zeros, is clearly dependent on the choice of base. The celebration of a 70th or 80th birthday, or a 50th wedding anniversary, the designation of centuries as historical units of comparison, are also tied to a system based on the number ten. In the duodecimal system, entirely different numbers, those divisible by 12, would be "round."

We have dwelt on the role of the number ten in our numerical system to show that ten has no essential mathematical properties which make it basic to counting, but that on the contrary any other positive whole number (greater than one) would do just as well [**12**]. What is decisive, is the *positional principle* on which all our representational systems rest, no matter what the base. This positional principle represents an arbitrary number by digits, each of which is assigned a positional value; a special symbol, our zero, is required for the positions not occupied by digits.

The reader has probably already asked himself where the mathematical problem is in all this? In ancient times or among primitive peoples, the development of a systematic method of counting and of representing numbers was in fact a problem of great cultural importance, whether or not it was consciously posed. Methods of counting were evolved gradually, by no one man. They culminated in the positional principle and in the choice of a base, which made it possible to represent any number, no matter how large, with a limited number of symbols (digits). This systematic representation of numbers is intimately linked with the perception—already

[6] If $N = n \cdot n = n^2$, the sides of the square must be divided into $n$ parts (in this example $n = 5$) to partition the square into $n^2 = N$ subsquares.

developed by Archimedes [13] in his grains of sand theory—that the sequence of numbers 1, 2, 3, $\cdots$ is infinite (see Chapter XII). The difficulty in evolving the positional system (which children now take for granted) is best illustrated by the history of zero, i.e. the introduction of a symbol for an unoccupied position [14]—a symbol which, as we know, the Romans lacked. To grasp the progress represented by the decimal system and its positional system (which gradually spread over Europe only after the year 1000) [15], consider the problem of conducting all our monetary, insurance, statistical and other numerical affairs in Roman numerals. Compare the time required to do a simple problem in addition in the decimal system with that required by the same problem using Roman numerals:[7]

| | |
|---:|---:|
| 146 | CXLVI |
| 1993 | MCMXCIII |
| 500 | D |
| 204 | CCIV |
| 59 | LIX |
| 140 | CXL |
| 98 | XCVIII |
| 301 | CCCI |
| 3441 | MMMCDXLI |

How much more time, energy and personnel would be necessary in ordinary business computation without the positional system [16].

It would not, then, make a great deal of difference to counting and calculating if man had been born with six fingers on each hand. It is not the preference accorded the number ten which matters, but rather the creation of a positional system for representing numbers, which is of decisive significance for our culture.

The origin of *whole* numbers in the *counting* process was the first mathematical activity of man. In addition, as long ago as the Babylonians and the Egyptians, man already knew fractions. A developed arithmetic dating back to 2000 B.C., with addition, subtraction, multiplication and division of fractions, was found in the Rhind papyrus. Later, the domain of numbers was extended in three ways, but each extension had to overcome many obstacles. The three generalizations which successively broadened the concept of number were those of negative, irrational, and finally of imaginary numbers.

If one follows the vicissitudes suffered by these numbers before they

[7] We could of course use the position system in this example in the same way the Romans used the abacus (see [15]).

gained full maturity and recognition,[8] one finds in each case the same childhood diseases and the same adolescent difficulties in the transition to a ripe, fully developed theory. First, there were tentative trials of the new numbers, whose foundations were uncertain; then a growing familiarity with them on the one hand, and a distinct aversion towards them on the other—if indeed their existence was recognized at all; at the same time a defense of the new acquisition, often on faulty grounds, was carried on by its champions.

Those who remember their own introduction to negative, then irrational and perhaps imaginary numbers, will agree that the stages in their learning process were analogous to those of the historical development of the subject and that the process is comparable to the well-known biological principle: ontogeny recapitulates phylogeny [**18**]. We will not discuss classroom reminiscences of imaginary numbers, even though these numbers are very important in the development of other branches of mathematics [**19**]. We must certainly recall our own resistance to the rule for multiplying negative numbers: $-1 \times -1 = +1$ (minus times minus equals plus). As for the irrational numbers, the high schools are forced to forego teaching them on a really rigorous basis, because this is much too difficult. High schools have to try to get by as cheaply as possible [**20**] without making the gifted students feel that they are being stuffed with material merely because it is prescribed [**21**], and hence to become disenchanted with the subject because of its apparent lack of rigor.

A major difficulty in understanding the new kinds of numbers—as evidenced both by their historical development and the learning process of the student—is the fact that their main function is no longer that of counting, but of *measuring*. Both fractions and negative numbers, however, do not lose their counting function completely. If I take several apples, about equal in size, and cut each of them into three parts, and then take five of these parts, the fraction $5/3$ still involves counting in the sense that 5 is a numerator or numberer. However, the part has replaced the whole as a unit. Negative numbers are used with positive ones in counting outgo and intake, so that commercial arithmetic has played a substantial role in the extension of the number domain [**22**]. But the fraction $5/3$ can also be interpreted as the measurement of a length (by dividing the length into three equal parts and then considering five such parts side by side). Negative and positive numbers can also be used to measure lengths by taking a fixed point on a line and specifying that measurements to the right of the point are positive and to the left negative. An example is the temperature scale of a thermometer.

[8] The long, painful history of the number zero is a chapter in itself [**17**].

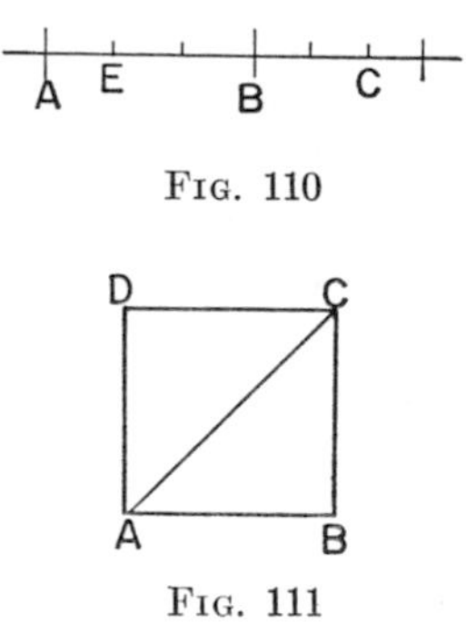


FIG. 110

FIG. 111

Before discussing the measuring functions of fractions and negative numbers any further, we must consider *irrational* numbers. A rigorous foundation for these numbers was not developed until the latter part of the 19th century, although their origin goes back to classical antiquity. Although we cannot fully treat the subject of irrational numbers here, we can indicate the nature of the problem solved by the introduction of irrational numbers.

Consider Fig. 110, in which $AB$ is the unit of length and the length of $AC$ is $5/3$. Consequently, $1/5$ of $AC$ is equal to $1/3$ of $AB$, that is $AC:AB$ as 5:3. Hence, *the two segments are in the ratio of two whole numbers.* In other words, $AC$ and $AB$ have a common measure, $AE$ (of which they are both multiples). Therefore, $AC$ and $AB$ are said to be *commensurable.*

The Greeks perceived that there are segments which are *not* in the ratio of two whole numbers, and therefore have no common measure or are *incommensurable.* The most familiar example is the one given by Euclid in the 10th book of his *Elements* (Fig. 111). The diagonal $AC$ and the side $AB$ of the square $ABCD$ are incommensurable, since the contrary assumption leads to a contradiction. For if $AC$ and $AB$ have a common measure, it is a segment which can be marked off exactly $m$ times on $AC$ and $n$ times on $AB$, with $m$ and $n$ suitable positive whole numbers; then the $m$th part of $AC$ is equal to the $n$th part of $AB$ and $AC:AB$ as $m:n$. It can be shown [**23**] that this implies that

$$m^2 = 2n^2.$$

Further, it can be proved [**24**] that whole numbers $m$ and $n$ cannot satisfy this equation (see [**23**] and [**24**]). Hence there cannot be two whole numbers $m$ and $n$ such that $AC$ and $AB$ are in the ratio $m:n$.[9]

[9] We can check this by carefully measuring the side and diagonal of a square. If $AB$ is divided into 1000 parts, measurement of $AC$ will yield 1414 of these parts so that $AC:AB$ is as 1414:1000, or 707:500. But, if $m = 707$, and $n = 500$,

$$m^2 = 499849$$

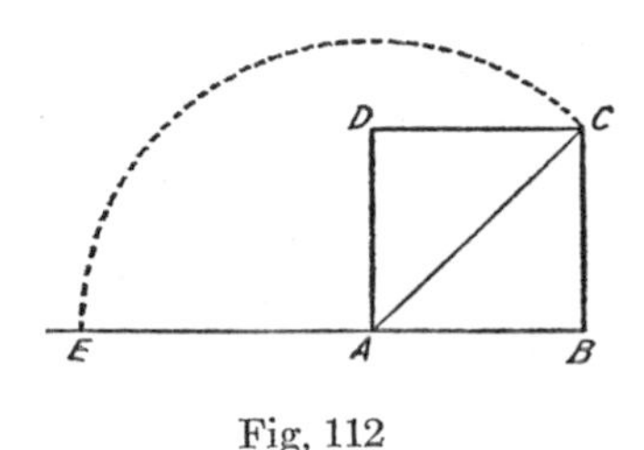


Fig, 112

Therefore, if $AB$ is the unit of length, the length of the segment $AC$ cannot be represented by any fraction $m/n$. Nevertheless, the need to assign *numbers* to the ratios of any two segments (commensurable or not) grew more and more imperative. This could be done only by extending the domain of fractions (rational numbers) by introducing new numbers—those we call irrational.[10]

Greek mathematics could compare two segments as equal (or larger or smaller); what it lacked was the concept of assigning numbers to lengths of segments incommensurable with a prescribed unit segment. While now we can simply say: If the side $AB$ is the unit of length, the length of the diagonal $AC$ is equal to $\sqrt{2}$,[11] this would have been impossible for the Greeks because $\sqrt{2}$ does not exist in the domain of rational numbers. Another example is the problem of adding $AE = AC$ to $AB$ (Fig. 112). We can write the sum $EB$ as $1 + \sqrt{2}$; the Greeks could add the two segments geometrically, but could not add them *arithmetically*.

The extension of the number system was required not only for geometric measurements, but also for the solution of algebraic equations. As a result, beginning with the Arab mathematicians, the use of irrational numbers spread after 1000 A.D. It was Michael Stifel (1487–1567) who gave them the name of irrational numbers. But it was not until the 19th century that

---

and

$$2n^2 = 2 \times 250000 = 500000,$$

so that $m^2$ and $2n^2$ are only approximately, but not exactly equal, as they must be if $m:n$ is to be the exact ratio of the diagonal to the side of a square.

One must thoroughly understand (as we emphasized in Chapter III) that the spirit of classical Greek mathematics was based on exactitude and went far beyond the practical considerations of surveying [25]. Therefore a sharp distinction must be made between approximate and absolutely exact relationships. Only a rigorously exact mathematics could make the distinction between commensurable and incommensurable segments—a distinction which would make no sense in practical measurements.

[10] Rational and irrational numbers together comprise the domain of *real numbers*. Imaginary numbers were a later development of mathematics (see the Postscript). Together with the real numbers they form the domain of complex numbers.

[11] Since the square of this length is 2 (see Footnote 6 in the Notes to this chapter).

rigorous theories of irrational numbers were developed. During the second half of the century, a period of critical activity and great discoveries, many leading mathematicians became interested in building a solid foundation for mathematics. Various theories of irrational numbers were evolved; among them the theory of Dedekind, which since then has been preferred by an ever growing number of mathematicians. Dedekind's theory of irrational numbers is too technical for discussion here, but we do want to say a few words about this great thinker.

Whoever is willing to agree that the outlook of all branches of mathematics is essentially determined by the ideas of outstanding investigators and the new concepts introduced by them, must recognize in Dedekind one of those creative spirits who have given modern mathematics its characteristic stamp. Dedekind's work (the theory of ideals) was in a field in which Gauss had been a pioneer; it was algebraic in origin and dealt among other things with problems of factorization analogous to the familiar problem of factoring a number into its prime factors, e.g.: $84 = 2 \cdot 2 \cdot 3 \cdot 7$. Kummer (1810–1893) had already illuminated part of this field. Dedekind's theory went on to embrace the whole field [26] and was so profound that it determined the development not only of algebra but of other branches of mathematics, and will no doubt continue to do so for a long time [27].

Dedekind's achievements had to do not with calculating but with the analysis of concepts, which made it difficult at the beginning for his contemporaries to enter into his new conceptual world. This was true even in the case of the theory of irrational numbers. Added to this barrier was the fact that the need for such a rigorous, systematic treatment of irrational numbers, first recognized by Dedekind, was by no means generally realized. He explained this need in 1858, in a lecture given while he was a Professor at Zürich. By the late fall of that same year he had evolved a systematic theory, but it was not until 1872 that he published it, under the stimulus of the appearance of other theories of irrational numbers [28]. Even then the new concepts were slow to influence the foundations of arithmetic and were still rejected by many [29].

Significant changes in mathematics and the great impetus they gave to new surges of development were conceived by a man whose outer life was so uneventful that it can be recounted in a few lines [30].

Richard Dedekind was born in Brunswick (the birthplace of the great Gauss), Oct. 6, 1831, where he lived until he was 19. After twelve years of study and teaching elsewhere, he returned to stay until his death in his 85th year. In 1850 he went to continue his studies, which he had begun at the Collegium Carolinum in 1848, in Göttingen. He received his doctorate from Göttingen in 1852 and in 1854 became a lecturer. In 1858 he was made Professor at the Federal Institute of Technology at Zürich, and in 1862 was called to the Technische Hochschule in Brunswick.

For many years Dedekind was the only surviving student of Gauss. At 19 he had heard Gauss lecture in the small auditorium of the Göttingen Observatory. While at Göttingen, Dedekind was a colleague and friend of Bernhard Riemann. Thus, for a decade and a half, Dedekind served as a living bond between the creative minds of the new century and the great men who had preceded him. But for a long time, the importance of Dedekind's work was not recognized. In 1904, an academic calendar appeared, with the motto "nulla dies nisi festiva," which gave the birth or death date of a mathematician for each day of the year. On it, Sept. 4, 1899 was marked as the day of Dedekind's death. Dedekind wrote to the publisher that Sept. 4 might be correct but 1899 certainly was not. He had spent the day, he volunteered, in the best of health and in a very stimulating discussion with his dinner guest and honored friend, Georg Cantor of Halle, who, Dedekind added, had used this opportunity to deal a death blow not to his friend, but to an error he had made. On February 12, 1916, his peaceful, academic life closed. Dedekind had lived to see his long unrecognized ideas gain acceptance, and begin to be accorded their true importance in mathematics.

Dedekind's theory of irrational numbers [**31**] gained wider and wider acceptance over other theories because, although it appears strange and abstract to the beginner, most mathematicians [**32**] agree that it most nearly approaches the essence of the matter.

You may be surprised to learn that several theories on a given subject, e.g. irrational numbers, may exist side by side, and that to some extent the choice of any one is a matter of individual taste. For example, there is a theory that before their separation by the Atlantic Ocean the Eastern and Western hemispheres were joined, and there is a second theory which maintains the opposite. One theory may sooner or later be proved incorrect, but meanwhile both are tenable. In the case of the irrational numbers, it is possible to have several equally valid theories, because their validity depends on consistency and not on empirical observation.

*Notes to Chapter VIII*

## COUNTING AND CALCULATING

**1** (p. 156). For material on number symbols, and also mathematical symbols, see {3}, {4}. The collection of number symbols in Fig. 113a, b is taken from {5}.

**2** (p. 156). See M. Cantor {5; p. 6}, for an account of the primitive origins of counting.

**3** (p. 158). In the above example, the most primitive method of counting would be to make as many notches on a long rod, or marks on a smooth surface, as there are people to be counted. This method would require a new word for every number, and would thus be applicable to a very restricted range of numbers.

**4** (p. 158). More recent historical research, especially that of G. R. Kaye, suggests that the Indian positional system (the decimal system) had its source in the Greek mathematics of classical antiquity, and that post-Christian Indian mathematics was of Greek and Chinese origin. See the informed and penetrating account in {4; pp. 16–18}, where references are to be found to the work of Kaye {6}, and others {7}, {8}; as well as the paper of Heinrich Wieleitner {9} describing these historical investigations.

**5** (p. 159). *Onze*, *douze*, etc. may of course be referred to the Latin *undecim*, *duodecim*, and (see {4; p. 5}) *elf* and *zwölf* may be traced to *ein-lif* (one more than ten) and *zwo-lif*. The assignment of names becomes really systematic starting with 13 (*dreizehn*) in German, with 17 (*dix-sept*) in French, and with 21 (*twenty-one*) in English.

**6** (p. 161). One might conjecture that the names of numbers originated in primitive languages, where they were the names of objects, and that number symbols may be primitive pictures of objects, which in some way represent numbers (see [**7**]). I have not been able to find anything further on this subject.

**7** (p. 161). But we must not be misled by the origin of the words *eleven* and *twelve* (see [**5**]), which refer to *one plus ten*, *two plus ten*, and therefore to the decimal system, for this would lead us astray if we wished to use the duodecimal system. Since the word *ten*, and the Latin *decem* which derives from the indo-germanic *tehun*, is related to the number of our fingers (Latin: *digiti*), we must ignore the original meaning when considering the hypothesis of hands with twelve fingers, and think of the word *ten* (or words in the Romance languages deriving from the Latin *decem*) as the name of the number shown in Fig. 103k, where it is *not* the total number of fingers.

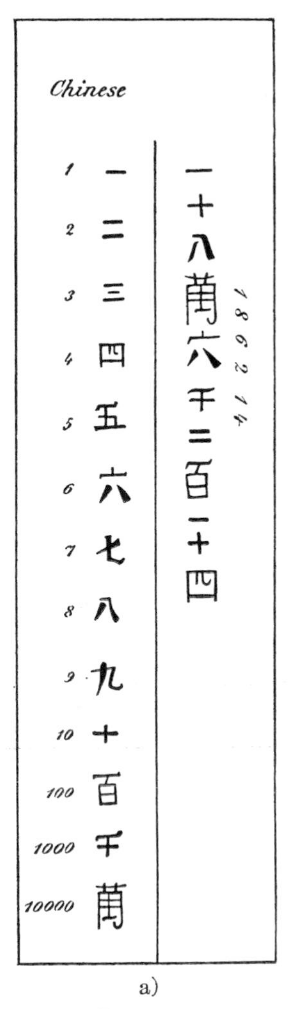


a)

Fig. 113a

**8** (p. 163). In Chapter VII, the choice of a base other than 10 would have had certain advantages. In the table on p. 121, as well as in Table 7 (Chapter I), the numbers are written in columns of ten. Hence the numbers in each row have the same final digit: the numbers in the first row end in 1, those of the ninth row end in 9. But in Table 12 (Chapter VII), where the numbers are written in columns of 12, this advantage is lost: the numbers of a row do not have the same final digit. However, if we were to use the duodecimal system, the numbers of the first row of Table 12 would read: **1**, **11**, **21**, **31**, $\cdots$ , and would therefore now end in a common digit.

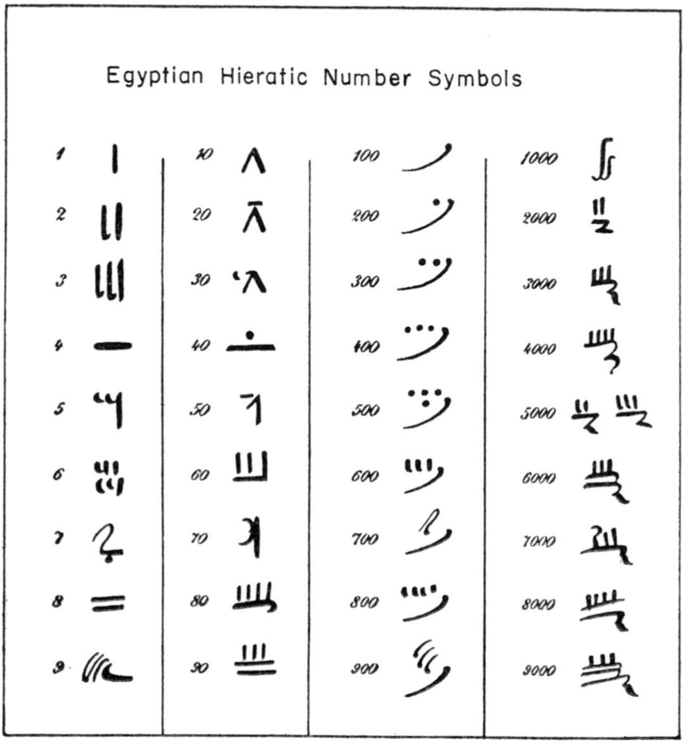

Egyptian Hieratic Number Symbols

| 1 | 10 | 100 | 1000 |
| --- | --- | --- | --- |
| 2 | 20 | 200 | 2000 |
| 3 | 30 | 300 | 3000 |
| 4 | 40 | 400 | 4000 |
| 5 | 50 | 500 | 5000 |
| 6 | 60 | 600 | 6000 |
| 7 | 70 | 700 | 7000 |
| 8 | 80 | 800 | 8000 |
| 9 | 90 | 900 | 9000 |

b)

Fig. 113b

The same would be true in Table 13 (Chapter VII), if we were to use a nonary system, which we discuss later in this chapter.

**9** (p. 163). Aristotle (384–322 B.C.) had already alluded to the anatomical origin of the decimal system. Blaise Pascal (1623–1662), Bishop John Caramuel y Lobkowitz (1602–1682), and Leibniz (1646–1716) considered bases other than ten. The famous French naturalist Buffon (1707–1788) advocated the introduction of the duodecimal system. See {4; p. 4} and {10}.

**10** (p. 164). As another example,

$$14 + 11 = 25$$

in the decimal system, is written as

$$\mathbf{12 + E = 21}$$

in the duodecimal system,[1] and as

$$\mathit{15} + \mathit{12} = \mathit{27}$$

in the nonary system;[2] while in the Roman system, which has no positional principle, we would write

$$\mathrm{XIV} + \mathrm{XI} = \mathrm{XXV}.$$

Analogously, in the case of multiplication:

$$3 \cdot 22 = 66$$

in the decimal system,

$$\mathbf{3 \cdot 1T} = \mathbf{56}$$

in the duodecimal system,

$$\mathit{3 \cdot 24} = \mathit{73}$$

in the nonary system, and

$$\mathrm{III} \cdot \mathrm{XXII} = \mathrm{LXVI}$$

in the Roman system.

**11** (p. 165). Thus, twenty-four is composite, since it can be factored into four times six (or two times twelve), whether it is written as 24 in the decimal system, **20** in the duodecimal system, or *26* in the nonary system. Similarly, the number twenty-three is prime whether it is written as 23, or **1E**, or *25*.

**12** (p. 165). Let $a$ be an integer greater than 1. In order to write numbers to the base $a$, we use the numbers[3]

$$0, 1, 2, \cdots, a - 1,$$

and the powers of $a$:[4]

$$a^0 = 1, a, a^2 = a \cdot a, a^3 = a \cdot a \cdot a, \cdots, a^n, \cdots.$$

It can then be shown that if $b$ is a positive integer, there are unique integers

$$n, c_0, c_1, c_2, \cdots, c_n,$$

where $n \geq 0$, $0 \leq c_i \leq a - 1$, $c_n \neq 0$, such that[5]

$$b = c_0 + c_1 a + c_2 a + \cdots + c_n a_n .$$

[1] This means: The sum of *twelve plus two* (= *year two*) and *eleven* (= *lambda*) is *two times twelve plus one* (= *two times year plus one*).

[2] This means: The sum of *nine plus two* and *nine plus five* is *twice nine plus seven*.

[3] If $a = 10$, these are the numbers 0, 1, 2, $\cdots$, 9, the digits of the decimal system.

[4] If $a = 10$, these are the numbers 1, 10, 100, 1000, $\cdots$.

[5] If $a = 10$,

$$b = c_0 + c_1 \cdot 10 + c_2 \cdot 10^2 + \cdots + c_n \cdot 10^n.$$

The case $a = 2$ is of practical importance. The digits relative to this base are then the numbers 0, 1. If $b$ is a positive integer, it is expressed in the dyadic system by

$$b = c_0 \cdot 1 + c_1 \cdot 2 + c_2 \cdot 2^2 + \cdots + c_n \cdot 2^n,$$

where each of the digits $c_0, \cdots, c_n$ is either 0 or 1. For example,

$$13 = 1 \cdot 1 + 0 \cdot 2 + 1 \cdot 2^2 + 1 \cdot 2^3.$$

The dyadic system is used in electronic computers for reasons of economy.

**13** (p. 166). Archimedes, who was born in 280 B.C., was killed in 212 B.C. during the conquest of Syracuse. It is said that he was killed in his study by a Roman soldier, and that while deeply immersed in the constructions on his sand-strewn floor, he called out without looking up, "Don't disturb my circles." This has the appearance of one of those typical situations in which two opposing temperaments meet: the mathematician who does not wish to be disturbed, and the soldier self-conscious of his power.

**14** (p. 166). For the origin of zero, see {5; p. 75, 432, 501, 521 ff.} and {4; p. 15 ff.}. On p. 18, in Note 95, of the last reference, it is reported that zero was used by the Babylonians in the second century B.C. See also {4; vol. 2, p. 56 ff.}.

**15** (p. 166). Leonardo of Pisa's (Leonardo Fibonacci, 1170–1250) book *Liber Abaci* (1202) was of great influence, particularly in Italy, where the Indo-Arabic system of calculating introduced via Spain was making slow headway, taking centuries to replace the Roman system. Noteworthy was a prohibition of the Florentine community (1299) against using the decimal system in commercial arithmetic, because, it is suspected, the civil officials did not have a sufficient command of it. See {4; p. 23 ff.}.

Moreover, computation in the Roman style during this whole period was performed on an abacus divided into columns, as it had been for the first thousand years, with the columns ordered to designate units, tens, hundreds, etc. See {4; p. 20, 21}.

**16** (p. 166). When one considers the inflation in Germany in the nineteen-twenties, one realizes that it would have been impossible to follow the astronomical figures of those days without a numerical system founded on a positional principle. Some people may doubt the value of human progress, and think that without this advanced system of counting and calculating, the inflation could never have reached such heights. They

---

For example,

$$1890 = 0 + 9 \cdot 10 + 8 \cdot 10^2 + 1 \cdot 10^3.$$

In this case, $n = 3, c_0 = 0, c_1 = 9, c_2 = 8, c_3 = 1$.

Carl Friedrich Gauß (1777-1855) in 1803 · Niels Henrik Abel (1802-1829)
Felix Klein (1849-1925) · Evariste Galois (1811-1832)

PLATE XII

Godefridus Guilielmus Leibnitius

Newton

C F Gauß

A. Cayley

Gottfried Wilhelm Leibniz (1646-1716) · Isaac Newton (1643-1727)
Carl Friedrich Gauß (1777-1855) · Arthur Cayley (1821-1895)

may even conclude that many discoveries and inventions which were meant to benefit mankind, are fated to be misused. We must not forget, however, that the reverse may also be true.

**17** (p. 167). There were still mathematicians in the 17th century who did not consider zero a number. See {4; vol. 2, pp. 56–59}.

**18** (p. 167). See {5; p. 3}.

**19** (p. 167). Their introduction meanwhile rests on a level no higher than the following: "Up to now we have dealt only with real numbers. Since the square $x^2$ of a real number $x$ is nonnegative, $x^2 + 1$ must be greater than or equal to 1. Hence, the equation $x^2 + 1 = 0$ has no solution (in real numbers). Therefore, in order to be able to solve this equation, we introduce a new number denoted by $i$ and called imaginary. It follows that $i^2 + 1 = 0$, or $i^2 = -1$.

This simple explanation is, of course, entirely inadequate for the construction of imaginary numbers. There is now, and there has been for some time, a rigorous foundation for the concept of imaginary number. For its great significance, see the Postscript.

**20** (p. 167). So, for example, if the irrational numbers are introduced by annexing the infinite nonperiodic decimal expansions to the already familiar periodic decimal expansions (which correspond to the rational numbers), the arithmetic rules applicable to the latter are extended without further ado to the former. Another example, to which a similar objection applies, is the use of the well known algorithm for calculating square roots to any degree of approximation. This is often used to calculate, say the $\sqrt{2}$, to several decimal places, and the result is used as an approximation to the $\sqrt{2}$. What is wrong here, of course, is that no attempt is made to prove that there is in fact an irrational number, $\sqrt{2}$, whose square is 2.

**21** (p. 167). The high school teacher who must maneuver around the unavoidable inadequacies of his exposition, doing as little damage to the subject matter as possible, must have intuition, pedagogical skill, and experience. His task is much more difficult than that of the college instructor who is developing a rigorous theory of irrational numbers.

**22** (p. 167). The Indian mathematician Brahmagupta, who was born in 598 A.D., used negative numbers in his calculations. But even in the 16th century, the negative numbers were still called *surdi* or *ficti* to indicate that they were absurd or contrived as opposed to the true (positive) numbers (*numeri veri*). There was no rigorous foundation for the negative numbers until the 19th century. See {4; vol. 2, p. 73 ff.}.

**23** (p. 168). Let $\mathfrak{S}$ be the segment which can be marked off $m$ times on $AC$ and $n$ times on $AB$.[6] If the square $ABCD$ is reflected about its side

[6] The main difficulty in the following geometric proof for most readers will no doubt lie in the fact that the concept of the length of a segment, as a number, is not

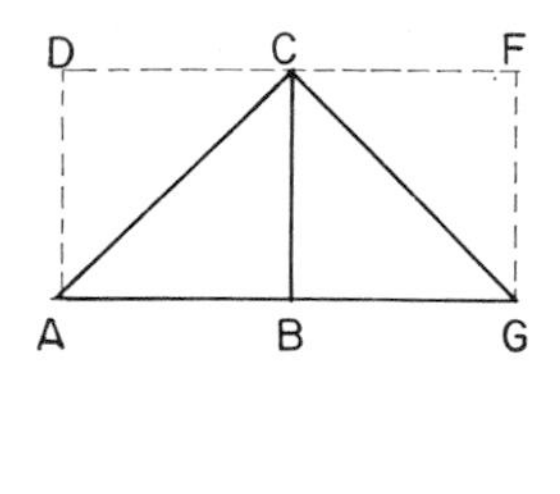


FIG. 114a

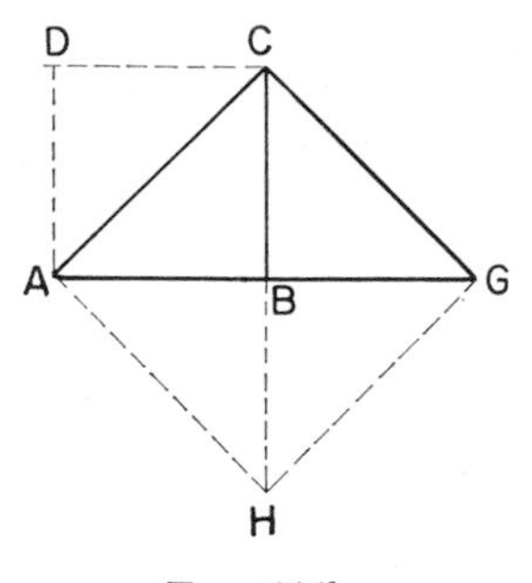


FIG. 114b

$BC$, the result (Fig. 114a) is a second square $BCFG$ of equal size. Since $BG = AB$, $\mathfrak{S}$ can be marked off on the segment $AG$ twice as many times as on the segment $AB$, that is, $2n$ times. Therefore, $AG:AC$ as $2n:m$. But triangles $ABC$ and $ACG$ are similar; therefore, $AC:AB = AG:AC$.[7] Hence,

$$m:n = 2n:m,$$

or

$$m^2 = 2n^2.$$

It may be of interest to consider a somewhat different proof, using areas. The square $ACGH$ of Fig. 114b can be divided into the four congruent triangles $ABC$, $BCG$, $BGH$ and $ABH$; the square $ABCD$ can be divided into the congruent triangles $ABC$ and $ACD$. Therefore, the area of $ACGH$ is twice the area of $ABCD$. Let $\mathfrak{Q}$ be the square with side $\mathfrak{S}$, and denote the area of $\mathfrak{Q}$ by $\mathfrak{F}$. If the length of $AB$ is $n$ times that of $\mathfrak{S}$, $ABCD$ can be divided into $n^2$ subsquares, each having the same area as $\mathfrak{Q}$. Hence, the area of $ABCD$ is $n^2\mathfrak{F}$. Since the length of $AC$ is $m$ times that of $\mathfrak{S}$, $ACGH$ can be divided into $m^2$ subsquares, each with the same area as $\mathfrak{Q}$; therefore, the area of $ACGH$ is $m^2\mathfrak{F}$. Since the area of $ACGH$ is twice the area of $ABCD$, it follows that

$$m^2\mathfrak{F} = 2n^2\mathfrak{F},$$

yet available to them. It is not possible to assign a numerical length to every segment until the irrational numbers are defined.

But it is possible, on the assumption that the ratio of $AC$ to $AB$ is the ratio of two integers $m$ and $n$ and that $AB$ is the unit of length, to assign the fraction $m/n$ to the length of $AC$. The geometric proof then shows that the square $m^2/n^2$ of this length must be 2.

[7] This can also be seen from Fig. 114b. $AB$ is a side and $AC$ is a diagonal of the square $ABCD$. But also $AC$ is a side and $AG$ is a diagonal of the square $ACGH$. Since the ratio of a diagonal to a side is the same for every square, it follows that $AG:AC = AC:AB$.

and so

$$m^2 = 2n^2.$$

**24** (p. 168). To show that the equation

$$m^2 = 2n^2$$

cannot be satisfied by positive integers $m$, $n$, we first prove two simple lemmas. First, the square of an odd integer is an odd integer. For if $U$ is an odd integer, $U = 2k + 1$ for some integer $k$. Hence

$$U^2 = (2k + 1)^2 = 4k^2 + 4k + 1 = 2(2k^2 + 2k) + 1.$$

Therefore, $U^2$ is also an odd integer.

Second, if positive integers $m$, $n$ satisfy the equation $m^2 = 2n^2$, and $m$, $n$ have a common factor $q$, so that $m = sq$, $n = tq$, where $s$, $t$ are integers, then $s$ and $t$ also satisfy the equation $m^2 = 2n^2$. For, substituting in the equation, we have

$$s^2q^2 = 2t^2q^2.$$

Hence,

$$s^2 = 2t^2.$$

By the second lemma, if $m^2 = 2n^2$ has a solution in positive integers $m$, $n$, then there is a solution for which $m$, $n$ are relatively prime, that is, $q = 1$. We shall now show that this leads to a contradiction. For, suppose that $m$, $n$ is a solution of $m^2 = 2n^2$. Since $2n^2$ is even, $m^2$ must also be even. Hence, by the first lemma, $m$ is even, and we can write $m = 2u$, where $u$ is an integer. Hence

$$4u^2 = 2n^2,$$

or

$$2u^2 = n^2.$$

Therefore, $n^2$ is even, and again by the first lemma, $n$ is even. Hence, both $m$ and $n$ are even, so that 2 is a common factor of both. Therefore, the equation $m^2 = 2n^2$ cannot have a solution in relatively prime positive integers $m$, $n$. In view of the above, this proves that the equation cannot have positive integral solutions.

**25** (p. 169). For some worthwhile remarks on the nature of classical Greek mathematics and its influence on the development of European scientific thought, see the essays of Paul Valéry {11}.

**26** (p. 170). This field is known as algebraic number theory. Kronecker (1823–1891), independently of Dedekind, and using, in part, somewhat different ideas, developed a theory of prime factor decomposition. The further development of the theory is due, however, to Dedekind. For an account of the development and modern achievements of this theory, see {12}.

**27** (p. 170). Richard Dedekind's Collected Mathematical Works {13} were published in 1930–1932 in three volumes. They were edited by Robert Fricke in Braunschweig, Oystein Ore in New Haven and Emmy Noether in Göttingen. Emmy Noether was the greatest of the very few women mathematicians whose names are remembered in the history of science. Among these are Hypatia,[8] the student and commentator of Diophantus of Alexandria, and Sonja Kovalevsky,[9] the student of Weierstrass. During her stay at Göttingen, she was the leader of a school of distinguished mathematicians, younger than herself, which was responsible for the further development of modern abstract algebra, especially along Dedekindian lines.[10]

Robert Fricke (1861–1930) died during the publication of Dedekind's Collected Works, and so was not able, as he wished, to contribute a biography of Dedekind based on personal reminiscences. Consequently, whatever information we have is scattered through the literature (see [**30**]).

[8] Hypatia was the daughter of the mathematician Theon of Alexandria. She was active in the neo-Platonic school of philosophy there. During this period, Alexandria was torn by the religious quarrels of post-Christian times. Hypatia was killed in 415 by a mob of fanatics. Nothing is known of her studies or her writings, since they were not preserved. But her life is treated in many works of fiction. See {21}.

[9] Sophie (Sonja) Kovalevsky (née Krukovsky), born January 15, 1850 in Moscow, married Vladimir Kovalevsky in 1868 in order to go abroad to study. She studied in Berlin, did graduate work in Göttingen, and in 1884 was made Professor of Higher Mathematics in Stockholm, where she died February 10, 1891. The story of her personal life is the subject of Leffler's *Sonja Kovalevsky* {22}. An autobiography, translated by Isabel F. Hapgood {23} is mentioned by D. E. Smith {21; p. 530}.

[10] Emmy Noether, daughter of Max Noether (1844–1921), who was himself a well known mathematician, was born March 23, 1882 in Erlangen. In 1907, she obtained her doctorate at Erlangen, and in 1922 was made a Professor at Göttingen. The events of 1933 led to her exile. She then taught at Bryn Mawr, and lectured at the Institute for Advanced Study in Princeton. As a result of unexpected complications following an operation, she died in Bryn Mawr, April 14, 1935. She is remembered by all who knew her personally for her temperament, ideal for a scholar, her direct, unconventional manner, her warmth, and her great readiness to be of help. For an account of her work, see van der Waerden's memorial article in the Mathematische Annalen {24}, and Hermann Weyl's memorial address {25}. Weyl sent me a copy of his memorial address in 1948, and its warmth touched me deeply. But van der Waerden's memorial article appeared in Germany; its author was at that time in Leipzig. Those who knew the situation in Germany at the time, or can imagine it, will be able to appreciate fully the courage of the author of the article and of the editors of the Annalen.

**28** (p. 170). One of these theories was developed by Charles Méray (1835–1911) and Georg Cantor, independently of each other. Dedekind first became aware of this through the papers of Eduard Heine (1821–1881) and Cantor in 1872. Méray published his paper first, and so has the priority. For Cantor, see Chapter XII.

A third theory was developed by Weierstrass (1815–1897) in his lectures. It became known through the papers of H. Kossak, S. Pincherle and O. Biermann (see {14} and {15}).

In passing, we note that the Foundations of Mathematics, of which the theory of irrational numbers is a part, is a very extensive field, developed in many different ways by mathematicians of the first rank. Unfortunately, we cannot pursue the matter further. (See Chapter XII, [**4**].)

**29** (p. 170). In the introduction to his book *Stetigkeit und Irrationale Zahlen* (*Continuity and the Irrational Numbers*) (1872), Dedekind recollects a long and lively conversation about his theory with his friend Durège, a few days after its publication (November 24, 1858). Letters written in 1876 to R. Lipschitz show the different positions of the two mathematicians (see {13; vol. III}, and in the same volume the introduction to Dedekind's book *Was Sind und Was Sollen die Zahlen?* (*The Nature and Meaning of Numbers*) published in 1880). For an account of du Bois-Reymond's campaign against the new arithmetic theories, see {16}.

**30** (p. 170). See Landau's memorial address in honor of Dedekind in {17}. Felix Klein's book {18} also contains a few facts about Dedekind and his work. Klein's book treats the whole sweep of 19th century mathematics, whereas most works on the history of mathematics are restricted to the mathematics of antiquity or periods long predating the 19th century. Klein's estimate of Dedekind is brief and inadequate, but this can be ascribed to the entirely different methods of research of the two men. Klein's method was impetuous and scornful of the foundations, Dedekind's the patient and meticulous construction of a theory on the basis of the new foundations. See Carathéodory's autobiographical notes {19} for a pertinent remark about Klein.

**31** (p. 171). A good book on the subject is {20}, which also contains brief accounts of the other theories and references to the literature.

**32** (p. 171). There was general agreement among the reviews of {20} (see [**31**]). However, one reviewer (in 1924) preferred Méray and Cantor's theory to that of Dedekind.

*Chapter IX*

# THE REGULAR POLYGON OF 17 SIDES

Carl Friedrich Gauss was perhaps the greatest mathematician of all time. In this chapter we are going to discuss one of his most famous discoveries. In his scientific journal there is a record of the exact date of his first great discovery: March 30, 1796, the very day on which, as a young man, he began the journal. Throughout his life he placed great importance on this discovery.

The problem concerns the regular polygons, and it belongs to the domain of geometry.

It is easy to explain what is meant by a regular polygon. To understand a regular octagon, for example, we first picture a circle. Beginning with a point $A$, we mark off a segment $AE$ (Fig. 115a, b, c) eight times in succession on the circumference of this circle. The final point depends of course on the choice of $AE$. It may be that the final point $Z$ is short of the point $A$, as in Fig. 115a; or that it overshoots $A$, as in Fig. 115b. If, however, the choice of the length $AE$ happens to be such that the final point $Z$ coincides with the initial point $A$, as in Fig. 115c, then the lines joining the eight points of division form a *regular* octagon.[1] In general, we may speak of a *regular polygon of n sides* or a *regular n-gon*. The regular polygons of 3, 4, 5, 6, etc. sides are usually called regular triangles, quadrilaterals, pentagons, hexagons, etc.[2]

The method we have described for obtaining a regular octagon, or for that matter any regular polygon, clarifies these concepts. But it is not a foolproof method for constructing a regular polygon. If, for example, we choose a segment $AE$ which proves to be too small, as in Fig. 115a, and we try a larger segment, it may still be too small, or it may be too large, as in Fig. 115b. And no matter how long we try, there may always be small deviations which will prevent the final point $Z$ from coinciding exactly with the initial point $A$.

To be sure, some deviations may be so small as to be insignificant for such practical purposes as drafting. But as we have already noted (in Chapters III and V), the science of geometry is concerned with the concept of *exact* constructions. Hence the problem is to find an exact construction of a regular polygon with a prescribed number of sides. We recall

[1] This definition implies that a regular polygon has equal angles, as well as equal sides.

[2] If $n = 4$, the regular quadrilateral is also a square; if $n = 3$, the regular triangle is also an equilateral triangle (Figs. 116 and 117). In the case of the triangle, the equality of the sides implies the equality of the angles; this is no longer true for $n > 3$ (if it is not required that the polygon be constructed on a circle).

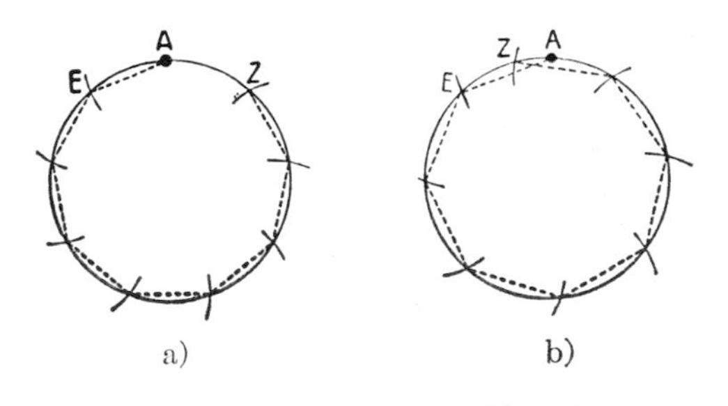


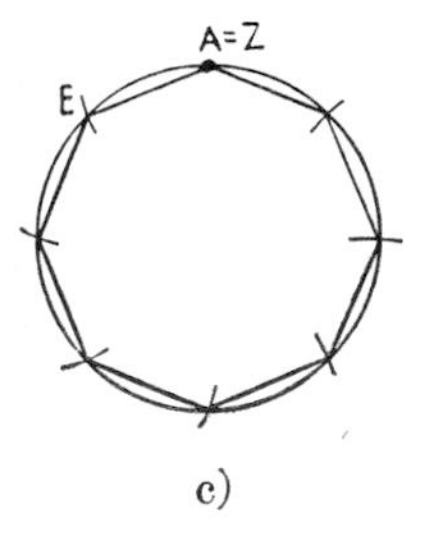


FIG. 115

that it is also essential to prescribe the aids and instruments allowed in the construction, and that since the days of classical antiquity the constructions which have aroused the greatest interest have been those which employ *straight edge* and *compass* alone.

What is the situation with regard to exact straight edge and compass constructions for regular polygons? It is clear that the relevant factor is the number of sides of the polygon. It may be easy, for example, to construct a regular polygon of 4 sides exactly with straight edge and compass, but it may be impossible to do this for a polygon with another number of sides.[3] The problem may be stated as follows: *For what values of n is it possible to construct a regular polygon of n sides with straight edge and compass alone? And for which values of n is this impossible?*

Let us begin with the regular *quadrilateral.* First we draw a circle with center $M$ (see Fig. 118a) and connect a point $A$ on the circumference with $M$. The line $AM$ extended intersects the circle at $C$. The perpendicular bisector of the diameter $AC$ is easily found by drawing two circles of radius $AC$, one with center $A$, the other with center $C$, finding their two points of intersection, and then connecting the two points with a straight line.[4] This connecting line cuts the original circle at two points, $B$ and $D$. It is obvious that $BD$ is the diameter of the circle perpendicular to $AC$. Then the four points $A$, $B$, $C$, $D$, are the vertices of a square (Fig. 118b). We have thus constructed a square, i.e. a regular quadrilateral, with straight edge and compass.

From the construction of a regular quadrilateral we may proceed immediately to that of a regular octagon. We need merely construct the perpendicular bisector of $AB$ (Fig. 119a) and find its point of intersection with the circle (the point $T$ in Fig. 119a). Then $AT$ is the side of a regular octagon obtained by marking off $AT$ eight times on the circumference.

[3] We have already discussed construction problems which have no exact solution with straight edge and compass alone (see Chapters III and V).

[4] Both circles are dotted in Fig. 118a. For the construction of a perpendicular bisector see Chapter III.

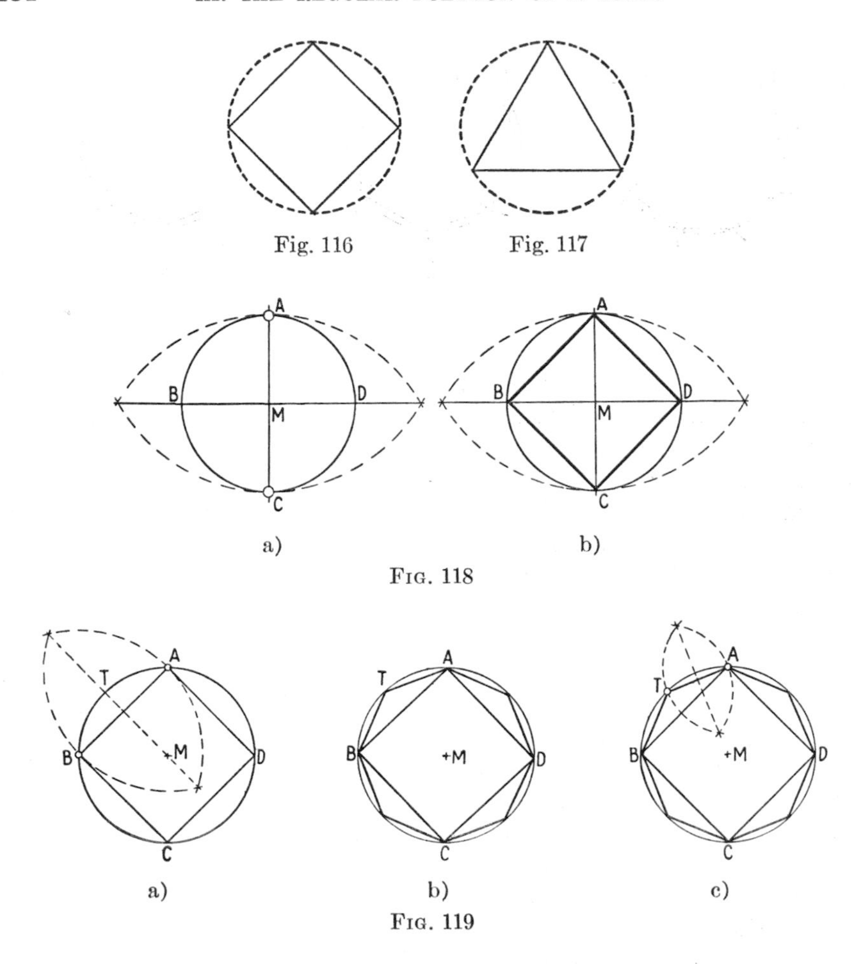


Fig. 116

Fig. 117

a) b)

Fig. 118

a) b) c)

Fig. 119

From the regular octagon of Fig. 119b we obtain a regular 16-gon by constructing the perpendicular bisector of $AT$. Fig. 119c shows only the perpendicular bisector but not the full 16-gon, since the scale of the figure makes it difficult to draw all 16 sides. Clearly, polygons of 32 sides, 64 sides, 128 sides, etc. are easily obtained by successive bisections.

We shall now consider the related figures of the *triangle* and the *hexagon*. For simplicity, we begin with the latter because it is known that the side of a regular hexagon inscribed in a circle is equal to the radius of the circle. One need simply strike off the length of the radius on both sides of $A$, as shown in Fig. 120a. Denote by $P$ one of the points obtained in this way (Fig. 120b). Marking off $AP$ on the circumference repeatedly, we get a regular hexagon. Starting with $A$ and skipping the vertex $P$, we obtain $AQ$ (Fig. 120c), the side of a regular (i.e. equilateral) triangle inscribed

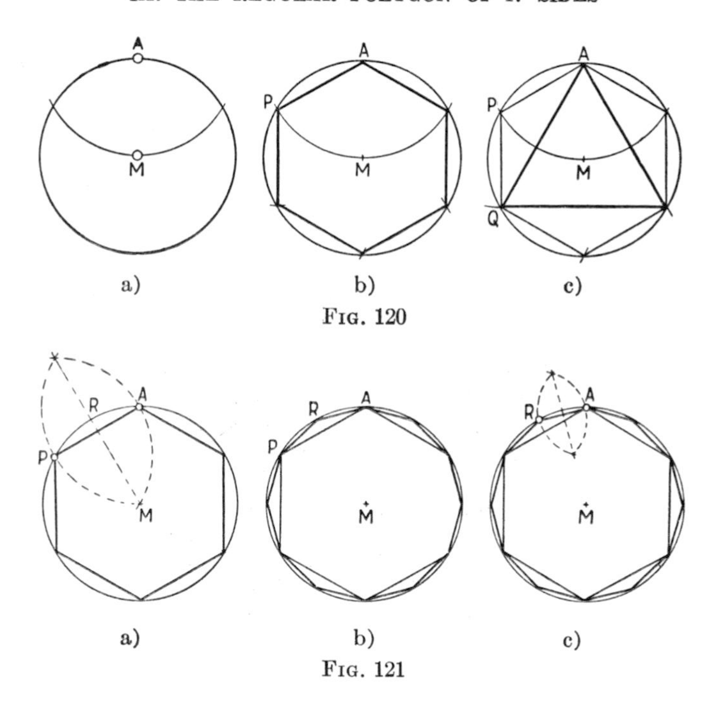


FIG. 120



FIG. 121

in the circle. On the other hand, by constructing the perpendicular bisector of $AP$ we get a side $AR$ of a regular 12-gon (Fig. 121a, b); and from this in the same way we obtain a regular polygon of 24 sides (Fig. 121c). It is clear that the same method will yield regular polygons of 48 sides, 96 sides, etc.

The construction of a regular pentagon is a little more complicated. We begin with the circle with center $M$, and the two perpendicular diameters $AC$ and $BD$ used in the construction of the square (Fig. 118). The next step in the construction is to draw the perpendicular bisector of the radius $MD$ (Fig. 122a). With $H$, the midpoint of $MD$, as center, we draw a circle passing through $A$ (Fig. 122b). The point of intersection of this circle with the diameter $BD$ is $G$. It can be proved [1] that $AG$ is then equal in length to a side of a regular pentagon inscribed in the circle. Marking off $AU = AG$ on the circumference, we get the side of a regular pentagon inscribed in the circle (Fig. 122c, d).

By constructing perpendicular bisectors (Fig. 123a, b) we can obtain from the regular pentagon a regular polygon of 10 sides, one of whose sides is $AV$, and then a regular polygon of 20 sides, etc. (Fig. 123b).

Finally we note that a regular polygon of 15 sides can be obtained by combining the construction of the triangle and pentagon. From Fig. 124a we see that the arc $AN$ is exactly $2/5$, and the arc $AQ$ $1/3$, of the total

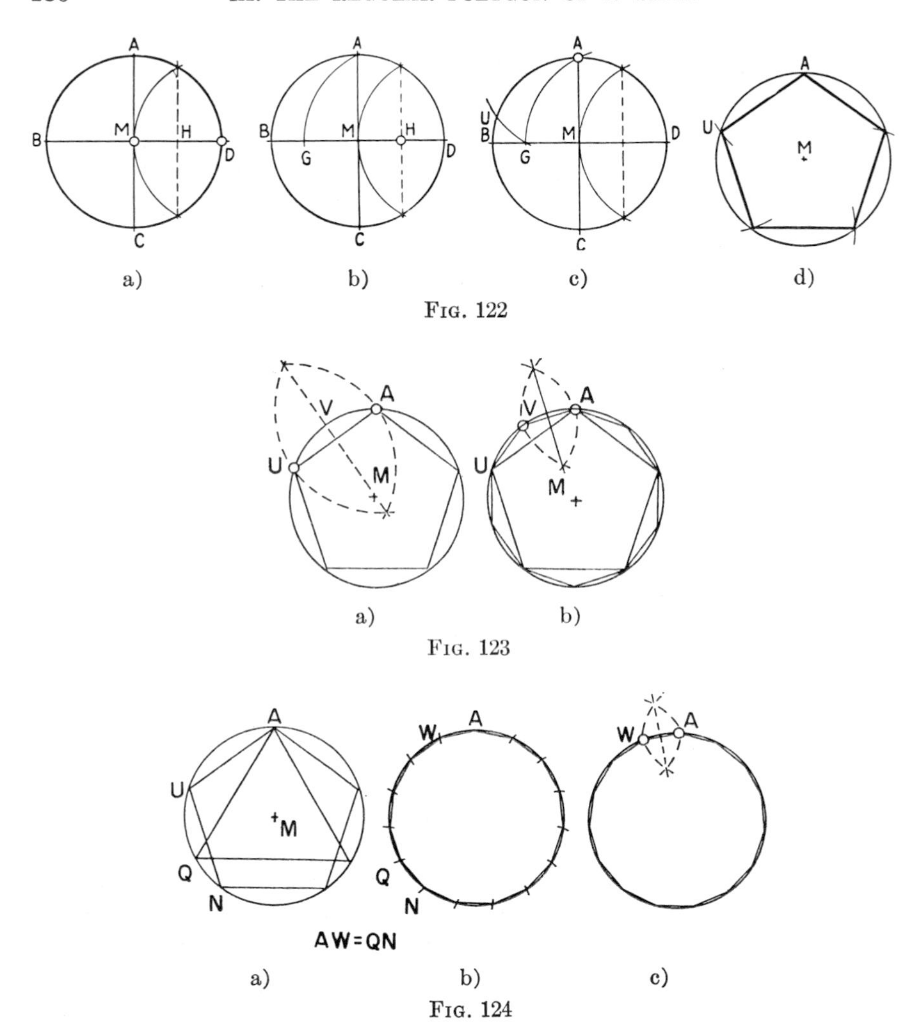


a) b) c) d)

FIG. 122

a) b)

FIG. 123

a) b) c)

FIG. 124

circumference. Hence the arc $QN$ is $2/5 - 1/3 = 6/15 - 5/15 = 1/15$ of the full circumference. To obtain a regular polygon of 15 sides we simply mark off $QN$ beginning at $A$. We then obtain regular polygons of 30, 60, 120, etc. sides by means of perpendicular bisectors (Fig. 124c).

We have now discussed all the exact constructions of the regular polygons with straight edge and compass known to antiquity [**2**]. All the constructions are based on those of the regular quadrilateral, the regular triangle and the regular pentagon. The regular 15-gon was easily obtained by a simple combination of constructions for the triangle and the pentagon. All the other constructions rest on successive doublings of the number of sides, so that the regular $n$-gons for which exact constructions with straight edge and compass were known, can be given in the following table:

$$n = 4, 8, 16, 32, 64, \cdots,$$
$$n = 3, 6, 12, 24, 48, \cdots,$$
$$n = 5, 10, 20, 40, 80, \cdots,$$
$$n = 15, 30, 60, 120, 240, \cdots.$$

On the other hand no exact constructions with straight edge and compass alone were known for a regular heptagon, or a regular nonagon or, in short, for the regular polygons of 7, 9, 11, 13, 14, 17, 18, 19, 21, 22, 23, 25, 26, 27, 28, 29, 31, 33, 34, 35, 36, 37, 38, 39, 41, 42, 43, 44, 45, 46, 47, 49, 50, 51, $\cdots$ sides; i.e., those not listed in the first table. This was the state of the problem at the time of Euclid (325 B.C.);[5] this knowledge was probably still much older and may have stemmed from the Pythagorean school of the 5th and 6th centuries B.C. [**3**].

During the next two thousand years no further constructions of the sort described were added to those already known. No wonder then that the belief arose that the domain of constructible regular polygons had been exhausted by the ancients; at various times this belief was flatly asserted as an indisputable fact [**4**]. This was the situation when Gauss made the unexpected discovery which reopened the problem. Specifically, Gauss' work made it clear that it is possible to construct a *regular polygon* of 17 sides with straight edge and compass alone.

How did Gauss go about solving this problem? You might think that he considered this or that regular polygon—the heptagon, the nonagon, etc.—for which there was no construction with straight edge and compass up to that time, and tried to see whether a sudden insight might help him to find such a construction. Perhaps luck was with him, and he stumbled on the 17-gon. But this was not what happened. Gauss' insight into this construction problem was the result of number-theoretic and algebraic considerations. Gauss was thus able not merely to find a construction for the regular 17-gon, but also to decide for which values of $n$ the construction of a regular $n$-gon was possible and for which not; in short, he solved the problem completely.

We shall now discuss Gauss' solution. To begin with we shall consider only those regular $n$-gons for which $n$ is a prime,[6] that is,

$$n = 3, 5, 7, 11, 13, 17, 19, 23, \cdots.$$

[5] For Euclid, see Chapter I. The regular polygons are treated in Book IV of his *Elements*.

[6] For the definition of prime number see Chapter I. The number 2 is also a prime, but is omitted here because a polygon must have at least three sides.

As we saw above, the problem had long been solved for $n = 3$ and 5. Gauss' solution was that a regular $p$-gon, $p$ a prime, is constructible if, and only if, $p - 1$ is a power of 2, that is,

$$p - 1 = 2 = 2^1, \qquad p - 1 = 2 \cdot 2 = 2^2, \qquad p - 1 = 2 \cdot 2 \cdot 2 = 2^3, \quad \text{etc.}$$

The question then is whether $p - 1 = 2^k$, that is whether $p$ is of the form $2^k + 1$.[7]

Applying this formula to the list of primes given above, we see first that $3 - 1 = 2^1$ and $5 - 1 = 2^2$; hence

$$3 = 2^1 + 1, \qquad 5 = 2^2 + 1.$$

Gauss' criterion thus confirms again the long established fact that the regular polygons of 3 and 5 sides can be constructed exactly But the prime

$$17 = 2^4 + 1,$$

is also of the form $2^k + 1$; while the primes 7, 11, 13, 19, 23 are not; for none of the numbers

$$7 - 1 = 6, \quad 11 - 1 = 10, \quad 13 - 1 = 12, \quad 19 - 1 = 18, \quad 23 - 1 = 22$$

is a power of 2. Therefore, the regular heptagon and the regular polygons of 11, 13, 19 and 23 sides are not constructible, while the regular 17-gon is! Thus, the latter is the simplest constructible regular polygon not known to the ancients.

We shall describe the construction of the regular 17-gon later; but first, we ask whether there are other primes, besides 5, 3 and 17, which are of the form $2^k + 1$. This is indeed the case. For $k = 8$, we get $2^8 = 256$, and $2^8 + 1 = 257$, which is a prime Hence a regular polygon of 257 sides can be constructed with ruler and compass. The same is true for the regular polygon of 65537 sides, since $2^{16} + 1 = 65537$ is a prime. Whether there are still other primes of the form $2^k + 1$ is not yet known; this is an unsolved problem in pure number theory, which is also relevant to the construction problem we have discussed [**5**].

In the sequel, it will be convenient to refer to the primes of the form $2^k + 1$ as the *Gauss primes*.[8] It is not difficult to determine those composite numbers $n$, for which constructible regular $n$-gons exist. We were able to derive the construction of a regular 15-gon from that of a triangle and a pentagon because of the relation $2/5 - 1/3 = 1/15$. In the same way, the constructibility of a regular 51-gon (51 is the product of the two Gauss

[7] We cannot go into the algebraic basis of Gauss' theorem.

[8] They are also called the Fermat primes (see [**5**] and the book by A. Scholz mentioned there).

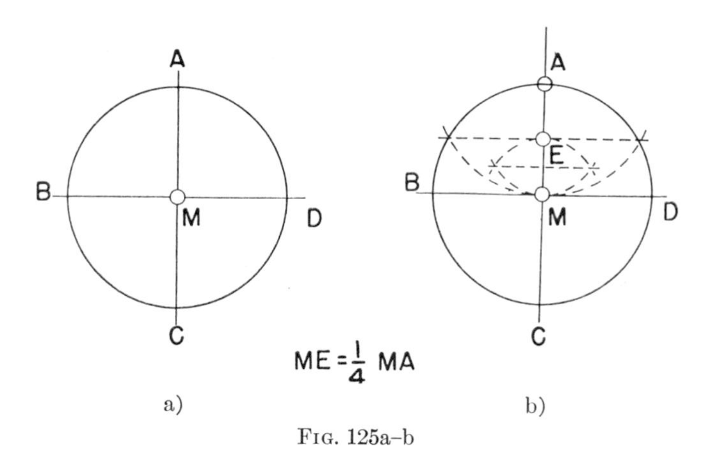


FIG. 125a–b

primes 3 and 17) follows from the relation $6/17 - 1/3 = 1/(3 \cdot 17) = 1/51$;[9] that of a regular polygon of 85 sides from $7/17 - 2/5 = 1/(5 \cdot 17) = 1/85$; and that of a regular polygon of $17 \cdot 257 = 4369$ sides from $121/257 - 8/17 = 1/(17 \cdot 257)$. In these examples we have combined two Gauss primes, but we can combine a still larger number. For example, since a polygon with $5 \cdot 17 = 85$ sides is constructible, a regular $n$-gon with $n = 255 = 3 \cdot 5 \cdot 17$ sides is also constructible because of the fact that $1/3 - 28/85 = 1/(3 \cdot 85) = 1/255$. In this way, we arrive at the conclusion that every regular $n$-gon, where $n$ is the product of two or more distinct Gauss primes, is constructible with straight edge and compass. Furthermore, as in the case of the triangle and the pentagon, the number of sides may be doubled one or more times by successive bisections.

We can now state Gauss' result: A regular $n$-gon is constructible with straight edge and compass if, and only if, 1) $n$ is a Gauss prime or the product of distinct Gauss primes; or 2) $n$ is the product of a number satisfying 1) and a power of 2; or 3) $n$ is a power of 2 (but at least 4) [6].

The construction of a regular polygon of 17 sides is shown in Figs. 125a–n, each representing a single step. We begin with a circle with center $M$ and two perpendicular diameters $AC$ and $BD$ (as in the case of the pentagon). In Fig. 125b the problem is to construct $ME = \frac{1}{4}MA$; the figure itself shows how $MA$ is first bisected, and the resulting half is again bisected so that $\frac{1}{4}MA = ME$. Fig. 125c shows an arc of the circle with center $E$ and radius $EB$ which intersects the straight line $AC$ at $G$ and $F$.

[9] The procedure is similar to that described in Fig. 124a, b. A regular triangle and a regular 17-gon are inscribed in a circle so that they have a vertex $A$ in common. Starting at $A$, and counting vertices in the same sense around the circle (both clockwise or both counterclockwise), the distance of the 6th vertex of the 17-gon from the first vertex of the triangle is equal to the side of a regular 51-gon.

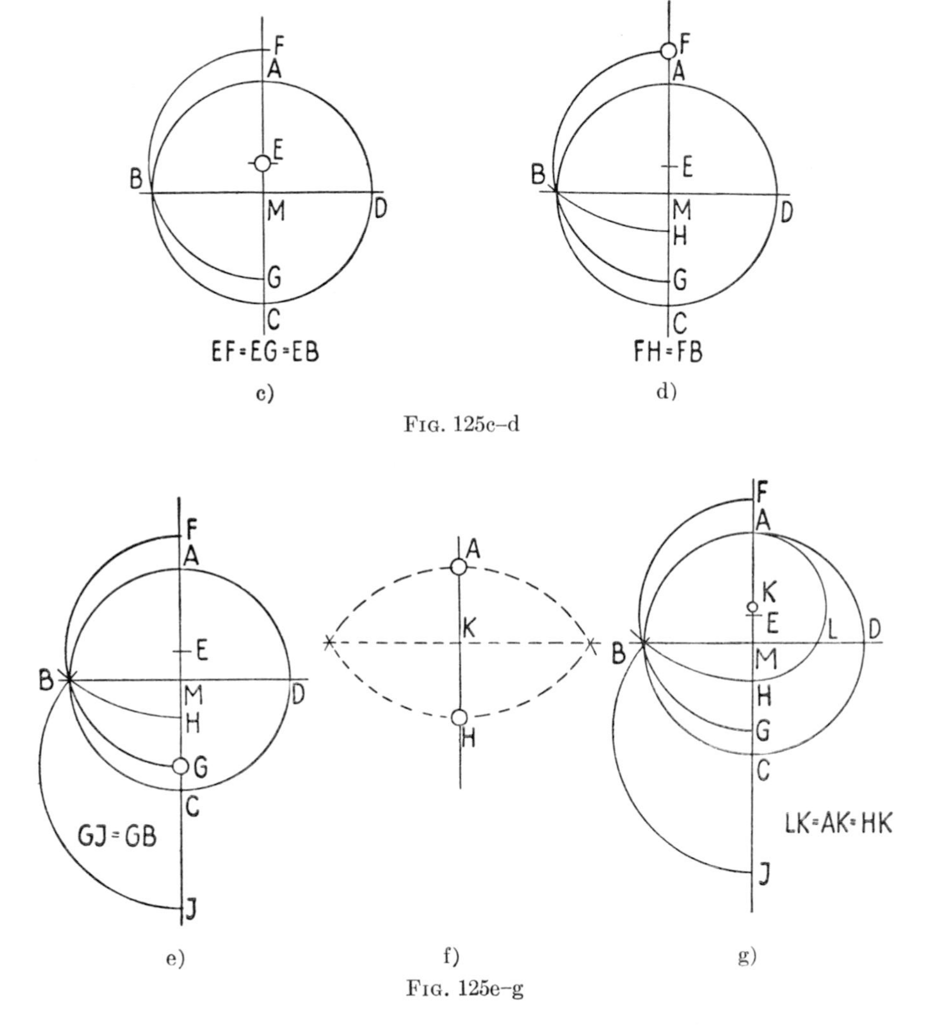


FIG. 125c–d

FIG. 125e–g

In Fig. 125d the point $H$ is located by drawing the circle with center $F$ through $B$. In Fig. 125e we get the point $J$. Bisecting $AH$ in Fig. 125f, we get $K$. Fig. 125g shows how the semi-circle constructed on the right side of the straight line $AC$ with $K$ as center cuts $BD$ to give the point $L$. In Fig. 125h, $LM$ is marked off once to the right of $L$ to give the point $N$, and in Fig. 125i, the circle with center $N$ and radius $MJ$ cuts $AC$ at $O$. Construction of one quarter of $OJ$ (Fig. 125j) yields $OZ$; striking a distance $OZ$ from $M$ we reach point $X$, and marking it off again, point $Y$ (Fig. 125k, l). Constructing the perpendicular bisector of $MY$ (Fig. 125l), which of course goes through $X$, we need only determine its point of intersection

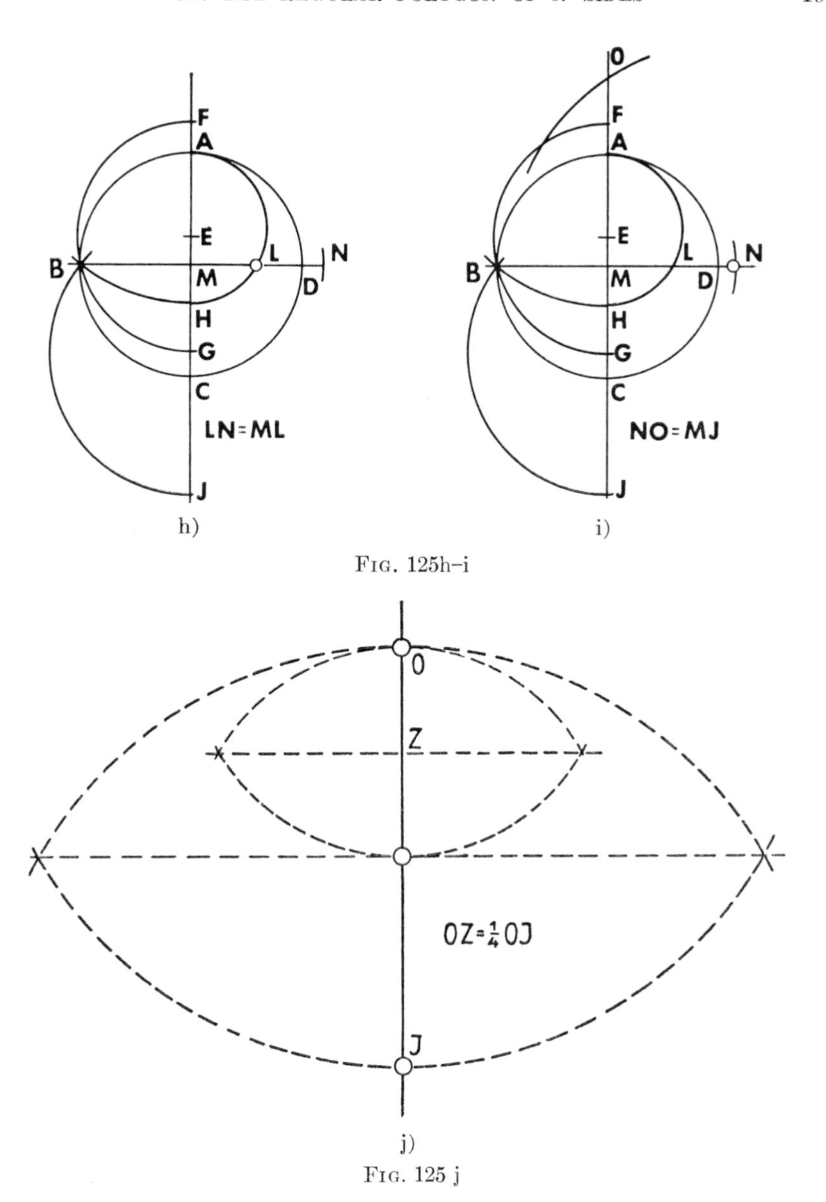


FIG. 125h–i



FIG. 125 j

$S$ with the original circle. $AS$ is then the side of a regular polygon of 17 sides [7]. The 17-gon itself, obtained by marking $AS$ off 17 times, is shown in Fig. 125m. It is of course again possible to obtain the regular polygon of 34 sides (Fig. 125n), 68 sides, etc. by bisection.

If the construction of the regular 17-gon is a great deal more complicated than that of the pentagon, that of the regular polygon of 257 sides

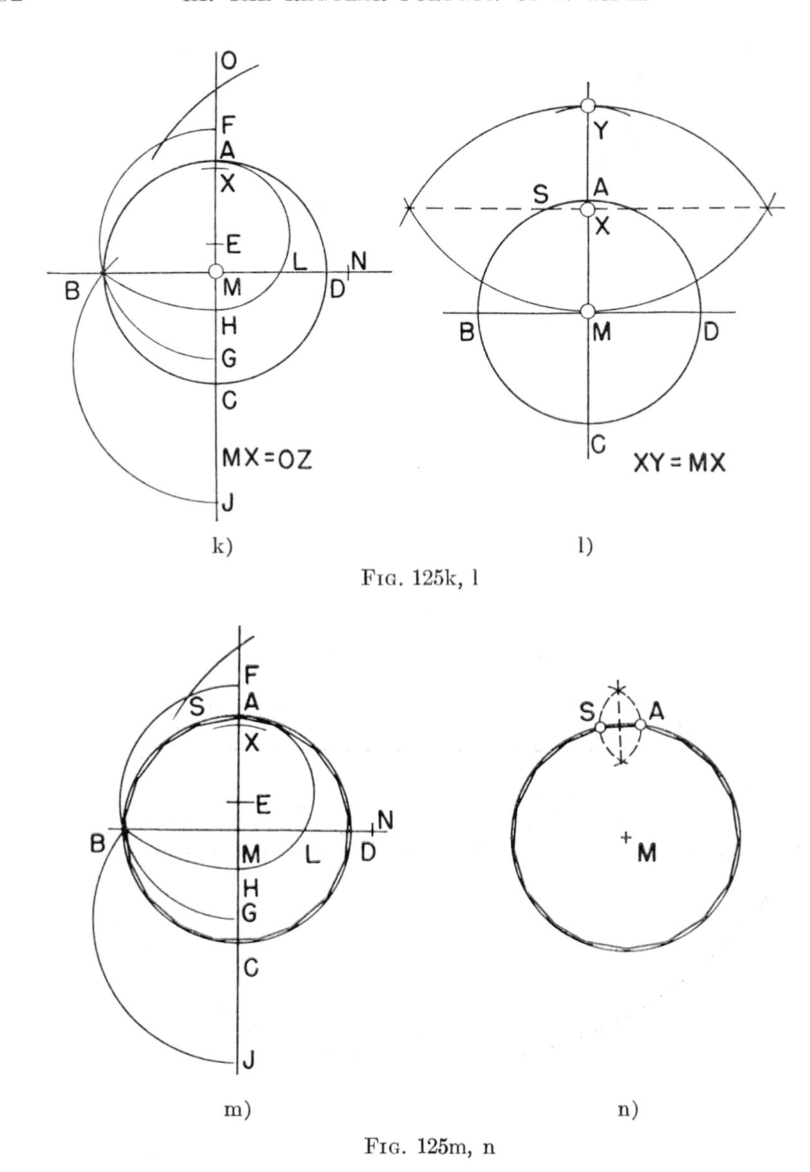


FIG. 125k, l



FIG. 125m, n

will be even more so. A book of 194 pages once appeared which gave the actual construction [8]. I hope therefore that you will appreciate my sparing you the details of this construction.

An amateur actually constructed a regular polygon of 65537 sides; he worked for ten years on the construction and the algebraic developments associated with it. The total work filled a chest which was given to the Department of Mathematics at the University of Göttingen for safekeeping [**9**], but it is unlikely that anyone has ever read it through.[10]

This is the third time that we have encountered a problem requiring an exact construction with straight edge and compass alone. But in the case of the other two, numerous attempts were made to solve them until it was proved that such constructions are impossible.[11] The problem of constructing regular polygons, however, has an entirely different history. The problem had long been laid aside in the belief that the ancients had exhausted all the possible constructions. But one day Gauss, then a relatively unknown young man, unexpectedly found that additional constructions were possible and found a theoretical solution of the whole problem [**10**]. The time came when his name resounded in the world of science, and Gauss became one of the immortals. But at this time he was a month short of nineteen. A friend, Professor E. A. W. Zimmermann sent a short notice of the discovery to the *Jenenser Intelligenzblatt* in 1796, and referred to the exceptional achievement of the young man [**11**]. The scientific publication of the theory on which the new result was based did not occur until five years later, perhaps because of printing delays. Gauss' original considerations were not geometric, so his discovery was first published in his *Disquisitiones Arithmeticae*.[12] This book was fundamental to the development of *number theory*, and in the last part treats the theory of the "equations defining the division of a circle."[13] The novelty and depth of its concepts made this book not at all easy to read. Nevertheless, everyone who was interested in number theory and the geometric problem we have just discussed was forced to read it. We have already mentioned how intensively Dirichlet studied this volume (see Chapter VII). Many years ago I happened to come across a copy of the original edition in a Viennese bookstore. On the flyleaf was inscribed the name of another famous mathematician, Liouville; and I was very happy to obtain this double souvenir.

Young as he was, the solution of the problem of regular polygons was not Gauss' first achievement. His *Disquisitiones Arithmeticae*, which appeared in 1801, had been preceded by other work. Gauss was born in Brunswick, on April 30, 1777. His family was not well off and his youth was attended with hardship. Even as a boy he had a passionate interest in calculations (which very often led to profound problems), and while

[10] Since Gauss' general theory decided all the basic questions, there is no scientific gain from an actual construction (except for the interest that may attach to the peculiarities of special cases). A proof of the formula $(a + b)(a - b) = a^2 - b^2$ for each pair of numbers $a$, $b$ up to a million would be equally interesting.

[11] See Chapters III and V.

[12] According to the custom of the time, the book appeared first in Latin, but was later translated into German.

[13] *De aequationibus circuli sectiones definientibus* is the Latin title.

still quite young asserted his right to follow his true calling against the wishes of his parents. He worked during the day, but at night he carried on extensive mathematical calculations. The lighting was poor, and sometimes, when paper was lacking, his figures were written in the margins of his books. But his schools recognized his mathematical and linguistic gifts. Influential people began to notice him, and Duke Ferdinand of Brunswick made it possible for him to attend the gymnasium and the university. From 1788 to 1795 he studied at the preparatory schools in Brunswick, and after a short period of study at the University of Göttingen, returned to Brunwick in 1798 [**12**]. During this time Gauss discovered his true bent. For many years he had also been interested in philology, but his construction of the regular 17-gon in 1796 finally decided him on a mathematical career. Many of the problems Gauss thought through at that time were not made public until decades later, when, after his death, in the course of compiling his Collected Works evidence of extensive unpublished research was found in his private papers and in his correspondence with other scholars. Near the conclusion of his studies at the gymnasium Gauss had intuitively discovered a law for the distribution of the primes. A rigorous proof of this law was found a century later, thanks to the techniques made available by an accumulation of research (see Chapter VII). Even earlier, he had been preoccupied with the axiom of parallels, and became convinced that this axiom was independent of the others.[14] As a result of this he gradually evolved the idea—without ever publishing anything on it—that the axiom of parallels has only approximate physical validity. Another discovery (published in 1795) was the method of least squares for minimizing the effect of errors inherent in any set of experimental data [**13**]. This method is used extensively in treating astronomical, geodesic and many physical measurements. It did not have long to wait before being tested. On the first night of the 19th century, January 1, 1801, Piazzi discovered the first of the so called small planets (planetoids or asteroids) at the Palermo Observatory. Our knowledge of the celestial bodies of our solar system had again been enlarged [**14**]. But when this new wandering star, visible only by telescope, disappeared into the West, and was sought again in the East at the proper time, it could not be found. The determination of the orbits and the calculation of the positions of the old planets, most of which are visible to the naked eye and can be located immediately, were based on longstanding and extensive observations [**15**]. But to find the planetoid again, its position

[14] The axiom of parallels is one of Euclid's axioms. It states that given a line and a point not on the line in the plane, there is precisely one line (a parallel) passing through the given point and not meeting the first line. Euclidean and non-Euclidean geometry will be discussed in Chapter XIV.

had to be determined with a great deal of precision on the basis of a small part of its path. Gauss' solution was so successful that the new planet Ceres was found again, but at a point far removed (14 full moon breadths) [16] from the spot which previous more primitive methods had predicted [17]. This far-reaching scientific achievement made Gauss, who was then only 24 years old, famous. He had received his doctoral degree only two years before, with a dissertation in pure mathematics [18]. This dissertation indicates that Gauss already had a clear insight into the nature of imaginary numbers and their value for many branches of mathematics [19], although he avoided using them in his thesis.

Another astronomical problem presented itself when Olbers (1758–1840) discovered a second planetoid, Pallas, at his private observatory in Bremen, March 28, 1802 [20]. Certain peculiarities of the orbit of Pallas required new theoretical investigations [21]. These involved Gauss in extensive calculations lasting for many years.

In 1807, Gauss fulfilled a personal ambition when he was made Professor and Director of the Observatory at the University of Göttingen, a position he held until his death, almost half a century later. But his worldly success did not free him from pressing personal problems. The patron of his student days, Ferdinand von Brunswick, at 71, was killed in the Battle of Jena, leading the Prussian army against Napoleon. Brunswick had been part of the state of Hannover, whose princes had occupied the throne of England since 1714. It had been occupied since 1803, when Napoleon was First Consul of France, and was now burdened with military imposts and strict police supervision. After the Battle of Jena, Brunswick, as well as other parts of Hannover, was given to the newly created Kingdom of Westphalia, to be ruled by Napoleon's youngest brother, Jerome. A few years later, in 1811, Hannover came under complete subjection to France. The war in Spain, the battle against Austria, the great march into Russia, all demanded military conscriptions not only in France, but in the "befriended countries" which were already suffering from their heavy war contributions. We know from Gauss' diary that during this war period wage payments were often suspended while at the same time taxes were being raised. He lived at a bare subsistence level; even his astronomical instruments were wholly inadequate [22]. Nevertheless, Gauss, who felt within him the pressure of many deep and unsolved problems, kept hard at work. Besides the thought he gave to a geometry without the axiom of parallels (already discussed above [23]), he also developed extensively, as is revealed by his private papers, a new mathematical theory, connected with certain problems of the integral calculus [24].[15]

[15] It is in the nature of the case that we can give a much more detailed account of

It was difficult for his family to understand a man who in the midst of privation and worry was totally immersed in his conceptual world. Indeed they thought him mad. But although he followed the path of his inner calling unswervingly, he was not without his agonizing moments. In one of his posthumous papers a cramped, pencilled note was found, written in the midst of a sketch for a mathematical problem: "Der Tod ist mir lieber als ein solches Leben"—"Death is preferable to this kind of life."

We do not know what Gauss' thoughts were about the politics of his times. His motto, even for his scientific activities, was "pauca sed matura" —"the few but the fully developed." He was known to hold back particularly where the expression of his ideas (as in the case of non-Euclidean geometry, which negated the axiom of parallels) might arouse the misunderstanding and enmity of the multitude, or the "cries of the mob," as he called them in one of his letters. How prudent it was, then, to remain silent on political matters, no matter how much events may have torn at his inner feelings.

After the Congress of Vienna in 1815, when peace came, George III of England claimed his ancestral land, and the status of Hannover was now raised to that of a kingdom. In 1816 the government commissioned Gauss to make a geodetic survey of Hannover, an assignment which took twenty-five years, and was of the greatest importance not only for the drawing of reliable maps, but for an increased knowledge of the exact shape of the earth. Gauss not only devised computational techniques of permanent significance, but also invented the heliotrope, an instrument vastly superior to any used previously. He personally participated in the measurements for five years, and no doubt found work in the field beneficial. Using the measurement (up to that time the largest made) of the triangle formed by the mountain peak Brocken (1142 m) in the Harz, Inselberg (915 m), about 20 km. south-east of Eisenach in the Thuringian Forest, and Hoher Hagen (508 m), about 12 km. south-west of Göttingen, he tried to determine the degree to which Euclidean geometry (based on the axiom of parallels) had physical validity.[16] His famous paper on the theory of surfaces (1827) is closely related to this work with the measurement of the earth.

At this time, Gauss was 50 years old, but many important problems and results in still other fields lay before him. By chance, at this time he extended his work to physics.

---

his practical achievements (those referring to geodesy, astronomy, physics), than of his accomplishments in pure mathematics.

[16] See Footnote 14. Examples of physical entities which are made to correspond to the straight lines of geometry are the axes of rotation of rigid bodies in mechanics, and light rays in a homogeneous (refractionless) medium in optics.

Three decades earlier, Goethe's idea of a society for the joint consideration of scientific problems had been rediculed by his brother-in-law Schlosser. Nevertheless a desire for unification and mutual enrichment of the various disciplines of the natural sciences led a group of scientists to found the Versammlungen Deutscher Naturforscher und Ärzte (Society of German Physicians and Natural Scientists) whose first meeting was called in 1822 by the natural philosopher Professor Lorenz Oken of Jena. Soon after, Alexander von Humboldt became one of the society's leading spirits [25].

In 1828 the society met in Berlin and Gauss was invited to attend as Humboldt's personal guest. It was on this occasion that he met the physicist Wilhelm Weber (1804–1891),[17] almost 30 years his junior. At the suggestion of Gauss, Weber was called to Göttingen, and the joint work of the two men began, work later commemorated by a Gauss-Weber memorial near the new Göttingen Institute. Between 1820 and 1831 a series of discoveries by Oersted, Biot and Savart, Ampère, and Faraday had exposed the relationship between electricity and magnetism. In addition to important refinements in methods of measurement, the collaboration of Weber and Gauss was responsible for the introduction of the so called absolute units of measurement,[18] and a general theory (based on the work of the French mathematicians, Lagrange, 1773, Laplace, 1782, and Poisson, 1813) of forces which obey the inverse square law [26]. Examples are gravitational, electric and magnetic forces.

Another product of Gauss' and Weber's research was the construction of the first *electromagnetic telegraph* in 1833, which allowed Weber's Institute of Physics to communicate with Gauss' Observatory. Previously, people had thought of the applications of electricity only to electro-chemical effects. Gauss now stated that at this point the only barriers to a world-wide communications system were technical and financial.

In conjunction with Weber, Gauss also applied himself to the study of

[17] At the death of William IV in 1837, Queen Victoria (1819–1901) ascended to the throne, but because of certain laws of inheritance, Ernst August von Cumberland succeeded to the throne of Hannover. When the latter overrode the constitution and demanded the cooperation of the state employees, seven professors at the University of Göttingen framed a proclamation of protest. They were immediately deprived of their positions and left the country. Wilhelm Weber was one of the "Göttingen Seven." Recalled in 1841, he remained at Göttingen, except for the years 1843–49, which he spent in Leipzig. Weber's famous fundamental law of electro-dynamics (for many years considered conclusive, until it was superceded by Maxwell's theory)—like Newton's theory of gravitation—assumed instantaneous action of the forces at a distance. Gauss, on the other hand (in a letter to Weber in 1845) thought, like Faraday, that the action of a force is propagated with a finite velocity. In this, as in many other cases, he anticipated the future development of science.

[18] In this system, all units of measurement are based on the fundamental units of length, time and mass.

*terrestrial magnetism,* familiar to us mostly through the magnetic needle of a compass and the phenomenon of the Polar lights. This activity was stimulated by Alexander von Humboldt, who, after his South American research trip (1799–1804), founded a world-wide society for the study of terrestrial magnetism. Gauss, who undertook to sift the data collected by the society, came to the conclusion that the earth is a large magnet, whose magnetic North and South Poles are not exactly the same as the geographical poles which lie on the earth's axis of rotation. Gauss calculated the position of the magnetic North and South Poles (the latter to a lesser degree of accuracy because of the smaller amount of data gathered in the southern hemisphere). A few years later, an American ship arrived in the vicinity of the magnetic South Pole and found that its location was in such close agreement with that predicted by Gauss (72°35′ south, 152°30′ east of Greenwich), that it far exceeded the expected accuracy of Gauss' calculations [**27**].

In discussing Gauss' achievements, we have been forced to overlook much of his work in the field of pure mathematics. Nevertheless this was the area he probed most deeply; a great deal of his research, extending over decades, he did not deem ripe for publication. He would not reveal initial results which he saw might yet lead to more profound conclusions. Occasionally he might utter a few cryptic remarks to the most intimate of his colleagues. It often happened that younger men would come to him to announce discoveries which had long been lying in the drawers of his desk; not unnaturally, when he said "These things are not new to me," they thought him perverse and envious. His posthumous papers have shown that he was speaking the truth: they prove that he had progressed much further than even his own remarks indicated. This retiring, secretive, unapproachable man, who was able to let himself go only in a few letters to old friends and students, was unquestionably the outstanding world authority of his time in the field of mathematics and its applications.

When he died, on February 23, 1855, Gauss was almost 78. In his honor, the reigning King of Hannover ordered a medal which hailed him as the prince of mathematicians.

In 1880 a memorial whose base was a polygon of 17 sides was erected to him in Brunswick. Gauss had once himself considered this figure as a possible decoration for his gravestone. It now stands in his native town as a symbol of its great son [**28**].

There is another, perhaps more beautiful, honor which must not go unmentioned. Felix Klein, in his lectures on the development of mathematcs in the 19th century at Göttingen from 1914 to 1919 (later published [**29**]) included this glowing tribute to Gauss:

"If we now inquire what was the unusual, the unique quality of this man, the answer must be: a combination of the greatest individual achievement in every chosen field with the greatest versatility; a complete balance between mathematical creativity, the strength for pursuing its development, and the practical sense for its application, including faultless observation and measurement; and finally, the presentation of this great self-created wealth in the most polished form.

"He had only two peers, Archimedes and Newton, who were equally gifted. In common with both, Gauss had the unusually long life span which makes possible a full development of personality."

In Klein's opinion, Archimedes personifies the scientific achievements of classical antiquity, Newton is the initiator of higher mathematics, while Gauss represents the emergence of a new mathematical era.

*Notes to Chapter IX*

# THE REGULAR POLYGON OF 17 SIDES

**1** (p. 185). The proof merely requires repeated application of the Pythagorean theorem and a few trigonometric formulas. We set the unit of length equal to the radius of the circle, so that $MA = 1$. Let $a$ be the length of $AH$, and $g$ the length of $AG = AU$. Then

$$a^2 = HM^2 + MA^2 = (\tfrac{1}{2})^2 + 1^2 = \tfrac{5}{4},$$

so that

$$a = AH = HG = \tfrac{1}{2}\sqrt{5}.$$

Hence,

$$MG = HG - HM = \tfrac{1}{2}\sqrt{5} - \tfrac{1}{2} = \tfrac{1}{2}(\sqrt{5} - 1).$$

Similarly,

$$g^2 = GM^2 + MA^2 = \tfrac{1}{4}(\sqrt{5} - 1)^2 + 1^2 = \tfrac{1}{4}(10 - 2\sqrt{5}),$$

so that

$$g = \tfrac{1}{2}\,(10 - 2\sqrt{5})^{1/2}.$$

Now, let $F$ be the midpoint of the segment $AU$ (see Fig. 122d and Fig. 126), and denote by $\varphi$ the angle $FMA$. Then

$$\sin\varphi = FA : AM = \tfrac{1}{2}AU : AM = \tfrac{1}{2}g : 1 = \tfrac{1}{4}\,(10 - 2\sqrt{5})^{1/2}.$$

Hence,

$$\begin{aligned}\cos^2\varphi &= 1 - \sin^2\varphi = 1 - (10 - 2\sqrt{5})/16 \\ &= (6 + 2\sqrt{5})/16 = [\tfrac{1}{4}(\sqrt{5} + 1)]^2.\end{aligned}$$

Therefore,

$$\cos\varphi = \pm\tfrac{1}{4}(\sqrt{5} + 1).$$

However, since $\varphi$ is an acute angle, $\cos\varphi$ must be positive, so that

$$\cos\varphi = \tfrac{1}{4}(\sqrt{5} + 1). \tag{1}$$

We now use the trigonometric identities

$$\begin{aligned}\cos(\alpha + \beta) &= \cos\alpha\cos\beta - \sin\alpha\sin\beta, \\ \sin(\alpha + \beta) &= \sin\alpha\cos\beta + \cos\alpha\sin\beta.\end{aligned}$$

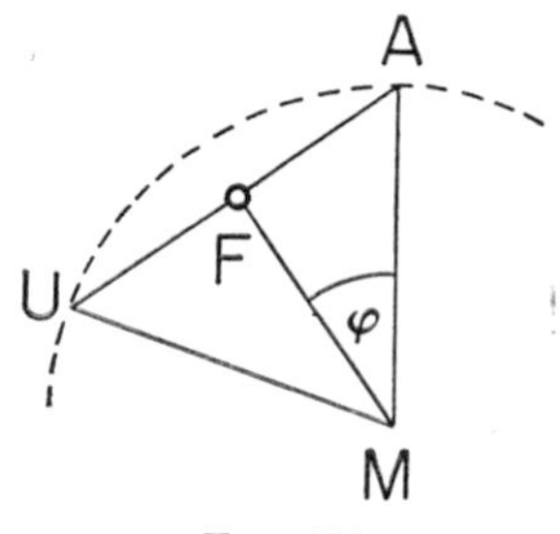


FIG. 126

In these identities, we put successively $\beta = \alpha$, $\beta = 2\alpha$, $\beta = 3\alpha$, $\beta = 4\alpha$, to obtain:

$$\begin{aligned}
\cos 2\alpha &= \cos^2\alpha - \sin^2\alpha = \cos^2\alpha - (1 - \cos^2\alpha) \\
&= 2\cos^2\alpha - 1, \\
\sin 2\alpha &= 2\sin\alpha\cos\alpha, \\
\cos 3\alpha &= \cos\alpha\cos 2\alpha - \sin\alpha\sin 2\alpha \\
&= 2\cos^3\alpha - \cos\alpha - 2\cos\alpha\sin^2\alpha = 4\cos^3\alpha - 3\cos\alpha, \\
\sin 3\alpha &= \sin\alpha\cos 2\alpha + \cos\alpha\sin 2\alpha = \sin\alpha\,(4\cos^2\alpha - 1), \\
\cos 4\alpha &= \cos\alpha\cos 3\alpha - \sin\alpha\sin 3\alpha = 8\cos^4\alpha - 8\cos^2\alpha + 1, \\
\sin 4\alpha &= \sin\alpha\cos 3\alpha + \cos\alpha\sin 3\alpha = \sin\alpha\,(8\cos^3\alpha - 4\cos\alpha),
\end{aligned}$$

and finally[1]

$$\begin{aligned}
\cos 5\alpha &= \cos\alpha\cos 4\alpha - \sin\alpha\sin 4\alpha \\
&= 16\cos^5\alpha - 20\cos^3\alpha + 5\cos\alpha, \\
\sin 5\alpha &= \sin\alpha\cos 4\alpha + \cos\alpha\sin 4\alpha \\
&= \sin\alpha\,(16\cos^4\alpha - 12\cos^2\alpha + 1).
\end{aligned} \tag{2}$$

We shall use (1) and (2) to calculate $\sin 5\varphi$ and $\cos 5\varphi$. First, from (1),

$$\begin{aligned}
\cos^2\varphi &= (\sqrt{5} + 1)^2/16 = (\sqrt{5} + 3)/8, \\
\cos^4\varphi &= (\sqrt{5} + 3)^2/64 = (3\sqrt{5} + 7)/32.
\end{aligned}$$

Hence,

$$\begin{aligned}
&16\cos^4\varphi - 12\cos^2\varphi + 1 = \tfrac{1}{2}(3\sqrt{5} + 7) - 3(\sqrt{5} + 3)/2 + 1 = 0, \\
&16\cos^4\varphi - 20\cos^2\varphi + 5 \\
&\qquad = \tfrac{1}{2}(3\sqrt{5} + 7) - 5(\sqrt{5} + 3)/2 + 5 = 1 - \sqrt{5}.
\end{aligned}$$

[1] The reader familiar with the elementary theory of complex numbers can obtain (2) more easily by using de Moivre's formula:

$$\cos n\alpha + i\sin n\alpha = (\cos\alpha + i\sin\alpha)^n.$$

To obtain (2), set $n = 5$ in this formula, expand $(\cos\alpha + i\sin\alpha)^5$ by the binomial theorem, set $\cos 5\alpha$ equal to the real part and $\sin 5\alpha$ equal to the imaginary part of the result, and simplify by using the identity $\sin^2\alpha = 1 - \cos^2\alpha$.

Therefore, according to (2), $\sin 5\varphi = 0$, and

$$\cos 5\varphi = (1 - \sqrt{5}) \cos \varphi = \tfrac{1}{4}(1 + \sqrt{5})(1 - \sqrt{5}) = -1.$$

It follows that $5\varphi = 180°$, so that $2\varphi =$ angle $AMU$ is $\tfrac{1}{5}$ of $360°$. Hence, the arc $AU$ is $\tfrac{1}{5}$ of a full circle. This proves our assertion that the segment $AU = AG$ is the side of a pentagon inscribed in the circle.

**2** (p. 186). Several constructions are known for each of the polygons we have discussed. In fact, various constructions for the pentagon and decagon were already known in antiquity. In this chapter, we are interested in determining those values of $n$ for which at least one construction of the corresponding regular $n$-gon exists.

**3** (p. 187). See {1}.

**4** (p. 187). See {1; p. 193}.

**5** (p. 188). It *is* known that $n = 2^k + 1$ is not a prime if $k$ is divisible by an odd integer $u > 1$. For then, $n = 2^{cu} + 1 = a^u + 1$, where $a = 2^c$. But, if $u$ is odd,

$$a^u + 1 = (a + 1)(a^{u-1} - a^{u-2} + a^{u-3} - \cdots + a^2 - a + 1);$$

hence $a^u + 1$ is composite if $u > 1$. Hence, if $n = 2^k + 1$ is to be a prime, $k$ cannot have any odd prime factors and must therefore be a power of $2: k = 2^s$. The problem reduces then to asking which primes are of the form

$$n = 2^{2^s} + 1. \tag{3}$$

As we have already seen, $s = 0, 1, 2, 3, 4$ yields the primes 3, 5, 17, 257 and 65537. Fermat (see Chapter XIII) had conjectured that (3) yields a prime for every value of $s$. But Euler, a century later, in 1732, showed that this conjecture was false, because $2^{2^5} + 1 = 2^{32} + 1 = 4294967297 = (641)(6700417)$ is composite; it had also been shown that $2^{2^s} + 1$ is composite for a whole sequence of values of $s$. See in this connection {2}, {1; p. 194} and {3}.

**6** (p. 189). That is, a regular $n$-gon is constructible if, and only if, $n = 2^g m$, where $n > 2$, $g$ is a nonnegative integer and $m$ is an odd integer $\geq 1$ whose prime factors are distinct Gauss primes.

**7** (p. 191). We shall not give a detailed proof of this assertion, although it can be carried out in the same elementary way as the proof in Note 1 for the pentagon; in this case, it is true, a considerably greater perseverance is required. The first step in the proof is to show, by repeated application of the Pythagorean theorem at each step of the geometric construction, that if $a$ is the length of the radius $MA$, then

$$MX = ab,$$

where

$$b = \tfrac{1}{4}[(c + d\sqrt{e} - 2\sqrt{f})^{1/2} + d + \tfrac{1}{2}\sqrt{e}],$$

and

$$\begin{aligned} c &= (17 + 3\sqrt{17})/4, \\ d &= (\sqrt{17} - 1)/4, \\ e &= (17 - \sqrt{17})/2, \\ f &= (17 + \sqrt{17})/2. \end{aligned}$$

Therefore,

$$b = MX/MA = MX/MS = \cos\gamma,$$

where we have set $\gamma$ = angle $AMS$.

The next step is to show that $\gamma = 360°/17$. To this end, we require a formula for $\cos 17\alpha$ in terms of powers of $\cos\alpha$. This can be obtained as follows. Starting with the formulas for $\cos 2\alpha$ and $\sin 2\alpha$ (see Note 1), we obtain, by repeated application of these formulas, formulas for $\cos 4\alpha$, $\sin 4\alpha$, $\cos 8\alpha$, $\sin 8\alpha$, and finally $\cos 16\alpha$ and $\sin 16\alpha$. Then putting $\beta = 16\alpha$ in the identity for $\cos(\alpha + \beta)$ (see Note 1), using the identities for $\cos 16\alpha$ and $\sin 16\alpha$, and substituting $1 - \cos^2\alpha$ wherever $\sin^2\alpha$ occurs in the result, we obtain

$$\begin{aligned} \cos 17\alpha = {} & 65536\cos^{17}\alpha - 278528\cos^{15}\alpha \\ & + 487424\cos^{13}\alpha - 452608\cos^{11}\alpha \\ & + 239360\cos^{9}\alpha - 71808\cos^{7}\alpha \\ & + 11424\cos^{5}\alpha - 816\cos^{3}\alpha + 17\cos\alpha. \end{aligned}$$

If we now set $\alpha = \gamma$, and substitute $\cos\alpha = \cos\gamma = b$ in the formula just obtained, we get, after performing the calculation,

$$\cos 17\gamma = 1.$$

On the other hand, it is not hard to see that

$$0° < 17\gamma < 720°.$$[2]

Since there is just one angle, 360°, satisfying this inequality whose cosine is 1, it follows that

$$17\gamma = 360°,$$

and

$$\gamma = 360°/17.$$

Of course, the same result can be obtained more quickly and in a much

[2] An approximate calculation shows that $b = .932 \cdots > \sqrt{3}/2 = \cos 30°$; hence $\cos\gamma > \cos 30°$, so that $\gamma < 30°$ and $17\gamma < 510° < 720°$.

more satisfying fashion if instead of performing these tedious calculations we use Gauss' algebraic development, which at the same time shows how the construction is to be carried out. Gauss' theory also shows that the regular 17-gon can be constructed in many other ways.

**8** (p. 192). This was a paper by J. F. Richelot (1808–1875, Königsberg) which appeared in four instalments in the *Journal für die reine und angewandte Mathematik* (*Journal for pure and applied mathematics*), vol. 9. More information about the historical development of the whole question can be found in {1; p. 181 ff.; cf. specifically p. 194}.

**9** (p. 193). This unusually diligent work, carried out by Professor Hermes in Lingen, is mentioned by Felix Klein {4}.

**10** (p. 193). Gauss' solution to the problem of the constructibility of regular $n$-gons is a complete solution in the following sense. Given a positive integer $n$, in order to decide whether the corresponding regular $n$-gon is constructible with straight edge and compass alone, it is only necessary to decompose $n$ into its prime factors and to determine whether the odd prime factors of $n$ are all distinct and that each of them is a Gauss prime, that is, of the form $2^k + 1$, and so necessarily of the form $2^{2^s} + 1$ (see Note 5). It is, to be sure, still an open question, as we have already noted, whether in addition to the five Gauss primes already known there are still more and whether there is perhaps an infinite number or only a finite number of such primes. The latter is still an unsolved problem (in pure number theory).

**11** (p. 193). The short report is written and signed by "C. F. Gauss of Brunswick, Studiousus in mathematics at Göttingen", and Professor Zimmermann adds: "It is worthy of notice that Herr Gauss is now in his 18th year and has devoted himself here in Brunswick to philosophy and classical literature with just as great success as to higher mathematics. April 18, 1796." See {5}.

**12** (p. 194). Gauss again expressed his gratitude to Duke Ferdinand in a beautiful dedication of the above mentioned *Disquisitiones Arithmeticae* which contains many noteworthy passages, and since it is difficult to fragmentize, may perhaps be reproduced here in its entirety. By presenting the original text, we give the preference to the Latinists among our readers, whom we do wish to woo to some extent. Posterity owes thanks to the prince, whose life and activity ended so unhappily, for the encouragement by means of which Gauss' path was opened to his destiny. The dedication reads:

Serenissimo Principi Ac Domino
Carolo Gvilielmo Ferdinando
Brvnovicensivm ac Lvnebvrgensivm Dvci

Princeps Serenissime

Summae equidem felicitati mihi duco, quod Celsissimo nomini *Tuo* hoc opus inscribere mihi permittis, quod vt *Tibi* offeram sancto pietatis officio obstringor. Nisi enim *Tua* gratia, Serenissime Princeps, introitum mihi ad scientias primum aperuisset, nisi perpetua *Tua* beneficia studia mea vsque sustentauissent, scientiae mathematicae, ad quam vehementi semper amore delatus sum, totum me deuouere non potuissem. Quin adeo eas ipsas meditationes, quarum partem hoc volumen exhibet, vt suscipere, per plures annos continuare literisque consignare liceret, *Tua* sola benignitas effecit, quae vt, ceterarum curarum expers, huic imprimis incumbere possem praestitit. Quas quum tandem in lucem emittere cuperem, *Tua* munificentia cuncta, quae editionem remorabantur, obstacula remouit. Haec *Tua* tanta de me meisque conatibus merita gratissima potius mente tacitaque admiratione reuoluere, quam iustis dignisque laudibus celebrare possum. Namque non solum tali me muneri haud parem sentio, sed et neminem ignorare puto, solennem *Tibi* esse tam insignem liberalitatem in omnes qui ad optimas disciplinas excolendas conferre videntur, neque eas scientias, quae vulgo abstrusiores et a vitae communis vtilitate remotiores creduntur, a patrocinio *Tuo* exclusas esse, quum *Tu* ipse intimum scientiarum omnium inter se et necessarium vinculum mente illa sapientissima omniumque quae ad humanae societatis prosperitatem augendam pertinent peritissima, penitus perspexeris. Quodsi *Tu*, Princeps Serenissime, hunc librum, et gratissimi in *Te* animi et laborum nobilissimae scientiae dicatorum testem, insigni illo fauore, quo me tamdiu amplexus es, haud indignum iudicaueris, operam meam me non inutiliter collocasse, eiusque honoris, quem prae omnibus in votis habui, compotem me factum esse, mihi gratulabor

Princeps Serenissime

Brunouici mense Julio 1801.

Celsitudinis Tuae seruus addictissimus
C. F. Gauss.

**13** (p. 194). Actually, the method is to minimize the sum of the squares of the errors.

**14** (p. 194). Seven of these celestial bodies were already known to antiquity; no others were known till the beginning of the 17th century, when, shortly after the discovery of the telescope, the four largest of the moons of Jupiter (also called court-followers or satellites) were discovered on the 7th and 13th of January, 1610 by Galileo[3]—and independently on January 8th by Simon Mayer. In the years 1655–1687 a moon of Saturn and the ring system around this planet, which had already been noticed as a peculiar change of form by Galileo and others, were added by Huyghens.[4] In addition, four more moons of Saturn were discovered by the elder Cassini[5]

[3] Galileo Galilei, the discoverer of the laws of gravity, advocate of the Copernican doctrine of the sun (not the earth) as the central body of the planetary system—a doctrine which, prosecuted by the Inquisition, he had to abjure in 1633; born February 15, 1564, in Pisa, died in blindness January 8, 1642, near Arcetri, Tuscany.

[4] Christian Huyghens (or Huygens), the creator of the wave theory of light and the inventor of the pendulum clock, born at the Hague April 14, 1629 as the son of a poet who was active for 62 years as the private secretary of three princes of Orange, died there July 8, 1695.

[5] Giovanni Domenico Cassini, ancestor of an entire dynasty of astronomers at the Paris Observatory, born 1625 in Perinaldo near Nice, died in Paris in 1712.

during this time. A century later Friedrich Wilhelm Herschel (1738–1822) discovered the planet Uranus, which is twice as far from the earth as Saturn; shortly thereafter some of the moons of Uranus and two more moons of Saturn were seen through the great telescope of the Greenwich Observatory. At present (July 1957) we know 1626 small planets, 2 moons of Mars, 11 of Jupiter, 10 of Saturn, 5 of Uranus. Neptune (with 2 known moons accompanying it at that time) was added to the large planets in 1846 (see Note 21), and the existence of a still more distant planet (Pluto) seems to be confirmed after its discovery in 1930 at the Lowell Observatory in Flagstaff, Arizona and after more recent observations (as was the case with Neptune, the existence of Pluto was first predicted by calculations).

As is well known, for a long time people regarded those heavenly bodies which changed their position between the fixed stars as "wandering stars" (planets) which circle around our *earth*, considered as the center of the universe, and they accordingly reckoned the sun and the moon together with Mercury, Venus, Mars, Jupiter and Saturn as belonging to the seven planets. The number of the days of the week and also their names have their origin in this belief.[6] Of course astrology and its faithful adepts took no notice of the fact that astronomy established the enormous variations in size, mass and attraction between these heavenly bodies,[7] and that new discoveries increased their number.

**15** (p. 194). The case of the planet Uranus also offered no difficulties, because of the slow change of its apparent position due to its long period of revolution around the sun (84 years) and because of the slightness of the deviation of its path from a circle. It was therefore possible to predict

[6] For example, germ. Montag, engl. Monday, fr. lundi = dies Lunae, day of the moon; or germ. Dienstag, ital. martedi = dies Martis, day of Mars; further, germ. Mittwoch = midweek, fr. mercredi = dies Mercurii, day of Mercury, and germ. Samstag, engl. Saturday = dies Saturni, day of Saturn. In the Slavic languages the designations for the days of the week are chiefly related to the number of the working day; in Turkish with the customary market days (bazaars). We must distinguish moreover between the relationships, which are often very old, between stars and divinities on the one hand and the relationships to the days of the week on the other. As I learn from friendly communications of my colleague M. San Nicolò, the Babylonians had a week of 7 or 5 days calculated according to each new month; the week to which we are accustomed running regularly 7 days was still not general in Graeco-Roman antiquity, and first emerged in Late Latin in firm connection with the planets or with names of Roman divinities, at times in a Germanic interpretation; only the designation of Sunday goes back in the Germanic languages to an older concept, which links this day to the Persian sun-god Mithras and testifies to the severe struggle of Christianity with the cult of Mithras (Late Latin deviates from this, dies dominicus, fr. dimanche).

[7] Thus Mercury, which remains on an average equally distant from the earth and the sun, has a mass less than 1/6000000 of that of the sun.

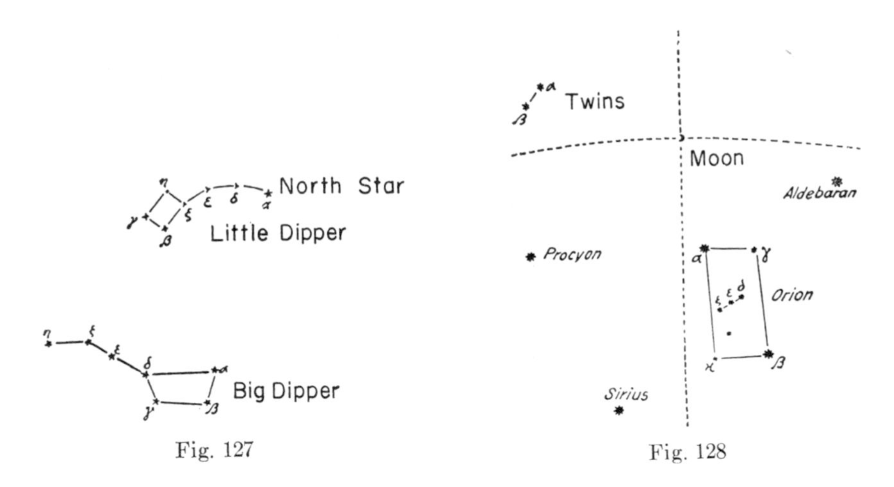


Fig. 127

Fig. 128

the position of its reappearance with accuracy. The same is true for the moons of some of the large planets, since the moons always remain in the immediate vicinity of the planets.

**16** (p. 195). In locating a celestial body in the sky, the important thing is to know the *direction* in which the telescope must be pointed. The star will not be seen if the difference between the direction in which the telescope is pointed and the direction of the star, that is, the angle between the two directions, is too great. This difference in direction (and not the distance in space) is what we meant when we spoke of the distance between positions in the sky. We can easily visualize such differences of direction by means of the image offered us by the full moon. The bearings which lead from our eye to two opposite positions on the edge of the moon's disk form an angle of about half a degree. Therefore, 14 full moon diameters are as much as 7°; in the sky this is approximately as much as the distance between the stars $\beta$ and $\gamma$ in the constellation of the Big Dipper (see Fig. 127), or between the stars $\alpha$ and $\gamma$ (Betelgeuse and Bellatrix) in Orion (see Fig. 128), or two and a half times the length of Jacob's Staff (the distance between $\delta$ and $\zeta$ in Orion).

**17** (p. 195). In these primitive methods, the calculations were based on the assumption that the path of the planet was a circle with the sun as center or very close to a circle. If this was not the case, the method failed. But, since the discovery by Kepler (1571–1630) of the laws of celestial mechanics bearing his name, it has been known that the orbits of the planets are conic sections (see Chapter VII, Footnote 11), and specifically ellipses with the sun at one focus (Fig. 9 in Chapter II shows an ellipse with $F$, $F'$ as foci). And the problem of calculating an elliptic path from observations of a rather short section of the path is considerably more difficult than the calculation of a circular path under the same conditions.

**18** (p. 195). The subject of the dissertation is a proof of the so called Fundamental Theorem of Algebra, a theorem which is considered today as belonging much more to function theory than to algebra. Gauss later proved this theorem in a great many other ways.

**19** (p. 195). This becomes still clearer if one considers how extensively Gauss concerned himself (as we see from the posthumous work) at an early age with the theory of elliptic functions whose double periodicity becomes apparent only if complex as well as real numbers are used.

**20** (p. 195). Wilhelm Olbers was active not only as a diligent observer, discovering in 1815 a comet named after him (as well as three more), but he also wrote a basic treatise on the determination of the paths of comets. Research has been able to gather much information from his correspondence with Gauss.

During a twelve day visit paid by the 26 year old Gauss in the summer of 1803 in Bremen, at the friendly invitation of Olbers, who was 20 years older, Gauss had his portrait painted by the portraitist Christian August Schwarz (1755–1814), who was highly valued for his pastel paintings. Gauss gave the painting to Olbers, whose later descendants thought it to be a portrait of one of their ancestors, name unknown. Through the efforts of Herr A. Wietzke in Bremen, it was discovered in 1928 in the home of a great-grandson of Olbers, the Hamburg merchant W. Gevekoht, who then gave it to the Göttingen Observatory (see {6}). A reproduction of this picture is shown in Plate XI.

**21** (p. 195). Just as Gauss had developed, when he predicted the reappearance of Ceres, the foundations of the theory of orbit determination, so he now developed a general perturbation theory. This theory takes into account, in astronomical calculations, not only the gravitational attraction of the sun, which is the main attractive force acting on a planet, but also the minor gravitational forces of the other planets. This perturbation theory made it possible for Leverrier (1811–1877) and J. C. Adams (1819–1892) to predict from the known orbit of Uranus the existence of another planet, Neptune, which then was discovered by Galle (1812–1910) in 1846 on September 23—the day of Leverrier's death at a later year.

**22** (p. 195). It is true that from 1811 on the establishment of the Göttingen Observatory was well under way, even if it was not completed till 1816. The library of Göttingen, by the way, at the time when Hannover was incorporated in the Kingdom of Wesphalia or the French Empire, had a higher budget for book binding than the Berlin library had for the procurement of books.

**23** (p. 195). This can be gathered from a letter written in 1808 by Gauss to his student, of almost the same age, Heinrich Christian Schumacher (1780–1850). At that time (1807–1810), and from 1821 on, Schumacher

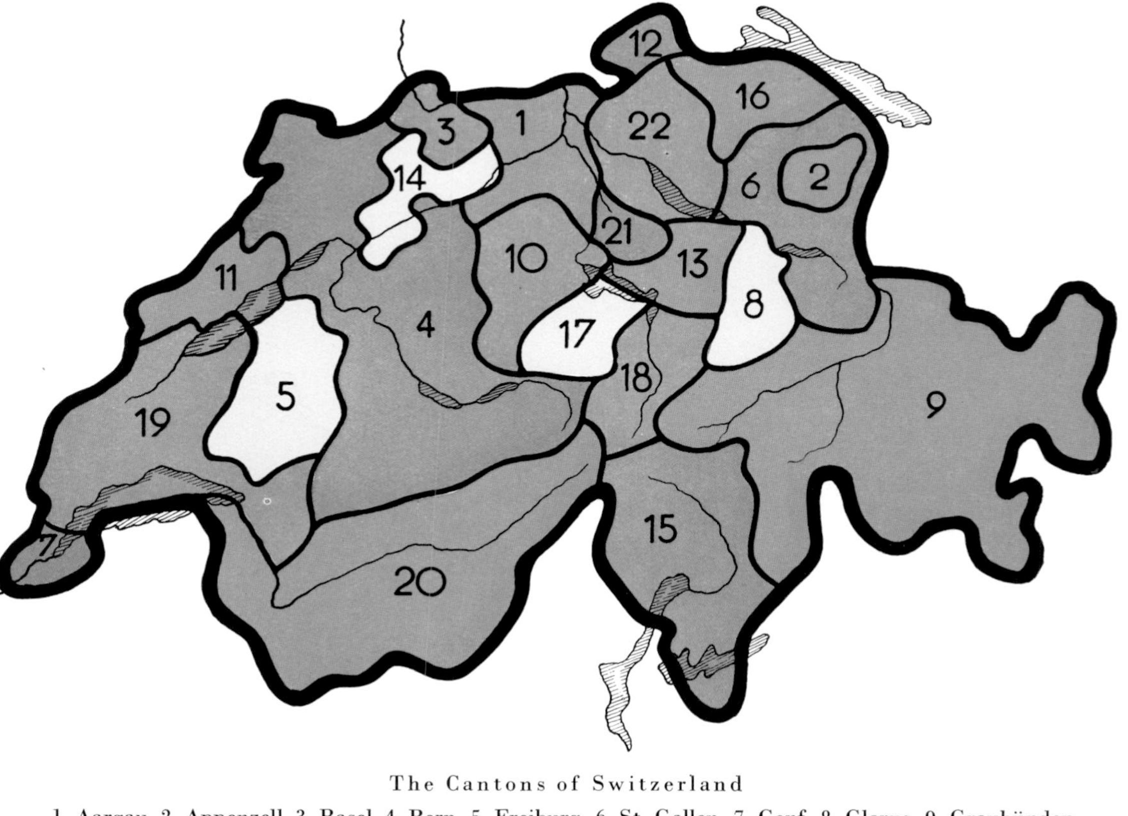


The Cantons of Switzerland

1. Aargau, 2. Appenzell, 3. Basel, 4. Bern, 5. Freiburg, 6. St. Gallen, 7. Genf, 8. Glarus, 9. Graubünden, 10. Luzern, 11. Neuchâtel, 12. Schaffhausen, 13. Schwyz, 14. Solothurn, 15. Tessin, 16. Thurgau, 17. Unterwalden, 18. Uri, 19. Waadt, 20. Wallis, 21. Zug, 22. Zürich

PLATE XIV

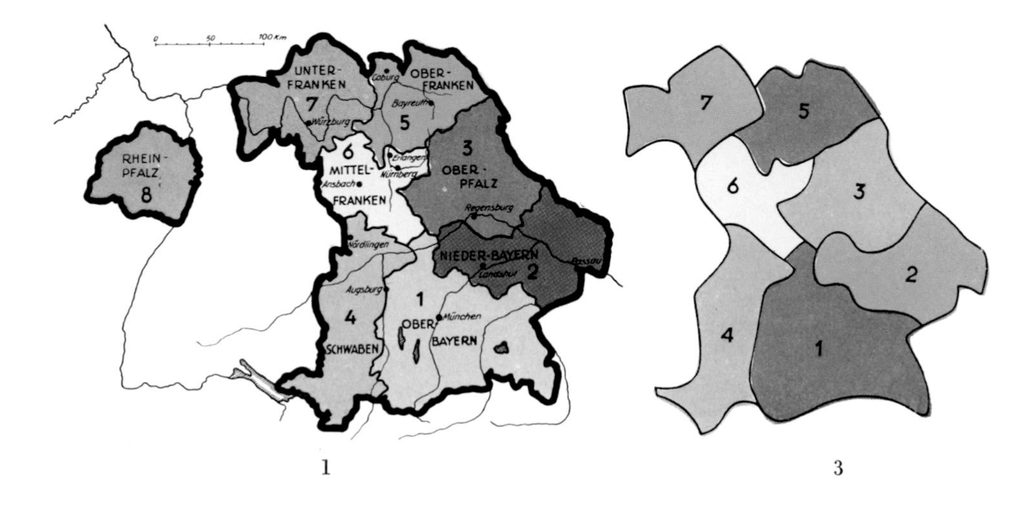


1 3

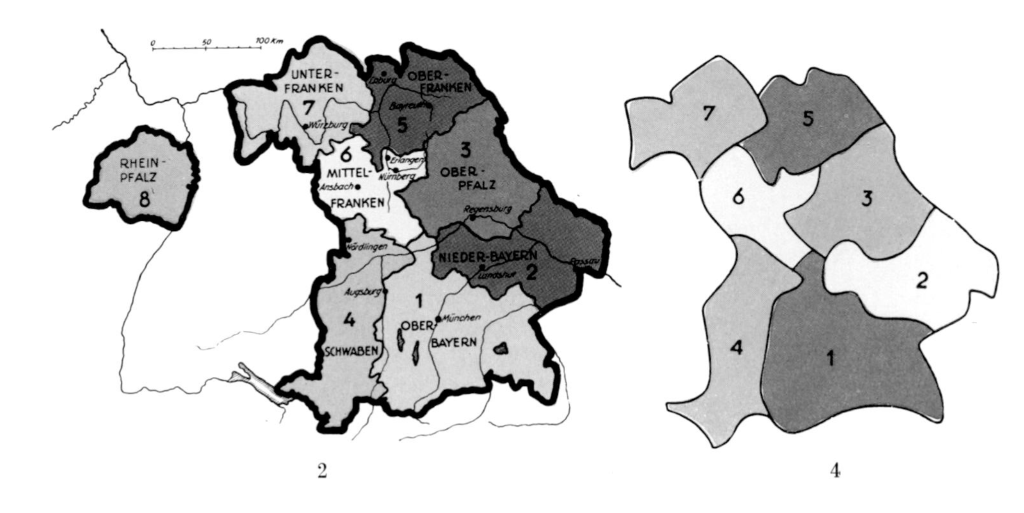


2 4

1 Upper Bavaria; 2 Lower Bavaria; 3 Upper Palatinate; 4 Swabria;
5 Upper Franconia; 6 Middle Franconia; 7 Lower Franconia; 8 Rhenish Palatinate

was active at the observatory in Altona (then Danish)—in the intervening years he was in Copenhagen.

**24** (p. 195). This was the theory of elliptic functions mentioned in Note 19.

**25** (p. 197). When Alexander von Humboldt was chairman, sessions for specialized fields were introduced besides the general sessions (see {7}). At the meeting held once more in Leipzig for the 100th anniversary of its foundation the society, which had long since been divided into two chief groups for natural science and medicine, comprised about 40 sections.[8] The attendance (several thousand took part) was greater than the attendance at the conferences of Vienna in 1913 and of Bad Nauheim in 1923—the last ones before World War One—but was exceeded by the gathering in Innsbruck in 1924.

**26** (p. 197). For the study of these forces Gauss introduced the concept of the potential, so that this field of study is called potential theory.

**27** (p. 198). See {8} and {9}. In these references Gauss, on the basis of observations made by Captain Wilkes, arrives at the values 72°21′ or 146°17′. (I am indebted for this information to the friendly communication of E. Schoenberg.)

**28** (p. 198). The significance which was attributed to the preeminent intellectual power of Gauss even in his own time has found expression in another way. In comparative anatomy, Gauss' contemporaries acted on the hypothesis that in the structure of the brain and the morphology of its convolutions there might appear not only differences in intellectual talents of various species, but in given cases of individual men. A head with a talent seldom seen even in a span of thousands of years had to be of special interest. And so—before the burial—secretly, it is true, to spare the feelings of the family who might have objected—Gauss' cranium was opened and the brain was prepared; the same thing was done four years later (this time probably with consent) with Dirichlet, Gauss' successor (see Chapter VII). The preparations were still exhibited, when I was a student, in the collection of the anatomical institute in Göttingen. Gauss' was without a name, known only in the circle of mathematicians—less clear, probably because of a defectiveness of the preservative fluid, Dirichlet's, labelled, clear and well preserved.

**29** (p. 198). See {10}. Felix Klein (1849–1925) delivered these lectures to a small circle in his home. After he became emeritus in 1913, he was suc-

[8] Connected with the conference of the section for mathematics was the conference of the German Association of Mathematicians, founded in 1890 by Georg Cantor, which in 1928 attained a membership of roughly 1100 (approximately 670 from Germany, approximately 70 from Austria which belonged to the area of the conference, but in addition approximately 360 from other countries, near and far).

ceeded by Constantin Carathéodory. However, until 1921 Klein was in charge of the mathematical collection and library; his successor in this respect was Richard Courant. The bibliographical treasures of this institute, which were of the greatest importance for the mathematical life of Göttingen, fell victim afterwards to the events of the second world war. Concerning Klein see also the Postscript, Note 6. Carathéodory, writing for the editorial staff of the *Mathematische Annalen* (in vol. 95), has testified to Klein's importance in the life of this journal.

*Chapter X*

# THE SOLUTION OF ALGEBRAIC EQUATIONS BY MEANS OF ROOT EXTRACTIONS

No one who has chosen mathematics as his field expects to make a fortune. As the saying goes, the mathematician must live on "roots" which he extracts with a great deal of labor [1]. The extraction of mathematical roots seems to many people, for reasons which are not hard to understand, a somewhat prepossessing task, and only a calculating nature could enjoy resquaring a square root calculated to many decimal places. It is easier, of course, to calculate with letter symbols. A simple example of this kind of calculation of roots is the solution of quadratic equations, that is, equations of the form[1]

$$(1) \qquad x^2 + ax + b = 0,$$

where $a$ and $b$ are given, and $x$ is the unknown. The solution is given by the formula

$$(2) \qquad x = -\tfrac{1}{2}a \pm (\tfrac{1}{4}a^2 - b)^{1/2}.$$

For instance, substitution of $a = -35/4$ and $b = 6$ into (2) gives $x = 8$ and $x = \tfrac{3}{4}$ as the solutions of the equation $x^2 - 35/4\, x + 6 = 0$.

But are there formulas such as (2) for equations of higher degree?

The answer will take us back to two different periods, the first half of the 16th century when the cubic and quartic equations were solved, and the first half of the 19th century, when after many unsuccessful attempts the problem of equations of degree higher than the fourth was solved.[2]

We shall begin with equations whose degree does not exceed four. First, we will go back to quadratic equations and rewrite the solution in a form more suitable to our later treatment of equations of the 3rd and 4th degrees. To this end, let $w$ stand for either $(\tfrac{1}{4}a^2 - b)^{1/2}$ or $-(\tfrac{1}{4}a^2 - b)^{1/2}$. Then

$$(3) \qquad w^2 = \tfrac{1}{4}a^2 - b.$$

Every solution $x$ of equation (1) can now be written as

$$(4) \qquad x = -\tfrac{1}{2}a + w.$$

[1] The general second degree equation is of the form

$$px^2 + qx + r = 0,$$

with $p$ different from zero. This can be transformed (without loss of generality) into equation (1) by dividing every term by $p$. Then the leading coefficient is 1 and $a = q/p$, $b = r/p$. We shall do the same in equations of higher degree.

[2] In contrast, the quadratic formula had already been known for more than 2000 years [2].

Thus, in the example given above (with $a = -35/4$ and $b = 6$) $w$ is either $29/8$ or $-29/8$ and $w^2 = 841/64$. Then by (4), $x = 35/8 + w$, and hence $x$ is either $35/8 + 29/8 = 8$, or $35/8 - 29/8 = 3/4$.

The general solution is summarized in the following table:[3]

TABLE I

*Solution of 2nd Degree (Quadratic) Equations*

$$x^2 + ax + b = 0,$$
$$w^2 = \frac{1}{4}a^2 - b,$$
$$x = -\frac{1}{2}a + w.$$

This solution of quadratic equations by means of root extraction is very old (see [**2**]). Attempts to find an analogous solution for cubic equations also go back to antiquity, but the solution was not discovered until the first half of the 16th century. It is given in the following table, and is explained below.

TABLE II

*Solution of 3rd Degree (Cubic) Equations*

$$x^3 + ax^2 + bx + c = 0$$
$$-\frac{1}{2}c + \frac{1}{6}ab - \frac{1}{27}a^3 = h$$
$$(W_1)^2 = -3(a^2b^2 - 4a^3c - 4b^3 + 18abc - 27c^2)$$
$$\left.\begin{aligned}(W_2)^3 &= h + \frac{1}{18}W_1\\ (W_3)^3 &= h - \frac{1}{18}W_1\end{aligned}\right\}\quad W_2W_3 = \frac{1}{9}a^2 - \frac{1}{3}b$$
$$x = -\frac{1}{3}a + W_2 + W_3$$

First, notice that $W_1$, $W_2$, $W_3$ are obtained by root extractions, and that

$$W_1 = (-3(a^2b^2 - 4a^3c - 4b^3 + 18abc - 27c^2))^{1/2},$$

where the square root symbol denotes *both* numbers whose square is the number under the square root sign.[4] Similarly,

[3] We use this form instead of the more usual and seemingly simpler formula (2) in order to avoid the use of imaginary numbers [**3**] which occur in the solution.

[4] $W_1$ is zero if and only if this number is zero. See [**3**].

$$W_2 = (h + \tfrac{1}{18} W_1)^{1/3}, \qquad W_3 = (h - \tfrac{1}{18} W_1)^{1/3},$$

where each cube root has three values;[5] and the values of $W_3$ must be paired with those of $W_2$ in such a way that $W_2 W_3 = \tfrac{1}{9} a^2 - \tfrac{1}{3} b$. Thus, there are no more than three pairs of values $W_2$, $W_3$, and hence no more than three solutions of the equation $x^3 + ax^2 + bx + c = 0$ [5].

The form of the solution of the cubic given above is essentially Cardano's formula [6], due to the Italian mathematician Hieronimo Cardano. Luigi Ferrari, a student of Cardano, went on to find a solution for the quartic equation by means of root extractions. This solution is summarized in Table III.

TABLE III

*Solution of 4th Degree (Quartic) Equations*

$$x^4 + ax^3 + bx^2 + cx + d = 0$$

$$A = \frac{1}{2}\left(b - \frac{3}{8}a^2\right)$$

$$B = \frac{1}{16}\left(b - \frac{3}{8}a^2\right)^2 - \frac{1}{4}\left(d - \frac{1}{4}ac + \frac{1}{16}a^2 b - \frac{3}{256}a^4\right)$$

$$C = -\frac{1}{64}\left(c - \frac{1}{2}ab + \frac{1}{8}a^3\right)^2$$

$$H = -\frac{1}{2}C + \frac{1}{6}AB - \frac{1}{27}A^3$$

$$(W_1)^2 = -3(A^2B^2 - 4A^3C - 4B^3 + 18ABC - 27C^2)$$

$$\left.\begin{aligned} (W_2)^3 &= H + \frac{1}{18}W_1 \\ (W_3)^3 &= H - \frac{1}{18}W_1 \end{aligned}\right\} \quad W_2 W_3 = \frac{1}{9}A^2 - \frac{1}{3}B$$

$$(W_4)^2 = -3, \quad \varepsilon = -\frac{1}{2} + \frac{1}{2}W_4, \quad \varepsilon^2 = -\frac{1}{2} - \frac{1}{2}W_4$$

$$\left.\begin{aligned} (W_5)^2 &= -\frac{1}{3}A + W_2 + W_3 \\ (W_6)^2 &= -\frac{1}{3}A + \varepsilon W_2 + \varepsilon^2 W_3 \\ (W_7)^2 &= -\frac{1}{3}A + \varepsilon^2 W_2 + \varepsilon W_3 \end{aligned}\right\} \quad \begin{aligned} &W_5 W_6 W_7 \\ &= -\frac{1}{8}\left(c - \frac{1}{2}ab + \frac{1}{8}a^3\right) \end{aligned}$$

$$x = -\frac{1}{4}a + W_5 + W_6 + W_7.$$

Thus, within a few decades, the schools of Italy made two important advances in the theory of algebraic equations; the solution of the cubic was the first advance in the subject since antiquity. But the question of

[5] Whenever the number under the radical sign is different from zero (see [3]) [4].

who made this discovery leads us to a dark chapter in the history of mathematics.

The solution of the cubic first appeared in Cardano's book *Ars Magna de Regulis Algebraicis*, printed in Nuremberg in 1545. Here—although in another form[6]—we find the solution of Table II for cubic equations with $x^2$ missing (that is, with $a = 0$), a form to which the general case can always be reduced (see [6]). But Cardano[7] did not claim the solution as his own. He first attributed the discovery in 1515 of the solution to Scipione del Ferro, and then to Nicolo Tartaglia.[8] This precipitated a violent struggle over the credit for this discovery, in which Cardano's student, Luigi Ferrari,[9] took an active part. In a book printed in Venice in 1546 (*Quesiti et inventioni diversi*) Tartaglia asserted that Cardano had promised him not to divulge the solution which Tartaglia had outlined to Cardano, and implied that Cardano had broken his word. The quarrel [8], in the manner of the time, was carried on with name-calling and mud-slinging of the lowest sort.[10] Besides the distribution of pamphlets whose main aim was to degrade one's opponent, quarrels such as this were carried on by numerous public disputations, in which the mere number of proponents on one side

[6] The symbols now used for powers or roots had not yet been adopted; even the signs for plus and minus were different. Brief formulas now express what at that time required long, detailed exposition [7].

[7] Hieronimo Cardano (1501–1576) did not occupy himself solely with mathematics, which he learned in Padua when he was barely 22. In 1526 he obtained the degree of Doctor of Medicine in Padua. He was asked to visit Denmark and Scotland, and in his turbulent life was even incarcerated in the debtor's prison in Bologna. He also traveled in France and Germany. In addition to numerous noteworthy works on mathematics, he also published treatises on philosophy and medicine.

[8] del Ferro, born 1465 (birthplace unknown), died in 1526 after 30 years of academic life at the University of Bologna. Tartaglia (1499–1557) was a teacher of mathematics at Venice and Brescia. His textbook on arithmetic, geometry and algebra (*General Trattato di Numeri et Misure*) went through several editions between 1556–1560, and subsequently was greatly esteemed.

[9] Luigi Ferrari, born 1522, became a student of Cardano at the age of 15. At 17 he lost all the fingers of his right hand in a brawl. He headed a land registry office in Milan, 1549–1556, but was forced to resign because of illness. Returning to his native city, Bologna, he studied mathematics until 1565. He died when still young, and it was rumored that his sister poisoned him.

Cardano included Ferrari's solution of the quartic in his work *Ars Magna*.

[10] One must remember that we are dealing with a time in which the invention of printing (about 1450) led to the first appearance of printed books of mathematics [9] (beginning with the last quarter of the 15th century). Up to this time there had been only a limited circulation of hand-copied scientific material. Most authors would disclose neither method nor proof, in order to prevent their application by others to their own problems. The usual custom was to challenge opponents to a contest over the solutions for a given problem. Only under the vow of secrecy was the veil lifted occasionally, and that only to a few.

or the other, as well as their vocal powers, often decided the outcome, and settled the "rights" of the case.

Tartaglia, who had his eye on a position in Brescia, agreed to hold such a debate with Ferrari. He lost, and ironically was regarded for a time as the rightful claimant, just because he had lost the debate. But today there is strong doubt as to the validity of his claim, while Cardano's writings have proved to be an indisputable contribution to our knowledge [10]. Perhaps, knowing what we do of the confusing history of this discovery, naming the above formula after Cardano is not wholly justifiable. Still, it seems more just to assign [11] the credit for this great advance in the field of algebraic equations to del Ferro and Cardano, than to Tartaglia.

The problem now was to find an analogous solution for equations of the fifth degree, and perhaps finally a general method for equations of any degree. The failure of subsequent attempts was ascribed to the forbidding computations involved. Even Euler (See Chapter XIII) believed, as is evident from publications dated 1732 and 1749 [12], that a solution by means of root extractions would eventually be found. A few scholars had deeper insight. Leibniz did not believe such a solution existed, as we can see in private letters dated 1678 and 1683 [13]. On the contrary, he claimed to have a proof that such a solution was not possible for equations of degree higher than the fourth. A century later, Gauss (see Chapter IX), in his doctoral dissertation (1799), alluded to the impossibility of solving equations of degree higher than the fourth by means of root extractions [14]. In the same year, Paolo Ruffini (1765–1822), in his *Teoria generale delle equazioni*, gave a proof of the impossibility of finding such a solution. However, his proof was not rigorous, and for the most part was ignored [15].

Thus the solution of equations of degree higher than the fourth was an enticing and challenging problem for the mathematical world at the beginning of the 19th century very much as the problem of trisecting an angle. Then in 1826, Abel gave the first rigorous proof that a general solution for equations of the fifth degree and higher by means of root extractions is impossible, thus vindicating Leibniz, Gauss and Ruffini.

This result, which shed a new light on the whole theory of algebraic equations, was the work of a young unknown. Niels Henrik Abel was born August 5, 1802, in Findoe, a small Norwegian village near Stavenger. His father was a minister. He contracted tuberculosis at an early age and lived only 27 years, mostly in severely trying circumstances. A melancholy temperament and a deep shyness characterized this young man, who nevertheless managed in his brief lifetime to make an extensive contribution to our knowledge. At the age of 16, under the influence of a new teacher [16], he became interested in mathematics, to which he had heretofore been indifferent. In 1821, Abel entered Christiania University, where he intensively studied the works of Euler, Lagrange, and Legendre, since there were no lectures on the more advanced topics of mathematics. He soon became familiar with the unsolved problems which were perplexing the best mathematical minds of his day. In 1823, he thought he had found a general solution for quintic equations; it was this erroneous conclusion that first attracted attention to him. But he soon discovered his error and went on to prove the impossibility of such a solution.

We have commented in Chapters III and V on the peculiar nature of such proofs. Similar considerations apply here. It is possible to extract the roots of the coefficients of a given equation in a great many ways, to combine the results and to extract their square, cube, etc. roots, and so on. It would therefore seem hopeless to test all possible expressions for solutions of the given equation. The surmise is correct. Such a program would be hopeless. As in the problem of proving the infinitude of the primes, what is needed is a new idea. But whereas Euclid's solution was simple enough to present here, Abel's proof is too technical and difficult for such treatment. Furthermore, Abel's result is also a consequence of Galois theory, which we shall mention later on.

Abel's discovery was published in 1824 in pamphlet form. The complete presentation followed in 1826, in the *Journal für die reine und angewandte Mathematik* (Journal for pure and applied mathematics), which had just been founded by Crelle (1780–1855).

As a result of this achievement, Abel was given a stipend which enabled him to make a study trip to Berlin, where he stayed during 1825–26. Shortly after his arrival he met Crelle, who recognized the youth's genius and became his attentive and encouraging friend.

Abel's achievements are by no means limited to his solution of the problem we have discussed. Other areas in the forefront of contemporary mathematical research occupied him, which it would require a more technical background to describe [**17**]. He obtained results of a wonderful generality in these fields, and left many concepts and theorems which still bear his name. Volume I of Crelle's Journal contained six papers by Abel, all written during the short interval he spent in Berlin. In February, 1826, together with some Norwegian friends, Abel went to Italy. From July until the end of the year he was in Paris, and at the end of October sent the Paris Academy a long paper entitled *Mémoire sur une classe très étendue de fonctions transcendantes*, in which he gave an exposition of his most important results [**18**]. However, Cauchy,[11] who was the referee, seems to have misplaced the manuscript. Later, in 1830, after Abel's death, Cauchy

[11] Augustin Louis Cauchy (1798–1857), the great French mathematician, was at this time at the height of his powers.

went into exile as a result of the July revolution, but entrusted his papers to the mathematician Gergonne. Abel's paper was finally printed in 1841 at the insistence of the Norwegian government.

Meanwhile, Abel was in touch with Legendre in Paris, but not with Cauchy. At the beginning of 1827, depressed because of the uncertain fate of his treatise, he returned to Berlin, where he became severely ill. He could have visited Gauss in Göttingen [**19**] on this trip, but had not done so because he had been warned by Legendre and others of Gauss' unapproachability. Back in Christiania in May of 1827, Abel was once again without a job or even any visible status. In 1828, however, he obtained a position as a substitute at the University.

However, he was not forgotten in Berlin. Under the influence of Alexander von Humboldt, and with the cooperation of the military, the development of a large polytechnic institute of the highest scientific caliber was planned—somewhat along the lines of the École Polytechnique, which with its Napoleonic tradition had always placed great emphasis on mathematics. Gauss had been offered the directorship of this institution in 1824, but he declined. After a time the military lost interest, and the plan for this scholarly institute was changed somewhat, but it was finally carried through, and in 1829 Abel was called to head the new institute. But before the news arrived in Christiania, Abel succumbed to his illness. He died on April 6, 1829. Lying on his miserable sick-bed he never heard the news that would have meant both status and income, nor did he have any idea that one day the annals of science would praise him as one of the most brilliant geniuses of his time; that all comprehensive texts would one day contain his discoveries; and that all over the world students of mathematics would learn his name. He had no reason even to suspect that one day his fatherland would erect a memorial to him, and that a yet unborn scholarly journal would dedicate several volumes to him on the centennial of his birth.

During Abel's last years another remarkable young genius developed a profound theory of algebraic equations which provided fresh insight into the problem of solving equations by means of root extractions. We are indebted to the young Frenchman Galois for the theory which will always bear his name.[12] Évariste Galois was born October 25, 1811, in Bourg-la-Reine, to the south of Paris. His life ended even more abruptly than Abel's. In 1828, while still a student at the Lycée, Collège Louis-le-Grand, he announced his first mathematical discovery. Interested as he was in the deepest problems in mathematics, he neglected the study of elementary mathematics as well as that of other fields [**20**]. In 1829 he tried to enter

[12] Several anticipations of Galois theory were found in Abel's posthumous papers.

the École Polytechnique. But, as he relates, the examination problems seemed so simple to him, that he felt it beneath his dignity to answer them. He failed the examinations twice. From the wilful way in which he engaged in his studies, there must have been great gaps in his education. In 1829 he entered the École Normale.

Young as he was, he was already involved in the political tensions of his day. His father, provoked by the ugly attacks of political opponents, had commited suicide, and the son subsequently became convinced that the world was governed unjustly and wickedly. He had greeted the July Revolution of 1830 with youthful enthusiasm, but soon began to feel it was as corrupt and oppressive as its predecessor, that its liberalism was a mask, and its leaders were irresponsible egoists and opportunists. Equally, Galois despised the director of the École Normale as fickle and cowardly. In 1830, after publishing an attack on the director in a student newspaper, he was expelled. The school discipline, designed to extract loyalty from its students by means of spying and the strictest supervision, was indeed repellent. Galois failed to get recognition for his superior mental abilities at school, and at the same time the Paris Academy refused to publish any of the three manuscripts he had submitted. The young firebrand interpreted these acts as the rule of unjust powers [**21**]. At the age of nineteen and a half he became involved in political agitations which he paid for with months of imprisonment at St. Pélagie. A year later, May 30, 1832, his life ended in a duel occasioned by a banal love affair. He never reached the age of 21.

And yet in this short period of time, he had not only studied the works of Lagrange, Gauss and Abel, but had developed a profound theory of algebraic equations, which went far beyond the then existing theory. His theory, however, was still unpublished when he was killed. On his last night, he composed a letter containing his mathematical testament to his friend Chevalier. An achievement of his magnitude is truly rare in so short a life.

In order to say a little about Galois' theory of equations, we must first expand the meaning of the word "root." Long before the time of Galois, the word had been used in a broader sense than we have so far assigned to it. In this chapter, a root, for example a cube root $W = \sqrt[3]{A}$, has meant a number $W$ satisfying the equation $W^3 - A = 0$. In general, an $n$th root $W = \sqrt[n]{A}$ has meant any number satisfying

$$W^n - A = 0. \tag{5}$$

We shall now mean by a root a number which satisfies an algebraic equation of the form

$$x^n + c_1x^{n-1} + c_2x^{n-2} + \cdots + c_{n-2}x^2 + c_{n-1}x + c_n = 0$$

(where $c_1, c_2, \cdots, c_{n-2}, c_{n-1}, c_n$ are the coefficients of the equation). For instance, the numbers $x_1 = 8$ and $x_2 = \frac{3}{4}$ are roots of the equation $x^2 - 35/4\, x + 6 = 0$. Up till now we have called these numbers solutions of the equation, in order to avoid confusion between the narrow and broad meanings of the word root. It was known at the time of Abel and Galois that the number of roots of an algebraic equation is equal to the degree of the equation [**22**]: a quadratic equation has two roots; a cubic equation, three, etc.; an equation of degree $n$ has exactly $n$ roots $x_1, x_2, \cdots x_n$.

To approach Galois theory, we first consider something which seemingly has nothing to do with algebraic equations. Think of the first row of seats in a lecture room, and specifically, of the seats marked 1, 2, 3. Suppose that these seats are occupied by three men, $A$, $B$, and $C$, in that order. There are six possible permutations for seating the three men in the three seats:[13]

1) $ABC$, 2) $ACB$, 3) $BAC$,
4) $BCA$, 5) $CAB$, 6) $CBA$.

Now consider changes in the permutation $ABC$. We can ask, for example, that the occupants of seats 1 and 3 exchange places. The permutation will then be $CBA$. The same request could have been made if the initial permutation had been, say $ACB$. Then the resulting permutation would be $BCA$. Clearly other exchanges of seats can also be made, which can be followed by still further exchanges. The essential point is that given an initial permutation and a final permutation which has been arrived at by a series of exchanges, it is always possible to effect the change from the first to the last permutation in exactly one step, that is, by means of exactly one exchange.[14] In other words, several consecutive changes of position can be replaced by one single, appropriate exchange [**23**]. This is true not only for three seats but for any number.

What does this have to do with the theory of equations? In the case of an equation of, say the third degree, three men exchanging seats are replaced by the three roots $x_1, x_2, x_3$ of the equation; and similarly in the case of an equation of degree $n$, we consider the permutations of the roots $x_1, x_2, \cdots, x_n$ of the equation. Since an adequate exposition of Galois theory would involve the theory of groups and extensions of fields, we can only say here that Galois theory studies what happens to certain expressions formed from the roots of the equation when the roots are permuted in the expressions. Here, as above, the decisive fact is that any finite number of

[13] Since the number of permutations is $1 \cdot 2 \cdot 3$. Similarly, the number of permutations of four people in four seats is $1 \cdot 2 \cdot 3 \cdot 4 = 24$; for five people and five seats, the number is $1 \cdot 2 \cdot 3 \cdot 4 \cdot 5 = 120$.

[14] For example, in the series of permutations 1)–6) above, 5) can be obtained from 1) by exchanging $A$ with $C$ and $B$ with $A$.

permutations of the roots, which turn one expression into another, can be replaced by one suitable permutation which has the same effect.

It is no doubt very surprising [**24**] to find that a simple thing like an exchange of seats is related to something complicated like the theory of equations. But it was no less surprising to find that what holds true for equations of degree less than or equal to four is no longer true for those of higher degree. And the key to this remarkable fact can, according to Galois theory, be found in the theory of permutation groups, of which the exchange of seats is an example.

This is another illustration of the fact that the history of mathematics is full of surprises, many more than most people would imagine.

*Notes to Chapter X*

# SOLUTION OF ALGEBRAIC EQUATIONS BY MEANS OF ROOT EXTRACTIONS

**1** (p. 211). This double meaning of the word "root," which is derived from Indo-Arabic sources,[1] is found in a number of languages, most commonly those related to Latin, but also in the non-Romance languages: radix (lat.), Wurzel (germ.), racine (fr.), radice (ital.), wortel (dutch), raiz (span.), raiz (portug.).

**2** (p. 211). For the earliest methods of solving quadratic equations (or the equivalent geometric problems) in classical antiquity or those employed by Indian and Arabic mathematicians see {1} and {2}.

**3** (p. 212). If $A$ is a positive number, $\sqrt{A}$ (or $\sqrt[n]{A}$) denotes a *positive* number[2] whose square (or $n$th power) is $A$.[3] For example, $\sqrt{841/64} = 29/8$. If $A = 0$, $\sqrt{A} = 0$ and $\sqrt[n]{A} = 0$.

On the other hand, when we come to a systematic development of the theory of real and complex numbers, this notation is no longer adequate. For it can then be shown that the equation $w^n - A = 0$ has $n$ distinct solutions for every natural number $n$ and every nonzero (real or complex) number $A$. For example, the equation $w^2 - 4 = 0$ has the two solutions $w = 2$ and $w = -2$. Similarly, the equation $w^5 - A = 0$ (where $A$ is a positive number) has the five solutions

$$w = \sqrt[5]{A},$$

$$w = \sqrt[5]{A} \cdot \frac{\tau + \varrho i}{2},$$

$$w = \sqrt[5]{A} \cdot \frac{-\sigma + \varrho \tau i}{2},$$

$$w = \sqrt[5]{A} \cdot \frac{-\sigma - \varrho \tau i}{2},$$

$$w = \sqrt[5]{A} \cdot \frac{\tau - \varrho i}{2}.$$

[1] See {14} and {2; vol. 2, p. 40}.

[2] It is shown in the theory of real numbers that every positive number has a well defined positive real $n$th root, which is then denoted by the root sign as above. We might add that the question of calculating an approximation to the root (by means of methods taught in elementary school or by the more refined methods of analysis) is a problem in itself and does not concern us here. Our concern here is the existence of closed forms for solutions of algebraic equations.

[3] The popular conception is that the root sign is a multiple-valued function, and that, say $\sqrt{4}$ stands for both 2 and $-2$; but, in mathematics, it is usual to consider only single-valued functions and thus better to write $\sqrt{4} = 2$ and $-\sqrt{4} = -2$.

Here, for brevity, we have set

$$\rho = [\tfrac{1}{2}(5 + \sqrt{5})]^{1/2}, \ \sigma = \rho^2 - 2, \ \tau = \rho^2 - 3.$$

As another example, if $A = \tau + \rho i$ ($\tau$ and $\rho$ as above), then the equation $w^2 - A = 0$ has the two solutions

$$w = (\sigma + i\rho\tau)/\sqrt{2} \quad \text{and} \quad w = -(\sigma + i\rho\tau)/\sqrt{2}.$$

Analogously, if $A$ is positive, the equation $w^3 - A = 0$ has the three solutions

$$w = \sqrt[3]{A}, \qquad w = \sqrt[3]{A}\tfrac{1}{2}(-1 + i\sqrt{3}), \qquad w = \sqrt[3]{A}\tfrac{1}{2}(-1 - i\sqrt{3}).$$

The solutions of the equation

$$w^n - 1 = 0$$

are of special interest. Every solution of this equation (and there are precisely $n$) is called an $n$th root of unity.[4] For example, 1 and $-1$ are the two square roots of unity. The imaginary number $i$, which is a solution of the equation $w^2 + 1 = 0$, so that $i^2 = -1$, also satisfies the equation $w^4 - 1 = 0$. Hence, $i$ is a 4th root of unity (the others are 1, $-1$, and $-i$).

The 3rd roots of unity are easy to find. For let[5]

$$\varepsilon = \tfrac{1}{2}(-1 + i\sqrt{3}).$$

Then

$$\varepsilon^2 = \tfrac{1}{2}(-1 - i\sqrt{3}),$$
$$\varepsilon^3 = 1,$$

so that

$$(\varepsilon^2)^3 = \varepsilon^6 = (\varepsilon^3)^2 = 1^2 = 1.$$

Hence, $w = \varepsilon$ and $w = \varepsilon^2$ are solutions of $w^3 - 1 = 0$. Since 1 also satisfies this equation, 1, $\varepsilon$, and $\varepsilon^2$ are the three 3rd roots of unity.

We have already noted that the imaginary numbers must be introduced in a systematic fashion (see Chapter VIII, Note 19). This is done in textbooks on modern algebra and function theory.

**4** (p. 213). For example, if $h + \tfrac{1}{18}W_1 = 8$, $W_2$ has the three values 2, $2\varepsilon$, and $2\varepsilon^2$, where $\varepsilon$ has the value assigned to it in Note 3.

[4] It is interesting to note the interrelations among the most various branches of mathematics; in this case, the relation between the regular polygons of Chapter IX and the $n$th roots of unity of this chapter, which divide the unit circle into $n$ equal parts. See {15}, {16}, {17}.

[5] Instead of using $i$, we could introduce the number $W = \sqrt{-3}$, which satisfies the equation $W^2 + 3 = 0$, and then let $\varepsilon = -\tfrac{1}{2} + \tfrac{1}{2}W$.

**5** (p. 213). If any set of possible values is assigned to $W_1$, $W_2$ and $W_3$ and the corresponding solution given by the last line of Table II is denoted by $x_1$, then the other two solutions are

$$x_2 = -a/3 + \varepsilon W_2 + \varepsilon^2 W_3,$$
$$x_3 = -a/3 + \varepsilon^2 W_2 + \varepsilon W_3,$$

where $\varepsilon$ is as in Note 3.

**6** (p. 213). Cardano's formula gives the solutions of the cubic equation in the special case that the coefficient of $x^2$ is 0, i.e., when $a = 0$ in Table II. Then the formulas of Table II become

$$x^3 + bx + c = 0, \qquad h = -c/2, \qquad W_1^2 = -3(-4b^3 - 27c^2),$$

so that

$$(W_1/18)^2 = (81c^2 + 12b^3)/18^2 = (c/2)^2 + (b/3)^3,$$
$$W_2^3 = -c/2 + W_1/18, \qquad W_3^3 = -c/2 - W_1/18, \qquad W_2 W_3 = -b/3,$$
$$x = W_2 + W_3.$$

The final formula above can then be given the following form known as Cardano's formula:

$$x = \sqrt[3]{-\frac{c}{2} + \sqrt{\left(\frac{c}{2}\right)^2 + \left(\frac{b}{3}\right)^3}} + \sqrt[3]{-\frac{c}{2} - \sqrt{\left(\frac{c}{2}\right)^2 + \left(\frac{b}{3}\right)^3}}.$$

Although this formula apparently gives the solutions of the cubic only for the case when $a = 0$, it is easy to see that a general cubic equation $x^3 + ax^2 + bx + c = 0$ can be reduced to this case. For, setting $x = z - a/3$ and substituting in the general cubic we get

$$z^3 + Bz + C = 0, \tag{1}$$

where

$$B = -a^2/3 + b, \qquad C = 2a^3/27 - ab/3 + c. \tag{2}$$

Applying Cardano's method to the simplified equation (1), we get

$$h = -C/2, \qquad W_1^2 = -3(-4B^3 - 27C^2),$$
$$W_2^3 = -C/2 + W_1/18, \qquad W_3^3 = -C/2 - W_1/18,$$
$$W_2 W_3 = -B/3, \qquad z = W_2 + W_3.$$

Substituting the values of $B$ and $C$ given by (2) and noting that $x = -a/3 + z$ we arrive at the solution of Table II.

**7** (p. 214). See {3} for the original form of Cardano's formula.

**8** (p. 214). For a more detailed discussion see {4}, {2; pp. 71–74}, and {5}.

**9** (p. 214). The first printed *Arithmetic Book* appeared anonymously in

Treviso in 1478; another appeared in Venice in 1484. In the first half of the 16th century, printers in Nuremberg, Strasbourg, Antwerp and other cities published various mathematics books. See {6}.

**10** (p. 215). When Cardano learned about this method of solution, he immediately devised a proof for its validity. Moreover, he was acquainted with the case of three real solutions (the so called *casus irreducibilis*, in which these solutions appear in apparently imaginary form). In addition, he took the imaginary solutions more into account than anyone before him, and it may have been this which led him to suspect that the number of solutions is the same as the degree of the equation. He also anticipated one of Descartes' rule of signs for the number of real roots.

**11** (p. 215). On the other hand, Cajori (see {7}) supports Tartaglia's claim.

**12** (p. 215). See {8}, {2; p. 92, Note 405}, and {7; p. 250}.

**13** (p. 215). See {8; pp. 110–113} and {2; p. 91, Notes 403, 404}. This correspondence was addressed to his friend Walter von Tschirnhaus of Kiesslingswalde (1651–1708), a member of an old Bohemian family, who was interested in mathematics. Tschirnhaus believed at first that the method of solution for the quartic could be generalized to higher degree equations. However, his communication of 1683 to the Paris Academy detailing his projected program for attacking this problem could not have been altogether honest, since it must have been clear to him by this time that the problem could not be solved in this way.

**14** (p. 215). See {9} and {2; p. 93, Note 411}.

**15** (p. 215). This is also true in Ruffini's later works on this problem; however, a treatise published by him in Modena in 1813 contained a perfectly valid partial solution. See {9a}, {10} and {2; p. 94, Note 412}.

**16** (p. 215). This was B. Holmboe of the Cathedral School. He was later responsible for the publication of the first edition of Abel's works which appeared in Christiania in 1839. See {7; p. 347} and {11}.

**17** (p. 216). For example, we owe to Abel the theorem which states that a power series is continuous in its circle of convergence. This is now an elementary theorem in function theory. But apart from this and other noteworthy results in function theory and his original investigations in elliptic functions, we owe to Abel far-reaching and profound investigations in the field of Abelian integrals of algebraic functions.

**18** (p. 216). The results had to do with a class of integral functions (the Abelian integrals of Note 17), of which elliptic integrals are a very special case. For example, the Addition Theorem in the theory of elliptic functions is the simplest case of Abel's theorem in the theory of Abelian integrals.

**19** (p. 217). See {11; pp. 29, 105} for a stimulating account of Abel's life and work.

**20** (p. 217). The brilliant account by George Sarton in *Osiris* (see {12}) [followed by Garrett Birkhoff's essay on Galois and group theory (see {12; pp. 260–268})] to which Carathéodory referred me, could have been substituted for the biographical sketch in the text. In his stimulating essay,[6] Sarton pictures with great warmth the fiery young genius, torn by inner crises in an age of crisis. He cites a recommendation given by one of his teachers (I quote the English text): "Tries to be original . . . Does absolutely nothing for the class. The furor of mathematics possesses him. . ."[7] One of his teachers, named Richard, who also had Leverrier and Hermite as students, recognized his superior ability and let him go his own way. Fourteen years after Galois' death, Liouville collected Galois' works for publication in the *Journal de Mathématiques pures et appliquées* (see {13}). A new edition was published in Paris in 1897 with an introduction by Émile Picard (1856–1941). This edition was a book of about 60 pages!

**21** (p. 218). A communication sent to Cauchy for refereeing was misplaced. This is not hard to believe, since in those critical times even scholars were affected by political events. A second communication of Galois to the Académie des Sciences in 1830 was taken home by Jean Baptiste Fourier (1768–1830), who was at the time permanent secretary, but he died before he had had a chance to referee the manuscript. This manuscript was never found. When Galois again submitted his paper, which contained an account of his new theory, in 1831, it was returned four months later by Poisson with the comment that he could not understand the paper. This was no doubt due to the newness and originality of the ideas, and the extreme compactness of the exposition, but it was certainly another misfortune for Galois.

**22** (p. 219). This is a consequence of the so called Fundamental Theorem of Algebra which states that every polynomial of positive degree (with real or complex coefficients) has at least one root (in the field of complex numbers). This theorem was difficult to prove [it was first proved by Gauss (see Chapter IX, Note 18)]; the fact that a polynomial of positive degree $n$ has precisely $n$ roots (which may not be distinct) is easy to prove once the Fundamental Theorem is established.

**23** (p. 219). Certain quite general theorems hold for these exchanges or permutations, and their theory, which was the original form of group theory, has now developed into the field of abstract group theory.

**24** (p. 220). We recall that Ruffini (see Note 15) had already made an intensive study of the permutations of roots in his work.

[6] This essay first appeared in {18} and was based on the full biography of Galois by Charles Dupuy {19}.

[7] Thanks to Dr. H. Garnir of the University of Liège, I am also able to quote the original text (in Dupuy {19; p. 256}): "Il vise à l'originalité . . . Il ne fait absolument rien pour la classe. C'est la fureur des Mathématiques qui le domine; . . ."

## *Chapter XI*
# THE FOUR COLOR PROBLEM

Let us think back to a geography class, and to the atlas with its colored maps. I am thinking, for example, of a map of Switzerland, not a physical contour map, but one which shows its 22 cantons (see Plate XIII for a schematic map of Switzerland). Now let us consider another map, of a region subdivided into less than 22 parts, such as Bavaria [1] with its 8 districts (Fig. 129). As in the map of Switzerland, the districts of Bavaria can be distinguished most easily by using a different color for each of the 8 districts (see Plate XIV, map 1).

But it is wasteful to use so many colors. Since the problem is simply to distinguish one administrative district from another, we could, for instance, use the same colors for the northern districts 5, 7, 8 as for the southern districts 2, 1, 4 (see Plate XIV, map 2). Five colors are now enough. Note that district 8 in Fig. 129 presents no problem, since it does not border on any other district, and therefore may be colored arbitrarily. For example, in map 1, it could have been colored pink, like district 7. Then seven colors would have been enough.

Essentially, the problem of using colors to differentiate the subdivisions of a larger domain is solved by adherence to one simple rule: *neighboring domains, that is, domains which have a border in common* (such as districts 1 and 2 in Fig. 129) *must be colored differently*. Further, if two domains have only isolated boundary points, but no boundary line, in common (see Chapter IV, Fig. 31a), one color will suffice for both.

This brings us to the problem we will consider in this chapter: What is the minimum number of colors necessary to distinguish the neighboring domains of all maps in the plane (or on a sphere)?

It was noticed by English cartographers that it had never been necessary to use more than four colors for any map. In 1850, it occurred to Francis Guthrie, a student of mathematics at Edinburgh, that if this were really so, it would be an interesting mathematical theorem. He discussed this idea with his brother Frederick,[1] who communicated it to Augustus de Morgan,[2] his teacher. Through de Morgan, other English mathematicians, for example, P. G. Tait,[3] learned of Guthrie's conjecture. Later,

[1] Frederick Guthrie (1833–1886) later became Professor of Chemistry and Physics at the newly created School of Science, South Kensington.

[2] Augustus de Morgan (1806–1871), Professor at the University College, London, and the author of *Budget of Paradoxes*, founded the London Mathematical Society.

[3] Peter Guthrie Tait (1831–1901) was Professor of Mathematical Physics at Edinburgh. The author, with William Thomson (1824–1907), of *A Treatise on Natural Philosophy*, he was also known for his work on the theory of knots (see {2}).

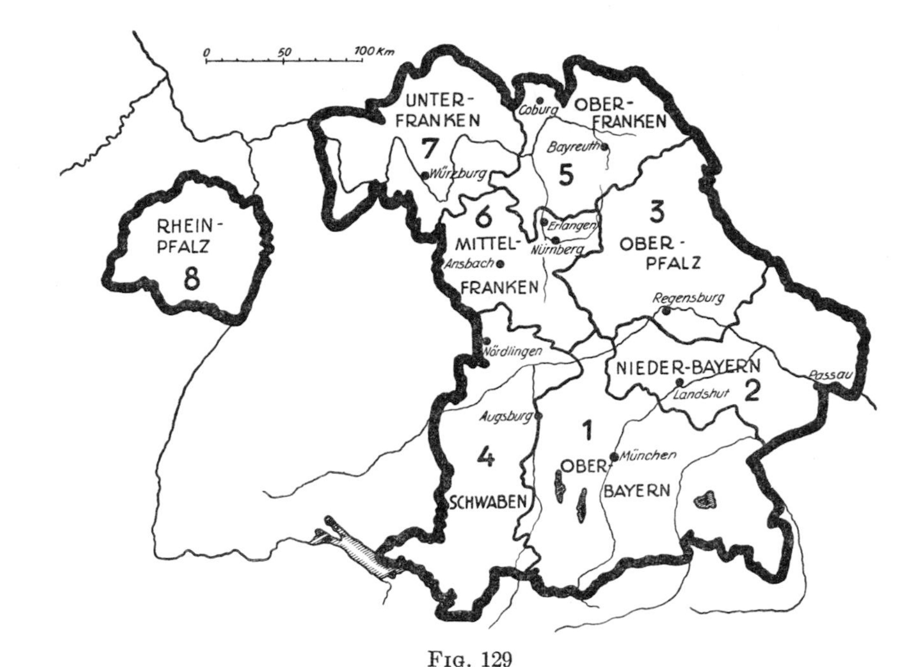


FIG. 129

the famous mathematician Arthur Cayley communicated the problem to the London Mathematical Society (1878) and the Royal Geographical Society (1879).

Guthrie's idea is still a conjecture rather than a theorem. A geometric theorem would have to hold for all possible maps (in the plane or on a sphere), and not only for those which have actually been drawn by cartographers. Such a theorem should maintain that at most four colors are enough for any map. Is the conjecture true? The truth is that we do not know, although some partial results in this direction have been obtained. The problem remains unsolved despite the many efforts that have been made to solve it. When the renowned Cayley confessed that with all his efforts he had been unable to prove the conjecture, he stimulated other mathematicians to attempt a solution.

Let us first approach the problem naively, by investigating some simple special cases. In Plate XIV, map 2 of Bavaria has five colors. From map 3 we see that four colors would have done as well; and map 4 shows[4] that even three colors would have sufficed. Furthermore, we cannot do with less than three colors. A glance at districts 3, 5 and 6, each of which borders

[4] The Palatinate (district 8) is omitted in maps 3 and 4 because, as we noted before, it makes no difference to the problem.

the other two, will show that three colors are required for these three districts alone.

Now, let us return to our first example, the division of Switzerland into cantons, and see whether four colors are enough. Plate XIII shows that this is indeed the case. Would three colors be enough in this case also? There are, of course, maps for which two colors are sufficient, such as map 1 (not the usual one) of Switzerland in Plate XV, which is colored in pink and white; or the blue and white coloring of map 2 of Bavaria (also not the customary one) in the same plate; or the black and white squares of any checker-board.

We have seen above that two colors will not suffice for *every* map. But if we try to outdo the British cartographers by using three colors instead of four, we find that we cannot. The map in Plate XIII shows that any attempt to use no more than three colors must fail. We shall discuss the reason for this later.

An example as complicated as a map of the Swiss cantons is unnecessary to show that four colors are sometimes required. Let us consider some simple examples. First, consider a circle divided into a number of sectors by radii (Fig. 130a–e). The circle is the country and the sectors are the districts which are to be colored. It is immediately clear that in the case of four, six, or any *even* number of sectors, *two* colors, $a$ and $b$, are enough. But an odd number of sectors requires three colors. For, if we begin by coloring the sectors alternately with $a$ and $b$, we shall ultimately come to a sector, the last one in the sequence, which requires a third color $c$, since this sector is bordered on one side by the color $a$, and on the other by the color $b$.

Here let us recall the principal concept of Chapter IV: the concept of

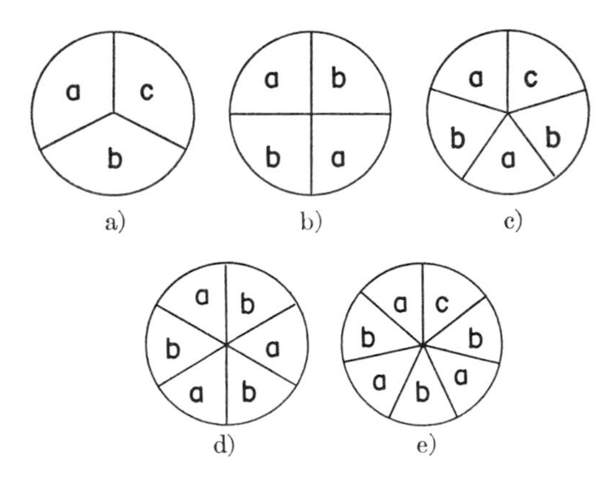


FIG. 130

neighboring domains, a set of domains each of which is a neighbor of every other, i.e., has a boundary line in common with every other domain of the set. Now, if we think of such a set of neighboring domains as a map to be colored, it is clear that each domain must have its own color; there must be as many colors as neighboring domains. Fig. 130a shows three neighboring domains, and this alone makes it clear that three colors are necessary. But on the other hand, it is noteworthy that the maps of Figs. 130c,e, which have five and seven sectors, respectively, certainly require three colors, although neither contains three sectors which form a set of neighboring domains. We emphasize this point in order to distinguish the problem of coloring maps with the least number of colors from the problem of neighboring domains.

Let us go on to a different type of map (Fig. 131a–e), in which an inner circle is surrounded by sectors of a ring. There is again an essential difference between an odd and an even number of sectors. With an even number, such as four or six (Fig. 131b,d), the alternation of two colors $a$ and $b$ is sufficient for coloring the ring sectors, just as in the maps of Fig. 130b,d. The interior circle which borders each sector along an arc requires a third color $c$. But if the number of sectors is odd, say three or five or seven, as in Fig. 131a,c,e, two colors are no longer enough for coloring the ring sectors. Another color $c$ is needed, for the same reason as in the maps of Fig. 130a,c,e. Obviously a fourth color $d$ is needed for the interior circle, which borders on each of the ring sectors. *Therefore, there are maps which require four colors.* Fig. 131a shows the simplest case of a set of four neighboring domains, which by its nature requires a different color for each domain. The same assertion is true of every map with more than four neighboring domains, since such a map contains a submap consisting of four neighboring domains, and therefore requires at least four colors. But

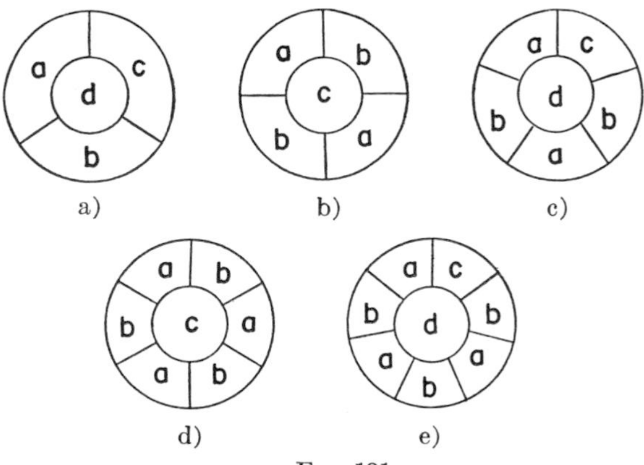


FIG. 131

Figs. 131c,e show (as will any map with an odd number of ring sectors) that there are maps without a set of four neighboring domains which nevertheless require four colors. It is easily verified that in a figure such as Fig. 131c there is no set of four neighboring domains, for such a set would have to contain three consecutive sectors, and in this figure the first and the third cannot neighbor each other [**2**]. *Therefore, there are maps which require four colors although they do not contain a set of four neighboring domains.*[5]

This fact deserves repeated emphasis, since many misunderstandings have arisen, even in professional circles. These misunderstandings confuse the problem discussed in Chapter IV, which concerns the maximum number of neighboring domains in the plane, with the problem of finding the minimum number of colors necessary to color any map in the plane. We call the latter number the *chromatic number of the plane* and denote it by $\chi$. The maximum number of neighboring domains in the plane will be denoted by $\nu$. In Chapter IV we saw that $\nu = 4$. The four color problem (in the plane or on a sphere) is to verify or disprove that $\chi = \nu = 4$. From the previous discussion it should be clear that

$$\chi \geq \nu.$$

It is, of course, possible that $\chi$ may be greater than $\nu$, since there are maps, such as those in Figs. 130 and 131, in which the number of colors needed is greater than the number of neighboring domains. We cannot, therefore, exclude the possibility that there are maps which require five, six, or even more colors. In such cases, of course, this would occur, *not* because of the existence of five or six neighboring countries, but because of the relative positions of the countries to each other on the map. As we have said, in practice cartographers have never required more than four colors for any map. But no mathematical proof has ever been found to

[5] The map of Switzerland contains a set of four neighboring domains: cantons 1, 3, 4 and 14; hence the map requires at least four colors. Another example is the configuration consisting of canton 10 surrounded by 13, 21, 1, 4 and 17, arranged as in Fig. 131c: five ring sectors surrounding an interior circle. In order to emphasize the relative positions of these cantons, which is the essence of the problem, we shall schematize the map of Plate XIII so that it becomes map 1 of Plate XVI. On this schematic map, it is easier to see the two configurations discussed above.

In contrast to map 1 of Plate XVI (or Plate XIII), map 2 of Plate XVI is an essentially altered map. This map is obtained from map 1 by uniting domains 14 and 1 into a single domain, 141; similarly, domains 11 and 5 are combined to form domain 115, and domains 13 and 17 into 1713. Map 2 shows that it is still possible to color all these domains with four colors. On the other hand, it is obvious that even the new map will require more than three colors. We defer further discussion of special features of map 1 [3].

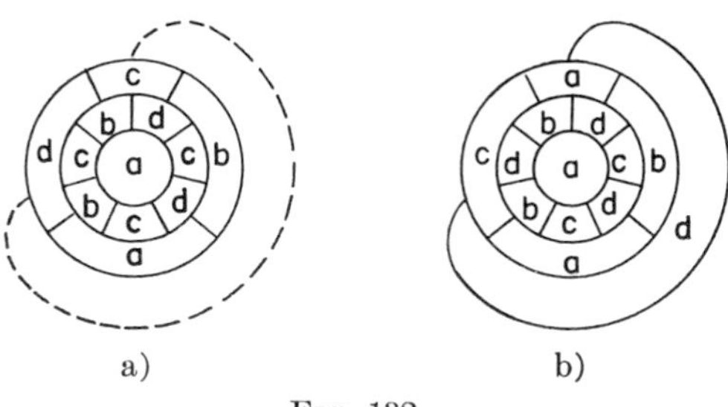


FIG. 132

show that maps requiring more than four colors cannot exist. Remarkably, however, no one has ever been able to construct an example of a map, no matter how complicated, which would require more than four colors.[6]

We might add that the same situation applies to a sphere. On a sphere there are also sets of four neighboring domains, so that there are maps on a sphere which require at least four colors. Moreover, no one has ever constructed an example of a map on a sphere for which more than four colors were necessary.

We have already seen that the chromatic number $\chi$ of the plane or sphere is *at least* 4. The English mathematician P. J. Heawood (1861–1955) proved in 1890 that $\chi \leq 5$. *Therefore, five colors will certainly suffice for plane or spherical maps.* Heawood's proof uses Euler's formula for polyhedral surfaces, which is rather odd, since a polyhedral surface is a surface composed of plane faces (for example, the surfaces of a cube, pyramid, prism, etc. are polyhedral surfaces), and polyhedral surfaces do not occur in the statement of the four color problem.[7] Euler's formula (see Footnote 7) is usually stated in terms of the vertices, edges and faces of a polyhedral

[6] Fig. 132a shows a circle divided into 12 domains which can be colored with four colors $a$, $b$, $c$, $d$. An attempt to construct a map requiring five colors by adding a thirteenth domain (shown by a dotted line) to this figure, so that the new domain is a neighbor of each of the four domains colored $a$, $b$, $c$, $d$, would fail. The reason is that an appropriate change in the original coloring would give a 4-coloring of the new map.

[7] Let $E$ be the number of vertices of a polyhedral surface, $K$ the number of its edges and $F$ the number of its faces. For example, $E = 8, K = 12, F = 6$ for a cube; $E = 4, K = 6, F = 4$ for a tetrahedron; $E = 10, K = 15, F = 7$ for a five-sided prism; $E = 6, K = 12, F = 8$ for an octahedron. These examples suggest that

$$E - K + F = 2$$

for polyhedral surfaces which are topologically equivalent to a sphere (i.e. which, roughly speaking, can be deformed into a sphere without tearing or pasting together). This is known as Euler's formula. Euler was unaware that this formula was already known to Descartes. (For Descartes see Chapter III; for Euler, Chapter XIII.)

surface, and in this form it applies only to such surfaces. But it can also be applied to maps on a sphere, and this is its significance for the map coloring problem. A proof of Heawood's five color theorem is too long to be included in the text. For a discussion of the proof see [**4**].

We shall now consider another fundamental aspect of the four color problem. Let us return to maps 3 and 4 of Plate XIV. These figures are partially schematized representations of part of Bavaria. What happens if we schematize still further in map 3 of Plate XVI, and concentrate only on the relative positions of the districts? It is easily seen that the mutual boundary relationships of the seven districts—abstracting, of course, from the incidental shape of the boundaries—are adequately represented. The problem of coloring map 3 in Plate XVI is exactly the same as that of coloring map 3 of Plate XIV, which is more accurate geographically. The coloring is exactly the same in both maps. Let us carry this schematization still further in maps 4 and 5, Plate XVI, where the map is deformed first into a semi-circle and then into a circle. The coloring problem remains the same so long as we maintain the *relative positions* of the districts. It is irrelevant to the coloring problem whether a boundary line, originally winding, has been straightened, or is later curved, or is changed in any of these particulars. It also does not matter that changing the figure increases the area of one domain or shrinks that of another, whether one is lengthened or another broadened. The 4-coloring of map 3, Plate XIV, and of map 3, Plate XVI, can be transferred, essentially unchanged, to maps 4 and 5 of Plate XVI. In the same way, it can be transferred to any other alteration of the figure resulting from stretching or compressing. Of course, the relative positions of the domains must be maintained, that is, existing boundary lines cannot be suppressed, nor new boundaries introduced. The same sort of transference applies to the 5-coloring of map 2, Plate XIV, as well as to the 3-coloring of map 4, Plate XIV. Thus, the map coloring problem depends solely on the positions of the individual parts of the figure relative to each other, but is completely *independent* of the incidental shapes involved. Neither size relationships nor the shape of the lines play any role.

We are therefore concerned only with those fundamental properties of a figure which remain unaltered under very general transformations. In this connection, it is convenient to think of the surface of the earth as plastic, or fluid like lava, to imagine changes of shape of whole countries, in the same manner as the transformations from map 3, Plate XIV, to maps 3, 4 and 5 of Plate XVI. In these changes, all the results of land measurements, all the angle, length and area measurements, are lost. But if we imagine the individual countries to be distinguished by the particular colors of their lava, then in spite of the volcanic catastrophe pictured here, an observer on the moon would be able to recognize the persisting color of each country and by means of this property note the position of each country relative to the others. The branch of mathematics which studies these fundamental properties of figures is called *topology*. The four color problem, as well as the problem of neighboring domains discussed in Chapter IV, is a topological problem.

One thing is clear: The map coloring problem, that is, the problem of coloring the domains of a map so that every two neighboring domains receive different colors, depends essentially on the type of surface on which the map lies. Of course, the plane and sphere (although in other respects not equivalent topologically) are not essentially different as far as the map coloring problem is concerned, because a sphere can be projected stereographically on a plane, as in a Mercator map. A map of Bavaria or Switzerland may be drawn equally well in the plane or on a sphere. If it could be proved that no map in the plane requires more than five colors, the proof could be easily modified to hold for a sphere, and for any other surface into which a sphere can be deformed without changing the boundary relations of the domains of the map **[5]**. For a sphere, as well as for a plane, the chromatic number $\chi$ is at least 4 and at most 5.

But (see Chapter IV), there are quite different types of surfaces, such as the torus (see picture 3, Plate I). We should expect that the map coloring problem on a surface so different from a sphere would yield completely different results. This is already clear from the fact that the number of neighboring domains possible on a torus is seven (see picture 1, Plate V), i.e., $\nu = 7$ on a torus. Since $\chi \geq \nu$ on a torus also, it follows that $\chi \geq 7$ on a torus. Is $\chi > \nu$ on a torus? This question may seem, at first glance, to be more difficult to decide on a torus than on a sphere or in the plane. Surprisingly, the opposite is true, for it can be proved that on a torus $\chi = \nu = 7$ **[6]**.

The map coloring problem has also been solved for the more complicated double torus (see picture 2, Plate V); for the double torus $\chi = \nu = 8$. Indeed, the map coloring problem has been solved for many other types of surfaces, partly as a result of older research, but mostly through more recent progress **[7]**. We have already distinguished between orientable (two-sided) surfaces and nonorientable (one-sided) surfaces (see Chapter IV, Notes 12, 13, 14). Ironically enough, the coloring problem has not been solved for many of the orientable surfaces, whereas it has been completely solved for the nonorientable ones **[8]**; for example, $\chi = \nu = 6$ for the Möbius band (see Figs. 40, 41 and Plate VI).[8] It is rare for a problem in the plane

[8] A generalization of the map coloring problem (as formulated in this chapter) has been investigated in the plane and on a sphere. Frequently, a domain is so divided that a number of its subdomains are separated (have no common boundary) although

and on a sphere to remain unsolved long after it has been solved for much more complicated surfaces. But remarkably, this is true for the four color problem.

We have called the map coloring problem a topological problem. Although topology has developed enormously during the last few decades [**10**], when the original four color problem in the plane and on a sphere was first proposed there was no field of topology. There were isolated problems,[9] but no discipline as such.[10] Since then an extensive theory has arisen which has been developed by many respected representatives of the field from all nations. Many difficult and far-reaching problems have been proposed and solved. Yet the modest problem of map coloring has withstood all efforts at solution.

In contrast with other serious problems in mathematics, there is something playful in this problem. However, many discoveries have originated in games, for example, the Dutch telescope, which came from the games of an optician's children who played with eye-glasses.

We have already mentioned Cayley as the mathematician who was instrumental in making the four color problem generally known in technical circles. Cayley is an important figure in the history of mathematics, and deserves more than a casual reference. The extensive and fruitful research of this indefatigable worker (his *Collected Mathematical Papers* comprise 13 large quarto volumes) attests to his versatility and energy. This is to be wondered at, because for many years his professional interest was directed elsewhere. Arthur Cayley was born in 1821 in Surrey. He grew up in St.

---

they belong together, say politically. It is then necessary to give such subdomains the same color. Obviously, this may increase the number of colors required for a map and thus lead to a completely new problem, e.g. the number of colors required for a map in which every country consists of two separated domains [**9**]. Every increase in the number of component parts (all requiring the same color) leads to a new problem. A good example is the map of Germany at the turn of the century, with numerous areas politically joined but geographically separated (e.g. the Saxon-Thuringian states, and the parts of Bavaria on the right and left banks of the Rhine). This map is not an example of the four color problem discussed in this chapter, but illustrates the generalized problem. This is also true of maps of the world in which all the dominions of the British Empire are given the same color, and similarly of all empires with geographically separated provinces.

[9] Another example is the Königsberg bridge problem (see {1}), current in Euler's time. The only branch of topology studied seriously at that time was the theory of knots (see {2}). But even this was only studied empirically, with no attempt to give a real proof for the classification of knots then current.

[10] At that time Riemann (see Chapter XIV, Footnote 12) had already arrived at a topological theory of surfaces, for application to the theory of complex functions; but it was not till much later that it became common scientific knowledge. To be sure, topology had already been prophetically foreseen by Gauss (see Chapter IX), even earlier by Euler (see Footnote 9) and perhaps still earlier by Leibniz (1646–1716).

Petersburg, where his father was a merchant. In 1838 he went to Cambridge, where he took Firsts in old English usage; by the time he was 20 he had begun to publish in the field of mathematics. From 1843–1863, he practiced law in London, and it is remarkable that it was during this time that he published his most significant mathematical papers. We can indicate one direction of his work. A projective property of a geometric figure is one which is unchanged under projection of the figure (see Chapter IV). From analytic geometry we surmise that certain algebraic facts will correspond to these projective properties. In this manner we arrive at *algebraic geometry* with its own computational methods [**11**]. Just as projective geometry had at an earlier date received particular attention in France, so now, according to Klein in his lively historical-mathematical lectures (see {18; vol. 1, pp. 147 ff. and p. 297}), a new school of algebraic geometry arose in England, whose foremost exponents were Cayley, Sylvester and Salmon. In addition to his papers on algebraic geometry, Cayley also published works on mechanics, astronomy and many other subjects.[11]

In 1863, Cayley was made Sadlerian Professor at the University of Cambridge, and a Fellow of Trinity College. He held this chair until his death in 1895. As is usual in England, he did not lecture to large audiences, but was the mentor of a small number of students, while also carrying on his scientific work and being active in the administration of the University.

The map coloring problem has a special charm, arising from the simplicity of its statement, which is in sharp contrast with the complexity of most modern mathematical problems. Amateurs and professional mathematicians alike, including Cayley, have been intrigued by this problem. But like so many other distinguished mathematicians, he did not succeed in finding a proof. We might add that a considerable number of incorrect proofs have been published.

There is no general agreement among mathematicians as to the correctness of the conjecture that the chromatic number of the plane (or sphere) is four. We cannot tell at this time whether, when a solution is found, the methods used will have wider mathematical significance. If this should turn out to be so, then the significance of the map coloring problem in the history of mathematics will be greater than that of an interesting precursor to topology.

[11] His research on the theory of graphs deserves to be noted here because of its connection with the map coloring problem (see Chapter IV, Note 4). The theory of graphs was also important in other fields: in determining the number of possible isomers in organic chemistry, in Kirchoff's theory of networks, etc. [**12**].

*Notes to Chapter XI*

# THE FOUR COLOR PROBLEM

**1** (p. 226). We chose the map of Bavaria because it has certain geometric properties. The discussion in the sequel will show that our interest is in the geometric properties of a map and not in whether the map is up to date geographically. A map showing the old duchies of France 200 years ago, or the occupation zones in Germany, or the postal zones of a city, or the districts of ancient Italy would have done just as well.

**2** (p. 230). The map of Fig. 133 is another good example. This map does not contain a set of four neighboring domains, but it can be shown that it requires more than three colors. It is called a dodecahedral subdivision. A dodecahedron is a regular polyhedron bounded by twelve pentagons. If such a (three-dimensional) figure is projected from a suitably chosen point $P$ onto a suitably chosen plane $E$, the result is a figure such as Fig. 133. In Fig. 133, $E$ is the plane of the paper and also the plane of one of the bounding pentagons (the central one in the figure) of the dodecahedron. The center of projection $P$ (not shown) was a point above the center of the pentagon opposite and above the central one in the figure.

**3** (p. 230). Cantons 4, 19, 11 and 5 are a set of four neighboring domains on the map of Switzerland (Plate XIII or Plate XVI, map 1). Canton 18 is surrounded by seven cantons: 9, 8, 13, 17, 4, 20 and 15, which are basically the same as the seven sectors of a circle surrounding a central circle (Fig. 131e); this is also true of the seven cantons surrounding canton 13. It is obvious that each of these submaps of the map of Switzerland requires more than three colors; this must also be true then for the whole map.

To be sure, cantons 5 and 11 do not have a common land boundary; their common boundary is Lake Neuchâtel. We could agree to color these two cantons alike, as in Plate XVI, map 2. This also applies to cantons 13 and 17, whose common boundary is Lake Lucerne. For this reason, they have been colored alike in map 2 of Plate XVI. Thus, in map 2, cantons 10 and 18 are surrounded by an even, instead of an odd, number of domains. We might, in addition, combine cantons 14 and 1, so that cantons 14, 1, 3 and 4 are no longer a set of four neighboring domains. This has been done in map 2 of Plate XVI. But even after this alteration, three colors do not suffice, since domain 1713 is now surrounded by an odd number of domains: 6, 22, 21, 10, 4, 18, 8. This configuration is equivalent to the map of Fig. 131e, which requires more than three colors.[1]

[1] We note that no domain on the border of Switzerland is colored yellow either in Plate XIII or in maps 1 and 2 of Plate XVI. Transferring these maps to a sphere, we could color the entire domain exterior to the map of Switzerland yellow, thus obtaining a division of a sphere into domains which require four colors.

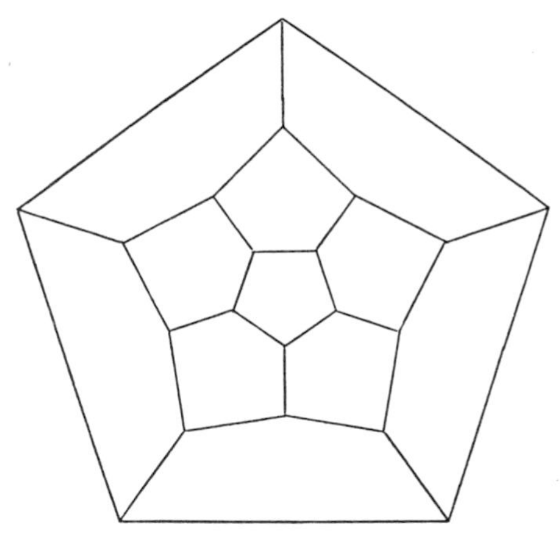

FIG. 133

**4** (p. 232). We shall outline the proof of Heawood's five color theorem in six steps, and show how the third step depends on Euler's polyhedral theorem.

I. We shall call any subdivision of a sphere into domains a map. A given map may contain a domain $A$ which surrounds one or more domains $B$, $C$, $\cdots$ and thus separates $B$, $C$, $\cdots$ from one or more domains $B'$, $C'$, $\cdots$. The boundary of the domain $A$ will then consist of two or more disconnected pieces. For example, consider the map obtained by dividing the earth into a domain $A$ consisting of the zone about the equator from 20° South to 20° North, and two classes of domains $B$, $C$, $\cdots$ and $B'$, $C'$, $\cdots$ which fill up each of the remaining spherical caps. Then $A$ surrounds $B$, $C$, $\cdots$ (or $B'$, $C'$, $\cdots$) and separates $B$, $C$, $\cdots$ from $B'$, $C'$, $\cdots$ (or $B'$, $C'$, $\cdots$ from $B$, $C$, $\cdots$), and its boundary consists of the two circles of latitude which bound it. As another example, consider the following map. The domain $A$ consists of all the oceans and all the islands; the domains $B$, $C$, $\cdots$ consist of the countries of North and South America; the domains $B'$, $C'$, $\cdots$ consist of the countries of Europe, Asia and Africa; the domain $A'$ is all of Australia. Then $A$ separates $B$, $C$, $\cdots$ from $B'$, $C'$, $\cdots$ and also from $A'$, and its boundary consists of several disconnected pieces.

We shall call a domain which does not surround one or more other domains and which has a connected boundary an *elementary domain*. A map all of whose domains are elementary domains will be referred to as a *normal map*. We shall also say that a map can be $n$-colored if $n$ colors suffice for this map.

Normal maps are important because of the following theorem:

*Theorem* 1. If *every normal* map on a sphere can be 5-colored (or, in general, $n$-colored), then every map on the sphere can be 5-colored ($n$-colored).

We shall not prove this proposition, but will try to indicate the proof on the assumption that the map has only one nonelementary domain. To make the argument concrete, consider the first of the above two examples, in which the map $M$ consists of a belt $A$ surrounding the equator and of domains $B, C, \cdots; B', C', \cdots$ filling in each of the spherical caps exterior to $A$. We assume that $B, C, \cdots; B', C', \cdots$ are all elementary domains, and that every normal map on the sphere can be 5-colored. Let us now combine the domains $A, B', C', \cdots$ into one domain $A_1$, leaving the domains $B, C, \cdots$ unaltered. Then the map $M_1$ consisting of $A_1, B, C, \cdots$ is a normal map on the sphere. Hence it can be 5-colored. Suppose that $A_1$ has the color $a$ in $M_1$; then the belt $A$ has the color $a$ in $M_1$.

Now construct a map $M_2$ by combining the belt $A$ with all the domains $B, C, \cdots$ to form a domain $A_2$, leaving $B', C', \cdots$ unaltered. Then $M_2$ is a normal map on the sphere and can be 5-colored. Suppose that the color $a$ is assigned to $A_2$ in the map $M_2$ (as it was in $M_1$). A moment's reflection will show that we have now succeeded in 5-coloring the original map $M$, since we have merely to assign to the domains $B, C, \cdots$ the colors they have in $M_1$, and to $B', C', \cdots$ the colors they have in $M_2$, at the same time retaining the color $a$ for $A$.

II. Theorem 1 of I (when proved) reduces the problem of coloring arbitrary maps to that of coloring normal maps. In the second step we reduce the problem further. To this end, let us call every isolated point at which three or more boundary lines of a map meet a *vertex* of the map. A vertex of a map at which exactly three boundary lines meet is called a 3-vertex, one in which exactly four boundary lines meet, a 4-vertex, etc. For example, on a checkerboard (see Plate XV) every vertex is a 4-vertex. We now define a *special map* to be a normal map all of whose vertices are 3-vertices. A checkerboard is normal but not special since its vertices are 4-vertices. Other examples of nonspecial (but normal) maps are the maps of Chapter IV, Fig. 32a (the vertex $B$ is a 4-vertex) and Fig. 31a (the vertex $B$ is a 5-vertex).

It can then be shown, although we will not reproduce the proof, that the coloring of normal maps can be reduced to the coloring of special maps. More precisely stated, and taking Theorem 1 into account, the proposition is

*Theorem* 2. If *every special* map on the sphere can be 5-colored (or $n$-colored), then *every arbitrary* map on the sphere can be 5-colored ($n$-colored).

III. We shall now consider certain formulas which hold for normal maps. Let $F_k$ be the number of domains (or countries) of the map which border (along a piece of boundary line) exactly $k$ other domains, and let $F$ be the total number of domains in the map. Then

$$F_2 + \cdots + F_n = F. \tag{1}$$

Now let us call a piece of boundary line of the map an *edge* if it begins and ends at a vertex (the initial and terminal vertices must be distinct) and contains no other vertices of the map. Denote the number of edges of the map by $L$. Then

$$2F_2 + 3F_3 + 4F_4 + \cdots + nF_n = 2L. \tag{2}$$

To see why (2) holds, note that if a domain borders exactly $k$ other domains, its boundary must be made up of exactly $k$ edges. Since there are $F_k$ domains of this sort, the number of edges contributed by them is $kF_k$. Hence the left-hand side of (2). However, each edge of the map is counted twice on the left-hand side of (2); hence the right-hand side of (2) is $2L$.

Now denote by $E$ the number of vertices of the map. Then

$$E - L + F = 2. \tag{3}$$

Formula (3) is a consequence of the Euler formula[2] (see Chapter XI, Footnote 7), which we cannot prove here.

IV. Now suppose that the map is a special map, that is, a normal map all of whose vertices are 3-vertices. Then formula (2) of III becomes

$$2F_2 + 3F_3 + \cdots + nF_n = 3E. \tag{4}$$

The reason is that a domain with exactly $k$ neighbors has $k$ vertices on its boundary. Therefore, the number of vertices in the $F_k$ domains each with $k$ neighbors is $kF_k$. The left-hand side of (4) therefore counts the total number of vertices (but more than once). Since each vertex is a 3-vertex, it is a vertex of three domains. The left-hand side of (4) therefore counts each vertex three times. This gives the right-hand side of (4).

Multiplying (3) by 6 and substituting for $6F$, $6L$ and $6E$ from (1), (2) and (4), we obtain

$$(6-2)F_2 + (6-3)F_3 + \cdots + (6-k)F_k + \cdots + (6-n)F_n = 12. \tag{5}$$

From (5) it is clear that the coefficients of $F_2$, $F_3$, $F_4$, $F_5$ are positive, the coefficient of $F_6$ is 0, and all the rest have negative coefficients. It follows that

$$4F_2 + 3F_3 + 2F_4 + F_5 \geq 12.$$

[2] If the polyhedral surface is projected from a point in its interior onto a sphere whose interior contains the surface, the result is a map in which every domain corresponds to a face of the polyhedral surface, each vertex to a vertex of the polyhedral surface and each edge to an edge of the surface. The numbers $F$, $E$, $L$ therefore have the same meaning as the numbers $F$, $E$, $K$ in the Euler formula (see Chapter XI, Footnote 7).

Therefore, not all the numbers $F_2$, $F_3$, $F_4$, $F_5$ can be 0. This proves

*Theorem* 3. A special map must contain a domain with at least two but no more than five neighbors.

V. A consequence of Theorem 3 is the following reduction theorem[3] (whose proof we omit):

*Theorem* 4. If $F > 5$, and if every special map with less than $F$ domains can be 5-colored, then every special map with $F$ domains can be 5-colored.[4]

VI. We are now ready for the conclusion of the outline of the proof. First, we note that if $F \leq 5$, the map can certainly be 5-colored. Hence, by Theorem 4 and induction we have

*Theorem* 5. Every special map can be 5-colored.

Combining Theorem 2 of II and Theorem 5 we finally arrive at

*Heawood's Five Color Theorem.* Every map on the sphere can be 5-colored.

This result is easily extended to maps in the plane. For, let $M$ be a map in the plane. Since the map consists of a finite number of bounded domains, the map itself is bounded. Now project the map $M$ stereographically onto a sphere. This is done by resting a sphere at some point $S$ of the plane (so that it touches the plane only at the point $S$) and joining the north pole $N$ of the sphere (the point opposite the point $S$) with every point $P$ of the plane. The point $P'$ at which $NP$ intersects the sphere is the stereographic image of $P$. The stereographic images of all points $P$ of the map $M$ together with all the rest of the sphere counted as one additional domain form a map $M'$ on the sphere. Since $M'$ can be 5-colored (by Heawood's theorem), so can $M$.

**5** (p. 233). Figs. 54 and 55 accompanying Note 5 of Chapter IV show how the surface of a tetrahedron can be projected on a sphere. Many other polyhedral surfaces can be similarly projected. This is why Euler's formula is applicable to subdivisions of a sphere as well as other surfaces topologically equivalent to a sphere.

**6** (p. 233). The proof[5] in this case—as well as the cases mentioned

[3] Compare with the period when English and American mathematicians first became interested in the color problem: A. B. Kempe (in London) published his first papers in {3}, {4}, {5}. Then William E. Story, in direct connection with Kempe's work, showed that the problem can be reduced to maps with 3-vertices (see II above and {6}). Besides the papers of Cayley mentioned before, see {7}.

[4] Kempe (see Footnote 3) believed that he had solved the four color problem because he had a proof of the theorem for four colors corresponding to Theorem 4. The proof was similar to the one outlined here, but involved a somewhat more complicated reduction process. However, Heawood showed that there was a gap in the proof. It is still an open question whether Kempe's reduction algorithm for four colors is valid for special maps.

[5] The proof is due to Heawood (see Footnote 4). Professor Heawood informed me in a letter of June 3, 1948 that he was still (in his 87th year) interested in the whole field, and that in addition to his papers of 1890 and 1898 (see {8}), he had published papers in 1936 and 1944 (see {9}, {10}) on the coloring problem.

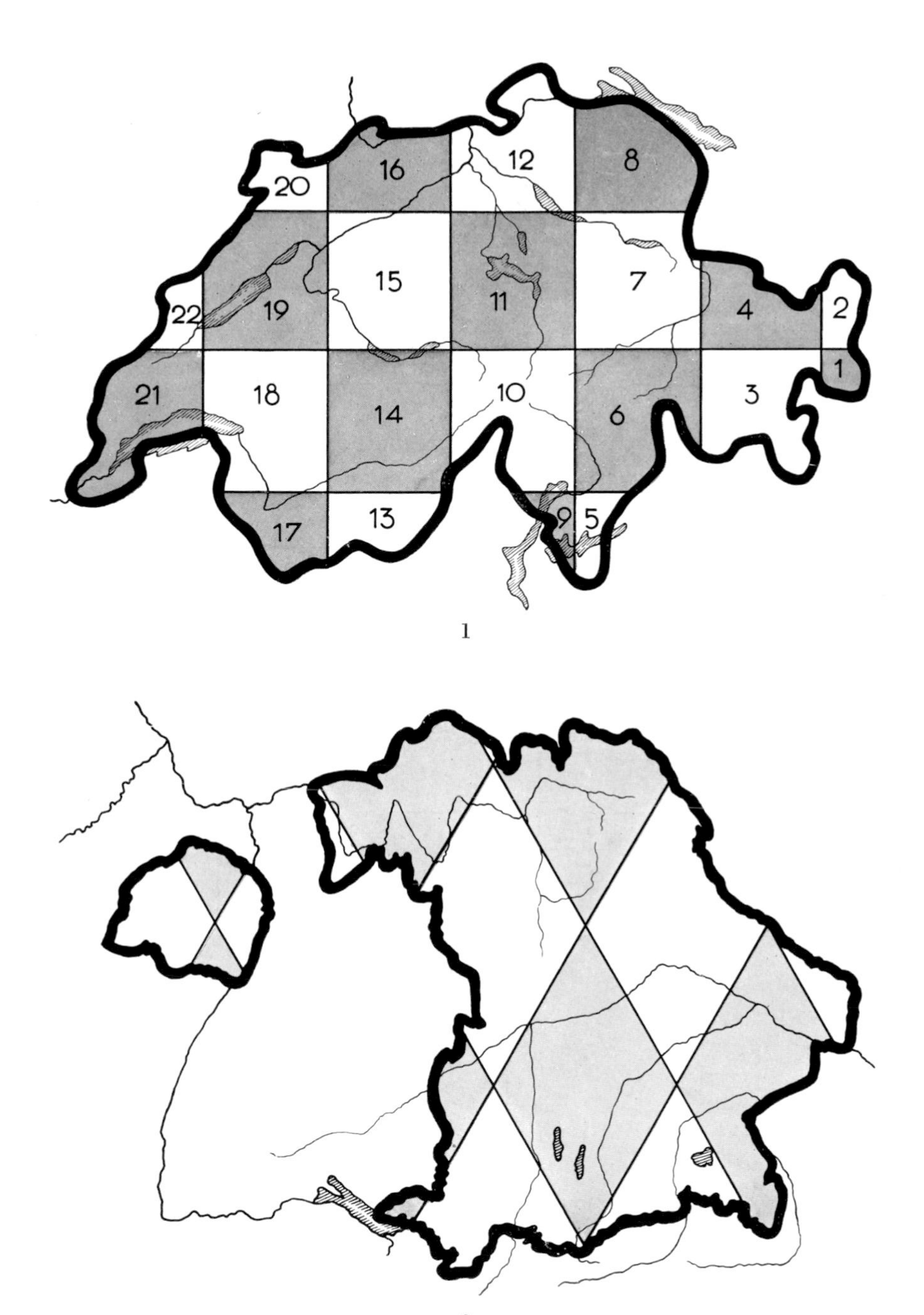


1

2

PLATE XVI

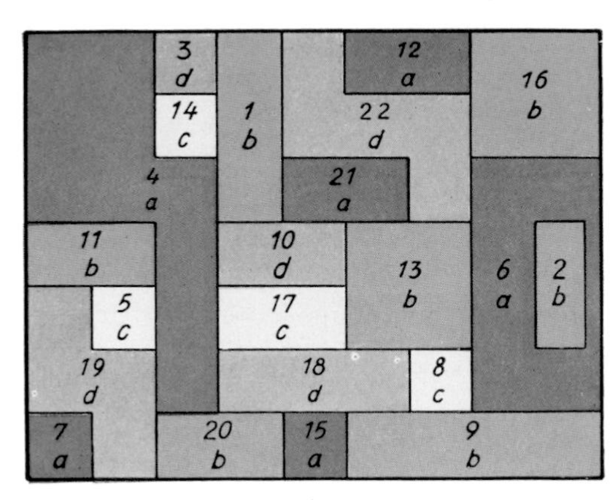


1

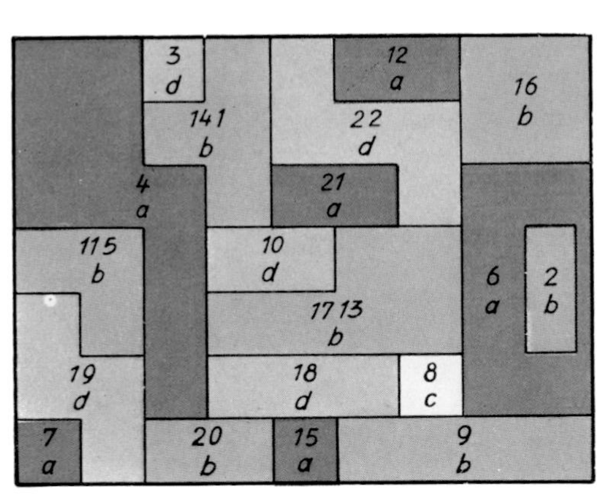


2

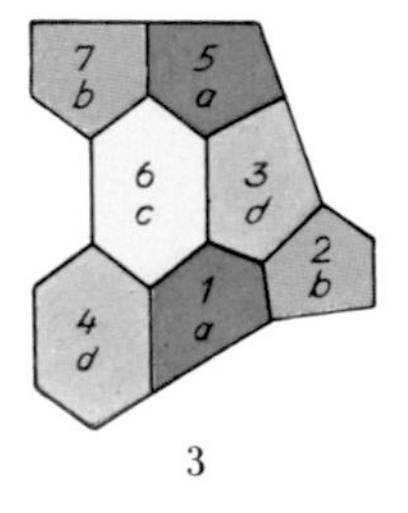


3

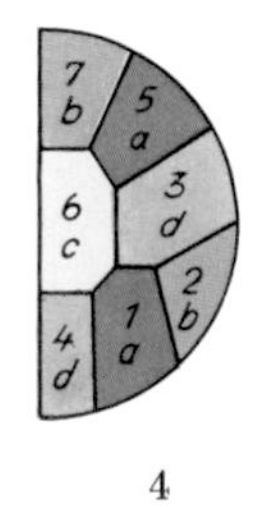


4

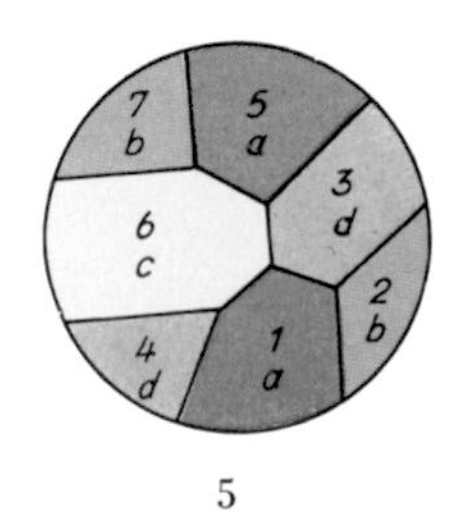


5

below—is similar to the proof of Heawood's theorem sketched in Note 4 for the sphere and plane. This proof, however, requires a generalization of Euler's formula to types of surfaces other than those topologically equivalent to the sphere. This generalization (the formula for the Euler characteristic) is one of the fundamental theorems of topology.—Indeed, Heawood showed that the chromatic number of a sphere with $p$ handles (for $p = 1$ the surface is a torus, for $p = 2$ a double torus, etc.), that is, a closed orientable surface of genus $p$, does not exceed $\frac{1}{2}[7 + (1 + 48p)^{1/2}]$. See also Chapter IV, Notes 7 and 8.

**7** (p. 233). We have emphasized that the chromatic number $\chi$ of a surface is to be distinguished from the maximum number $\nu$ of neighboring domains on the surface, and have noted that $\chi \geq \nu$. But G. A. Dirac in a paper {11} published in 1952 has shown that for many types of surfaces the problems of finding $\chi$ and $\nu$ are closely related. Indeed, he has shown that for most types of surfaces the fact that a map on the surface requires a certain number $n$ of colors implies the existence of $n$ neighboring domains in the map. In other words, $\chi = \nu$ for these surfaces. But his result does *not* hold for the plane and sphere (and nonorientable surfaces of genus 1 and 3).

**8** (p. 233). See the references cited in Chapter IV, Notes 2 and 14. For further map coloring problems, see {12} and {13} and the references cited there.

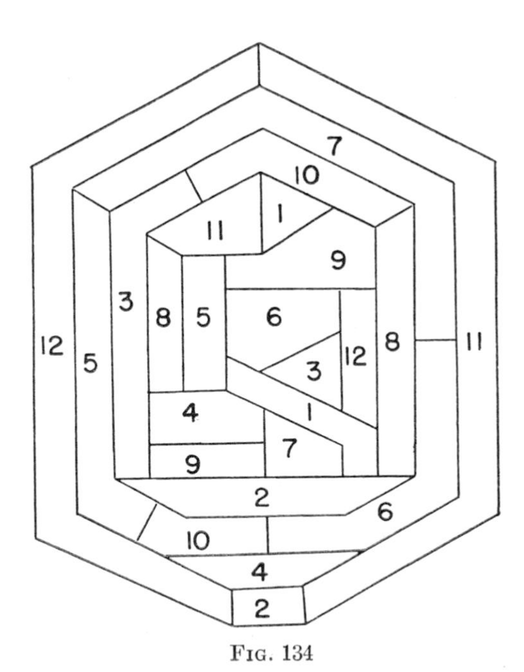


FIG. 134

**9** (p. 234). For such maps we denote the chromatic number by $\chi_2$, to distinguish it from the chromatic number $\chi_1$ of maps whose domains are connected, that is, consist of one piece. Remarkably, the more complicated problem was solved completely by Heawood, who found that $\chi_2 = 12$ for the sphere.[6]

The results cited for the torus and Möbius band, together with references to the literature, can be found in {1; Chapter XVIII, §§ 3, 4, pp. 216–219}.

**10** (p. 234). The first introductory text in this field was written by Oswald Veblen {14}. Soon after, a book by B. v. Kerékjártó appeared {15}. In addition to these we might mention several other papers and books {16}. Newer books are given in {17}.

**11** (p. 235). Classical algebraic geometry is concerned with the theory of invariants and this involves the use of matrices and determinants. Matrices and determinants are also used to study systems of linear equations, a topic most students study in school. Cayley had begun to develop matrix theory as early as 1858, a fact which should be of interest to physicists, since finite and infinite matrices are now extensively used in theoretical physics. Cayley also extended algebraic geometry to the study of $n$-dimensional algebraic varieties. See also the relevant sections of Felix Klein's book {18}.

**12** (p. 235). For more details see {19}.

[6] Heawood proved that 12 colors always suffice, i.e. $\chi_2 \leq 12$, and also gave an example (see Fig. 134) in which 12 colors are necessary. In the example, the 12 domains, each consisting of two parts, form a set of 12 neighboring domains.

*Chapter XII*

# INFINITY IN MATHEMATICS

Surrounded as the word *infinity* is with an air of mystery and awe, the mathematician who deals with this concept in a cool, detached manner is likely to inspire considerable puzzlement in the outsider. But the same words may have very different meanings in various branches of knowledge. We shall not be concerned here with the usual poetic or theological connotations of infinity and eternity so dear to the heart of man, but with specific well defined mathematical concepts. These definitions will serve to distinguish not only between *finite* and *infinite*, but also between various *degrees of infinity*, that is, between a hierarchy of *infinite numbers*, called *transfinite numbers*. At the end of the chapter, we will try to give a rough idea of a famous unsolved problem in the theory of transfinite numbers, the continuum problem.[1] In addition, this chapter will once again demonstrate the fascination unsolved problems have for the true mathematician.

Once again, as in Chapter VIII, we must return to the beginnings of mathematics. These origins extend beyond the human consciousness, for even among animals there are indications of an awareness of the concept of number, e.g. the "number" of their young, and the concept of "more" or "less." Indeed, experiments have shown that some animals can learn to distinguish a specific number from a larger or a smaller one [**1**].

To start with, we note that the process of "counting" in its restricted sense, that is, ordinal enumeration, is not always necessary if the number of objects is small. In such cases, one learns, with a little practice, to apprehend the total number of objects in a collection without consciously enumerating the objects one after the other.

The formal process of counting really begins when we have to deal with larger collections of objects, as in an exchange of goods or money. Then definite number names or symbols are used to refer to the objects of the collection, one after another. We take an object and say "one"; we take another and say "two"; when we take the last object, the number we have reached gives the total number of objects in the collection.

In the usual process of counting, therefore, we range the objects to be counted in some specific order, and then tick them off one by one with the aid of the positive integers. It would then appear that the number of objects in a collection depends on the particular order in which they are counted; another enumeration of the same objects, but in a different order, might give another result. This sometimes happens when the people in a

[1] The problem has been solved since this was written. See Footnote 17.

room are counted first in one order and then in another. But we are then convinced that we have made an error, and start over. Indeed, we know from experience, that the particular order selected for enumerating the objects of a collection is immaterial. Just as irrelevant to the number of objects in a collection are the various properties of the objects, such as size, color, the English names attached to them, etc. For these reasons, we shall be concerned for the most part (later in the chapter we will have to take order into account) with abstract collections of objects. Such collections, in which no account is taken of the particular nature of the objects making up the collection, are called *sets*. A *set* is thus a technical mathematical term, and its meaning in this context must not be confused with any other connotations it may have. We shall refer to the objects (all assumed to be distinct) comprising the set as the *elements* of the set. A set may have just one element or none at all. The set which has no elements is called the *empty set*.

Let $M$ be a set. A set $A$ is called a *subset* of $M$ if every element of $A$ is also an element of $M$. In this definition we do not exclude the possibility that $A$ contains *all* the elements of $M$. Thus, $M$ itself is a subset of $M$. We say that two sets $M$ and $N$ are equal ($M = N$) if $M$ is a subset of $N$ *and* $N$ is a subset of $M$, i.e. $M$ and $N$ have exactly the same elements. A set $A$ is called a *proper subset* of $M$ if $A$ is a subset of $M$ and if there is at least one element of $M$ which is not an element of $A$. In other words, a proper subset $A$ of $M$ is a subset of $M$ which is not equal to $M$. The reason for introducing this seemingly subtle distinction is to simplify the following discussion. To illustrate these definitions, let $M$ be a set whose elements are white and black sheep. Then the set $A$ of black sheep is a subset of $M$ (since every black sheep is also a sheep), and indeed $A$ is a proper subset of $M$ (since the white sheep are elements of $M$ but not of $A$).

If $M$ is a set and $A$ is a subset of $M$, the subset of $M$ consisting of the elements of $M$ which are *not* elements of $A$ is called the complement of $A$ in $M$, and is denoted by $A'$. We also say that $M$ is the *union* of $A$ and $A'$. In the example above, $A'$ is the subset of white sheep.

Now suppose that we are given two sets, and are required, not to count, but merely to *compare* the number of elements in each, that is, to determine whether or not they have an equal number of elements. For example, let $A$ be a set of black marbles and let $B$ be a set of white marbles. To compare the two sets, we need merely remove one black and one white marble at a time, lay them aside, and go on until the marbles of one color are exhausted. If both colors are exhausted at the same time, $A$ and $B$ have the same number of marbles. If the black marbles are used up first, $B$ has more marbles than $A$; in the contrary case, $A$ has more marbles than $B$. An analogous procedure can be applied to determine whether there are more women than men in a given gathering. Let each man simply choose one woman to escort to dinner. If there are women left over, the number of women is greater than the number of men.

In each of the above examples, the procedure for comparing the number of objects in each set consisted in assigning to each element of one set an element of the other set, or, in other words, pairing elements of the two sets, as long as possible. We add that, just as in counting, the order in which the elements are paired is irrelevant.

Our future discussion will be simplified if at this point we introduce another mathematical term to denote the pairing described in the examples above. A 1–1 (read one-to-one) correspondence between two sets $M$ and $N$ is a pairing of the elements of $M$ and $N$ which 1) assigns to every element of $M$ exactly one element of $N$, 2) two distinct elements of $M$ are assigned distinct elements of $N$ and 3) every element of $N$ is assigned to some element of $M$. If there is a 1–1 correspondence between $M$ and $N$, the sets $M$ and $N$ are said to be in 1–1 correspondence or *equivalent*. For instance, if a gathering consists of 5 men and 5 women, and the set $M$ is the set of 5 men, $N$ the set of 5 women, $M$ and $N$ are in 1–1 correspondence because each man can be assigned a woman (partner) in such a way as to satisfy 1), 2) and 3) above. The definition of 1–1 correspondence applies also to infinite sets, but before discussing infinite sets we want to formulate more precisely the remarks made above on the comparison of *finite* sets, since all our examples have so far been taken from the physical world. This reformulation is in the form of two propositions, (a) and (b), which describe in terms of set, subset and 1–1 correspondence the assertions: "The set $M$ has the same number of elements as the set $N$," and "The set $M$ has more elements than the set $N$."

PROPOSITION (a). *Two finite sets $M$ and $N$ have the same number of elements if there is a* 1–1 *correspondence between $M$ and $N$, that is, if $M$ and $N$ are equivalent.*

PROPOSITION (b). *A finite set $M$ has more elements than a finite set $N$ if there is a* 1–1 *correspondence between a proper subset $T$ of $M$ and all of $N$; in other words, if $N$ is equivalent to a proper subset $T$ of $M$.*

We shall now consider infinite sets, which are indispensable in mathematics. At this point we leave the world of immediate experience and enter the world of speculative thought, since infinite sets are purely mental constructs for which no examples exist in the immediate physical world.

Archimedes, in his work *The Sand Reckoner*, posed the problem of calculating the number of grains of sand in a sphere extending from the earth to the fixed stars. He had neither names nor symbols to designate such enormous numbers [**2**]. Nevertheless, Archimedes showed how with a systematic computational scheme one could represent numbers of even this magnitude.[2]

This example indicates that at the basis of any mode of dealing with extremely large, but finite, numbers, that is, with finite sets, is the assumption that the sequence of natural numbers

$$1, 2, 3, \cdots$$

is unending.[3] To be sure, the sequence has a beginning—the number 1 is the first element of the sequence—but it has no end: every number has a successor [**4**].

The set of all natural numbers is the most immediate and important example of an *infinite set*.[4] Other examples are: the set of all even numbers

$$2, 4, 6, 8, 10, \cdots ;$$

the set of all odd numbers

$$1, 3, 5, 7, 9, 11, \cdots ;$$

and the set of all powers of 2:

$$1, 2, 4, 8, 16, 32, \cdots$$

(see [**5**]). Still another example is the set of numbers

$$1/2, 1/4, 1/8, 1/16, \cdots ,$$

where each number is one half its predecessor.

A somewhat different example is the set of all points on a segment $AB$ (see Fig. 135a). It is obvious that the set of these points is also infinite; in fact, we need not consider the set of all points on $AB$, but only the subset of $AB$ consisting of the points $C$, $D$, $E$, etc. (see Fig. 135b), where $C$ is the midpoint of $AB$, $D$ is the midpoint of $AC$, etc.[5] Then this subset [**6**] of $AB$ is itself an infinite set [**7**].

Further examples of infinite sets are: the set of points on a straight line,

[2] See {1} and {2}.

[3] It makes no essential difference that we have names and a decimal system to symbolize much larger numbers than was possible in Greek mathematics. The magnitude of the numbers which can be expressed by means of our positional system is still limited [**3**].

[4] In mathematics it is necessary to make a strict distinction between finite sets—no matter how large—and infinite sets, whereas the word "infinite" has a much vaguer meaning in every-day speech and in poetry, e.g. a mother's infinite patience, infinite sorrows, etc.

[5] The subset of the segment $AB$ consisting of the points $C$, $D$, $E$, $\cdots$ is in 1–1 correspondence with the set of numbers $1/2$, $1/4$, $1/8$, $\cdots$ , since it is these numbers which give the relative distances of the successive points of the subset from the point $A$.

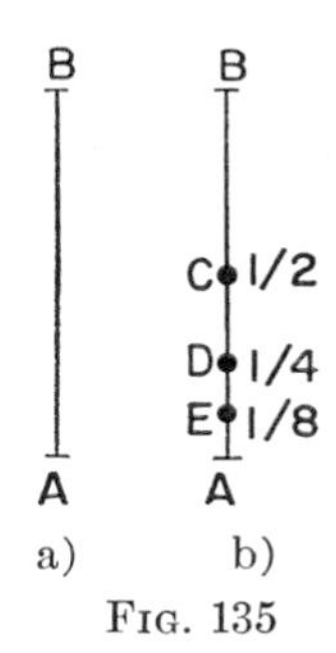


FIG. 135

the set of points on a half line, the set of points in the plane or in space, the set of all circles in the plane, and the set of all straight lines in space.

The infinite sets in these examples are quite dissimilar, but, as in the case of finite sets, we can try to compare infinite sets with each other. To understand the rather surprising results of this attempt, we must again start at the beginning and follow the historical development of the subject.

In 1851 Bernard Bolzano's[6] book, *Paradoxes of the Infinite*, was published; the title is well suited to the nature of our subject. Bolzano was a precursor of Georg Cantor, who in the last third of the 19th century created the theory of sets, on which is based the comparison of infinite sets. This theory has had a very pervasive influence on all branches of modern mathematics [**9**].

In contrast with the controversy aroused by his theory of sets, Cantor's outer life was quiet and uneventful, much like the scholarly life led by Dedekind, who for many years exchanged ideas with Cantor in a friendly correspondence. The two men, about fifteen years apart in age, had many professional interests in common, especially their interest in the infinite in mathematics, which is the basis of all mathematics; and they were continually concerned with it.[7] Statements which many of their contempo-

[6] Bernard Bolzano (1781–1848) became a lay priest in 1805. In 1820 he was dismissed from his post as Professor of Comparative Religion in Prague for heresy. He was also an opponent of Kant's philosophy. In 1817 he published a work in pure mathematics, in which he proved himself superior in critical acumen to most of his contemporaries [8]. His *Paradoxes of the Infinite* (a work that presaged modern dimension theory) was published three years after his death by a student he had befriended.

[7] In this connection we should also mention the theory of irrational numbers (see Chapter VIII). The irrational and rational numbers together comprise the real numbers, by means of which all points on a real line may be represented. Dedekind's theory of irrational numbers, published in 1872, is probably the oldest in conception, even though an equivalent theory was published by Charles Méray in 1869. Méray's theory went unnoticed at the time. It was republished in 1872. A theory identical with Méray's was developed independently by Cantor, who published it the same year. During Cantor's lifetime, Weierstrass and Heine also published theories of irrational numbers.

raries regarded as self-evident appeared to them to require proof; for this reason, as we have noted before, Dedekind's work on the foundations of the theory of real numbers had to overcome a great deal of misunderstanding before it was accepted. Cantor was faced with quite different obstacles. Dedekind's concern was to study the properties of the infinite which differentiate it from the finite, and to clarify the nature of proof by mathematical induction, which is based on one of the most important properties of the infinite sequence of natural numbers. But Cantor's preoccupation was with ordering and analysing the infinite itself. His theories were met not merely with indifference, but with much hostility. Nevertheless, they aroused increasing interest and gradually gained recognition.

Georg Ferdinand Louis Philippe Cantor was born in 1845 in St. Petersburg, where his father, a broker from Copenhagen, had moved in his youth. While still in elementary school in Petersburg, Cantor was strongly impelled to study mathematics. When he was eleven the family left Petersburg for Germany. There he attended the Gymnasium in Wiesbaden, then a private school in Frankfurt-am-Main, next a non-classical secondary school in Darmstadt, and in 1860, the Technical Institute where he studied engineering, to please his father. In 1862, his father finally agreed to allow his son to follow a career in mathematics.

One semester of study in Zürich was followed by a long period in Berlin, where his teachers were Kummer (1810–1893; see Chapter XIII), Kronecker (1823–1891) and Weierstrass (1815–1897). Weierstrass apparently influenced him most. In 1867, after receiving his doctorate, Cantor went to Halle, where Heine [**10**] was at the time. In 1869 he became a privat-dozent (a private lecturer recognized by the University) at the University of Halle. He was later promoted to a professorship, which he held until he retired in 1905. He died in Halle in 1918.

Before his death, his ideas, at first so violently opposed, had been accepted, and had begun to influence many branches of mathematics. Up to the seventies his main published work was in the field of trigonometric series. Then, after many delays and hesitations, he published his research on the theory of sets. His work aroused vehement opposition in his former teacher Kronecker, but Weierstrass recognized its value immediately.

How was it possible for such speculative research to influence and alter the highly technical mathematics of Cantor's time? The answer is that Cantor had concerned himself not only with general investigations of the infinite, but had also applied his results to point sets on a line, in the plane and in space. It follows from the remark in Footnote 7 that the points of a line and the set of real numbers are in 1–1 correspondence. One may therefore speak of sets of real numbers and sets of points on a line interchangeably. But points and numbers have always been mathematical objects, so that it was now possible to unify many earlier results [11] by means of the new concepts of the theory of point sets. This theory also led to the formulation of new problems and methods of proof which would have been impossible without it [12].

The disputes over the theory of sets, and especially its rejection by the influential Kronecker, led Cantor to devote a great deal of energy towards the founding of the Deutsche Mathematiker Vereinigung or German Mathematical Union (see Chapter IX, Note 25 and Footnote 8 in the Notes), which for many decades received the highest respect. Cantor was the first chairman (1890), serving two three year terms. The Union was meant to be an international forum for a free discussion of controversial problems. It is significant of Cantor's temperament, as well as of the spirit of the time, that he asked Kronecker to deliver the initial lecture, and that Kronecker declined on the grounds of ill health. Problems on the *power* or *cardinality* of infinite sets (the new field of transfinite numbers introduced by Cantor) were again of primary interest at the Heidelberg Congress of 1904.

Of the numerous honors which were bestowed on Cantor, the Sylvester medal of the British Royal Society deserves special mention because it is so rarely given.

Let us now return to the problem of comparing infinite sets. We cannot, of course, count infinite sets as we do finite sets. If we were to count infinite sets by assigning the number 1 to some element, the number 2 to another element, etc., we would never arrive at a number corresponding to the totality of elements in the set.

Nevertheless, the procedure described above for comparing two finite sets $M$ and $N$ can be extended to infinite sets by means of the definition of the relation of equivalence between sets. The definition of equivalence did not involve in any essential way the notion of finiteness; it depended only on the notion of pairing or correspondence, and this idea can be applied to all sets, whether finite or not. Therefore, as in the case of finite sets, we will say that two arbitrary sets $M$ and $N$ are *equivalent* if there is a 1–1 correspondence between $M$ and $N$. The definition of 1–1 correspondence is exactly the same as that given for finite sets (see p. 245): In a 1–1 correspondence every element of $M$ is paired with precisely one element of $N$ and conversely.

Here is a simple example. Let $M$ be the set of odd natural numbers, $N$ the set of even natural numbers. The pairing

$$1,\ 3,\ 5,\ 7,\ \ 9,\ 11,\ \cdots,$$
$$2,\ 4,\ 6,\ 8,\ 10,\ 12,\ \cdots,$$

where beneath each odd number we place the succeeding even number

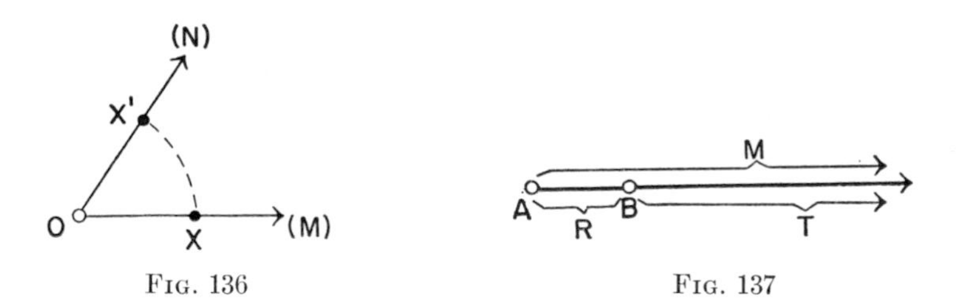


FIG. 136

FIG. 137

(the element $n$ of $N$ corresponding to the element $m$ of $M$ is given by the formula $n = m + 1$), is an example [**13**] of a 1–1 correspondence between two sets. We therefore conclude that the two sets are equivalent.

As another example consider two half-lines $M$ and $N$ emanating from a common point $O$. A 1–1 correspondence between $M$ and $N$ is established by a rotation about $O$ that carries every point $X$ of $M$ into a corresponding point $X'$ of $N$ (Fig. 136). This is clearly a 1–1 correspondence between $M$ and $N$ since the rotation can be reversed [**14**].

We recall that the equivalence of two *finite* sets implied that they had the same *number* of elements; it was appropriate to use the word *number* to describe the totality of elements of a finite set, since we are already acquainted with the numbers 1, 2, 3, etc. (although in a systematic development of the foundations of arithmetic these would also have to be defined). But we must, at least for the time being, avoid using the word *number* in connection with infinite sets [**15**], since we have no definition or acquaintance with numbers corresponding to infinite sets as yet. Thus, we shall be careful not to say "the number of even numbers is equal to the number of odd numbers" or "one half-line has the same number of points as another half-line."

It would be wrong, moreover, to think that infinite sets behave exactly like finite sets. The following example makes this clear. Let $M$ be the set of all natural numbers 1, 2, 3, $\cdots$, and let $N$ be the set of all even numbers 2, 4, 6, $\cdots$. The correspondence

$$\begin{array}{l} 1, 2, 3, 4, \ \ 5, \ \ 6, \cdots, \\ 2, 4, 6, 8, 10, 12, \cdots \end{array}$$

shows that the two sets are equivalent: the correspondence assigns to every element $m$ of $M$ the element $n = 2m$ of $N$. (The element $n$ of $N$ is thereby assigned to the element $m = n/2$ of $M$.)

The remarkable thing about this equivalence is that $N$ is a proper subset of $M$, for $M$ contains both the even and the odd numbers. This cannot happen in the case of a finite set, for if $M$ is a finite set, it contains a definite number of elements (given by some natural number), while every proper subset of $M$ contains a smaller number of elements. It follows that there can be no 1–1 correspondence between $M$ and any of its proper subsets (see Proposition (b)).

In the case of infinite sets, however, we can find many examples in which a set is equivalent to one of its proper subsets. For instance, let $M$ be the set consisting of a point $A$ and a half-line originating at $A$ (Fig. 137). Let $B$ be a point of $M$ different from $A$, and let $T$ be the proper subset of $M$ obtained by deleting from $M$ all points of the segment $AB$ other than $B$. To see that $T$ is equivalent to $M$, translate $M$ to the right so that $A$ coincides with $B$, and make correspond to every point of $M$ the point of $T$ into which it is carried by the translation.

As another example, let $M$ be the set of all natural numbers $1, 2, 3, \cdots$; and let $T$ be the proper subset of $M$ consisting of all natural numbers $\geq 2$. The correspondence

$$1, 2, 3, 4, 5, 6, \cdots,$$
$$2, 3, 4, 5, 6, 7, \cdots$$

shows that the two sets are equivalent: to each number $x$ of $M$ we assign the number $x + 1$ of $N$ [**16**].

Let us take still another example. The two half-lines shown in Fig. 138a represent two sets of points $M$ and $N$. The two half-lines can be put in 1–1 correspondence by a suitable parallel projection, making each point $X$ of $M$ correspond to a point $X'$ of $N$. Hence $M$ and $N$ are equivalent. Now, if we project the half-line $N$ perpendicularly onto the proper subset $T$ of $M$ consisting of the half-line starting at $C$ (Fig. 138b), we then have a 1–1 correspondence between $N$ and a proper subset of $M$. This shows that $N$ is also equivalent to a proper subset of $M$.

The two examples above indicate that in the case of two infinite sets $M$ and $N$, it is possible for *$N$ to be equivalent to all of the set $M$ as well as to a proper subset $T$ of $M$*. Indeed, if an infinite set $M$ is equivalent to an infinite set $N$, then $N$ is always equivalent to a proper subset of $M$, and conversely [**17**].

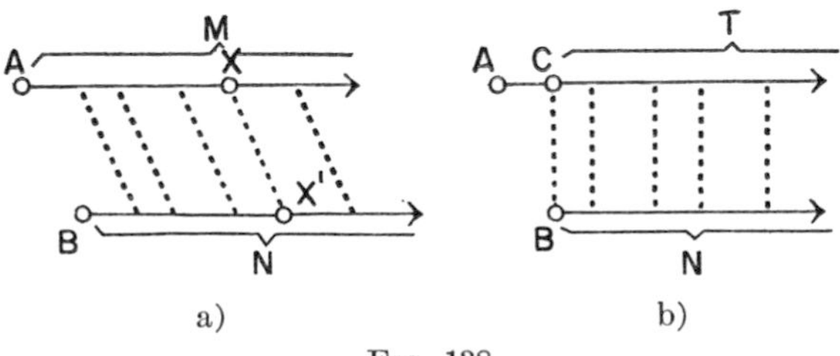


FIG. 138

Thus, in the case of infinite sets the equivalence of a set $N$ with a proper subset of a set $M$ does not imply the nonequivalence of $N$ and $M$.

This is the reason why in comparing two arbitrary sets—particularly infinite sets—it becomes necessary to reformulate Propositions (a) and (b) (p. 245) as definitions. In addition, instead of using the phrase "number of elements of a set," which is associated with finite sets, we introduce the set theoretic term *power* of a set. We then have

DEFINITION (A). *Two sets $M$ and $N$ are said to be equivalent or to have the same power if there is a* 1–1 *correspondence between $M$ and $N$.*

DEFINITION (B). *We shall say that the power of a set $M$ is greater than the power of set $N$ if* (1) *there is no* 1–1 *correspondence between $M$ and $N$, i.e. $M$ is not equivalent to $N$, and* (2) *there is a* 1–1 *correspondence between $N$ and a proper subset of $M$, i.e. $N$ is equivalent to (has the same power as) a proper subset of $M$.*[8]

These two definitions provide the criteria for comparing arbitrary sets and are the starting point of an important part of the theory of sets.

Let us examine a few elementary results on the comparison of infinite sets.[9]

We divide these results into two groups. The first group concerns sets which are equivalent to the set $Z$ of all natural numbers $1, 2, 3, 4, \cdots$. Examples of such sets are the set of all even numbers $2, 4, 6, \cdots$, and the set of all odd numbers $1, 3, 5, 7, \cdots$. The essential property of a set $M$ which is equivalent to $Z$ is that every element of $M$ can be assigned a natural number, so that the elements of $M$ can be written as a sequence indexed by the natural numbers; in other words, the elements of $M$ can be enumerated. We shall call such sets *denumerable*.[10]

Some of the following examples of denumerable sets may be unexpected.

### *Examples of Denumerable Sets*

$D_1$) The set of even numbers $2, 4, 6, \cdots$ is denumerable [**19**].

$D_2$) The set of odd numbers $1, 3, 5, \cdots$ is denumerable [**19**].

[8] Condition (1) is superfluous in the case of finite sets, since condition (2) implies condition (1) [**18**].

[9] We shall generally omit the proofs or give them in the Notes. For the mathematician, these proofs provide an insight into the essence of the problem, but the nonmathematician might only be confused by some of the technicalities in the methods of proof.

[10] The term *denumerable* should not be confused with the *number* of elements in the set. For a denumerable set is, of course, an *infinite* set (like the set $Z$ to which it is equivalent), and therefore does not have a definite number of elements. The term merely means that it is possible to enumerate the elements of the set—a process analogous to counting—but the enumeration never ends, as it does in the case of finite sets.

$D_3$) The set of all integers

$$\cdots, -4, -3, -2, -1, 0, 1, 2, 3, 4, \cdots$$

is denumerable [20].

$D_4$) Divide the plane into an infinite number of squares like a checkerboard. The set of squares is denumerable [21].

$D_5$) The set of all cubes of a decomposition of three-dimensional space into cubes is denumerable.

$D_6$) The vertices of the squares of Example $D_4$ form the *lattice points* of a plane lattice. The set of lattice points is denumerable [22].

$D_7$) If the plane is divided into four parts or quadrants by two perpendicular lines, and one of the quadrants is divided into squares (as the whole plane was in Example $D_4$), the set of these squares is denumerable [23].

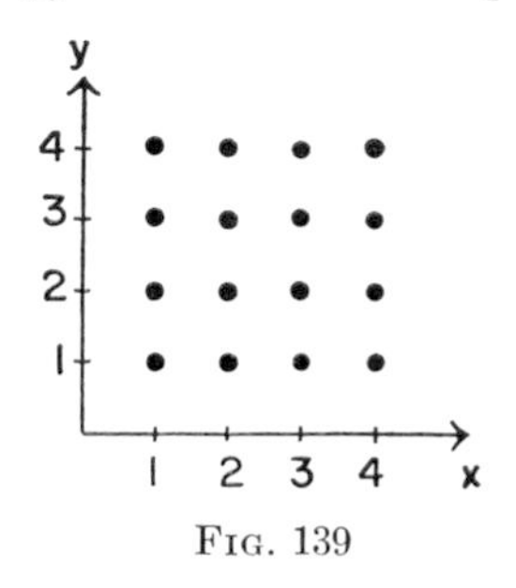

FIG. 139

$D_8$) The set of all points in the plane whose coordinates are positive integers, that is, all the lattice points of a quadrant (see Example $D_6$) , is denumerable [24] (see Fig. 139).

$D_9$) The set of all pairs $(m, n)$, where $m$ and $n$ are natural numbers, is denumerable [25].

$D_{10}$) A positive fraction, that is, a ratio of two natural numbers, is called a positive *rational number*. The set of all positive rational numbers is denumerable [26].

$D_{11}$) The set of all rational numbers (positive, negative and zero) is denumerable [27].

$D_{12}$) The set of all rational numbers between 0 and 1 is denumerable [28].

$D_{13}$) The set of all terminating decimals, such as 0.1, or 13.5, or 3.142, etc., is denumerable [29].

$D_{14}$) The set of all prime numbers[11] is denumerable.

[11] See Chapter I, where it is proved that the set of primes is infinite. Since it is a subset of the set of natural numbers, it is necessarily denumerable (see the end of Note 19). It remains an unsolved problem (see the end of Chapter I) whether the set of prime twins is finite or infinite. If it is infinite, it is denumerable; otherwise, it is finite.

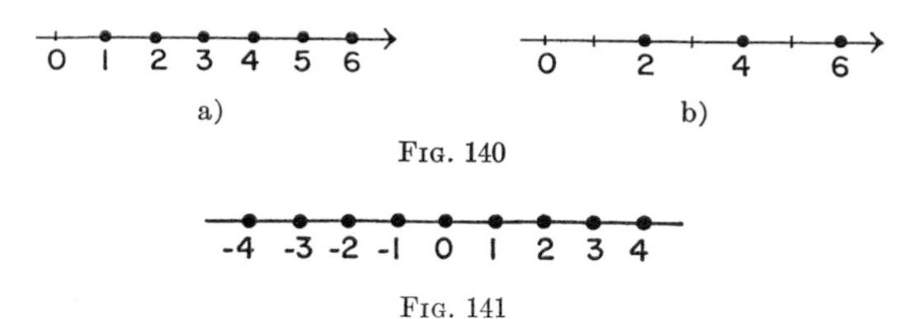


FIG. 140

FIG. 141

Some of these examples are illustrations of the fact that a set may be equivalent to one of its proper subsets. For instance, the sets $D_3$ and $D_{11}$ are both denumerable, that is, they are both equivalent to $Z$; they are, therefore, equivalent to each other.[12] However, since $D_{11}$ consists of all the rational numbers, while $D_3$ consists of only the whole rational numbers, $D_3$ is a proper subset of $D_{11}$.

We should now be accustomed to the equivalence of a set with one of its proper subsets. This was true of the set of all even numbers and the set of all natural numbers. To see this example geometrically, we represent these numbers as points on a straight line (Fig. 140a, b). In comparing the set $D_{11}$ of all rational numbers with the set $D_3$ of integers (Fig. 141), it is instructive to consider which points on the line represent the rational numbers.

The midpoints of the intervals between the integers correspond to the fractions (rational numbers) whose denominator is 2. If the intervals between the integers are divided into thirds, the points of division correspond to the fractions whose denominator is 3, etc. In this way we see that the points on the line corresponding to the rational numbers are *dense* on the line, that is, every (open) interval of the line contains at least one rational point. This is the geometric representation of the set $D_{11}$. In contrast, the set $D_3$ is represented in Fig. 141 by the widely separated points corresponding to the integers. The equivalence of $D_{11}$ and $D_3$ is therefore quite unexpected.

The points of the line corresponding to the set $D_{12}$ are obtained by retaining the rational points on the line between 0 and 1 and deleting all other points on the line (including 0 and 1). This set, which seems to be a small part of the set $D_{11}$, has the same power as all of the set $D_{11}$, because both sets are denumerable and therefore equivalent.

We now turn to another equally surprising group of equivalent sets. We begin with the set of all points on a straight line. For the time being, let us disregard the question of whether the set of all points on a straight line is denumerable, like the other sets we have studied, or whether it is

[12] It can be shown that if two sets are equivalent to a third, they are also equivalent to each other [**30**].

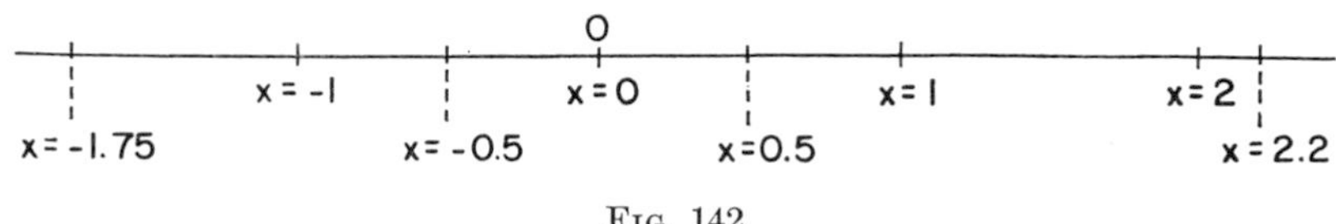


FIG. 142

not. As long as this question remains unanswered, we must consider the possibility that the power of the set of all points on a straight line is different from that of the denumerable sets. It is quite easy to concede this possibility, since after looking at the points on the line of Fig. 140a which represent the natural numbers we would hardly be inclined to assume that this sparsely distributed set could be equivalent to all the points of the line. Whatever the answer is, we shall call the power of the set of all points on the line the *power of the continuum* at least until the question is decided. Thus the second group of results deals with sets which have the power of the continuum. We label the examples[13] below as $C_1$, $C_2$, $C_3$, etc., where the set of points on a straight line is $C_1$. In discussing these sets, we refer to their elements interchangeably as points of a line and as real numbers, since we assume that there is a 1–1 correspondence between the real numbers and the points on a line (Fig. 142).

### *Sets Having the Power of the Continuum*

$C_1$) The set of points on a straight line (the set of all real numbers) has the power of the continuum.

$C_2$) The set of points on a half-line excluding its initial point, e.g. the set of all numbers $x > 0$, has the power of the continuum.

$C_3$) The set of points of a half-line including the initial point of the half-line, e.g. the set of all numbers $x \geq 1$, has the power of the continuum.

$C_4$) The set of points of a closed interval (that is, an interval containing both its endpoints; for example, the interval $0 \leq x \leq 1$) has the power of the continuum. It is clear that any other closed interval would do just as well.

$C_5$) The set of points of a half-open interval (that is, an interval containing one of its endpoints, but not the other; for example, $0 < x \leq 1$, or $0 \leq x < 1$) has the power of the continuum. (A rotation of $0 < x \leq 1$ about the point $\frac{1}{2}$ transforms it into $0 \leq x < 1$.)

$C_6$) The set of all points of an open interval (that is, an interval without both its endpoints; for example, the interval $0 < x < 1$) has the power of the continuum.

$C_7$) The set of all points on the circumference of a circle has the power of the continuum.

[13] The proofs are given in the Notes.

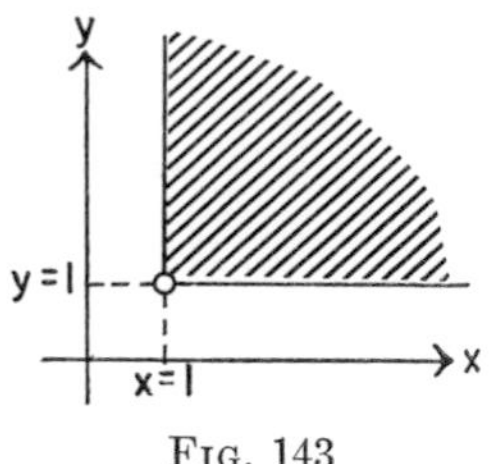


FIG. 143

$C_8$) The set of all points on the circumference of a circle with the exclusion of one point on the circumference has the power of the continuum.

$C_9$) The set of all points of a semi-circle without its endpoints has the power of the continuum.

$C_{10}$) The set of all points in the plane (the set of all pairs of real numbers $(x, y)$) has the power of the continuum.

$C_{11}$) We noted in Example $D_7$ that the plane can be divided into four quadrants by two perpendicular lines. We shall denote by $C_{11}$ the set of points in one of these quadrants including its boundary points (the points in the half-lines bounding the quadrant); for example, $C_{11}$ is the set of points in the first quadrant including its boundary points (that is all points $(x, y)$ for which $x \geq 0$, $y \geq 0$). Then $C_{11}$ has the power of the continuum. The power of $C_{11}$ is independent of the choice of the two perpendicular lines or of the particular quadrant. For example, the hatched quadrant in Fig. 143 bounded by the lines $x = 1$ and $y = 1$ (that is, the set of points $(x, y)$ for which $x \geq 1$ and $y \geq 1$) will do just as well.

$C_{12}$) The set of points in a quadrant without its boundary points (the set of all pairs $(x, y)$ in which both $x$ and $y$ are positive) has the power of the continuum.

$C_{13}$) The set of all points of three-dimensional space (triples of real numbers $(x, y, z)$) has the power of the continuum.

$C_{14}$) The set of all points $(x, y, z)$ of three-dimensional space for which $x \geq 1$, $y \geq 1$ and $z \geq 1$ has the power of the continuum. These points form an octant in space.

$C_{15}$) The set of all triples $(a, b, c)$ of real numbers with $c$ positive has the power of the continuum.

$C_{16}$) The set of all circles in the plane with a common center $O$ (concentric circles) has the power of the continuum.

$C_{17}$) The set of all circles in the plane has the power of the continuum.

$C_{18}$) The set of all straight lines in the plane has the power of the continuum.

$C_{19}$) The set of all straight lines in space has the power of the continuum.

We note in passing that the elements of the sets $C_1$–$C_{19}$ are very different. The elements of the sets $C_1$–$C_{14}$ are points; the elements of $C_{16}$ and $C_{17}$ are

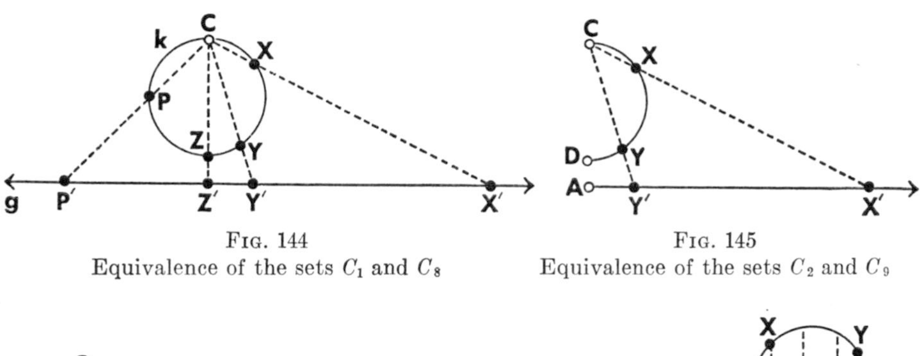


FIG. 144
Equivalence of the sets $C_1$ and $C_8$

FIG. 145
Equivalence of the sets $C_2$ and $C_9$

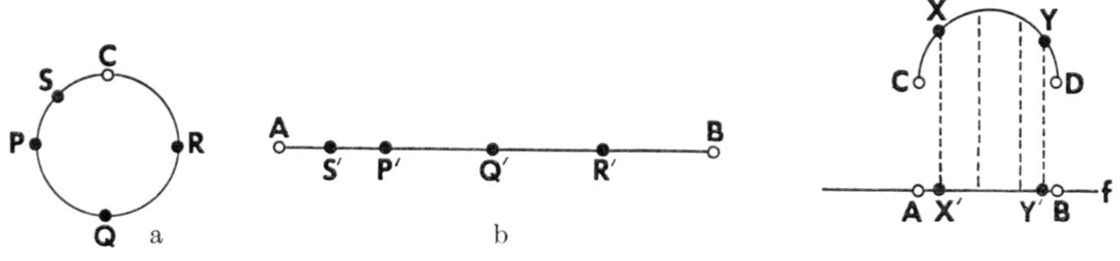


FIG. 146
Equivalence of the sets $C_6$ and $C_8$

FIG. 147
Equivalence of the sets $C_6$ and $C_9$

circles; those of $C_{18}$ and $C_{19}$ are straight lines. Example $C_{15}$ is completely ungeometric: the elements of this set are triples of numbers. Thus $C_{15}$ is a purely arithmetic example. But many arithmetic examples are related to geometric examples because of the analytic representation of the geometric point sets. The elements of the sets $C_1$–$C_6$ are single numbers $x$; $C_{10}$, $C_{11}$ and $C_{12}$ are sets whose elements are pairs of numbers $(x, y)$; $C_{13}$ and $C_{14}$ are sets whose elements are triples of numbers.

As far as the proofs of the equivalence of the sets $C_1$–$C_{19}$ are concerned, we shall have to be content with a few suggestions. Some of the equivalences are indicated in Figs. 144–147.[14] A further set of equivalences is implied by the proposition (see [16]) which states that if one element is omitted from an infinite set, then the resulting set is equivalent to the original set.

[14] In Fig. 144, $C_1$ is represented by the straight line $g$, and $C_8$ by the circle $k$ minus the point $C$. A projection from $C$ yields a correspondence between $k$ (minus $C$) and $C_1$ in which $X$ is paired with $X'$, $Y$ with $Y'$, $Z$ with $Z'$, $P$ with $P'$, etc. The right half of Fig. 144 yields Fig. 145; this figure indicates the correspondence between $C_2$, represented by the half-line with initial point $A$ (minus the point $A$), and $C_9$, represented by the semi-circle (minus the points $C$ and $D$). In Fig. 146, the segment $AB$, minus its endpoints, represents $C_6$. We have taken its length equal to the circumference of the circle, which, except for the point $C$, represents $C_8$. To obtain a correspondence between $C_6$ and $C_8$, imagine that $C_8$ is a string. Then wind $AB$ around the circle, beginning at $C$, so that $S, P, Q, R$ correspond to $S', P', Q', R'$, respectively. In Fig. 147, the correspondence between $C_6$ and $C_9$ is shown by projecting the semicircle onto a straight line $f$ parallel to the diameter $CD$.

This shows that the sets $C_1$, $C_8$, $C_6$, $C_9$, $C_2$ are all equivalent (see Footnote 12).

Accordingly, $C_3$ is equivalent to $C_2$, $C_4$ to $C_5$, $C_5$ to $C_6$, and $C_7$ to $C_8$. From this and from the correspondences indicated in Figs. 144–147 we may, therefore, conclude that the sets $C_1$–$C_9$ are all equivalent [**31**].

In a similar way we can show [**32**] that the sets $C_{10}$, $C_{11}$ and $C_{12}$ are equivalent to each other.[15]

It is especially noteworthy that the sets $C_{10}$–$C_{12}$ are also equivalent to the sets $C_1$–$C_9$. Therefore, e.g. the *set* $C_{10}$ *consisting of all points of the plane is equivalent to the set of all points on a straight line.*

This consequence of Cantor's theory is particularly startling. For this reason, it would perhaps be best for the reader to prove it for himself. As an aid, a method of proof is suggested in [**34**]. Finally, the set $C_{13}$, that is, the set of points in three-dimensional space (and also the sets $C_{14}$, $C_{15}$ and $C_{17}$) can be shown to be equivalent to the set of points of a straight line. For a proof, see [**35**].

We now consider another aspect of the equivalence of all these varied sets. One of the reasons why some of these equivalences are so startling is that different dimensions are involved. The straight line has one dimension, the plane has two dimensions, while space has three. One would be inclined to assign a greater power to the higher dimensional sets. But we must not forget that the concept of dimension involves considerations entirely different from those on which the concepts of equivalence and the power of sets are based.[16] The sharp and clear distinction between the two concepts is a more recent development. Indeed, the older literature contains many discussions of dimension which do not stand the test of modern rigor [**36**]. This is another example of how profoundly a half century of critical thought has affected large areas of mathematics.

In view of the surprising and seemingly paradoxical equivalence of some of the sets we have discussed, it would seem natural to ask: *Are not all infinite sets perhaps equivalent?* The infinite sets considered up to now can be divided into two classes of equivalent sets: the class of denumerable sets and the class of sets having the power of the continuum. We may then first consider the following question: *Is the power of the denumerable sets equal to the power of the continuum?* In particular: *Is the set of all points on a straight line denumerable?* In other words, can all the points on a straight line be enumerated?

[15] The equivalence of the sets $C_{13}$, $C_{14}$, $C_{15}$ and $C_{17}$ can be proved in the same manner [**33**]. The proof of the equivalence of $C_{18}$ and $C_{19}$ is simpler and we shall not discuss it.

[16] The concept of dimension was discussed in Chapter VI. We saw there that the dimension of a set of points depends decisively on the neighborhood relationships between the points of the set. Hence, dimension is a topological concept. Equivalence of sets, however, is a purely set-theoretic notion: in constructing a 1-1 correspondence between sets, we may ignore neighborhood relationships completely.

Encouraged by the equivalence of very dissimilar sets we might well expect an affirmative answer. But in fact the answer is no. *The points on a straight line cannot be enumerated; this set is not denumerable.*

To prove this, let us consider the equivalent set $C_3$ of all points of a half-line (including its endpoint), say the set of real numbers $x \geq 1$. We represent the numbers of this set by continued fractions of the form

$$a_1 - \frac{1|}{|a_2} - \frac{1|}{|a_3} - \frac{1|}{|a_4} - \cdots,$$

where $a_1, a_2, a_3, \cdots$ are integers $\geq 2$. Each of these continued fractions represents a number $\geq 1$ [**34**]; conversely, each number $\geq 1$ can be expanded in a unique continued fraction of this form.

We shall give an *indirect* proof (a proof by contradiction) that the set $C_3$ is not denumerable. First, we assume the contrary, that is, that the set $C_3$ is denumerable, and that consequently a natural number can be assigned to each point of $C_3$. If this assumption leads to a contradiction, our original assumption must be discarded, and we will have proved that the set of points $x \geq 1$ is not denumerable.

Let us therefore assume that $C_3$ is denumerable, and that consequently the points of $C_3$ can be enumerated by means of the natural numbers 1, 2, 3, $\cdots$. We denote the point of $C_3$ which is assigned the number 1 by $P_1$, the point assigned the number 2 by $P_2$, etc. We shall dispense with a picture because the positions and distribution of the points $P_1, P_2, \cdots$ on the half-line are irrelevant to the proof. What is essential is the assumption that every point of the half-line is assigned a natural number, and that therefore the infinite sequence of points

$$(S) \qquad P_1, P_2, P_3, P_4, P_5, \cdots$$

contains *all* the points of the half-line.

Now, to each of the points of $(S)$ there corresponds a number $\geq 1$, the coordinate of $P_1$. We denote by $x_1$ the coordinate of $P_1$. The number $x_1$ can be expanded in an infinite continued fraction:

$$x_1 = a_1 - \frac{1|}{|a_2} - \frac{1|}{|a_3} - \frac{1|}{|a_4} - \frac{1|}{|a_5} - \cdots$$

(where $a_1, a_2, a_3, a_4, a_5, \cdots$ are integers $\geq 2$). In the same way the coordinate $x_2$ of the point $P_2$ can be represented by an infinite continued fraction:

$$x_2 = b_1 - \frac{1|}{|b_2} - \frac{1|}{|b_3} - \frac{1|}{|b_4} - \frac{1|}{|b_5} - \cdots,$$

where again $b_1, b_2, b_3, \cdots$ are integers $\geq 2$. Continuing, we have

$$x_3 = c_1 - \frac{1|}{|c_2} - \frac{1|}{|c_3} - \frac{1|}{|c_4} - \frac{1|}{|c_5} - \cdots,$$

$$x_4 = d_1 - \frac{1|}{|d_2} - \frac{1|}{|d_3} - \frac{1|}{|d_4} - \frac{1|}{|d_5} - \cdots,$$

$$x_5 = e_1 - \frac{1|}{|e_2} - \frac{1|}{|e_3} - \frac{1|}{|e_4} - \frac{1|}{|e_5} - \cdots,$$

for $P_3$, $P_4$, $P_5$, etc.

Our assumption was that the sequence $P_1$, $P_2$, $P_3$, $\cdots$ contains *all* the points of the half-line. This assumption will be contradicted as soon as we find a point of the half-line not included in the sequence $(S)$. This is easily done. To this end, we write the continued fraction

$$X = A_1 - \frac{1|}{|A_2} - \frac{1|}{|A_3} - \frac{1|}{|A_4} - \frac{1|}{|A_5} - \cdots,$$

where $A_1 = 2a_1$, $A_2 = 2b_2$, $A_3 = 2c_3$, etc. Hence

$$X = 2a_1 - \frac{1|}{|2b_2} - \frac{1|}{|2c_3} - \frac{1|}{|2d_4} - \frac{1|}{|2e_5} - \cdots.$$

It is clear that $X \geq 1$, since all the numbers $A_1$, $A_2$, $\cdots$ are natural numbers $\geq 2$ (in fact they are $\geq 4$). Therefore, $X$ is the coordinate of a point $Q$ of the half-line.

Now the point $Q$ is different from $P_1$. For, if $Q = P_1$, then $X = x_1$, and

$$A_1 = a_1,\ A_2 = a_2,\ A_3 = a_3,\ \cdots.$$

But $A_1 = 2a_1$. Therefore, $Q \neq P_1$.

In the same way, $Q$ cannot be $P_2$. For, if it were, then $X$ would equal $x_2$, and

$$A_1 = b_1,\ A_2 = b_2,\ A_3 = b_3,\ \cdots.$$

But $A_2 = 2b_2$. Therefore, $Q \neq P_2$.

Continuing in this manner, we see that the point $Q$ cannot be equal to any of the points $P_1$, $P_2$, $P_3$, $\cdots$.

Thus $Q$ is a point of the half-line which is not contained in the sequence $(S)$ [**37**]. Therefore, we must reject the assumption that this sequence of points includes all of the points of the half-line. It is, therefore, impossible to enumerate all the points of a half-line, and so this set is not denumerable. Hence, *the continuum is not denumerable* [**38**].

After all the paradoxical results on the equivalence of the most unlikely sets we were ready to believe that all infinite sets were equivalent. We have now seen that this is not so. The situation is not quite so simple.

There are at least two different powers: the power of denumerable sets, and the power of the continuum.

Are there then only two powers and no others? Cantor's answer was: There are an infinite number of powers, of increasing magnitude. In the hierarchy of infinite powers, the lowest power is that of the denumerable sets, that is, the power of the set of natural numbers. It is called *aleph zero*. The next higher power is called *aleph one*, etc. Each aleph is called a transfinite number, and it is the theory of transfinite numbers, as well as the theory of sets, which we owe to Cantor. The construction of the alephs depends on the notions of a *well ordered set* and of the *order types* or *ordinal numbers* of such sets. We shall discuss these ideas very briefly.

A well ordered set is a generalization of the set of natural numbers. In the present context, the relevant properties of the set of natural numbers are: 1) The set of natural numbers is an ordered set, that is, every two natural numbers are either equal or one is less than the other. 2) Every nonempty subset of the natural numbers, that is, every subset which contains at least one element, has a first or smallest element. Abstracting these two properties of the set of natural numbers, we say that a set $W$ is well ordered if 1) $W$ is an ordered set, and 2) every nonempty subset of $W$ has a first element. It is clear that every finite ordered set is well ordered, and of course the set of natural numbers is well ordered. An example of a set which is not well ordered is the set of integers

$$\cdots, -3, -2, -1, 0, 1, 2, 3, \cdots.$$

It is true that this set satisfies condition 1) above, since it is ordered. But it does not satisfy condition 2), because it contains a subset, namely itself, which does not have a first element.

Now suppose that $W_1$ and $W_2$ are two well ordered sets. We say that $W_1$ and $W_2$ have the same *order type*, or the same *ordinal number* if the following two conditions are satisfied: 1′) There is a 1–1 correspondence between $W_1$ and $W_2$. 2′) The 1–1 correspondence is order preserving. By this is meant that if $w_1$, $w_1'$ are two elements of $W_1$, and $w_1 \leq w_1'$ in $W_1$, then $w_2 \leq w_2'$ in $W_2$, where $w_2$, $w_2'$ are the elements of $W_2$ corresponding to $w_1$, $w_1'$.

Clearly, two finite sets have the same order type if, and only if, they have the same number of elements; in the contrary case, they could not satisfy condition 1′), much less 2′). Therefore, each finite set represents a distinct order type. But since each finite set is characterized by the number ($n = 0, 1, 2, \cdots$) of its elements, it follows that the set of distinct order types of finite sets is denumerable. In other words, the set of ordinal numbers corresponding to finite sets is denumerable. It is the power or transfinite number of this set of ordinal numbers which is denoted by aleph zero. This may be taken as the definition of aleph zero, the first transfinite number.

Having now defined aleph zero, we could go on to consider the other alephs, which are also defined as the powers of certain sets of ordinal numbers, in this case ordinal numbers of infinite sets. However, for simplicity, we shall restrict ourselves to the definition of aleph one, which is defined by means of the order types or ordinal numbers of denumerable sets.

Let us therefore consider a denumerable set. We know that the elements of a denumerable set can be enumerated, so that its elements can be written as

$$E_1, E_2, E_3, \cdots.$$

These elements may be ordered in many ways. For example, they may be ordered by the magnitude of their subscripts:

$$(1) \qquad E_1, E_2, E_3, E_4, E_5, E_6, E_7, E_8, \cdots,$$

so that $E_1$ is first, $E_2$ second, etc. Or, their order may be

$$(2) \qquad E_2, E_1, E_3, E_4, E_5, E_6, E_7, E_8, \cdots,$$

so that the order of $E_1$ and $E_2$ is reversed, but that of all other elements remains unchanged. Or, they may be ordered as in

$$(3) \qquad E_2, E_1, E_4, E_3, E_6, E_5, \cdots,$$

where each pair of successive elements in (1), beginning with the first, is interchanged, but the relative order of the pairs is unchanged. The order types of (1), (2) and (3) are the same. In each case, the order type is the same as that of the natural numbers ordered with respect to magnitude.

On the other hand, the order type of

$$(4) \qquad E_2, E_3, E_4, E_5, E_6, \cdots, E_1,$$

in which $E_1$ follows all the elements $E_2$, $E_3$, $E_4$, etc. is not the same as that of the natural numbers, because (4) has a last element, whereas the natural numbers do not.

Still another order type is

$$(5) \qquad E_1, E_3, E_5, \cdots, E_2, E_4, E_6, \cdots,$$

where $E_2$, $E_4$, $E_6$, $\cdots$ in that order follow all the elements $E_1$, $E_3$, $\cdots$. It is clear that the order type of (5) is different from that of (1) (because $E_2$ does not have an immediate predecessor in (5)), and also from (4) (because (5) has no last element). It is also clear that the order type of

$$(6) \qquad E_2, E_4, E_6, \cdots, E_1, E_3, E_5, \cdots$$

is the same as that of (5). Another type of order is

(7) $E_1, E_4, E_7, \cdots, E_2, E_5, E_8, \cdots, E_3, E_6, E_9, \cdots,$

and we could go on to give many other examples.

We shall not discuss ordered sets which are not well ordered, since this would require a chapter in itself [**39**], but rest content with a few more words about well ordered sets. There are, of course, types of well ordered denumerable sets which are different from (1), (4), (5) and (7). In fact, the set of such order types or ordinal numbers is very large. It is *not* even denumerable; its power is greater than that of the set of natural numbers. Hence, the set of all denumerable well ordered order types or ordinal numbers cannot be enumerated. The power of the set of all denumerable ordinal numbers is called *aleph one.* Aleph one is, therefore, the transfinite number of the set of all ordinal numbers of denumerable sets.

In the same way, *aleph two* would be defined as the power of the set of all ordinal numbers (that is, of all distinct well ordered order types) of sets of power aleph one; *aleph three* as the power or transfinite number of the set of all ordinal numbers of sets of power aleph two, etc. In this way we are led to construct a whole transfinite hierarchy of alephs, and it can be shown that aleph zero < aleph one < aleph two < aleph three < $\cdots$ . Furthermore, an addition and multiplication can be defined for the alephs (as well as for the ordinal numbers), and this makes it possible to have a transfinite arithmetic.

In conclusion we mention an unsolved problem. In the previous brief discussion of well ordered sets, our examples have been confined to denumerable sets, and we have called the power of the set of all denumerable well ordered order types aleph one, etc. Now the question is: What is the position of the power of the continuum (that is, the power of the set of real numbers or points on a line) in the hierarchy of the alephs? More precisely: Is the power of the continuum equal to aleph one? We have shown that it is not aleph zero (the power of the natural numbers). This is the famous *continuum problem.* It was proposed by Cantor a half century ago and has never been solved. Cantor's conjecture (the *continuum hypothesis*) that the power of the continuum is indeed equal to aleph one has never been proved or disproved.[17]

[17] The continuum problem was solved by Paul Cohen of Stanford University in 1963. He showed that the continuum hypothesis is independent of the commonly accepted axioms of set theory, so that it is not possible to either prove or disprove the conjecture within this system. See P. J. Cohen, *The independence of the continuum hypothesis*, Proc. Nat. Acad. Sci. U. S. A. **50** (1963), 1143–1148. For a review of this paper, see Mathematical Reviews **28** (1964), 221, Review No. 1118. (Ed.)

*Notes to Chapter XII*

# INFINITY IN MATHEMATICS

**1** (p. 243). See {3}, {1; p. 4} and {4}.

**2** (p. 245). For references on the history of number symbols see {5}.

**3** (p. 246). The large numbers denoted by the words trillion, quadrillion, etc. are after all limited by the number of words at our command. Much larger numbers can be obtained by using powers of 10 like $10^{10}$, $10^{10^{10}}$, etc., but there is a limit even to this notation. In contrast, the idea of an *unending* sequence of numbers transcends experience and the designation of particular numbers; it is purely conceptual.[1]

**4** (p. 246). The method of proof known as mathematical induction, which goes back to Pascal (see Chapter XIII, Note 14), is based on the assumption that each natural number has a successor. See Hermann Weyl's book {6}. Compare also the works of Dedekind and Russell mentioned in Footnote 2.

We have already noted in Chapter VIII, Note 28 that mathematicians and mathematical logicians of the first rank are still investigating the foundations of mathematics and especially of set theory. However, a discussion of the foundations is beyond the scope of this book.

**5** (p. 246). There is an oriental legend connected with the first 64 numbers of this sequence. It seems that the inventor of chess was asked by his Prince to choose his reward. He asked for a grain of wheat for the first square of his chessboard, 2 for the second, 4 for the third, etc. The Prince, who at first was disappointed by the modesty of this request, soon discovered that it could not be fulfilled even by emptying all the world's granaries. The total number (18,446,744,073,709,551,615) of grains would cover the surface of the earth with 3 or 4 grains for each square centimeter; it would cover Europe, Asia and Africa with a surface $\frac{1}{2}$ cm. thick. If the Prince were to present this gift to the inhabitants of a kingdom of 100 million people, each person would receive 3.67 million kilograms of wheat (on the assumption that each grain weighs $\frac{1}{50}$ gram).

**6** (p. 246). The geometric examples of infinite sets are as removed from physical experience as the numerical examples. In geometry, every line segment, no matter how small, can be bisected ad infinitum. In the physical world, of course, the number of bisections is finite.

As an example of speculative thought, we may mention one of the para-

[1] The Indian mathematicians seem to have been preoccupied, partially for religious reasons, with the idea of very large numbers. We owe to them the introduction of zero and the consequent development of the positional system. See {2; Section A, pp. 3–29}.

doxes of Zeno of Elea (5th century B.C.). Achilles is one mile behind a tortoise. Achilles runs 1000 times as fast as the tortoise. Will Achilles catch the tortoise? Zeno's answer was no. For, by the time Achilles has run the mile, the tortoise will have crawled $1/1000$ of a mile. By the time Achilles has covered this $1/1000$ of a mile, the tortoise will have crawled another $1/1000000$ of a mile, etc. The solution, of course, is that Achilles will catch the turtle after he has run

$$1 + 1/1000 + 1/1000^2 + 1/1000^3 + \cdots = 1 + 1/999$$

miles. The solution depends on the concept of the sum of an infinite series, which in turn is defined in terms of the limit of the infinite sequence of partial sums of the series.

**7** (p. 246). This follows from the proposition that every subset of a *finite* set is finite. Hence, if the set of points on the segment $AB$ were finite, it would follow that the set of points $C$, $D$, $E$, $\cdots$ (as a subset of $AB$) is also finite. Since this not the case, the set of points on $AB$ is infinite. In general, therefore, the first proposition implies that a set cannot be finite if it has an infinite subset.

**8** (p. 247). The note to § 40 of Bolzano's *Paradoxes of the Infinite* (pp. 80, 81 of the original edition; the original edition was reprinted by Mayer & Müller, Berlin, 1889) points to the modern definition of the dimension of a point set. The title of the work in pure mathematics mentioned in Chapter XII, Footnote 6 was *Rein analytischer Beweis des Lehrsatzes, dass zwischen je zwei Werten, die ein entgegengesetztes Resultat gewähren, wenigstens eine reelle Wurzel der Gleichung liege* (Pure analytic proof of the theorem: If an equation assumes opposite signs for two different values of the variable, it has a root between these two values). The work appeared in Prague in 1817; an edition by Jourdain was published in Ostwald's Classical Series (No. 153, 1905). The object of the paper was to prove what is known today as the Intermediate Value Theorem for continuous functions. The proof of the theorem is not obvious, and the validity of the theorem cannot be referred simply to the fact that geometrically it is intuitively obvious.

**9** (p. 247). As Carathéodory in his book {7} points out, the entire theory of functions of a real variable—including the theory of Lebesgue integration—is based on the theory of point sets, "the imperishable creation of Georg Cantor." See also Note 12.

**10** (p. 248). Heinrich Eduard Heine's (1821–1881) best known book is a work on spherical functions, which find frequent application in problems of applied mathematics and physics.

**11** (p. 249). An example is the field of trigonometric series mentioned as Cantor's first field. Properties of point sets had already been studied by Paul du Bois-Reymond (1831–1889) and Axel Harnack (1851–1888).

**12** (p. 249). See Note 9. The development of topology, and the branch of topology known as dimension theory, are examples. Before the development of topology, point set theory was applied to function theory, especially by Mittag-Leffler (1846–1927) and Poincaré (1854–1912). These applications demonstrated the value of set theory to the mathematical world. Its importance was also underscored by David Hilbert (1862–1943).

**13** (p. 250). The indicated correspondence is only one of the possible correspondences between the two sets. There are, of course, many others (the same observation applies to all the other examples). For example, another 1–1 correspondence between the two sets is:

$$1, 3, 5, 7, \ 9, 11, \cdots,$$
$$4, 2, 8, 6, 12, 10, \cdots.$$

**14** (p. 250). Two parallel half-lines furnish another simple example: an appropriate parallel displacement takes every point of the first half-line into a corresponding point of the second half-line. The correspondence is 1–1, and this establishes the equivalence of the two lines.

It is now easy to establish the equivalence of any two half-lines. First, turn one of the half-lines until it is parallel to the second. Then perform the parallel displacement suggested above.

**15** (p. 250). It is obvious that no finite set can be equivalent to an infinite set. For, let $M$ and $N$ be two sets, and suppose that $M$ is a finite set with $n$ elements, $E_1, E_2, \cdots, E_n$. If $N$ is equivalent to $M$, there is a 1–1 correspondence between $M$ and $N$. Let the elements of $N$ which correspond to the elements of $M$ under this correspondence be $E_1', E_2', \cdots, E_n'$. Therefore, $N$ has a finite number $n$ of elements, and is finite.

**16** (p. 251). It is, in fact, true in general that every infinite set contains a proper subset to which it is equivalent.[2] We shall give a rough proof of this proposition (a rigorous proof requires more care). Let $M$ be an infinite set, and let $E_1$ be an element of $M$. Since $M$ is infinite, the complement $M_1$ of the set consisting of $E_1$ in $M$ is not empty, and therefore contains an element $E_2$, etc. Having chosen elements $E_1, E_2, \cdots, E_n$ of $M$ in this fashion, consider the complement $M_n$ in $M$ of the set consisting of $E_1, \cdots, E_n$. Since the latter set is finite and $M$ is infinite, $M_n$ is not empty, and therefore contains an element $E_{n+1}$. Hence, by induction, there is an infinite sequence of distinct elements

[2] Dedekind, in his book *Was sind und was sollen die Zahlen?* (Brunswick, 1888), used this property to distinguish between finite and infinite sets, that is, he defined an infinite set as one which contains a proper subset equivalent to the whole set, and a finite set as any set which does not have this property. See Dedekind's book {13} and Bertrand Russell {14}.

(1) $$E_1, E_2, \cdots, E_n, E_{n+1}, \cdots$$

in $M$. Denote this set by $H$, and the complement of this set in $M$ by $K$.

We shall now show that $M$ is equivalent to $M_1$ (the complement in $M$ of the set consisting of $E_1$). (This will also prove the proposition: If $M$ is an infinite set and an element of $M$ is deleted, the resulting set is also infinite.) To do so, define the following 1–1 correspondence between $M$ and $M_1$: If $P$ is an element of $K$, assign to $P$ itself. If $P$ is an element of $H$, it is one of the elements $E_1, E_2, \cdots$, say $E_i$. Then assign to $P = E_i$ the element $E_{i+1}$, that is, the element of (1) which follows it in the sequence. We have, therefore, assigned to every element of $M$ an element of $M_1$, and conversely, in a 1–1 fashion. This proves the proposition.

**17** (p. 251). This follows from the proposition proved in Note 16.

**18** (p. 252). In the technical literature of set theory, the definition of "The power of the set $M$ is greater than the power of the set $N$," is given a different, but equivalent, form. See {8} and {9}.

**19** (p. 252). The set $D_1$ is denumerable because the correspondence $m = 2n$, where $n$ is any element of $Z$ (the natural numbers) and $m$ is an element of $D_1$, is a 1–1 correspondence between $Z$ and $D_1$. Similarly, $D_2$ is denumerable because $m = 2n + 1$ is a 1–1 correspondence between $Z$ and $D_2$. More generally, the following proposition is true: *Every subset of the natural numbers is denumerable.* For, every subset of the natural numbers is a subsequence of 1, 2, 3, $\cdots$ and may be written as

$$a_1, a_2, a_3, \cdots, a_n, \cdots,$$

where each of the $a_i$ is a natural number and has the same order in this sequence as it does in the sequence of all natural numbers. Then the correspondence or pairing $(n, a_n)$ is a 1–1 correspondence between $Z$ and the given subset of $Z$. This proves that the subset is denumerable.

The proposition: *Every infinite subset of a denumerable set is denumerable,* can be proved in the same way. For, let $M$ be a denumerable set. Since there is then a 1–1 correspondence between $M$ and $Z$, the elements of $M$ can be written in a sequence

$$a_1, a_2, \cdots, a_n, \cdots,$$

where each $a_i$ is an element of $M$ and all the elements of $M$ occur in this sequence. If $N$ is an infinite subset of $M$, then the elements of $N$ form a subsequence of the above sequence. Therefore, the elements of $N$ can be written as

$$a_{i_1}, a_{i_2}, \cdots, a_{i_n}, \cdots,$$

an infinite sequence in which the $a_{i_j}$ are distinct elements of $M$ which belong to $N$, and $i_1, i_2, \cdots$ is an increasing sequence of natural numbers.

Then the correspondence or pairing $(n, a_{i_n})$ is a 1–1 correspondence between $Z$ and $N$. Hence $N$ is denumerable.

**20** (p. 253). The 1–1 correspondence

$$\begin{array}{ccccccccccc} 0, & 1, & -1, & 2, & -2, & 3, & -3, & \cdots, \\ 1, & 2, & 3, & 4, & 5, & 6, & 7, & \cdots \end{array}$$

(in other words, the pairing $(n, 2n)$ if $n > 0$ and $(n, -2n + 1)$ if $n \leq 0$) shows that $D_3$ is denumerable.

**21** (p. 253). That $D_4$ is denumerable can be seen by choosing an arbitrary square and labeling it 1, then labeling the eight squares surrounding the first one with the numbers from 2 to 9, etc. (see Fig. 148).

**22** (p. 253). We note that each lattice point is the upper right vertex of exactly one square. It can, therefore, be labeled with the number assigned to this square. Hence the set $D_6$ of lattice points is denumerable.

**23** (p. 253). $D_7$ is an infinite subset of $D_4$. Hence, by the second proposition of Note 19, $D_7$ is denumerable.

**24** (p. 253). $D_8$ is an infinite subset of $D_6$. See Notes 23 and 19.

**25** (p. 253). The set of pairs $(m, n)$, where $m$ and $n$ are natural numbers, is the set of lattice points of a quadrant in the plane. Hence $D_9$ is the same as $D_8$. Specifically, if the pairs $(m, n)$ are written in the same order they are assigned in Note 22 as a subsequence of $D_6$, we have

$$(A_0) \quad (1, 1), (1, 2), (2, 2), (2, 1), (1, 3), (2, 3), \\ (3, 3), (3, 2), (3, 1), (1, 4), (2, 4), (3, 4), \cdots.$$

**26** (p. 253). Actually, $D_{10}$ is an infinite subset of $D_9$; hence it is denumerable. To see this, note that every positive fraction or rational number is of the form $m/n$, where $m$ and $n$ are natural numbers. Therefore, every element of $D_{10}$ can be thought of as a pair $(m, n)$, which is an element of $D_9$. However, $D_{10}$ is a proper subset of $D_9$, since two fractions, such as $m/n$ and $2m/2n$, may be equal in $D_{10}$, without being the same pair in $D_9$ (in $D_9$, $(m, n)$ and $(2m, 2n)$ are distinct pairs). Therefore, $D_{10}$ is a subsequence of the sequence $(A_0)$, and its elements may be written in the same order

| | | | | |
|---|---|---|---|---|
| 22 | 23 | 24 | 25 | 10 |
| 21 | 8 | 9 | 2 | 11 |
| 20 | 7 | 1 | 3 | 12 |
| 19 | 6 | 5 | 4 | 13 |
| 18 | 17 | 16 | 15 | 14 |

FIG. 148

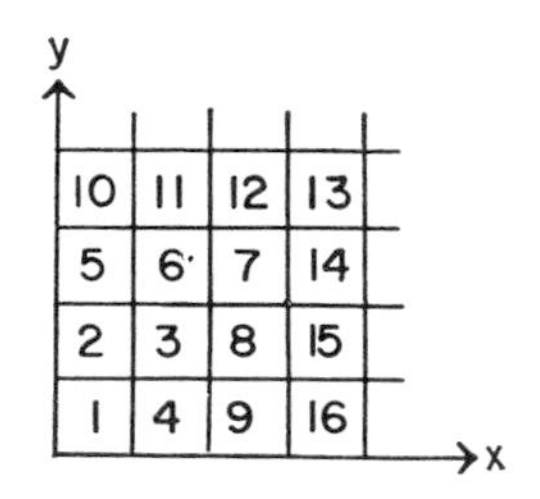


FIG. 149

in which they occur in $(A_0)$. Thus, we obtain the following sequence in which only fractions whose numerators and denominators are relatively prime occur:

$$(A_r) \qquad 1/1,\ 1/2,\ 2/1,\ 1/3,\ 2/3,\ 3/2,\ 3/1,\ 1/4,\ 3/4,\ \cdots .$$

**27** (p. 253). Let the sequence $(A_r)$ of Note 26 be

$$r_1,\ r_2,\ r_3,\ \cdots,\ r_n,\ \cdots,$$

where $r_1 = 1/1$, $r_2 = 1/2$, etc. Then $D_{11}$ (the set of all rational numbers) can be written in the following sequence:

$$0,\ r_1,\ -r_1,\ r_2,\ -r_2,\ r_3,\ -r_3,\ \cdots,\ r_n,\ -r_n,\ \cdots,$$

that is,

$$0,\ 1,\ -1,\ 1/2,\ -1/2,\ 2,\ -2,\ 1/3,\ -1/3,\ \cdots .$$

**28** (p. 253). This follows from the fact that $D_{12}$ is an infinite subset of $D_{10}$. Specifically, the elements of $D_{12}$ can be written as a sequence by omitting from $(A_r)$ all those fractions which are $\geq 1$:

$$1/2,\ 1/3,\ 2/3,\ 1/4,\ 3/4,\ \cdots .$$

**29** (p. 253). $D_{13}$ is an infinite subset of $D_{10}$. For example, $0.1 = 1/10$, $13.5 = 27/2$, $3.142 = 1571/500$.

**30** (p. 254). Let $M$, $N$ and $S$ be three sets, and suppose that $M$ is equivalent to $N$ and $N$ is equivalent to $S$. Let $m$ be an element of $M$, let $n$ be the element of $N$ corresponding to $m$, and $s$ the element of $S$ corresponding to $n$. Then the pairing $(m, s)$ is a 1–1 correspondence between $M$ and $S$. Hence $M$ is equivalent to $S$.

**31** (p. 258). The equivalence of $C_{16}$ and $C_2$ (and therefore of $C_{16}$ with all the sets $C_1 - C_9$) is obvious. For, each circle of $C_{16}$ is characterized by its radius, so that each circle corresponds to a positive real number; conversely, every positive real number corresponds to a circle of $C_{16}$ with that radius.

**32** (p. 258). We can use the equivalence between $C_1$ and $C_3$ to prove the equivalence between $C_{10}$ and $C_{11}$. Because of the equivalence of $C_1$ and $C_3$, each real number $u$ corresponds to a real number $x \geq 1$. Now let $(u, v)$ be a point in the plane, that is, $(u, v)$ is a pair of real numbers. Let $y \geq 1$ be the element of $C_3$ corresponding to $v$. Then the assignment of $(x, y)$ to $(u, v)$ is a 1–1 correspondence between $C_{10}$ and $C_{11}$. Similarly, the equivalence of $C_{11}$ and $C_{12}$ follows from that of $C_3$ and $C_2$.

**33** (p. 258). The equivalence of $C_1$ and $C_2$ implies that every real number can be paired with a positive real number. Hence, if $(x, y, z)$ is an element of $C_{13}$, let $u = x$, $v = y$ and let $w$ be the positive number corresponding to $z$. Then the assignment of $(u, v, w)$ to $(x, y, z)$ is a 1–1 correspondence between $C_{13}$ and $C_{15}$. Now, let $k$ be any element of $C_{17}$ ; then $k$ is a circle in the plane with center $(a, b)$ and radius $r > 0$. Hence every circle in the plane is characterized by three numbers, the first two of which are arbitrary and the third is positive. Therefore, $C_{17}$ is equivalent to $C_{15}$. The equivalence of $C_{14}$ and $C_{13}$ is proved in the same way as the equivalence of $C_{11}$ and $C_{10}$ in Note 32.

**34** (p. 258). By the proposition of Note 30, in order to prove the equivalence of $C_1$ and $C_{10}$, it is enough to prove the equivalence of $C_3$ and $C_{11}$, since $C_1$ is equivalent to $C_3$ and $C_{10}$ is equivalent to $C_{11}$.

Now let $x$ be an element of $C_3$. Then $x \geq 1$ and can be represented by a continued fraction

$$(K) \qquad x = a_1 - \frac{1|}{|a_2} - \frac{1|}{|a_3} - \frac{1|}{|a_4} - \cdots,$$

where $a_1$, $a_2$, etc. are natural numbers $\geq 2$. For example,

$$\sqrt{3} = 2 - \frac{1|}{|4} - \frac{1|}{|4} - \frac{1|}{|4} - \cdots$$

(where $a_1 = 2$ and $a_2$, $a_3$, etc. are all 4). The notation $(K)$ for a continued fraction has the following meaning. Let

$$x_1 = a_1,$$

$$x_2 = a_1 - \frac{1}{a_2},$$

$$x_3 = a_1 - \cfrac{1}{a_2 - \cfrac{1}{a_3}},$$

$$x_4 = a_1 - \cfrac{1}{a_2 - \cfrac{1}{a_3 - \cfrac{1}{a_4}}},$$

etc.[3]

Then $x$ is the value approached by or the limit of the sequence

$$x_1, x_2, x_3, \cdots, x_n, \cdots.$$

For example, in the case of the continued fraction representation of $\sqrt{3}$ above:

[3] The expressions $x_1$, $x_2$, $x_3$, etc. are called the *convergents* of the continued fraction. Simple rules for the calculation of continued fractions have been developed. See the references in Footnote 7.

$$x_1 = 2,$$

$$x_2 = 2 - \frac{1}{4} = 7/4 = 1.75,$$

$$x_3 = 2 - \cfrac{1}{4 - \cfrac{1}{4}} = 26/15 = 1.7333 \cdots,$$

$$x_4 = 2 - \cfrac{1}{4 - \cfrac{1}{4 - \cfrac{1}{4}}} = 97/56 = 1.73214 \cdots,$$

etc.,

and the limiting value of $x_1, x_2, \cdots$ is $\sqrt{3}$.

As further examples, the continued fraction representations of $\pi$ and 1 are:[4]

$$\pi = 4 - \frac{1|}{|2} - \frac{1|}{|2} - \frac{1|}{|2} - \frac{1|}{|2} - \frac{1|}{|2} - \frac{1|}{|2} - \frac{1|}{|17} - \frac{1|}{|294} - \frac{1|}{|3} - \frac{1|}{|4} - \cdots,$$

$$1 = 2 - \frac{1|}{|2} - \frac{1|}{|2} - \frac{1|}{|2} - \cdots.$$

Now let $(x, y)$ be an element of $C_{11}$, that is, a pair of real numbers, with $x \geq 1, y \geq 1$; and let

$$(K') \qquad x = a_1 - \frac{1|}{|a_2} - \frac{1|}{|a_3} - \frac{1|}{|a_4} - \cdots,$$

$$(K'') \qquad y = b_1 - \frac{1|}{|b_2} - \frac{1|}{|b_3} - \frac{1|}{|b_4} - \cdots$$

be the continued fraction representations of $x$ and $y$. Then assign to the pair $(x, y)$ the real number $t$ represented by the continued fraction

$$(\S) \qquad t = c_1 - \frac{1|}{|c_2} - \frac{1|}{|c_3} - \frac{1|}{|c_4} - \frac{1|}{|c_5} - \frac{1|}{|c_6} \cdots,$$

[4] The continued fraction expansion of a given number $x$ can be derived as follows: Let $a_1$ be the least integer greater than $x$. Then $0 < a_1 - x \leq 1$ and $q_1 = 1/(a_1 - x) \geq 1$; hence $x = a_1 - 1/q_1$. Next, let $a_2$ be the least integer greater than $q_1$ and set $q_2 = 1/(a_2 - q_1)$, so that $q_1 = a_2 - 1/q_2$. Now let $a_3$ be the least integer greater than $q_2$, etc.

where

$$c_1 = a_1\,, \quad c_2 = b_1\,, \quad c_3 = a_2\,, \quad c_4 = b_2\,, \quad c_5 = a_3\,, \quad c_6 = b_3\,, \text{etc.}$$

Of course, the continued fraction representation of $t$ in turn determines the continued fraction representations of $x$ and $y$, since

$$x = c_1 - \frac{1|}{|c_3} - \frac{1|}{|c_5} \cdots, \quad y = c_2 - \frac{1|}{|c_4} - \frac{1|}{|c_6} - \cdots.$$

Since $c_1$, $c_2$, $c_3$, etc. are natural numbers $\geq 2$, it follows that $t \geq 1$.[5] The above assignment is, therefore, a 1–1 correspondence between $C_{11}$ and $C_3$.

*Addendum.* If in $(K)$ we allow $a_1$ to take any integral value, while restricting the values of $a_2$, $a_3$, etc. to natural numbers $\geq 2$ as before, $(K)$ assumes all real values.[6]

The representation of real numbers by the kind[7] of continued fractions we have used above has certain advantages over other representations.

[5] For example, let $x = \sqrt{3}$, $y = 1$. Then

$$t = 2 - \frac{1|}{|2} - \frac{1|}{|4} - \frac{1|}{|2} - \frac{1|}{|4} - \frac{1|}{|2} - \cdots$$

(where $t = \sqrt{2} = 1.414 \cdots$).

[6] In general, if $g$ is an arbitrary integer and the coefficients of $(K)$ are required to satisfy the conditions $a_i \geq g + 1$, $a_i \geq 2$ $(i > 1)$, then every $x \geq g$ has a continued fraction representation of the form $(K)$. We can, therefore, obtain a 1–1 correspondence between the set of all pairs $(x, y)$, with $x \geq g$, $y \geq g$, and the set of all real numbers $t \geq g$ by using the scheme of Note 34.

[7] The continued fraction $(K)$ all of whose "numerators" are $-1$ is called a *reduced simple* continued fraction. A real number $x$ may also be represented by a simple continued fraction, that is one whose "numerators" are all $+1$. For example, the expansion of $\sqrt{2}$ as a simple continued fraction is

$$\sqrt{2} = 1 + \frac{1|}{|2} + \frac{1|}{|2} + \frac{1|}{|2} + \cdots$$

There are, in fact, many continued fraction representations of the same number. For example, $\sqrt{2}$ may also be expanded as

$$\sqrt{2} = 2 - \frac{1|}{|1} + \frac{1|}{|2} - \frac{1|}{|1} + \frac{1|}{|2} - \cdots.$$

Finite continued fraction expansions are also of importance. In this case, the representation of rational numbers by simple continued fractions is not unique. For instance,

$$\frac{16}{13} = 1 + \frac{1|}{|4} + \frac{1|}{|3} = 1 + \frac{1|}{|4} + \frac{1|}{|2} + \frac{1|}{|1}.$$

For the theory of continued fractions see {15}–{19}.

Blaise Pascal (1623-1662) · Pierre de Fermat (1601-1665)
Joseph Louis Lagrange (1736-1813) · Leonhard Euler (1707-1783)

PLATE XVIII

Georg Cantor (1845-1918)· David Hilbert (1862-1943)
Nikolai Ivanowitch Lobatschefskij (1793-1856)· Bernhard Riemann (1826-1866)

For one thing, the continued fraction is always an infinite sequence, whereas the decimal representation, for instance, is finite for certain rational numbers. Then again, the continued fraction representation chosen here is unique. These properties render unnecessary additional remarks required in the case of decimal representations. For example, let $t = {}^{151}\!/_{275} = .54909090 \cdots$. Using the same scheme as that above in the case of continued fractions, we assign the pair $x = .5999 \cdots$, $y = .4000 \cdots$ to $t$ by choosing alternate digits of the decimal expansion of $t$ for $x$ and $y$. But then $t = {}^{16}\!/_{25} = .64000 \cdots$ determines the pair $x = .6000 \cdots$, $y = .4000 \cdots$, which is the same as the first pair since $.5999 \cdots = .6000 \cdots$. Since the two values of $t$ are different, the decimal representation would not yield a 1–1 correspondence. The difficulty is that the decimal representation is not unique ($.5999 \cdots = .6000 \cdots$). There are difficulties even with representations by simple (see Footnote 7) continued fractions, and this is why we have chosen the representation by reduced simple (see Footnote 7) continued fractions.

**35** (p. 258). Since $C_1$ is equivalent to $C_3$ and $C_{13}$ is equivalent to $C_{14}$, to prove that $C_1$ is equivalent to $C_{13}$ it suffices to show that $C_{14}$ is equivalent to $C_3$. Let $(x, y, z)$, $x, y, z \geq 1$, be an element of $C_{14}$, and let

$$x = a_1 - \frac{1 |}{| a_2} - \frac{1 |}{| a_3} - \cdots,$$

$$y = b_1 - \frac{1 |}{| b_2} - \frac{1 |}{| b_3} - \cdots,$$

$$z = c_1 - \frac{1 |}{| c_2} - \frac{1 |}{| c_3} - \cdots,$$

be the reduced simple continued fraction representations of $x$, $y$ and $z$. Then assign to $(x, y, z)$ the real number $t \geq 1$ given by

$$t = a_1 - \frac{1 |}{| b_1} - \frac{1 |}{| c_1} - \frac{1 |}{| a_2} - \frac{1 |}{| b_2} - \frac{1 |}{| c_2} - \frac{1 |}{| a_3} - \frac{1 |}{| b_3} - \frac{1 |}{| c_3} - \cdots.$$

This assignment is then a 1–1 correspondence between $C_{14}$ and $C_1$.

**36** (p. 258). The statements, "A line has $\infty^1$ points, the plane has $\infty^2$ points, space has $\infty^3$ points" convey the wrong impression by implying that a line has less points than the plane and that the plane has less points than space. As we have seen, this is not correct. This mistake was made even by von Staudt in his book {10} (for quotations from this book see {11}). Of course, the distinction to be made between the line, plane and space is one of dimension and not the power of the sets concerned; and the concept of dimension involves 1–1 *bicontinuous* correspondences, not simply 1–1 correspondences. This distinction is made very clearly in {12}.

**37** (p. 260). It is not difficult to see that the method of proof described in the text can be varied in many ways to obtain a point $Q$ of the half-line $x \geq 1$ which does not appear in the sequence $(S)$. It is, of course, not essential that $A_1 = 2a_1$, $A_2 = 2b_2$, etc. It is merely necessary that $A_1 \neq a_1$, $A_2 \neq a_2$, etc.; there are several ways of doing this. The method of proof itself is called the Cantor diagonal method, a name which is suggested by the following scheme:

$$\begin{array}{cccccc}
\boxed{a_1}, & a_2, & a_3, & a_4, & a_5, & \cdots \\
b_1, & \boxed{b_2}, & b_3, & b_4, & b_5, & \cdots \\
c_1, & c_2, & \boxed{c_3}, & c_4, & c_5, & \cdots \\
d_1, & d_2, & d_3, & \boxed{d_4}, & d_5, & \cdots \\
e_1, & e_2, & e_3, & e_4, & \boxed{e_5}, & \cdots \\
\cdots & \cdots & \cdots & \cdots & \cdots & \cdots
\end{array}$$

In the table, the numbers $a_1$, $b_2$, $c_3$, etc. have been enclosed in boxes to show that if $A_1$, $A_2$, etc. are chosen so that they differ from these numbers, then the continued fraction with the $A_i$'s as coefficients will differ from $P_1$ in its first coefficient, from $P_2$ in its second coefficient, etc. Furthermore, the continued fraction representation is not necessary. The decimal representation of real numbers can also be used if one is careful to exclude representations such as .4999 $\cdots$ for .5000 $\cdots$, etc.

**38** (p. 260). The importance of this theorem is confirmed by considering a second proof, also due to Cantor. The second proof is also by contradiction. We assume that all the points of the half-line $x \geq 1$ can be written in a sequence, and show that this leads to a contradiction.

To begin with, the point $x = 1$ is on the half-line. Therefore, it is a point of the sequence, say $P_{80}$. To make the proof a little simpler, but with no restriction on generality, we may assume that $x = 1$ corresponds to $P_1$. This can be accomplished by simply exchanging the order of $P_1$ and $P_{80}$ in the sequence and renumbering, so that $P_{80}$ is now $P_1$ and $P_1$ is now $P_{80}$. All the points of the half-line $x \geq 1$ are now written in a sequence

$$(1) \qquad P_1, P_2, P_3, \cdots, P_n, \cdots,$$

where $P_1$ now corresponds to $x = 1$. Let us denote the numbers or coordinates corresponding to $P_1$, $P_2$, etc. by $x_1$, $x_2$, etc. Hence $x_1 = 1$. Since all the points of the half-line satisfy the inequality $x \geq 1$, it follows that $x_2$, $x_3$, etc. are all $> 1$.

Now consider the interval $P_1P_2$ (Fig. 150a). Since (1) contains all the points of the half-line, it must also contain all the points of $P_1P_2$. We now look in the sequence $P_3$, $P_4$, $P_5$, $\cdots$ for the first point, that is, the point

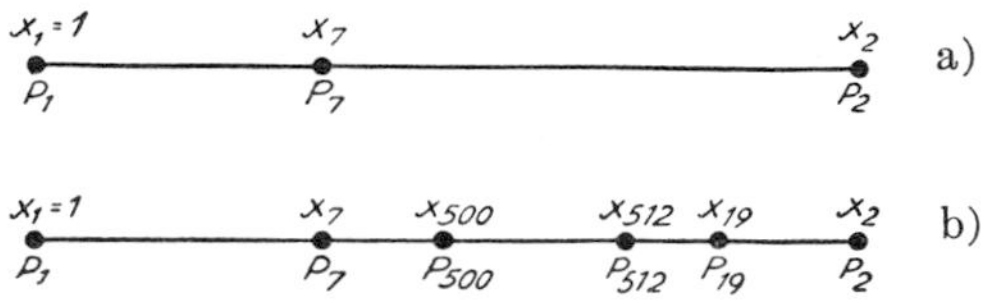

FIG. 150

with least subscript, which is in the interval $P_1P_2$. For concreteness, suppose that it is $P_7$ (Fig. 150a). Hence $x_1 < x_7 < x_2$. We emphasize for later use that *no* $P_i$ *with* $i < 7$ *lies in the open interval* $P_1P_2$ (the interval with the endpoints $P_1$, $P_2$ excluded), i.e. $x_1 < x_i < x_2$ implies that $i \geq 7$.

We next consider the interval $P_7P_2$, and look in the sequence $P_8, P_9, P_{10}, \cdots$ for the first point (the point with least subscript) which is in the interval $P_7P_2$. For concreteness, suppose that this point is $P_{19}$ (Fig. 119b). Hence $x_7 < x_{19} < x_2$. It is again clear that *no* $P_i$ *with* $i < 19$ *is in the open interval* $P_7P_2$.

We now go on to consider the interval $P_7P_{19}$ and the sequence $P_{20}, P_{21}, P_{22}, \cdots$, and to choose the first point of the sequence which is in the interval. Suppose this point is $P_{500}$. Then, as before, *no* $P_i$ *with subscript less than* 500 *is in the open interval* $P_7P_{19}$.

In the next step, we choose the first point of the sequence $P_{501}, P_{502}, \cdots$ which is in the interval $P_{500}P_{19}$, say $P_{512}$. Then *no* $P_i$ *with subscript less than* 512 *is in the open interval* $P_{500}P_{19}$.

By continuing this process we obtain a decreasing sequence of intervals

$$P_1P_2, P_7P_2, P_7P_{19}, P_{500}P_{19}, P_{500}P_{512}, \cdots \tag{2}$$

whose left-hand endpoints

$$x_1, x_7, x_{500}, \cdots \tag{3}$$

form an increasing sequence, while its right-hand endpoints

$$x_2, x_{19}, x_{512}, \cdots \tag{4}$$

form a decreasing sequence; furthermore, every element of (3) is less than every element of (4). Therefore, according to a fundamental property[8] of the real numbers, there is a real number $z$ which is greater than all the numbers of (3) but less than all the numbers of (4).[9] Let $Q$ be the point

[8] This property is the *completeness* of the real numbers. The completeness of the real number system may be formulated in several equivalent ways. Of particular relevance to the proof of Note 38 is the following formulation: Every bounded increasing or decreasing sequence of real numbers has a limit (that is, the numbers of the sequence approach a definite value). The term *bounded* means that all the numbers of the sequence are contained in some interval.

[9] From the completeness property stated in Footnote 8 it follows that (3) has a

of the half-line corresponding to $z$. Then $Q$ is an element of every interval of (2).

We shall now show that $Q$ cannot occur in the sequence (1), in contradiction to our assumption that (1) contains every point of the half-line. Suppose $Q$ is a point of the sequence (1). It must then have a definite subscript, say $k$: $Q = P_k$. First, we note that $P_k$ cannot be an endpoint of any of the intervals of (2), since $z$ is greater than any number of (3) and less than any number of (4). Therefore, since $P_k$ is an element of the open interval $P_1P_2$, $k \geq 7$; since $P_k$ is an element of the open interval $P_7P_2$, $k \geq 19$; since $P_k$ is an element of the open interval $P_7P_{19}$, $k \geq 500$; since $P_k$ is an element of the open interval $P_{500}P_{19}$, $k \geq 512$; etc. It follows that if $n$ is an arbitrary natural number, then $k \geq n$. Hence $Q$ cannot be a point of the sequence (1), and the theorem is proved.

**39** (p. 263). An example of a denumerable order type which is not well ordered is the set of integers ordered with respect to magnitude (see p. 261). Another example, of a different kind, is the set of rational numbers ordered with respect to magnitude (according to Note 27, the set of rational numbers is denumerable).

---

limit $a$ and (4) has a limit $b$; and from the fact that every number of (3) is less than every number of (4) we deduce that $a \leq b$. If $a = b$, then there is just one number $z$ with the stated property and $z = a = b$. If $a < b$, then the set of points $z$ with the stated property is infinite, since every $x$ such that $a \leq x \leq b$ has this property. See, for example, {19}.

*Chapter XIII*

# FERMAT'S LAST PROBLEM

In the concluding chapter we will be dealing with problems which are more difficult to state than those previously discussed, because they are more technical in nature. In this chapter, therefore, we will conclude our discussion of the problems which can be simply stated.

Our final problem of this nature will be Fermat's great or last problem (1665). It is not as old as the geometric construction problems of antiquity we have discussed earlier, but it is equally famous. One of the reasons for its notoriety is that in 1908 Dr. Paul Wolfskehl of Darmstadt, a scientist, offered a prize of 1000000 marks for its solution. A flood of amateur solutions, full of errors and misconceptions, were sent to him for more than ten years, until post-World War I inflation devalued the prize [**1**]. Some professional mathematicians, who had worked on this or related problems in the past, did return to it, at least for a time, but they were aware of the difficulties of the problem, which had defied the efforts of the greatest mathematicians. They also knew of the profound theories which must be mastered before it is possible to appreciate the work already done in the field; and they recognized that some problems are more suited than others to individual aptitudes.

Let us now turn to this still unsolved problem. Remarkably, although its difficulties have up till now proved insurmountable, it is simple enough to state, because its statement involves only the natural numbers.

We begin the discussion of the problem by considering the following table:

$$
\begin{array}{l}
1, 2, 3, 4, 5, 6, 7, 8, 9, 10, 11, 12, 13, 14, 15, 16, 17, \cdots \\
1, \cdots, 4, \cdots\cdots\cdots, 9, \cdots\cdots\cdots\cdots\cdots\cdots\cdots\cdots\cdots\cdots, 16, \cdots\cdots \\
1, \cdots\cdots\cdots\cdots\cdots\cdots, 8, \cdots\cdots\cdots\cdots\cdots\cdots\cdots\cdots\cdots\cdots\cdots\cdots\cdots \\
1, \cdots\cdots\cdots\cdots\cdots\cdots\cdots\cdots\cdots\cdots\cdots\cdots\cdots\cdots\cdots\cdots\cdots, 16, \cdots\cdots \\
1, \cdots\cdots\cdots\cdots\cdots\cdots\cdots\cdots\cdots\cdots\cdots\cdots\cdots\cdots\cdots\cdots\cdots\cdots\cdots\cdots
\end{array}
$$

The first row consists of the natural numbers, the second of their squares, the third of their cubes, and the $n$th row of their $n$th powers (the $n$th power of a number is the number multiplied by itself $n$ times).

With the table in mind we can ask a few simple questions. To begin with, looking at the second row of squares, *is the sum of two squares ever itself a square?* For example, $1^2 + 2^2 = 5$ is not a square; neither are $1^2 + 3^2 = 10$ and $2^2 + 3^2 = 13$. But $3^2 + 4^2 = 25 = 5^2$ is a square. Thus we see that the answer to the question is yes. Without much effort,[1] we can find still other examples of Pythagorean triples (three natural numbers $x$, $y$, $z$ which satisfy the equation $x^2 + y^2 = z^2$ [2]): $5^2 + 12^2 = 169 = 13^2$, $15^2 + 8^2 = 289 = 17^2$. In fact, the Greeks had developed a simple formula for finding all Pythagorean triples, of which there are an infinite number.[2] This formula will later (see Part III of [19]) play a role in our discussion.

Looking now at the third row of the table, the row of cubes, we again ask: Is a cube ever the sum of two cubes? It is not possible to give an example in this case because no one has ever been able to find three natural numbers $x$, $y$, $z$ satisfying the equation

$$x^3 + y^3 = z^3,$$

although there have been many attempts to do so. This failure led many mathematicians to suspect that such numbers did not exist. From a work of Abu Dschafar Muhamed Ibn Allusain, we gather that the Arab astronomer and mathematician Alhogendi had tried in 970—unsuccessfully—to prove that the equation $x^3 + y^3 = z^3$ has no solution in natural numbers $x$, $y$, $z$. Later the Persian mathematician Beha Eddin (1547–1622) made the same assertion [5].

Attempts to find positive integral solutions of the equation

$$x^4 + y^4 = z^4$$

also proved futile; it would appear that either such solutions do not exist or, if they do, that they are very large numbers. The above table shows that the cubes are more dispersed than the squares, and that the fourth powers are still more dispersed, so that there is less prospect of finding a number in the fourth row which is the sum of two other numbers in the row. This alone

[1] We need only multiply three numbers which satisfy the equation $x^2 + y^2 = z^2$ by the same factor to obtain another such triplet. Multiplying 3, 4, 5 by 2, we get $x = 6$, $y = 8$, $z = 10$, and $6^2 + 8^2 = 36 + 64 = 100 = 10^2$; multiplying by 3, we get $x = 9$, $y = 12$, $z = 15$, and $9^2 + 12^2 = 15^2$. The solutions $x$, $y$, $z$ of the equation $x^2 + y^2 = z^2$ which are of real interest are those which are relatively prime, that is, have no common factor except 1. Only such solutions will be used as examples.

[2] The following theorem can be proved [3]: Three natural numbers $x$, $y$, $z$ are a Pythagorean triple if and only if

$$x = (a^2 - b^2)d, \quad y = 2abd, \quad z = (a^2 + b^2)d,$$

where $a$, $b$, $d$ are natural numbers and $a > b$. A simple calculation will verify that this condition is sufficient [4].

We note further that a Pythagorean triple $x$, $y$, $z$ is relatively prime if and only if 1) $d = 1$, 2) $a$ and $b$ are relatively prime (hence $a$ and $b$ cannot both be even), and 3) $a$ and $b$ are not both odd (hence one of the two numbers $a$, $b$ must be odd and the other even). (See [3] for a proof.) For instance, setting $d = 1$ and $a = 2$, $b = 1$; or $a = 3$, $b = 2$; or $a = 4$, $b = 1$; we obtain the examples given in the text: (3, 4, 5), (5, 12, 13), (15, 8, 17).

would of course not be a decisive reason for believing that there are no solutions. Nevertheless, some mathematicians before Fermat very likely conjectured that the equation [5a]

$$x^n + y^n = z^n$$

has no positive integral solutions for $n > 2$. (In the sequel we shall say that the above equation is *solvable* if it has positive integral solutions, and *nonsolvable* otherwise.)

Fermat's name became permanently associated with the problem, however, because he claimed to have a *proof* that $x^n + y^n = z^n$ is nonsolvable for $n > 2$; and this claim, coming from one of the greatest mathematicians of his time, was not to be lightly dismissed. The circumstances surrounding this claim, and indeed the manner in which so many of his results were made public, deserve special attention.

In Chapter III, we discussed Fermat's great contemporary and rival René Descartes. They lived in the troubled days of the Thirty Years' War. But while Descartes spent his time traveling about Europe, Pierre de Fermat's life was relatively quiet. Unlike Descartes, he stayed aloof from the religious-political and military wars of his time. Fermat was born in Toulouse in 1601, and seldom left his native region. Here he studied law; in 1631 he became a parliamentary lawyer, married soon thereafter, and was then made a member of the nobility. He died on January 12, 1665. But what a wealth of ideas, in the most diverse fields of mathematics filled the mind of this man whose days were occupied in the legal life of his town. Problems which, after Newton and Leibniz were solved by means of the differential and integral calculus, were handled in Fermat's day by ingenious special methods. Like Descartes, Fermat achieved significant results by solving isolated, special geometric problems; among other things, he devised an ingenious method for dealing with maximum-minimum problems. If we date the beginning of analytic geometry with the famous *Géométrie* (1637) of Descartes (see Chapter III), we must mention that Fermat, as can be shown by his correspondence with other scholars, had independently developed the basic concepts of this geometry. This does not dispute of course Descartes' priority. At that time outlets for the publication of new discoveries were very different from those of today, when a recognized author can choose among many established technical and academic periodicals. No such periodicals existed then. Recall, for example, the quarrels over Cardano's formula for cubic equations (see Chapter X). It was the custom to hold back a solution until a competitor had disclosed his. This was still the custom two generations after Fermat, when the widely publicized quarrel of the brothers Jakob and Johann Bernoulli took place. Contact with the scientific world, including foreign countries, was maintained through correspondence alone. Fermat conducted most of his correspondence through an intermediary, Father Mersenne (1588–1648) of Paris, a man with extensive scientific contacts [6]. Even in direct communications it was the custom to limit oneself to a statement of results without disclosing how they were obtained. Just as one guards one's luggage on foreign travels, so did the scholars of that time guard their intellectual possessions, for fear of theft. This caused many a reputation to be blackened [7].

Descartes (whose opportunities for publication at Leyden were relatively good) and Fermat were also involved in difficulties because of the indiscretions of a third person, concerning some research in optics. But after an exchange of letters they settled their differences with courteous formality.

In algebra (Descartes' *Géométrie*, in spite of its title, contained a great deal of algebra) Descartes must be judged the superior of Fermat, whose accomplishments in this field were by no means insignificant. But in number theory (Fermat's problem belongs to this field) Fermat had no superiors among his contemporaries or his successors. Among his predecessors, only Diophantus of Alexandria is to be judged Fermat's peer in number theory. The first part of Diophantus' *Arithmetic* [8] contains a pedagogical lecture[3] on the elements of algebra, in which Diophantus introduced a systematic, albeit rather primitive, algebraic notation. A second part of the book contains a large number of exercises, and the general propositions connected with many of these are important results in number theory. According to the introduction, Diophantus' *Arithmetic* was to contain thirteen books, but not all of these are extant. What it originally contained is a question whose answer is still sought by historians of science. When we read ancient texts, we must remember that we are usually dealing with copies, which are, moreover, translations, whose accuracy was subject to the understanding of the copyists who transcribed them, and of their translators. The only knowledge we have of Diophantus' personal life comes from a puzzle poem [9] which he composed in the terminology of his own problems. We know that he reached the age of 84, but beyond a few references to a wife and child which are woven into the poem, we learn only that he lived in Alexandria. It has been conjectured that he was a contemporary of Julian the Apostate who reigned from 361 to 363 A.D.

Over thirteen centuries—perhaps more—elapsed before the first *printed*

[3] In a way which is as appropriate today as it was then, he impresses upon the student he is addressing the necessity of serious application to his studies: "I see, my dear Dionysius, with what zeal you apply yourself to the solution of arithmetic problems. Now I have tried to give you a systematic picture of the science. The subject matter, still unfamiliar to you, may seem a little difficult, and as a beginner you may at times despair of making progress; but your zeal and our instruction will lead you to a comprehension of the subject, because learning comes quickly when zeal and instruction meet." See {9; vol. 1, Ch. 23, pp. 394–416}.

edition [10] of Diophantus' *Works* in 1621. One copy of this edition—Fermat's copy—is especially significant. His marginal comments include many new[4] and deep number theoretic results [11], but no proofs are given. The responsibilities of his position as Parliamentary Counselor did not favor hasty divulgence of proofs, nor did his own inclinations, which were in the spirit of the times. Among these marginal notes, we find one which asserts the nonsolvability of the equation $x^n + y^n = z^n$ for all $n > 2$. Moreover, Fermat expressly adds:

"I have discovered a truly wonderful proof of this, but the margin is too small to contain it."[5]

This claim was made in an edition of Diophantus published by Fermat's son after his father's death (1670), which reproduces Fermat's marginal notes.

Did Fermat, who was always very careful about his claims [12], really possess a valid proof? All the extant letters and papers touching on the problem have been thoroughly examined [13], but Fermat's proof has never been found. But the problem, still unsolved today, has remained permanently associated with Fermat's name, and has spread his fame farther than any of his unquestionable mathematical results.

Nevertheless, a clue to the method of proof Fermat may have had in mind can be obtained from hints given elsewhere. Indeed, early results, which later led to the proof of at least some special cases of Fermat's conjecture were based on his idea (see [19] for the case $n = 4$). To explain the idea, we first recall that, for example, the equation $x^4 + y^4 = z^4$ had already been shown to be nonsolvable for very large values of $x$, $y$. Thus, if $x^4 + y^4 = z^4$ is solvable, its solutions are extremely large numbers. Suppose now that it were possible to prove that if the equation $x^4 + y^4 = z^4$ has a very large solution, then it must also have a smaller solution, say at most half as large. Then, for example, if there were no solutions less than 10000, there would also be no solutions less than 20000; for the contrary would imply that there were solutions less than 10000. But then there could not be solutions less than 40000, because if there were, there would also be solutions less than 20000, etc. This argument does away with the need for further testing.

[4] One of the most important is a theorem (later greatly generalized) named after Fermat: If $p$ is a prime and $a$ is not divisible by $p$, then $a^{p-1} - 1$ is divisible by $p$. For instance, if $p = 5$ and $a = 3$, then $3^4 - 1 = 81 - 1 = 80$ is divisible by 5. This theorem, which is very important in number theory, is called the *little Fermat theorem*, to distinguish it from Fermat's great or last theorem, which is the subject of this chapter. We have called the latter Fermat's great problem, because it is not really a a theorem, since it has never been proved.

[5] See {9; vol. 2, p. 705}. In the original Latin: "Cuius rei demonstrationem mirabilem sane detexi; hanc marginis exiguitas non caperet."

In a fragment of an unfinished essay discovered in the Leyden Library, Fermat speaks of a method "of infinite or unlimited descent" ("la déscente infinie ou indéfinie"), a term which accurately describes the essence of the method of proof described above [**14**].

Whether Fermat actually possessed such a method of proof for the general case and not only for $n = 4$ will always remain a mystery, although we must assume with some degree of probability that he did [**15**]. Despite results achieved in special cases, we must remember that for two and a half centuries the efforts of many different investigators to find a proof based on the idea outlined above have proved fruitless [**16**].

But Fermat's ideas and the problems he posed—not least those among has marginal notes in the works of Diophantus—greatly stimulated the further development of number theory. The problem which bears his name played a major role in this respect, because it led to the creation of entirely new branches of mathematics.

For the time being, however, we shall confine ourselves to a discussion of the status of the problem in Fermat's time and its later development. Fermat's conjecture was first proved for $n = 4$. The first proof seems to be due to Frénicle de Bessy (about 1602–1675); his proof appeared in 1676, and his method coincided with the one proposed by Fermat for $n = 4$ [**17**]. Independently of Frénicle, with whose work he was not acquainted, Euler seventy years later obtained the same result. He was also the first to solve (in 1763) the essentially more difficult case of $n = 3$. He is therefore to be regarded as a pioneer in the solution of this famous problem. We would have to go too far afield to discuss the case $n = 3$ [**18**], and will therefore have to be content with a brief discussion of the case $n = 4$.

The proof in this case is based on the observation that every 4th power is a square. Hence, if we set $x^2 = u$, $y^2 = v$, $z^2 = w$ in the equation $x^4 + y^4 = z^4$, we obtain

$$u^2 + v^2 = w^2.$$

Therefore, $(u, v, w)$ is a Pythagorean triple. Since the case $n = 2$ has already been solved (see Footnote 2 and [**3**]), we have a starting point for further deductions. (The proof is not especially difficult, but we shall not give it here in order not to interrupt the continuity of the discussion. The proof is given in [**19**].)

We note further that the nonsolvability of the problem for $n = 4$ implies its nonsolvability for all exponents divisible by 4. Therefore, Euler's proof of 1747 implies that

$$x^{4s} + y^{4s} = z^{4s} \qquad (s = 1, 2, \cdots)$$

is nonsolvable.

Similarly, the nonsolvability of the equation $x^3 + y^3 = z^3$ implies the nonsolvability of the equation

$$x^{3s} + y^{3s} = z^{3s} \qquad (s = 1, 2, \cdots).$$[6]

More than half a century passed before the case $n = 5$ was solved, and 14 years later the case $n = 7$ was solved.[7] Did Gauss (see Chapter IX), then the foremost living mathematician, who had solved so many difficult problems, ever concern himself with Fermat's problem? From Gauss' posthumous papers [**20**] we learn that he had sketched proofs for the cases $n = 5$ and $n = 7$, which were the same as those later published by Dirichlet and Lamé.[8] Perhaps he regarded these as only preparatory to a *general* proof, and subsequently felt that the state of number theory did not yet warrant it.

But we have not yet discussed everything now known about Fermat's problem. First, we make the obvious remark that for each exponent $n$,

$$x^n + y^n = z^n$$

is either solvable or not solvable. (Whether or not we actually know which assertion holds for a given $n$ is irrelevant at this point.) In the second case, we shall call the exponent $n$ a *Fermat exponent*, because it satisfies Fermat's conjecture; in the first case, we shall call it a *non-Fermat exponent*. The exponent $n = 2$ is a non-Fermat exponent because, as we have seen, Pythagorean triples do exist. The same is true of $n = 1$, since $x + y = z$ is solvable.

Next, we divide the set of all natural numbers into three classes as follows:

*Class I* consists of numbers not divisible by 2, that is, all odd numbers

$$1, 3, 5, 7, \cdots.$$

*Class II* consists of all numbers which contain the factor 2 exactly once; that is, the doubles of all odd numbers:

$$2, 6, 10, 14, 18, 22, \cdots.$$

[6] In general, the nonsolvability of $x^n + y^n = z^n$ implies that of $x^{ns} + y^{ns} = z^{ns}$ $(s = 1, 2, \cdots)$. For suppose the last equation has a solution $X, Y, Z$. Then $X^s, Y^s, Z^s$ is a solution of the first equation, which is a contradiction.

[7] The proof that $x^5 + y^5 = z^5$ is not solvable is due to Dirichlet (see Chapter VII). His papers of 1825 and 1826 were submitted to the French Academy by Lacroix and Legendre, who was working on the same problem at the time. The proof for $n = 7$ (1839–1840) was given by Gabriel Lamé (1795–1870) and Victor Amédée Lebesgue (1791–1875). Dirichlet's result (1832) that $x^{14} + y^{14} = z^{14}$ is not solvable is therefore a special case of the Lamé-Lebesgue theorem.

[8] Other evidence that Gauss had occupied himself with Fermat's problem is found in letters written in 1804 and 1807 to the mathematician Sophie Germain (1776–1831), who believed she had solved the problem for certain categories of exponents; see {2; vol. 2, Ch. 26, pp. 731, 734}.

*Class III* consists of all numbers divisible by $4 = 2^2$:

$$4, 8, 12, 16, 20, 24, \cdots .$$

Now we know, because of Frénicle's and Euler's proof, that every multiple of 4 is a Fermat exponent; hence, all the numbers of Class III are Fermat exponents. Therefore, only Classes I and II can contain non-Fermat exponents. Further, Class I contains $n = 1$ and Class II contains $n = 2$, and both are non-Fermat exponents. The question then is: Do Class I or Class II (or both) contain other non-Fermat exponents? If Fermat's conjecture were correct, the answer would be no, for in that case there would be no non-Fermat exponents except $n = 1$ and $n = 2$. But we do not know whether this is true.

It is now of particular importance to examine the *primes*

$$2, 3, 5, 7, 11, 13, 17, 19, 23, \cdots$$

to see whether or not any of the primes are Fermat exponents. Euler, Dirichlet and Lamé showed that 3, 5, and 7 are Fermat exponents, and we know that 2 is a non-Fermat exponent. Without prejudging Fermat's conjecture, we now divide the primes into two categories:

*Category A* consists of all prime Fermat exponents $p$.

*Category B* consists of all prime non-Fermat exponents $p$. Then Category B contains $p = 2$.

It is not known whether Category B contains any prime except 2. Fermat conjectured that it does not. If his conjecture is substantiated, all the odd primes must belong to Category A.

We are now faced with the question: *Are all odd primes Fermat exponents, i.e., is the equation*

$$x^p + y^p = z^p$$

*nonsolvable for every odd prime p?*

This question would seem to cover only a special case of Fermat's problem, since the problem is concerned with exponents which are not only primes but also composite numbers. But, actually, the whole problem is reducible to the case of *prime* exponents. This is based on the fact that every composite number is a product of its prime factors (see Chapter I). First, we can immediately disregard numbers divisible by 4, since we know that the numbers of Class III are Fermat exponents. The numbers of Class I and Class II remain, with the exception of $n = 1$ and $n = 2$, which are known to be non-Fermat exponents. If we denote any odd number greater than 1 by $U$, Fermat's problem is reduced to a consideration of the numbers $U$ of Class I and the numbers $2U$ of Class II. For example, 45 and 247 are in Class I; 30, 6 and 2389298 are in Class II. Each number $U$ is either an odd prime, or the product of odd primes. Therefore, each number $U$ or $2U$ is divisible by at least one odd prime $p$. Now if every odd prime $p$ were a Fermat exponent, then according to Footnote 6, every number divisible by $p$ would also be a Fermat exponent. In other words, every number $U$, as well as every number $2U$, would be a Fermat exponent.

Thus the special case of the odd primes is crucial: If it can be proved that the odd primes are Fermat exponents, Fermat's problem is solved. For, then all numbers of Class I, with the exception of $n = 1$, as well as all numbers of Class II with the exception of $n = 2$, would be Fermat exponents; and since Class III contains only Fermat exponents, every number $n > 2$ would be an exponent for which $x^n + y^n = z^n$ is not solvable [**21**].

This makes it clear why all the efforts to solve this problem have been concentrated on the odd primes. We have already seen that the primes $p = 3, p = 5, p = 7$ are Fermat exponents. But even before Lamé published his proof for $p = 7$, there appeared in 1837 the first of a series of papers by Kummer, which subsequently led to a much more general result: a proof that a certain class of primes consists of Fermat exponents. The author of this paper, Ernst Eduard Kummer (1810–1893) also contributed to many other fields of mathematics [**22**], but he owes the permanent place he occupies in the history of mathematics to his achievements in number theory in connection with Fermat's problem. In 1849 the Paris Academy had endowed a gold medal valued at 3000 francs for the complete solution of Fermat's problem. When no paper which met the conditions of the grant was submitted, even on extension of the terminal date, the medal was presented to Kummer as the author whose research most merited the prize.

We may briefly summarize the total effect of Kummer's work [**23**] on the present state of Fermat's problem as follows [**24**]:

*As a result of Kummer's work, we can state that the odd primes less than* 100 *are Fermat exponents. On the other hand, there is a set of odd primes for which the question has not been decided* [**25**]. *Nevertheless, up to now no odd prime non-Fermat exponent has been found.*

Thus, Fermat's conjecture has not been refuted, but neither has it been completely substantiated. And it is difficult to prophesy how long this uncertainty will continue.

Kummer's great achievement was not only a step forward in the solution of Fermat's problem, but also had a much deeper significance. At the beginning of the 19th century, Gauss' *Disquisitiones Arithmeticae* (1801), laid the foundations for a broadening of number theory which would not have been possible earlier. Much was accomplished in the newly extended field, but a problem which had long before been solved in the older number theory—the decomposition of an integer into its prime factors—now assumed an entirely different aspect. So far-reaching was the change that it seemed hopeless to find a generalization of the concept of prime number, which would play a role in the new theory analogous to that of the usual primes in elementary number theory. Kummer's great achievement was to do just this. His concept of "prime numbers," now called prime ideals, was later further generalized, and is now a fundamental concept of modern number theory and algebra. The significance of his achievement is comparable to that of the mathematicians of classical antiquity, who proved that an integer can be uniquely decomposed into its prime factors [**26**].

Perhaps some day Fermat's problem will be completely solved. It will be a real achievement. And if the solution yields new methods of research and new problems, it will be a new milestone. If not, our desire for knowledge will have been gratified, but Fermat's problem in itself would then occupy no more than a modest place in the history of mathematics, and this principally because it stimulated Kummer's work.

Felix Klein has compared a historical epoch in science to a chain of Alps. Looking back over this chapter, we can imagine ourselves in the midst of the mountains, where from a high peak on a clear day we can see other giant mountains rising far in the distance. Thus, we recognize in the development of number theory the peaks leading from Diophantus over Fermat and Euler to Gauss, as to the highest point of the mountain chain, only to view from that point the craggy, steep mountainsides of a newly discovered chain. At this point we will briefly describe the life and work of Euler, who is a prominent link in this chain.

Leonhard Euler was born April 15, 1707 in Basle, a city which has contributed many important mathematicians to the world. Foremost among these was the Bernoulli family, with so many members that many histories of mathematics present a family genealogy, as historians give genealogies of royal families. In Euler's generation the brothers Jakob (1654–1705) and Johann Bernoulli (1667–1748) were particularly prominent in the mathematical world. Euler spent his youth outside the city on the right bank of the Rhine, in a place where his father was a minister. This man, who educated his son himself, was able to give him a good background in mathematics, having studied with Johann Bernoulli. While attending the University of Basle to study theology, Euler became friendly with Johann's sons, Nicolaus (1695–1726) and Daniel (1700–1782). Despite the difference of seven years between them, Euler kept pace with Daniel, and in 1723 took his M.A. In 1727, when he was only 19, he won a prize from the Paris Academy for his treatise on the design of ship masts.

In 1725, the second wife of Peter the Great, Catherine, a highly gifted person, succeeded her husband on the Russian throne. In accordance with her husband's wishes, she founded the Petersburg Academy, modeling it after the pattern of the Paris and Berlin Academies. Many famous scholars from all over the world were called to it. Nicolaus and Daniel Bernoulli went there as early as 1725, and wrote to Euler to tell him that a position would be waiting for him if he would extend the field of his interest to physiology. To prepare himself for this post, Euler began the study of medicine at the University of Basle in 1726. He reached Petersburg in 1727, having travelled by ship and foot, but soon the Empress died, and conditions for scientific work became highly unfavorable. He then became a ship's officer and considered transferring to the Navy. But when the Empress Anna assumed the throne in 1730 conditions improved again, and Euler joined the mathematical staff at the Academy. Three years later he was made Professor of Physics. In the same year he married the daughter of a painter from St. Gall, who bore him 13 children.

In 1735, a record feat cost Euler the sight of his right eye. The Paris Academy had set the problem of determining the time from observations of the height of the sun. Several able competitors had reported that two or three months would be necessary to carry out this project. Euler computed the required tables in three days,[9] but lost the sight of his right eye as a result. Nevertheless, he continued to publish papers in many different fields. Some of these appeared in the Proceedings of the Petersburg Academy, and some, such as a work on mechanics, were published independently.[10] In 1740, he received another prize from the Paris Academy, one of ten he was to receive during his life from that Academy, for a work on the causes of ebb- and flood-tide.

After Czarina Anna died in 1740, the position of the Academy again worsened, and in 1741 Euler accepted a post in Berlin offered him by Frederick II, who had just ascended the throne. An insight into conditions at Petersburg is afforded by the following story. During a reception at the Court in Berlin given by the Queen Mother, Euler, because of his timid, monosyllabic responses, was asked why he was so shy. He replied: "Madame, because I come from a country where any one who says anything is hanged [**29**]." In 1744 he became Director of the Mathematics Department of the revived Prussian Academy. In the two and a half decades he spent in Berlin, Euler wrote an enormous number of papers in all of the contemporary branches of mathematics and their applications. However, the atmosphere of the court, on which Voltaire thrived, did not suit Euler's simpler nature, so that he remained aloof and devoted his energies to research.

[9] Gauss was able to do this later in an hour, due to superior methods [**27**].

[10] Everyone familiar with the use of the Greek letter $\pi$ to describe the relationship between the circumference of a circle and its diameter will be interested to know that this letter symbol was first used in a paper of Euler's (about 1738) on infinite series [**28**]. In a somewhat earlier work (1734–1735) Euler used the letter $p$ instead of $\pi$.

But the youthful Frederick II was capricious [**30**]. He greeted Euler's arrival in Berlin with a flattering letter of welcome, but mathematics itself did not greatly interest him. He could only understand its value when it was applied to shipbuilding, the construction of fortifications, the handling of artillery, or similar pursuits. In 1749, Euler had to busy himself with such projects as the levels of a canal, a lottery, and the water displays in the gardens of Sans Souci. At the request of the king he translated a book from English into French on "new principles of artillery," and while doing so developed a complete theory of ballistics. This won him more favor than any successes in number theory. But his intellect encompassed both fields, and he was equally adept in pure and applied mathematics. As a result, this versatile man could handle successfully any of the demands made on him. It is ironical that the son of a country whose rulers had for centuries striven to preserve the peace, spent his career in the service of a monarch noted for his military exploits and for his skill in power politics.

But Euler did more than meet the demands of his position; his genius served all humanity. His productivity and the range of his work is unrivaled. Most important of all, his work in analysis enriched the differential and integral calculus of Leibniz and Newton and allied fields. He also founded the calculus of variations (see the Postscript). He did not confine himself to the numerous problems in number theory stemming from Fermat's marginal notes in the works of Diophantus, but devoted himself so wholeheartedly to the most varied fields that his name is forever associated with many techniques, theorems and theoretically interesting numerical values [**31**]. He simultaneously pursued investigations in algebra and mechanics, in elementary and analytic geometry of the plane and in space, in the theory of optical instruments, and in celestial mechanics. His habit of working in so many areas at once is different from that of many other great mathematicians, who have preferred to concentrate on one problem at a time.

The manner in which Euler's work was made public also contrasts sharply with the secrecy customary earlier, as in Fermat's time. In his extensive publications, Euler often described not only how he arrived at his results but also the errors he had made at the beginning. He gave reasons for rejecting unsuccessful methods of attacking a problem and corrected earlier work, disclosing information earlier generations had kept from the mathematical world. This frankness was in part due to Euler's temperament, but also he had opportunities for publication in newly established Academy journals not available to earlier mathematicians.[11] In addition, Euler wrote

[11] But not all mathematicians were as generous as Euler in the presentation of their material. This was true even of Lagrange, his successor at the Berlin Academy (see {38; p. 251}). There are many later instances of authors who spent great effort on compressing material into the sparsest form—even at the cost of readability.

a series of expository works on the contemporary status of various fields of mathematics, which were printed by Bousquet in Lausanne.

During the decades Euler spent in Berlin, a considerable part of his work was published in the journals of the Petersburg Academy,[12] from which he derived a part of his income. His reputation there was such that when in 1760 Russian troops occupied Berlin Euler was given a personal guard. When his estate in Charlottenburg was plundered by Saxon troops, he received compensation and later a present of 4000 gulden from the Empress Catherine II. This second Catherine ascended the Russian throne in 1762 after the murder of Peter III, and held it for 34 years. She took personal charge of the judicial, administrative and educational functions of the government, and was strongly interested in the development of the sciences. At her request Prince Dolgorucki asked Euler to return to Petersburg, promising favorable conditions for his work. In 1766, Frederick II reluctantly granted Euler and two of his sons permission to move. Euler's youngest son, an 18 year old lieutenant in the Artillery of the Prussian Army, was at first forced to stay behind, but was later permitted to join his brothers.

Upon Euler's arrival in Petersburg, the Empress granted the means to purchase a home. Shortly afterwards, his left eye began to fail, but this did not prevent him from publishing his famous *Vollständige Anleitung zur Algebra* (*Complete Introduction to Algebra*), a book noted for its clarity and content. Euler dictated it to one of his servants and found the presentation satisfactory when his servant independently solved all the pertinent problems in algebra and number theory.[13] In 1771 his house burned. Euler was saved by a Basle laborer but became totally blind. His wife and manuscripts were rescued by Count Orloff.

But Euler would not permit his blindness to hamper his activities. At his request Nicolaus Fuss (1755–1825) was called from Basle (he was later to succeed Euler's oldest son as Secretary of the Academy), and with his aid papers on shipbuilding, navigation, optics, and the course of the moon continued to pour forth.

In 1783 there was great excitement in the small town of Annonay, near Lyon. On June 4 the brothers Montgolfier made their first public attempt

[12] These journals did not contain all his papers. For example, three volumes of *Opuscula* appeared in Berlin at various times between 1746–1751.

[13] In the year 1770 in which the *Anleitung zur Algebra* appeared, he also published *Briefe an eine deutsche Prinzessin über verschiedene Gegenstände der Physik und Philosophie* (*Letters to a German Princess on Various Topics in Physics and Philosophy*). The publication of this work was occasioned by Euler's instruction of the daughters of the Margrave Heinrich von Brandenburg-Schwedt in Berlin. This popular work was well known in its time. Yet Lagrange once stated that it could have remained unprinted without any loss. I myself have not seen the book, and must refrain from passing judgment.

to rise in a balloon. On August 28, 200000 Parisians witnessed the ascent of a balloon filled with hydrogen. Euler, who was then 76, succeeded at the beginning of September of the same year in integrating the difficult differential equations governing the motion of the balloon. But in the course of the work he suffered several spells of dizziness; his death followed on the 18th of September.

Euler had once said that the presses of the Petersburg Academy would still be publishing his papers twenty years after his death; in fact, it took 35 years to publish them all. About 50 years ago, it was planned to publish an edition of his collected works. Of the 70 quarto volumes planned, about half have appeared [**32**]. Constantin Carathéodory was charged with the publication of the two volumes on the calculus of variations. The Collected Works, when completed, will be monumental.

At the time of Euler's death, Gauss was six years old. The bridge between Euler and Gauss is the great school of French mathematicians at the end of the eighteenth century [**33**]. An account of this school would, however, take us far beyond the framework of this chapter.

We have thus far been able to discuss a few great mathematicians, but there are many others, both successful and famous, whom we could hardly even mention [**34**], because their work is too far removed from the problems we have chosen. In order to discuss their achievements, moreover, we would have had to assume a certain mathematical sophistication on the part of the reader, which we have not wanted to do. Our aim has been to show that mathematics is *living and growing*, and not a closed field of static knowledge; and to indicate the hard work involved in solving mathematical problems, work which demands devotion and self-sacrifice, but which does not always reward research with satisfying results [**35**].

The efforts of thousands of mathematicians over several millenia have not been in vain. Something *permanent* has been created, more permanent than history's "lasting" peaces, "holy" alliances and "conclusive" diplomatic decisions. Without the 2000 year old Pythagorean theorem the greatest part of contemporary mathematics, as well as that of physics and technology, would not exist; without the knowledge of the spherical nature of the earth (first discovered by the Pythagorean school) and the discovery of the New World which depended on it, our lives would be wholly different. These mathematical discoveries were made at the time of the political debates of the Athenians regarding ostracism, when the Persian Wars were being fought, and when the Roman Wars converted Rome from a kingdom to a republic. These events certainly had their part in shaping the future, but for the mathematician the significance of these political events is far less immediate than the scientific discoveries of the time.

The activities of Archimedes of Syracuse as a military engineer, the weapons he invented, are but passing events compared to the gains in knowledge he achieved. Archimedes' mastery of the mathematics of classical antiquity anticipated the mathematics of modern times. His law of levers was the foundation for the building of machines; his famous discovery of the apparent loss in weight of bodies immersed in water became the basis of fluid mechanics, which led to the theory of ships and air-craft. His methods in geometry are forerunners of the integral calculus which is so important to the natural sciences; and his measurements of the circle and sphere are still applicable to current problems.

As we attempt to distinguish between what is permanent and what is transitory in man's efforts, we should not forget the inestimable value we obtain from the masterpieces of art. But the satisfaction of the pure quest for knowledge is a source of joy not only to the initial discoverer, but also to those who follow him and attain the same insight for themselves. The search for knowledge enriches the life of all.

*Notes to Chapter XIII*

# FERMAT'S LAST PROBLEM

**1** (p. 277). Details on the conditions governing the award of the prize can be found in {1}. An error-free proof for *all* exponents $n$ printed in a technical journal, and refereed by the editorial board of the journal was required. The commission charged with administering the prize money could use the interest on the endowment to award prizes for partial solutions, or for other scientific purposes, such as inviting foreign speakers to give lectures. The most significant were the six lectures given by Poincaré at Göttingen in April, 1909, on selected topics in pure mathematics and mathematical physics. These were printed in Leipzig in 1910. The unusual size of the endowment was criticized as a threat to the purity of number theory, but nevertheless it did do a great deal of good before it was dissipated. See {2; vol. 2, p. xix}.

**2** (p. 278). According to the Pythagorean theorem, three numbers $x$, $y$, $z$ (even when they are not integers) which satisfy the equation $x^2 + y^2 = z^2$ represent the lengths of the three sides of a right triangle. If $x$, $y$, $z$ are integers, such as 3, 4, 5, a triangle with these sides can easily be constructed.

Nevertheless, the significance of right triangles whose sides are integers must not be overestimated. In reality, it was the fact (a consequence of the Pythagorean theorem) that there are triangles with *incommensurable* sides which was of decisive significance for the future development of mathematics, because it led to the introduction of the irrational numbers (see Chapter VIII). This insight of Pythagoras and his school was fundamental to the rigor and purity of the geometry of antiquity, and raised it far above the level of empirical approximation. See Paul Valéry {4} for remarks on Greek mathematics which are sympathetic to this view. See also a collection of papers {5} by Fréchet, Got, Dubreil, Denjoy, etc. on the great currents in mathematical thought.

**3** (p. 278). The proof is based on several simple lemmas. The first two are immediate consequences of the prime factorization theorem and we omit their proofs. In the sequel all numbers are natural numbers (positive integers). We will also denote the greatest common divisor of two natural numbers $A$, $B$ by $(A, B)$. If $(A, B) = 1$, we say $A$, $B$ are relatively prime.

*Lemma A*. If $W^2$ is divisible by $T^2$, i.e. $W^2 = VT^2$, then $W$ is divisible by $T$, i.e. $W = UT$. Hence, $V$ is a square, since $W^2 = VT^2 = U^2T^2$, so that $V = U^2$.

*Lemma B*. If $W^2 = AB$, and $(A, B) = 1$, then $A$ and $B$ are squares, that is, $A = C^2$, $B = D^2$. Hence $W = CD$.

*Lemma C*. If $W$ is a square, then $W = 4n$ or $W = 4n + 1$.

To prove this, note that the square of an even number is a multiple of 4, and the square of an odd number is of the form $4s + 1$:

$$(2m)^2 = 4m^2 = 4n,$$

$$(2m + 1)^2 = 4m^2 + 4m + 1 = 4s + 1.$$

Since a square is the square of either an even or odd number, the lemma is proved.

*Proposition D.* If $X$, $Y$, $Z$ is a solution of the equation

$$x^2 + y^2 = z^2, \tag{1}$$

then $X$ and $Y$ are not both odd.

For if $X$ and $Y$ are both odd, then by Lemma C, $X^2 = 4k + 1$ and $Y^2 = 4s + 1$. Hence $Z^2 = X^2 + Y^2 = 4k + 1 + 4s + 1 = 4n + 2$, which contradicts Lemma C.

*Proposition E.* If $X$, $Y$, $Z$ is a relatively prime solution of (1) (that is, the greatest common divisor of all three numbers $X$, $Y$, $Z$ is 1), then $(X, Y) = 1$. (It can of course happen in general that three numbers $u$, $v$, $w$ are relatively prime, whereas, say $u$, $v$ are not relatively prime, e.g. $u = 10$, $v = 12$, $w = 15$.)

Indeed, let $t = (X, Y)$, and suppose that $X = tu$, $Y = tv$. Then

$$Z^2 = X^2 + Y^2 = t^2u^2 + t^2v^2 = t^2(u^2 + v^2).$$

Hence $Z^2$ is divisible by $t^2$. Therefore, by Lemma A, $Z$ is divisible by $t$. Since $X$ and $Y$ are also divisible by $t$, it follows from the relative primeness of $X$, $Y$, $Z$ that $t = 1$. Therefore, $(X, Y) = 1$.

*Remark.* Since $X^2 = Z^2 - Y^2$ and $Y^2 = Z^2 - X^2$, an entirely similar proof will show that $X$, $Z$ and $Y$, $Z$ are also relatively prime (if $X$, $Y$, $Z$ is a relatively prime solution of (1)).

Therefore, according to Propositions D and E, if $X$, $Y$, $Z$ is a relatively prime solution of (1), one of the numbers $X$, $Y$ must be even and the other odd, say $X$ is odd and $Y$ is even. (Since (1) is symmetric in $X$, $Y$, it makes no difference which one we assume to be odd and which even.) Then $X^2$ is odd and $Y^2$ is even (by Lemma C). Therefore, $Z^2$ is odd, and so $Z$ is odd (also by Lemma C).

We now rewrite (1) as $y^2 = z^2 - x^2$, substitute $X$, $Y$, $Z$ and factor the right-hand side to obtain

$$Y^2 = (Z + X)(Z - X). \tag{2}$$

Since $X$ and $Z$ are both odd, $Z + X$ and $Z - X$ are both even. Let

$$Z + X = 2r, \qquad Z - X = 2s, \tag{3}$$

where $r$ and $s$ are positive integers and $r > s$. ($Z - X$ is positive since $Z^2 = X^2 + Y^2$ implies that $Z > X$.)

Adding and subtracting the two equations (3), we get

$$Z = r + s, \qquad X = r - s. \tag{4}$$

Now, $r$ and $s$ are relatively prime. In the contrary case, $X$ and $Z$ would have a common factor $>1$, an eventuality which is excluded by the remark following Proposition E. Hence $r$ and $s$ cannot both be even. Furthermore, $r$ and $s$ cannot both be odd; if they were, $X$ and $Z$ would both be even, whereas $X$ and $Z$ are both odd.

Substituting (3) in (2) we get

$$Y^2 = 4rs. \tag{5}$$

Since $Y$ is even, $Y = 2w$ and $Y^2 = 4w^2$. Substituting this in (5) we obtain

$$w^2 = rs. \tag{6}$$

Since $r$ and $s$ are relatively prime, we can apply Lemma B to write

$$r = a^2, \qquad s = b^2, \tag{7}$$

where $a > b$ since $r > s$. Clearly, $a$ and $b$ are relatively prime; for if $t$ is the greatest common divisor of $a$, $b$ and $a = tc$, $b = td$, then $r = t^2c^2$, $s = t^2d^2$. Hence $t$ divides both $r$ and $s$. Since $r$ and $s$ are relatively prime, $t = 1$, and the assertion holds. Furthermore, one of the numbers $a$, $b$ is even and the other odd, since this is true of $r$ and $s$.

Substituting (7) in (5), and taking (4) into account, we finally get

$$X = a^2 - b^2, \qquad Y = 2ab, \qquad Z = a^2 + b^2, \tag{8}$$

where $a$, $b$ are relatively prime, $a > b$, and one of the numbers $a$, $b$ is even, the other odd.

The relations (8) give all the relatively prime solutions of (1). Every other solution can be obtained by multiplying each of $X$, $Y$, $Z$ by a common factor $d$.

**4** (p. 278). Euclid (4th century B.C.) obtained a representation of Pythagorean triples equivalent to the one derived in Note 3. As a matter of fact, special classes of Pythagorean triples were already known to Pythagoras (6th century B.C.) and Plato (429–348 B.C.). Euclid's representation is

$$x = ghd, \qquad y = \tfrac{1}{2}(g^2 - h^2)d, \qquad s = \tfrac{1}{2}(g^2 + h^2)d, \tag{8'}$$

where $g$ and $h$ are relatively prime odd numbers and $g > h$. This representation can be obtained in a manner similar to that of Note 3, this time setting

$x^2 = (z + y)(z - y)$. The solutions (8) can be obtained from (8′) by setting

$$a = \tfrac{1}{2}(g + h), \qquad b = \tfrac{1}{2}(g - h),$$

and (8′) can be obtained from (8) by setting

$$g = a + b, \qquad h = a - b.$$

[The Indian mathematician Brahmagupta (598 A.D.) had a representation similar to the Euclidean representation but somewhat different in form.] The Pythagorean triples (3, 4, 5), (5, 12, 13) and (15, 8, 17) can be obtained from (8′) by putting $g = 3$, $h = 1$; $g = 5$, $h = 1$; $g = 5$, $h = 3$, respectively. [It may be of interest to note a theorem of Frénicle (1676) to the effect that if $(x, y, z)$ is a Pythagorean triple, then $xyz$ is divisible by 60.]

The Euclidean representation (8′) can be found in Euclid's *Elements*, Book X, Proposition 29, Lemma 1. The Diophantine representation (8) is in Diophantus' *Works* (see Tannery's edition {6}). See also {7} and {8; vol. 3, p. 111 ff.}.

**5** (p. 278). Abu Mohammed Alhogendi (d. 1000 A.D.) is one of the three [the other two were the astronomer Abul Wafa (940–998) and Abu Nasr (960–1015)] independent discoverers of the sine theorem in spherical trigonometry, which applies to all triangles on a sphere and is important in the calculation of terrestrial and celestial triangles. Prior to this time, the theorem was known only for right triangles on a sphere. Beha Eddin compiled many earlier results in a book called *Essence of the Art of Calculation*, in which a great variety of algebraic and geometric problems is treated. See {9; vol. 1, p. 646 and pp. 672–675}, {10} and {8; vol. 3, p. 114 and vol. 5, p. 136}.

**5a** (p. 279). The use of exponents goes back to Descartes, who introduced them in his *Géométrie*. See {3}, {9; vol. 2, p. 723} and {8; vol. 2, p. 124}.

**6** (p. 280). For scholars, like Descartes and Mersenne, extensive travel was a means of acquainting themselves with their professional colleagues and of exchanging scientific information; these trips played the role of our scientific meetings. In addition to Mersenne, Fermat also corresponded with Pierre de Carvacy and Digby, an Englishman who had emigrated to France for political reasons.

**7** (p. 280). Because proofs and experimental evidence were omitted in correspondence, it was quite possible for a scholar, on learning of another scholar's discovery through a letter, to claim the discovery as his own (again without elaboration of the method involved) in a letter to a third scholar. For instance, the mathematician Giles Persone de Roberval (1602–1675) made unpleasant and questionable accusations against the physicist and mathematician Evangelista Torricelli (1608–1647) after the latter's death. See {9; vol. 2, Ch. 80}.

**8** (p. 280). For details see {9; vol. 1}.

**9** (p. 280). For the poem see {9; vol. 1, p. 395}.

**10** (p. 281). The editor Claude Gaspard Bachet de Méziriac (1587–1638), who made valuable contributions to number theory, published in 1612 a book entitled *Problèmes plaisants et délectable qui se font par les nombres*. The first edition of this book is no longer extant, while copies of the second edition of 1624 are very rare. The 3rd–5th editions were reprinted in 1884. For fairly recent books of a similar nature see {11}–{18}.

**11** (p. 281). We will mention here only two of Fermat's theorems (Bachet and Fermat thought it possible that the first of these was known to Diophantus): 1) Every natural number is a sum of at most four squares (e.g. $7 = 2^2 + 1^2 + 1^2 + 1^2$). 2) Diophantus had remarked that no prime of the form $4n + 3$ is a sum of less than three squares. Fermat proved that every prime of the form $4n + 1$ is a sum of two squares (e.g. $5 = 2^2 + 1^2$, $13 = 3^2 + 2^2$, $17 = 4^2 + 1^2$). Fermat added that he could prove these theorems by the method of infinite descent. Theorem 1) was first proved by Lagrange (1770). For this reason it is often known as Lagrange's theorem. The second theorem was proved by Euler (1749).

Fermat is also responsible for the first result (given without proof) in the theory of quadratic residues. This theory was later developed by Euler and Legendre, and brought to a finished form by Gauss in 1801.

**12** (p. 281). Fermat was firmly convinced that his conjecture that every number of the form $2^{2^s}$ is a prime was correct. Euler later showed that the conjecture is wrong. However, Fermat never claimed to have a proof of the conjecture in his letters to Frénicle (1640) and Pascal (1654), although later he seems to have believed that he had a proof by the method of infinite descent (see {19} and {2; vol. 1, Ch. 15, p. 375}).

**13** (p. 281). Charles Henry, who together with Tannery edited Fermat's *Works* {19}, conducted an extensive search among the relevant manuscripts. His complete report can be found in {20}.

**14** (p. 282). It does not seem at all necessary to seek the sources of Fermat's method of infinite descent (Moritz Cantor in {9; vol. 1, p. 710} indicates Campanus as a possible source). Nevertheless, Legendre, for example, in presenting the proof of Fermat's theorem for $n = 4$ [that is, when he gives the proof of the nonsolvability of the equation $x^4 + y^4 = w^2$ (see [**19**])] in his *Theory of Numbers* {21} is not content merely to exposit the proof, but takes pains to point out how greatly the range of numbers in which there can be no solutions (for $n = 4$) is extended, all in one stroke.

Moreover, as far as I know, the historical accounts have nowhere (except for {22}) clearly pointed out that the method of infinite descent is essentially the same as Pascal's method of mathematical induction, introduced by him before 1654 (see Chapter XII, Note 4). To see this we merely need to modify the outline of the proof given in the text (see also Note 19) as follows: Assume that the equation $x^4 + y^4 = z^4$ is nonsolvable for all $x$, $y$, $z$ such that $z < n$. Then the equation is nonsolvable for all $x$, $y$, $z$ such that $z < n + 1$. For if there is a solution with $z < n + 1$, it can be shown that there is a solution with $z < n$, which contradicts the original assumption. Therefore, by induction there can be no solution (since there is no solution with $z < 2$).

**15** (p. 282). See {23} and {8; vol. 3, p. 113}.

**16** (p. 282). The oldest (erroneous) proof for arbitrary $n > 2$ was that of Claude Jaquemont (1651–1729). It is in a manuscript originally thought to be by Nicolas Malebranche (1638–1715). See {2; vol. 2, p. 733}.

**17** (p. 282). See {23}, {8; vol. 3, p. 113} and {24; vol. 2, p. 598}.

**18** (p. 282). For an elementary proof of Fermat's theorem for $n = 3$ see {24; vol. 2, pp. 600–604}. The theorem can also be (and usually is) proved in the theory of algebraic number fields (see {25}). As a matter of fact, algebraic number theory was developed as a result of work on Fermat's problem.

**19** (p. 282). We will give Euler's proof (1747) for the nonsolvability of the equation

$$x^4 + y^4 = z^4. \tag{1}$$

It later appeared in his book *Vollständige Anleitung zur Algebra* (1770).

Actually, Euler proved a stronger theorem, namely that the equation

$$x^4 + y^4 = w^2 \tag{2}$$

is nonsolvable (in natural numbers). The nonsolvability of (2) immediately implies the nonsolvability of (1). For if (1) has a solution $X$, $Y$, $Z$, then $X^4 + Y^4 = Z^4 = (Z^2)^2 = W^2$, and $(X, Y, Z^2 = W)$ is a solution of (2), which is a contradiction.

The proof of the nonsolvability of (2) depends on two lemmas. As in Note 3, all numbers are natural numbers, and we use the notation

$$(A, B) = 1$$

to mean that $A$ and $B$ are relatively prime.

*Lemma F.* If $(A, B) = 1$ and $(A, C) = 1$, then $(A, BC) = 1$. More generally, if

$$(A, B_1) = 1, (A, B_2) = 1, \cdots, (A, B_n) = 1,$$

then $(A, B_1B_2 \cdots B_n) = 1$.

We omit a proof of this proposition. The first part is an immediate consequence of the prime factorization theorem and can be found in any book on elementary number theory. The second part can be proved by induction.

*Lemma G.* If $W^2 = A_1 A_2 \cdots A_m$ is a product of $m$ factors every two of which are relatively prime, i.e. $(A_i, A_j) = 1$ for $i \neq j$, $1 \leq i, j \leq m$, then every factor is a square:

$$A_1 = C_1^2, \cdots, A_m = C_m^2.$$

For $m = 2$, Lemma G reduces to Lemma B of Note 3. Therefore, Lemma G can be proved by induction. It is true for $m = 2$. Assume that it is true for all $k < m$. Then

$$W^2 = A_1 \cdots A_m = A_1(A_2 \cdots A_m) = A_1 B,$$

where we have set $B = A_2 \cdots A_m$. Now by Lemma F, $(A_1, B) = 1$. Therefore, by Lemma B, $A_1$ and $B$ are squares: $A_1 = C_1^2$, $B = D^2 = A_2 \cdots A_m$. Since the last product has only $m - 1$ terms, by the inductive hypothesis each of the numbers $A_2, \cdots, A_m$ is a square, $A_i = C_i^2$, $2 \leq i \leq m$. This proves the lemma.

We now proceed to prove the nonsolvability of (2) in seven steps. The proof is by contradiction.

I. Assume that (2) has a solution $X, Y, W$, so that

$$X^4 + Y^4 = W^2. \tag{3}$$

Let $(X, Y) = H$, and

$$X = Hx, \qquad Y = Hy. \tag{4}$$

Then $(x, y) = 1$. Substituting (4) in (3), we get

$$W^2 = H^4(x^4 + y^4).$$

If we set $H^2 = T$, this becomes

$$W^2 = T^2(x^4 + y^4).$$

Therefore, $W^2$ is divisible by $T^2$, and it follows from Lemma A of Note 3 that $W$ is divisible by $T$. Hence

$$W = Tw = H^2 w. \tag{5}$$

Substituting for $X, Y, W$ from (4) and (5) in (3), we obtain

$$x^4 + y^4 = w^2,$$

where $(x, y) = 1$. We have, therefore, proved that if (2) has a solution, then it has a solution for which $(x, y) = 1$.

II. Now suppose that $x, y, w$ is a solution of (2), with $(x, y) = 1$. Then $x$ and $y$ cannot both be even. We shall now show that $x$ and $y$ cannot both be odd. For suppose that $x$, $y$ are both odd. Then $u = x^2$, $v = y^2$ are both odd (see Lemma C of Note 3). Since

$$u^2 + v^2 = w^2, \tag{6}$$

$u$, $v$, $w$ is a Pythagorean triple in which both $u$ and $v$ are odd. This contradicts Proposition D of Note 3, and proves the assertion. Hence one of $x$, $y$ is odd and the other even. Since $x$ and $y$ occur symmetrically in (2), we can suppose without loss of generality that $x$ is odd and $y$ is even. Therefore, $u = x^2$ is odd and $v = y^2$ is even.

III. Since $(x, y) = 1$, it follows from Lemma F by setting $A = y$ and $B = C = x$ that $(y, x^2) = 1$; moreover, putting $A = x^2$, $B = C = y$ in Lemma F, we get $(x^2, y^2) = 1$, Hence $(u, v) = 1$. Hence $(u, v, w) = 1$, and since $u$, $v$, $w$ is a solution of (6), $u$, $v$, $w$ is a relatively prime Pythagorean triple. The three numbers $u$, $v$, $w$ can therefore be written in the form

$$u = p^2 - q^2, \qquad v = 2pq, \qquad w = p^2 + q^2 \tag{7}$$

(see (8) of Note 3), where $(p, q) = 1$, one of $p$, $q$ is odd and the other even, and $p > q$.

IV. Since $u = x^2$, $x^2 = p^2 - q^2$, so that

$$x^2 + q^2 = p^2. \tag{8}$$

Since $(p, q) = 1$, $(p, q, x) = 1$; therefore, $x$, $q$, $p$ is a relatively prime Pythagorean triple. Hence by Proposition D of Note 3, one of $x$, $q$ is odd, the other even. Since $x$ is odd (see the end of II), $q$ must be even. Therefore, once more by (8) of Note 3,

$$x = a^2 - b^2, \qquad q = 2ab, \qquad p = a^2 + b^2, \tag{9}$$

where $(a, b) = 1$, $a > b$ and one of $a$, $b$ is odd, the other even.

V. From (7) and (9) it follows that

$$y^2 = v = 2pq = 4ab(a^2 + b^2).$$

Hence $y$ is even: $y = 2k$. Therefore,

$$4k^2 = y^2 = 4ab(a^2 + b^2),$$

so that

$$k^2 = ab(a^2 + b^2). \tag{10}$$

Since $(a, b) = 1$, setting $A = a$, $B = C = b$ in Lemma F, we get $(a, b^2) = 1$. Now suppose that $(a, a^2 + b^2) = d$, and $a = dg$, $a^2 + b^2 = dh$. Then $b^2 = dh - a^2 = dh - d^2g^2 = d(h - dg^2)$, i.e. $d$ is a common factor of $a$ and $b^2$. Therefore, $d = 1$, and

$$(a, a^2 + b^2) = 1.$$

Similarly,

$$(b, a^2 + b^2) = 1.$$

Hence we have shown that every pair of factors of $k^2$ (see (10)) is relatively prime.

Putting $m = 3$, $A_1 = a$, $A_2 = B$ and $A_3 = a^2 + b^2$ in Lemma G, we see that each of these is a square:

$$a = r^2, \qquad b = s^2, \qquad a^2 + b^2 = t^2. \tag{11}$$

We note that $(r, s) = 1$. For if $(r, s) = g$, then

$$g^2 = (r^2, s^2) = (a, b) = 1,$$

so that $g = 1$.

VI. From (11) it follows that

$$r^4 + s^4 = t^2. \tag{12}$$

Now from (9), $p = a^2 + b^2$. Since $a \geq 1$, $b \geq 1$, it follows that $p \geq 2$. Therefore, $p^2 > p$. From (7), $w = p^2 + q^2$. Since $p \geq 2$ and $q^2 > 0$, it follows that $w \geq 2$; hence $w^2 > w$. Since $w = p^2 + q^2 > p^2$, we have shown that

$$w^2 > w > p^2 > p = t^2. \tag{13}$$

VII. According to I–VI, therefore, if $x$, $y$, $w$ is a relatively prime solution of (2), there must be a relatively prime solution $r$, $s$, $t$ of (2) with $t^2 < w^2$. There must therefore be a solution of (2) for which $w^2 = 1^2$. Since there is no solution of $x^4 + y^4 = w^2 = 1^2$, we have arrived at a contradiction. This proves Fermat's theorem for $n = 4$.

**20** (p. 283). See {26}. For references to the papers of Dirichlet, Legendre, Lamé and Lebesgue mentioned in Footnote 7 (of Chapter XIII) see {2; vol. 2, p. 731, 734}, {8; vol. 3, p. 114}, {27}, {28} and {29}.

**21** (p. 285). If it should turn out that some odd primes are non-Fermat exponents, things would not be so simple; for then it would have to be determined whether $x^n + y^n = z^n$ is solvable for $n$ a product of non-Fermat primes.

We could also ask questions of a more special kind. For example, can $x^p + y^p = z^p$, $p$ a prime, have a solution $x$, $y$, $z$ such that $(x, p) = (y, p) = (z, p) = 1$, i.e. such that none of $x$, $y$, $z$ is divisible by $p$. At the present time it is known that there are no solutions of this kind for many primes $p$, but they may perhaps have other solutions (see {25} for the theorems of Wieferich and Mirimanoff).

**22** (p. 285). In 1836 Kummer published a famous paper on the theory of hypergeometric series. The Kummer convergence criterion (1835) is a standard theorem in the theory of infinite series. Even more well known is the Kummer surface, discovered by him in connection with work on infinite sets of lines in space (1864–1866). For an evaluation of this work see {30}.

**23** (p. 285). Kummer was wrong about the significance of his first papers on Fermat's problem. In 1834 he sent Dirichlet the manuscript of a paper in which he thought he had proved Fermat's conjecture. However, the proof contained an irreparable error. But Kummer persisted and with the aid of new and deep concepts was able to lay the foundation for a series of highly successful papers. See Hilbert's famous report {31} for a simpler and more modern exposition of Kummer's results. See also {32} and {28}.

**24** (p. 285). We cannot give here a more precise definition of the class of primes which Kummer proved were Fermat exponents, because the definition would entail a lengthy technical introduction involving the number of ideal classes of an algebraic number field, of the corresponding quotient field and Bernoulli numbers (for the latter see {33}). The calculation of the primes of Kummer's class depends on the calculation of the Bernoulli numbers, which are recursively defined, and so must be calculated one by one.

As a matter of fact, it is not easy to say what the least prime is for which it is not known whether or not it is a Fermat exponent. In 1955, T. L. Selfridge, C. A. Nicol and H. S. Vandiver showed by means of computations on the high speed computer SWAC in Los Angeles that Fermat's conjecture is correct for all odd primes $p < 4003$ (see {34}).

**25** (p. 285). This is due to the fact (remarked in Note 24) that the determination of the primes of Kummer's class depends on the available tables of Bernoulli numbers. As Landau pointed out in {25; p. 202} it is not even known yet whether the set of primes in Kummer's class is finite or infinite. Logically, there are three possibilities: 1) There are an infinite number of primes in Category A (Fermat exponents), but only a finite number (perhaps none except for $p = 2$; this is Fermat's conjecture) in Category B (non-Fermat exponents). 2) There are a finite number of primes in Category A, but an infinite number in Category B. 3) Both Category A and Category B contain an infinite number of primes.

**26** (p. 286). Kummer's theorem is known as the prime ideal factorization theorem. It was first stated and proved in full generality by Dedekind and independently in another form by Kummer's student Leopold Kronecker (1832–1891). The newer field mentioned in the text is algebraic number theory. A modern introduction can be found in {35}; for an older classical exposition see {36}; see also David Hilbert's (at that time) comprehensive report in {31}.

**27** (p. 287). See {37}.

**28** (p. 287). The notation sin, cos, tan was also introduced by Euler;

also the letter $e$ for the number 2.718 $\cdots$, the base of the natural logarithms. The functional notation $f(\cdots)$, where the dots stand for a variable, is also due to him (1735). See {9; vol. 3, pp. 637, 645, 855} and {38; pp. 249, 250}.

**29** (p. 287). See {39} and {38; p. 248}.

**30** (p. 288). Although Euler could turn seemingly trivial occurrences into interesting mathematical problems (on a boat trip he would analyze the wave motion and the motion of the ship), he showed little interest in Frederick's polished verses. Frederick went so far as to lampoon Euler as "un gros cyclope de géométrie" who, at the opera, was interested only in the acoustics, optics and spatial geometry of the hall. See the article in honor of Euler's 200th birthday in {40}. The same article (pp. 9–12) also touches on Euler's unfortunate excursion into philosophy occasioned by his personal difficulties with Maupertuis and Samuel König.

**31** (p. 288). Euler also obtained noteworthy results in the theory of infinite series, but by methods of reasoning which were faulty and lacked all the standards of modern rigor, as witness the following untenable equations:

$$1 - 3 + 5 - 7 + \cdots = 0,$$

$$\cdots + 1/a^2 + 1/a + 1 + a + a^2 + \cdots = 0,$$

etc. An uninitiated reader would certainly gather the wrong impression from the works of that time. One of the Bernoullis, Nicolaus (1687–1759), a nephew of Jakob and Johann Bernoulli, felt that the absence of rigor was unjustified and that the use of divergent series should be avoided. Curiously enough, he finally let himself be convinced by Euler (in an exchange of letters 1742–1743). The theory of divergent series is of course now a well established field of mathematics. See {9; vol. 3, pp. 666–669} and {38; p. 251}.

**32** (p. 290). At the Dresden Congress of German Scientists and Physicians, the mathematics division, in commemoration of Euler's 200th birthday, heard lectures on the various fields in which he was active. Many of the participants were amazed at his versatility. At last, one of the lecturers, the mathematician Alfred Pringsheim, began his lecture by saying that after all these talks on Euler the astronomer, Euler the shipbuilder, etc., he would like to discuss Euler the mathematician, since that was what he had been above all.

**33** (p. 290). The foremost mathematicians of the French school were Joseph Louis Lagrange (1736–1813), Pierre Simon Laplace (1749–1827) and Adrien Marie Legendre (1752–1833). For biographical details and evaluations of their work see Felix Klein's lectures (Legendre is discussed in detail, but Lagrange and Laplace are merely mentioned), {38}, {41} and {42}.

**34** (p. 290). We have not had occasion to discuss or even mention many of the mathematicians who appear in Felix Klein's *Vorlesungen über die Entwicklung der Mathematik im* 19. *Jahrhundert.*

**35** (p. 290). See the Postscript, Note 8 for the fantastic growth of modern mathematical productivity.

## *Chapter XIV*

# SPACE CURVATURE

It was only after serious reflection that I decided to add a chapter on space curvature to this book.

There are several reasons against its inclusion. Mathematics students do not study space curvature until they reach graduate school, by which time they have been prepared for it by a technical course in differential geometry. Would it then not be pointless even to introduce it to nonmathematicians?

On the other hand, this subject is so misunderstood by the general public, that it does seem worthwhile to make an effort to present a correct version.

However, the reader's lack of technical equipment, while a severe limitation, is not the main objection to discussing this problem. In many of the earlier chapters, a *complete* presentation would have required more extensive mathematical knowledge. Our tactic in such cases was to present the more difficult part of the material in a very general and necessarily vague way, but to attempt at the same time to give some idea of the nature of the problems involved.

But in this particular subject, there are special difficulties. First, we must understand how mathematical knowledge, particularly geometric knowledge, is acquired, both historically and individually. Then, we must examine the relation between this kind of knowledge and the absolute certainty of mathematical theorems, which we have not troubled the reader with, thus far, because there seemed no need to do so. Another troubling factor is that there are alternative ways of presenting this subject. Even though they are all technically valid, their multiplicity and lack of unity tend to cause confusion. Moreover, certain technical terms commonly used by mathematicians tend to be misunderstood by nonmathematicians. *Space curvature* is an eminent example of such a term.

It may prove useful to preface an explanation of this concept with a few remarks on nomenclature in mathematics. Some sciences have developed a systematic notation, such as, in chemistry, the formulas for compounds in terms of their elements and the structure of a molecule in terms of its atoms. Symbolic notation is often complicated, but it gives a compact characterization of very complex and varied laboratory products.

Mathematics has its own formal apparatus, as systematic as that of chemistry, and universally understood by anyone who has learned it. It is therefore often possible to understand a mathematical paper written in a foreign language simply because the *symbolism conveys the meaning*. *Verbal* designations of concepts are, of course, more difficult to decipher, since they may change from language to language.

Mathematicians must and do attach the greatest importance to clear definitions and to painstakingly rigorous statements and proofs of theorems. Whenever this rigor is relaxed, as it may be, during periods of accelerated discovery, it is sooner or later carefully restored. The introduction of suitable symbols and formulas is usually given careful consideration. But perhaps for that very reason, the choice of mathematical *terminology* has not always been felicitous; for mathematicians, concepts and their definitions are important, the words used to denote the concepts are not [**1**]. Carelessly chosen technical expressions might occasion some inconvenience, but in the splendid isolation which mathematicians enjoyed in the past, no other misfortunes were to be expected.

But times have changed and now men outside the field approach it without the necessary preparation and training; they tend to depend on the *word* rather than on the *concept*, and often think it unnecessary, and at times even find it impossible, to understand what is meant. The confusion caused by the term *space curvature*, a term which was coined in the previous century, could have been avoided by choosing a word other than *curvature*, but the term proved tenacious. The advent in this century of the theory of relativity and its popularization finally fixed the term so firmly in the public mind, that it is impossible to dislodge it. [It may be of interest at this point to note that the geometric concepts on which the general theory of relativity is based were developed by Riemann in 1854, in his Habilitationsvortrag (a lecture required of a beginning University Lecturer). This lecture made a deep impression on the aged Gauss, and he praised it very highly. But it did not arouse a great deal of attention outside the scientific world.]

The misleading connotation of the term space curvature is due to the fact that mathematicians use the term *curvature* in two essentially different ways. We shall try to distinguish these two ways by discussing *measurements* on various *surfaces* such as the plane, a sphere, etc.

Before doing so, however, let us first consider *how our geometric perceptions and concepts are formed.* Measurement played an essential role in this process. We learned on drawing paper how to measure the lengths of the three sides of a triangle $ABC$ with a ruler and the size of its angles with a protractor. If we verified by measuring the sides of two triangles $ABC$ and $A'B'C'$ that corresponding sides of the two triangles were equal, we knew that we could cut out one of the triangles and superimpose it on the other. (Corresponding angles of the two triangles would then have to be equal.) The fact that the triangles can be superimposed could be established in other ways; for example, by ascertaining by measurement that angle $A$ = angle $A'$, and $AB = A'B'$, $AC = A'C'$.[1] Moreover, two triangles which

[1] The condition is more complicated for two quadrilaterals; the equality of four

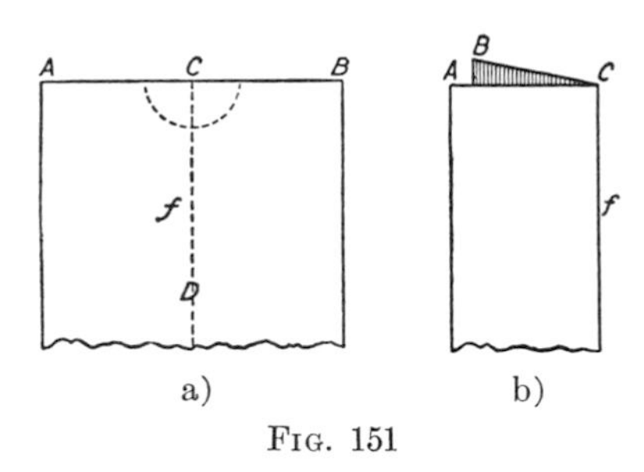


Fig. 151

can be superimposed on a third can be superimposed on each other. These experiments in measurement prepare us for the concept of *congruence* and the *congruence theorems* on triangles.

Many other concepts, simpler than that of congruence, which belongs to a fairly well developed stage of geometry, may be traced back to *experience*. Take one of the most primitive geometric concepts, that of the *straight line*. We may represent the straight line between two points by a taut string stretched between two points. To see that the string is really straight we sight along it (see Chapter II). In the same way, we sight along the edge of a table to see whether it is planed straight. We see, on the other hand, that a board stretched across a brook does not lie in a straight line, but is buckled in the middle by its weight. Again it is vision which establishes whether a wire is straight or bent.

We can also obtain a representation of a straight line by folding a piece of paper. Paper folding introduces still other concepts, e.g., the concept of a *right angle*. If $AB$ is a straight edge of a sheet of paper and we fold the paper so that $A$ is joined to $B$, the fold $f$ passes through the midpoint $C$ of the segment $AB$, and forms two right angles (angle $ACD$ and angle $BCD$ in Fig. 151a) at $C$. The concept of symmetry can also be illustrated by folding paper: For example, if we fold a square of paper along a diagonal, we see from the fact that the two parts cover each other that the diagonal is a line of symmetry of the square.

Other visual experiences can illustrate other geometric concepts. The concept of *parallelism* can be seen in railroad tracks lost in the distance on a broad plain. The two rails are nailed to ties of equal length, spaced at equal distances from each other. Sighting along each rail we see that they are straight. There are lines then which are straight visually, and which are at a constant distance from each other: we say the two rails are *parallel*. If the railway has several tracks, we confirm the fact that two rails parallel to a third are parallel to each other (i.e. parallelism is a transitive relation).

corresponding sides does not imply the congruence of the two quadrilaterals. However, if we call a side or angle of a quadrilateral an item, then the two figures are congruent if any five corresponding items are equal.

All of the above observations belong to the world of *experience*, and are comparable to such procedures as the weighing of two objects—we find that if they are equal in weight to a third object, they will balance each other on the scale. Similarly, if two correctly regulated watches are synchronized with a third watch, they will show the same time. However, there is a difference between experience with objects and clocks (part of the subject matter of physics) and geometric experience. The former has to do with physical concepts such as weight and time; while the latter has the barest of content, that which is relevant only to spatial relationships, abstracted from time and other possibly interesting qualities, such as temperature, color, or taste. Our primitive geometric concepts are based on the exploration of form alone.

On the other hand, geometric statements based on observation pertain to the world of experience just as the statements of any other natural science in which measurement and number are used. It would be more proper to call this aspect of geometry, a geometry of physics, or practical geometry.

But on a higher level of instruction in geometry we encounter an entirely different, nonempirical, approach. The student may expect that in advanced geometry he will be dealing with more complicated plane or solid figures than triangles or rectangles, yet the reverse is true. Advanced geometry returns to the simplest concepts, such as point, line, plane. The most primitive statements (for example: two distinct points determine a line which contains the two points) are singled out and called axioms. Then *logical conclusions* or theorems are derived from the axioms. In this way we obtain further statements, some of which may seem as obvious as the axioms. But the propositions must be proved; it must be shown that they follow logically from the axioms, or from propositions which have already been proved from the axioms.

This is, of course, Euclid's achievement. His axioms are the foundation on which his structure is erected systematically, stone by stone from the ground up. The procedure is always the same: each new proposition is proved by means of the axioms or propositions already proved. Even when the theory is later extended to include numbers, which makes it possible to define the length of a segment, the size of an angle, or the area of a surface, there is no change in the logical step-by-step procedure. New propositions in geometry are never obtained by observing, measuring, or by means of any other physical experiments, but only by logical deduction. (Diagrams used as teaching aids are of course not part of the proof.) The proposition that the perpendicular bisectors of the three sides of a triangle all pass through the same point, and the Pythagorean theorem, are established by *proof*, and not by empirical construction or measurement. In this manner, an immense structure—far beyond what is taught in the class-room—has been built over the centuries, and we can only be astonished by the number of propositions that have been discovered by mathematicians [2]. And all these propositions rest on the validity of the axioms—the primitive statements on which the whole structure is built. This geometry of the plane, based on Euclid's axioms, is known as *Euclidean geometry*.

What is the relation between this theoretical structure and the practical geometry of the natural sciences? Are we correct in assuming that the propositions of pure geometry are fully confirmed in the world of experience? First of all, it is not possible to speak of absolute exactitude in natural science, since all measurements, constructions and experiments involve a certain degree of error, no matter how refined the methods, the apparatus and the training and alertness of the observer may be. This inexactitude is encountered in all experimental verification of propositions involving even the simplest geometric concepts.

This inexactitude is obvious in the simplest of all figures, a point. A point drawn on paper with a pencil, seen through the microscope, becomes an extended heap of graphite. A point in the distance—a church steeple or a star—is in reality a large piece of metal or an enormous astronomical body.

The same inexactitude is inherent in experimental testing of propositions, such as the one which states that there is exactly one straight line through two points. Let us fix two points in the ground by means of two markers. We may then ask whether a cross on top of a distant mountain is on the straight line determined by the first two points. There will always be small deviations, depending on the observer, atmospheric conditions, the instruments, etc., as well as the fact that the cross, small as it may appear through the telescope, may actually be of considerable size.

The same holds for the concept of parallelism. We can verify whether opposite edges of a table are parallel by measuring the width of the table at several points; but the measurements will be exact only within certain limits. And so with the parallel rails of a railroad track. Similarly, if we draw a straight line on the ground and attempt to draw a line parallel to it through a point not on it, the result will be uncertain. The Euclidean axiom of parallels [3] which states that there is exactly one parallel (that is, a line which has no point in common with the first line and such that both lines are contained in a plane) to a line through a point not on the line—as well as all the other axioms—can have only a relative accuracy in the physical world of the natural sciences [4]. This is as true for geodetic measurements as for geometric constructions on paper. No matter how expensive and well-made the instruments, inaccuracies always occur and must be taken into account.

Accordingly, the theoretical structure of Euclidean geometry is an

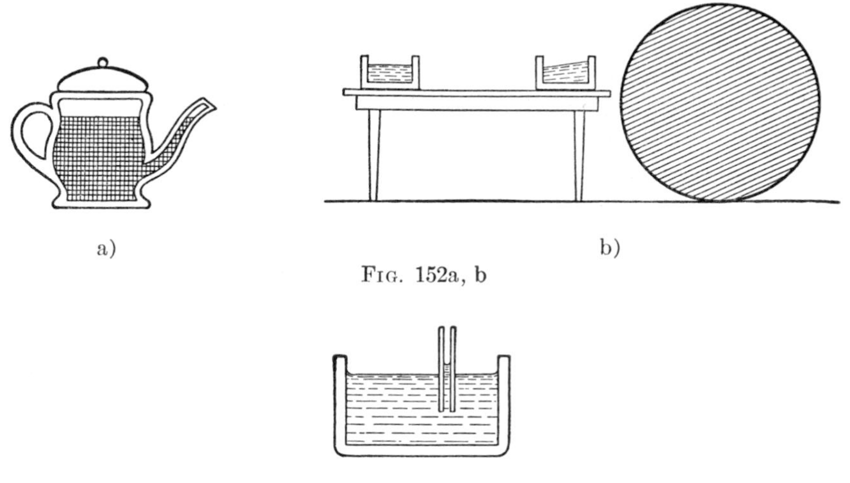


Fig. 152a, b

Fig. 152c

*idealization* of our inexact geometric perceptions. This idealization consists in claiming that certain propositions are precisely valid, but all our physical observations and measurements can never substantiate this degree of exactitude. Certain propositions of the theory are actually impossible to verify, e.g. the proposition that a segment on a straight line can be marked off repeatedly. This proposition concerns the infinite extent of a straight line, and by its very nature is outside the range of practical observation and construction [**5**]. The same is true of propositions which involve division of a straight line segment into arbitrarily small parts by repeated bisection; in practice, this procedure is rendered impossible as soon as the endpoints of a segment are so close together that they can no longer be differentiated [**6**]. And even for those propositions of Euclidean geometry which permit a comparison with the real world, the agreement between theory and practice holds only within certain limits.

This is also true of any other scientific theory which must take into account unavoidable inaccuracies in actual observations. For example, take a vessel, such as a pail, a bowl, a rectangular tank for tropical fish, or a pitcher, and fill it with water. According to Archimedes' law on the equilibrium of liquids, the surface of the water will be parallel to the ground, that is, horizontal. If we pour tea or coffee into a pot, the liquid in the pot will be at the same level in the pot as in the spout, no matter what the shape of the spout (Fig. 152a). But these observations are always made with a margin of error, and so we become aware that physical laws as well can lay no claim to absolute accuracy. As a matter of fact, there are cases in which definite deviations occur, so that the relevant theory has to be modified in certain respects to account for these deviations. For example, the attraction of a massive lead ball may cause the surface of the water to deviate from the horizontal position (Fig. 152b); or capillary attraction may cause the liquid to rise a little at the edge of a vessel, or in an immersed narrow tube (Fig. 152c). The same limitations hold in every other scientific field. In the process of burning, according to a long standing chemical law, the weight of the ash plus other products of the oxidation process, including the gases given off, is equal to that of the burned matter plus the oxygen used in the process. But the weighing process, no matter how refined, has its limits of accuracy. And when the law of conservation of matter is seen to be subject to certain modifications in special cases (e.g., radioactive phenomena), it becomes necessary to revise the theory.

Spatial experience, that is, practial geometry, is also part of the phenomenal world. If spatial experience is compared with the propositions of Euclidean geometry, only approximate agreement is achieved. But if the difference between observation and theory is so small that it can be accounted for by the unavoidable inaccuracies involved in each measurement —no matter how fine the instruments—then we say that Euclidean geometry agrees with experience within certain limits of accuracy.

But we must also consider the possibility that, because of refined methods or better instruments, even very small differences between the Euclidean propositions and our measurements may *not* always remain within the permissible margins of error. The deviations would then be similar to those from the law of equilibrium of fluids or the conservation of matter. We could not in that event regard Euclidean geometry as a faithful representation of physical space, but would have to credit it with merely approximate validity. Indeed, it may be necessary as a result of especially fine measurements to revise it or to replace it. Gauss had seriously considered this possibility at the beginning of the nineteenth century (see Chapter IX).

What would be the significance of a revision or replacement of Euclidean geometry? Would Euclidean geometry no longer have mathematical certainty? What about its propositions, such as the Pythagorean theorem and all its consequences, which are two thousand years old? Would they all have to be discarded?

As it turns out, nothing as drastic as this is necessary. The validity of Euclidean geometry rests on the fact that is is a deductive system derived from a set of primitive propositions or axioms. Its mathematical certainty is completely independent of the results of experiments carried out in the physical world. Nevertheless, its propositions do hold experimentally to a considerable extent. Drawings on the draughting table, constructions of architects and engineers, geodetic measurements on the surface of the earth, and astronomical observations show that Euclidean geometry is in substantial agreement with physical experience. The agreement is indeed such that although our methods of measurement have been increasingly refined in the course of centuries, we continue to depend on Euclidean geometry in such practical applications. This validity would not change even if more refined measurements should indicate a deviation between theory and practice. In a broad range of practical applications, the propositions of Euclidean geometry could, and would as before, meet all the demands of accuracy, and a suitably revised theory would be needed only in those highly special cases where fine differences between the two theories were crucial. This situation is analogous to that of the surface of a liquid at rest: in many cases—if we do not come too close to the walls of the vessel—capillary action can be disregarded; again, in chemical research, the law of the conservation of matter continues to hold as long as the deviations due to radioactive phenomena are negligible.

It behooves us to examine the position of a purely mathematical theory in the framework of physical investigation. A mathematical theory has certain basic assumptions, whose logical consequences are derived by means of long chains of deductions. It is assumed that the axioms are completely valid. In the development of a theory, all the proofs are examined for gaps, to make sure the propositions follow rigorously from the axioms. In the application of such a theory to a branch of natural science, or to a practical physical procedure, it is then assumed that *if* the axioms of the mathematical theory apply with sufficient accuracy, *then* so do all the further propositions developed in the theory.

In astronomy, for instance, Newton's law of gravitation states that the attraction of two astronomical bodies is inversely proportional to the square of the distance between them (that is, if $m'$ and $m''$ are the masses of the two bodies and $r$ is the distance between them, then the force of attraction between them is $m'm''/r^2$). All theoretical calculations in celestial mechanics are based on this law (and on Newton's other laws). The calculations are purely mathematical: they yield the logical consequences of the law of gravitation [7]. The task of astronomers is to compare the theoretically calculated positions of astronomical bodies with their observed positions. It was the wonderful agreement between the predicted and the actual orbits of the planets, and other phenomena, which assured the long reign of Newton's law of gravitation in celestial mechanics.[2]

[2] Because of certain deviations in the motion of the planet Mercury, the astronomer von Seeliger suggested that better agreement with observation might be obtained by replacing the Newtonian force $m'm''/r^2$ with one of the form $m'm''/r^c$, where $c$ is slightly less than 2. One would then have to check whether calculations based on the new law agreed not only with the observed motion of Mercury but also with that of the other celestial bodies. In the theory of relativity, the motion of Mercury is deduced from the new relativistic law of gravitation, which is based on very profound changes in our conception of space, and not from trivial changes in the Newtonian force as above.

Let us take another example, this time from the theory of heredity. One may cross different types of the same species of plant, say a red and a white type. One then investigates subsequent generations to compare the results of the crosses with each other as well as with the original types. According to Gregor Mendel (1822–1884), certain rules govern the average distribution of descendants among the various types. There are at hand numerous examples of crossings of plant and animal types. If equally fertile types, undisturbed by external influence, are crossed, purely mathematical calculations on the basis of the Mendelian laws predict the proportions in which the various types will occur from generation to generation and the ultimate distribution of types [**8**]. Here too mathematics is concerned only with the problem of drawing conclusions from certain assumptions. The problem of comparing these predictions with what is actually observed in particular cases is another matter. If there were no agreement, we would have to conclude that Mendel's assumptions were not valid for the cases considered.

Thus there is a *division of labor* in all the sciences which use mathematical tools. On the one hand, we have a mathematical theory characterized by axioms or laws, the premises from which strictly logical deductions are drawn; on the other, the data of experiments and observations, which must be compared with the theoretically predicted values.[3] If there is no agreement, or the discrepancies are greater than the unavoidable experimental inaccuracies, further investigation may lead to a revised or even a new theory which better describes the observed phenomena.

In the natural sciences, it often happens that the development of a general law begins with a conjecture on the part of an investigator, whose problem then is to determine the range of validity of the conjecture. In many cases this can be done only by deriving the consequences of the hypothesis mathematically, in order to compare them with experience. Hence one is often forced to develop a mathematical theory on the basis of a mere hypothesis. The *physical suitability* of the mathematical theory is a problem in itself, and in no way affects its mathematical consistency. For example, the ring of Saturn stimulated mathematical investigations to determine whether, on the basis of Newton's law of gravitation, a rigid ring body can maintain its equilibrium while rotating about a body at its center. The fact that the ring of Saturn is not a single large rigid solid ring,

[3] Both are, of course, indispensable to the development of the sciences. The purely mathematical development of a theory can solve many difficult problems, as in celestial mechanics, to which many great mathematicians like Laplace, Gauss and Poincaré devoted intensive research. But physical experimentation and intuition are necessary to give insight into the nature of the objects dealt with and to provide clues as to the most suitable theory.

but rather a host of small bodies which fill up a ring-shaped flat disk, has nothing to do with the question of the mathematical correctness of the theory [9].

It must always be kept in mind, also, that one scientific problem may lead to several hypotheses. Different basic assumptions will then yield different mathematical theories, and only a comparison with observation will decide which theory corresponds most closely to the data at hand. Thus, the hypothesis that the molecules of a gas are infinitely small elastic spheres, which collide at enormous speeds with each other and the walls of the vessel in which the gas is contained, led to a kinetic theory of gases which explained much of the experimental data on pressure, temperature, etc. A second theory, which assumed that the elastic spheres had a finite diameter, explained still other phenomena in the behavior of a gas [10]. Other examples of rival or revised theories, which thereby did not lose their *mathematical* validity, are Wilhelm Weber's law of electromagnetism, the corpuscular and wave theories of light, and Kepler's theory of elliptic planetary orbits which replaced the theory of circular orbits (see also Footnote 2).

Returning to geometry, it is clear that the problem of deciding which propositions are valid in the physical world is no different from the analogous problem in the natural sciences. Of course, since classical antiquity, Euclidean geometry has agreed very nicely with the results of constructions and measurements in practical geometry. But as we have pointed out refined measurements may yield deviations from the theory large enough to require a new or revised theory. It is indeed possible first to develop alternative geometries and then to see which theory is closest to experience.

This was undertaken long ago. An alternative to Euclidean geometry was developed and called *non-Euclidean geometry*,[4] and careful measurements for distinguishing between the two theories experimentally were proposed.

What is *non-Euclidean* geometry? Like Euclidean geometry, it is a purely mathematical theory in which purely logical deductions are rigorously proved from certain axioms. The only difference lies in the axioms. By contradicting one or more of the axioms of Euclidean geometry (each axiom has several contradictories) new propositions can be obtained from the new set of axioms, and the result will be a theory different from Euclidean geometry. Thus it is possible to have not one but many non-Euclidean geometries, depending on the changes made in the axioms.

However, the term *non-Euclidean geometry* usually refers to the geometry

[4] We refer here to the oldest of the non-Euclidean geometries. For this reason, we shall refer to it as the classical non-Euclidean geometry, to distinguish it from another non-Euclidean geometry, which we shall call the romantic non-Euclidean geometry and will discuss later [11].

obtained by replacing a certain Euclidean axiom by one of its contradictories, retaining all the others unchanged. Which axiom is it? Is there one axiom in particular which causes most difficulty when tested?

The fact is that several of Euclid's postulates are sources of difficulty, and therefore, there are many axioms which one might be inclined to change. Among these there is one, the axiom of parallels, which mathematicians first thought of changing. The reason for this is historical [**12**]. In any case, the first or classical non-Euclidean geometry differed from Euclidean geometry only in contradicting the axiom of parallels.

The Euclidean axiom of parallels states that if $g$ is a straight line in the plane and $P$ is a point not on $g$, then there is precisely one straight line $h$ in the plane containing $P$ and not meeting $g$. This proposition cannot be verified experimentally, since we cannot follow a straight line to infinity. It is an unprovable idealization. We would, therefore, be justified in replacing this axiom with one which asserted that there is more than one straight line containing $P$ and not meeting $g$ [**13**].

This is the axiom which replaces the Euclidean axiom of parallels in the oldest or classical non-Euclidean geometry. This second geometry is, like the first, a self-contained structure built upon rigorous, logical deductions. Its mathematical certainty—which has nothing to do with its applicability—is the same as that of Euclidean geometry. The only difference is that the propositions of the two geometries are different.

Classical non-Euclidean geometry was developed independently more than a hundred years ago by Nikolai Ivanowitsch Lobatschefskij (1793–1856), Johann Bolyai (1802–1860) and Gauss.[5]

But it was Gauss who thought of comparing both theories experimentally. His opportunity came during the geodetic survey of Hannover in 1821–1841. We must remember that as a rule the axioms of a geometry are not susceptible to experimental verification. But there may be other propositions of the theory, which are more suited to this purpose.[6] In this context, the proposition of greatest interest is the one concerning the sum of the angles of a triangle. In Euclidean geometry, this sum is always two right

[5] For Gauss see Chapter IX. Lobatschefskij and Bolyai first published their results between 1827 and 1832, whereas Gauss, who had had a clear insight into the possibility of a non-Euclidean geometry a generation before, published nothing on this subject during his lifetime. For a detailed account, including a history of the subject, see {1}.

[6] For instance, it would be impossible to compare Newton's law of gravitation with an alternative law directly, since it is not possible to isolate two bodies from all others which act on them. It is possible, however, to compare the motion of, say, the planet Mercury predicted by the two laws, and so arrive at an indirect verification.

angles, that is 180°. In non-Euclidean geometry this sum is always less than 180°, but varies with the size of the triangle, and approaches 180° as the triangle becomes smaller.

Gauss used this fact as a starting point for comparing the two theories. An especially large triangle in the Hannover survey was chosen to test the propositions on the sum of the angles of a triangle. The result was a value so closely approximating 180° that the difference remained within the unavoidable margin of error. The experiment thus gave no reason for departing from the assumptions of Euclidean geometry insofar as measurements of the size used in this survey were concerned. Of course the question remained open for larger scale measurements.

A comparison of Euclidean geometry with non-Euclidean geometry shows that, in addition to the propositions on the sum of angles of a triangle, there are many other propositions which differ from each other significantly. Many formulas, such as those for solving triangles, computing areas and volumes, etc. are different in non-Euclidean geometry (although for small magnitudes the differences are negligible in practice), and confirm the natural expectation that different axiom systems imply different sets of propositions.

This is of course true for other changes in the Euclidean axioms. As we mentioned, there are some axioms, such as those which express the fact that straight lines are infinite in extent, which cannot pretend to physical validity. As we said, it is theoretically possible to obtain non-Euclidean geometries quite different from the classical one. One of these, which we shall temporarily call the *romantic* non-Euclidean geometry (see Footnote 4 and [**11**]), is especially noteworthy. In this geometry, there is no parallel line through a point $P$ not on the straight line $g$. Moreover, the straight lines are *not* infinite but have a finite length (although this may be extremely large) [**14**]. This peculiarity of the theory may justify the use of the term *romantic*. The difference between the romantic and Euclidean geometries is again a function of the size of the figure and is small for relatively small distances. It also contains many propositions different from those of Euclidean geometry. But in contrast to the classical non-Euclidean geometry, the sum of the angles of a triangle is now larger than 180° (and the excess over 180° is smaller the smaller the triangle). One might, therefore, call the romantic non-Euclidean geometry a non-Euclidean geometry of *positive type*, and the classical non-Euclidean geometry one of *negative type*. This terminology has a more scientific flavor than the labels classical and romantic.

But the sum of the angles of a triangle is only *one* of the many differences between non-Euclidean and Euclidean geometries. The formulas for other quantities, such as lengths, areas and volumes are also different. Another difference is in the measure of curvature, which we began with, and shall return to later.

We have not mentioned space curvature till now, and it may therefore seem that we have not yet reached the real subject of this chapter. But actually, we have attained our goal without using this confusing term. We can now explain how this terminology arose, and how, in particular, the *measure of curvature* came to express the difference between the Euclidean and non-Euclidean geometries.

We have already mentioned that the difference between the non-Euclidean and Euclidean geometries varies with the size of the figures considered, and that the difference decreases with the magnitude of the figures. The magnitude at which deviations become appreciable depends on the quantity measured: there are quantities which require extremely large magnitudes or extremely fine measurements before they show a deviation (for example, in the measurement of angles), and there are other quantities for which the deviation is significant in the range of less extreme magnitudes. Accordingly, in verifying non-Euclidean geometries experimentally, or in comparing them with respect to their deviation from Euclidean geometry, it is not only the type of theory—positive or negative—which is relevant, but also the critical magnitudes at which appreciable deviations begin to occur. If it were not for its awkwardness, one might use the term *measure of non-Euclideanness.*

There is another matter to consider: How can one visualize a non-Euclidean geometry, either of the classical or romantic sort? Spatial intuition is not of much help, since the propositions of Euclidean geometry are physically valid to a great degree of accuracy, and what we want to visualize are the cases in which the deviations are appreciable. Is there some way of constructing geometric models of non-Euclidean geometries, which will allow us to picture the differences? Actually, it is possible, if we agree to limit ourselves to plane, that is, two-dimensional geometries, to construct models of non-Euclidean plane geometries on *curved surfaces.*

Curved surfaces were discussed in Chapter II. We shall now consider *measurements* on these surfaces. One of these surfaces, the *pseudo-sphere* (see Plate IV, pictures 6 and 7, and Fig. 154) was mentioned in passing in Chapter II, as one of many types of surfaces. This surface, however, is intimately connected with the classical non-Euclidean geometry (negative type). We shall see that there is also a curved surface model for the romantic non-Euclidean geometry (positive type).

But first, let us clarify the concept of a curved surface. We assume that the surfaces are situated or imbedded in Euclidean three-dimensional space.

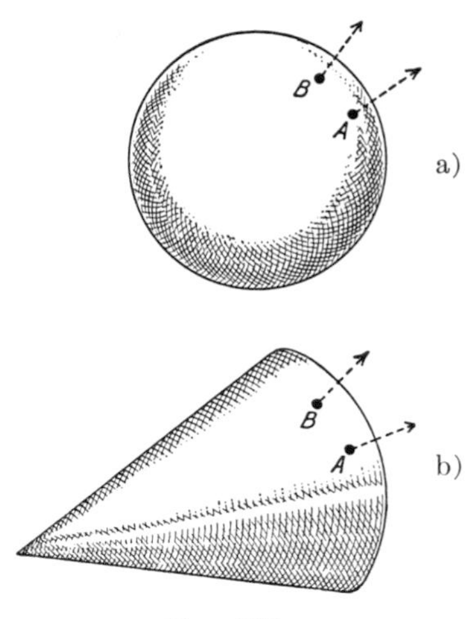


FIG. 153

What properties distinguish the curved surfaces from the plane or flat surfaces?

A simple example of a curved surface is a piece of the surface of a sphere, say a piece of the surface of the earth. We can erect a perpendicular or normal at every point of the spherical surface, but the direction of the normal will change from point to point. For example, we cannot see the same star through a telescope in Athens as we can in Bamberg (see Fig. 153a), if both are directed normal to the surface of the earth. This shows that the surface of the earth is neither a plane nor a piece of a plane. When we say that a spherical surface is curved, what we mean is that the direction of the normal varies from point to point on the surface. Thus, the property of a surface of being either curved or flat (plane) clearly depends on the possibility of drawing normals to the surface into the surrounding three-dimensional space.

The same is true of the pseudo-sphere: normals erected at various points of this surface will have different directions. A curved surface may therefore be distinguished from a plane or flat surface by the fact that all the normals to the plane have the same direction.

These examples show that the property of being curved or non-curved is an *imbedding property*, that is, it expresses a relation between the surface and the space in which it is imbedded or which surrounds it. The reason is that the curvedness of the surface is measured by drawing normals to the surface, and in order to draw normals to the surface it is necessary to have something outside the surface into which to draw them, that is, a surrounding space.

In addition to imbedding properties, such as curvature, surfaces also have *inner* properties, which depend only on the surface and not on the space in which it is imbedded. It is with inner properties that we are concerned when we make measurements, such as land surveys, on the surface. To carry out such measurements, we must imagine ourselves as living entirely on such a surface, or on part of it, and must disregard the surrounding space. For example, people living on the surface of a sphere would have two-dimensional bodies which fit on the surface and do not stick out into the surrounding three-dimensional space. Such people would have to carry out all their measurements on the surface of the sphere. This is roughly analogous to the existence of a heavy fog which obscures all relationships to the surrounding three-dimensional space [**15**]. In other words, we must ask ourselves the following question: If we lived on such a surface, how would the computational formulas for land measurements change in comparison with the formulas of Euclidean geometry? These changes will of course vary with the surface chosen. But for us the significant thing is that for each two-dimensional non-Euclidean space there is a curved surface imbedded in three-dimensional Euclidean space, on which measurements agree with the corresponding non-Euclidean formulas.

Which surfaces are related to non-Euclidean geometries? How far does the similarity extend? Are there surfaces which correspond, as far as measurements are concerned, to the classical (negative) and the romantic (positive) non-Euclidean geometries?

The third question is to be answered in the affirmative, provided only that a bounded area of the curved surface is used as a model for measurements in a bounded portion of the non-Euclidean plane. For example, the pseudo-sphere (Fig. 154) is a surface model for the classical non-Euclidean geometry if the geodesics (see Chapter II) of the surface are chosen as

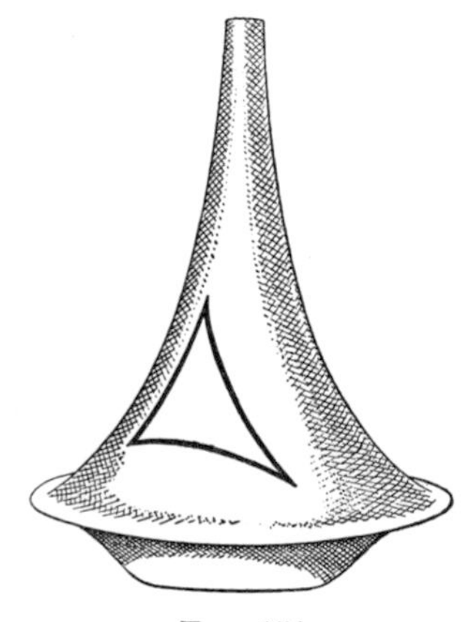

Fig. 154

the straight lines. Exactly the same formulas hold for measurements on a bounded portion of this surface as for the classical non-Euclidean geometry. For instance, on this surface the sum of the angles of a triangle formed by three geodesics is always less than 180°, and the deviation from 180° decreases with the size of the triangle.[7] This then is a model of the negative non-Euclidean geometry, provided the conditions stated above are adhered to.

It is even simpler to construct a surface model for the romantic (positive) non-Euclidean plane geometry, provided similar conditions are imposed. Any sphere, or a piece of a sphere which is not too large, with the geodesics (in this case, great circles) as straight lines, will do as a model.[8] It is known from spherical trigonometry that on a sphere the sum of the angles of a triangle is greater than 180°, and that the excess decreases with the size of the triangle. For sufficiently small triangles the differences between the formulas for spherical and plane Euclidean geometry become negligible, as we know from experience. The magnitude of the deviation from Euclidean plane geometry therefore depends essentially on the size of the sphere. The computations for a triangle whose great circles are 20 feet long on a sphere 200 feet in diameter will show marked deviations from the corresponding computations in the Euclidean plane; while the deviation for a triangle whose sides are also 20 feet long, but which now lies on a larger sphere, say 2000 feet in diameter, will be substantially smaller. And if a triangle with sides 20 feet long is constructed on a sphere the size of the earth, the great circle sides of the triangle will not be distinguishable from straight-line segments, and the formulas of plane Euclidean geometry will be completely accurate for this triangle. A number which decreases as the radius of a sphere increases might therefore be used as the measure of the deviation from Euclidean geometry [**17**].

It is clear that there is a connection between curvature and the positive non-Euclidean geometry: the smaller the radius of the sphere, the greater the difference in the formulas of the two geometries; the smaller the radius of the sphere, the more pronounced its curvature.

But, on the other hand, the curvature of a sphere (or any other surface) is an imbedding property, while measurements on the surface involve only inner properties. Thus, the problem of finding valid formulas for measurements is a problem intrinsic to the surface itself, and must be sharply distinguished from the concept of curvature.

[7] This is intuitively obvious. A very small piece of a curved surface is indistinguishable from a plane, its geodesics are indistinguishable from straight line segments and its triangles from plane triangles.

[8] It is essential that the part of a sphere chosen be small enough so that it contains no semi-circle of a great circle, i.e., so that it does not contain a pair of antipodal points [**16**].

We cannot undertake a complete analysis of formulas having to do with measurements on surfaces. So far, we have mentioned only the proposition concerning the sum of the angles of a triangle. It will be instructive to consider another proposition having to do with measurement on a surface.

We shall again compare a sphere with a plane, both imbedded in three-dimensional space. We again carry out our constructions without using the imbedding space. Suppose the plane is the surface of a table. We mark a point on the table, and draw a circle of radius 10 inches with the point as center. The circumference of the circle is then $2\pi r$, or 62.83 inches, correct to two decimals.

Now let us do the same on the surface of a sphere. For instance, take a large stone ball 100 inches in radius, mark a point on its surface, and proceed on the surface (along great circles through the point) of the ball 10 inches in all possible directions. The endpoints of these paths again form a circle, whose circumference is smaller than that of the circle constructed on the plane table top. It is easily calculated [**18**] to be 62.73 inches, that is, one tenth of an inch less than the circumference of the circle on the plane table top. The difference becomes much more pronounced as the radius of the sphere is decreased. For instance, if in the preceding example the radius of the sphere is reduced by half, but the radius of the circle is left unchanged, the circumference of the circle will now be 62.41 inches. The difference between this figure and the one obtained on the table top is more than .4 inches.

Let us now consider larger magnitudes. It would be possible to show that the surface of the earth is not a plane even if a continuous thick fog were to obscure the stars, that is, it could be shown by measurements confined to the surface of the earth. If from a point on the surface of a sphere the size of the earth arcs of great circles are drawn in all directions a distance of 62.137 miles, the endpoints of these arcs will lie on a circle whose circumference is 28.43 yards less than it would be on a plane [**19**]. Thus, land surveys on the earth must be carried out by means of formulas other than those which hold for a plane [**20**]. The difference of 28.43 yards between the circumference of a circle in the plane and of the same circle on a sphere can be regarded as a measure of the difference between measurement in the plane and on a sphere. Since the circumference on a sphere is smaller than the corresponding circumference in the plane, we may speak of a contraction of the spherical surface as compared with the plane. The number 28.43 could be used as a measure of the contraction, which decreases as the radius of the sphere increases.

Similar measurements can be made on other surfaces (see Chapter II for examples of surfaces). Again all constructions are confined to the surface. Starting with a point on the surface, paths of equal length are marked off in all directions along the geodesics through the point, and the curve formed by the endpoints of all these paths is then considered. The length of this curve is then compared with the circumference of the corresponding circle in the plane [**21**]. Does contraction take place on surfaces other than a sphere? Or does the opposite occur?

In fact, the opposite does occur on the surface of the pseudosphere: the circumference of the curve formed by the endpoints of paths of prescribed length all issuing from a fixed point is *larger* than the corresponding circumference in the plane [**22**].

Returning now to the distinction between curvature as an imbedding property and measurement on the surface as an intrinsic property, we shall give another, perhaps clearer, example to illustrate the difference. A sheet of paper rolled into a cone represents a curved surface, since the normals to the surface (see Fig. 153b) vary in direction. However, measurements on a cone are exactly the same as those on a plane. For, bending a flat sheet of paper into a cone introduces no change in the size of angles and lengths of paths, straight or curved. If the surface of the earth were a large cone, surveyors would use exactly the same formulas as those used on a plane. The sum of the angles of every triangle on a cone is 180°; there is no magnification or contraction as on a spherical or pseudo-spherical surface. This example shows that, as far as measurement is concerned, deviations from the Euclidean model do not occur solely because of the presence of curvature.

The tempation to interchange these two problems, or to combine them, instead of making a clear distinction between them, is of course very great, because the totality of properties of a given surface stand in a certain reciprocal relation to each other. If the radius of a sphere is small, its normals change direction quickly, and so the curvature of the sphere is large; at the same time there is a large contraction in the circumferences of circles, and a marked excess over 180° in the sum of the angles of even small triangles. A small sphere is, therefore, not only sharply curved, but also has a large non-Euclidean index.[9] If $R$ is the radius of a sphere, $1/R$ increases as the radius decreases. Hence $1/R$ can be used as a measure not only of the curvature, but also of the deviation from the Euclidean model. Then the proposition that the deviation of a sphere of radius $R$ imbedded in Euclidean space, that is, a sphere with curvature $1/R$, from the Euclidean model increases with the curvature is clearly true.

But this proposition, while true, is irrelevant to our present interest in curved surfaces, particularly to the sphere and pseudo-sphere. Our interest is due to their use as models for non-Euclidean geometries. Furthermore,

[9] The same is true for the relation between curvature and intrinsic measurements on other surfaces, in particular, the pseudo-sphere [**23**].

they are models which emphasize the difference between the familiar Euclidean plane geometry and non-Euclidean plane geometry, and are models which enable us to visualize non-Euclidean geometry. In using the models we must be careful, however, to use the purely intrinsic term *non-Euclidean index*, which measures the deviation from the Euclidean plane, and not the term *curvature*, an imbedding property, even though both are measured by the same number. The confusion in the subject we mentioned at the beginning of the chapter, and which we hope has now been cleared up, is due to the incorrect use of the term space curvature instead of non-Euclidean index.

We must now extend our discussion to three-dimensional non-Euclidean geometries. This was our original intent, but we considered two-dimensional geometries first in order to obtain visual models. Returning now to the three-dimensional problem, we ask whether Euclidean geometry is valid for the physical space of our experience. The problem now concerns intrinsic measurements in a three-dimensional space, whereas previously it concerned only intrinsic measurements in a two-dimensional space. Another difference is that the three-dimensional space of experience is not imbedded in a higher-dimensional space. However, the problem of determining whether Euclidean geometry or some non-Euclidean geometry is valid in space is similar to the two-dimensional problem discussed above. Again we ask whether certain contraction phenomena occur.

In order to test this, we must again imagine equal distances, say 100 miles, marked off in all directions in *space*. If the space is Euclidean, the endpoints of the segments will lie on the surface of a sphere whose surface area is given by the formula $4\pi r^2$, where $r$ is the radius of the sphere, in this case 100. But if measurement of the area of the surface [**24**] were to yield a smaller value, we would again have a contraction, and the size of the difference could again be used as the non-Euclidean index [**25**]. Euclidean geometry would then have to be replaced with a suitably modified geometry. We note, however, that actual measurements made in space show the non-Euclidean index to be so small that it becomes noticeable only for distances far greater than 100 miles.

Why is the meaningfulness of this problem so often denied? The reason would seem to be that in the preceding century, the term *curvature index* had unfortunately made its way into the language, rather than *non-Euclidean index*, or *contraction index*. The terminology alone caused the confusion. The difficulty is clear. If three-dimensional space is curved, it must be imbedded in a higher-dimensional space, and if this is not the case, the term has no meaning, since curvature is an imbedding property [**26**]. However, the non-Euclidean index is an intrinsic property, and is perfectly meaningful in the absence of imbedding. Hence, everything we have said in discussing the problem of space curvature indicates that it would be preferable to speak of a deviation from Euclidean geometry and to avoid the term space curvature.

In retrospect we may add that the use of surface models for non-Euclidean geometries in the two-dimensional case has two drawbacks. First, measurements on a surface model are a poor substitute for measurements in the space itself, particularly because of the limitation to small regions. Secondly, expressions which are meaningful only on surface models are bound to cause confusion when they are carried over to the corresponding non-Euclidean theory. Our presentation of three-dimensional geometry has avoided some of these difficulties, because it is not possible to use three-dimensional models, which would have to be imbedded in a space of more than three dimensions [**27**]. In avoiding the term space curvature, we also escape the danger of incorrectly extending to a non-Euclidean geometry of space the properties of an approximate representation, which do not hold in the non-Euclidean space.

There is one property of space, its *homogeneity*, which we have not yet mentioned. The homogeneity of space means that it has the same properties at every point. This implies, for instance, that if a construction is carried out at one point in space, it can also be carried out at every other point in exactly the same way. The same measurements which a Roman cohort used for constructing a camp in Africa can be used in Scotland. The construction of the Eiffel tower in Paris can be copied exactly in Chicago or Sidney. The geometric laws governing shadows are the same on the moons of Jupiter, in our solar eclipses, and under a living room lamp. This is certainly not true of other areas of experience. If a pendulum is moved from the harbor of Archangel to the high plains of Peru, its rate of oscillation will decrease significantly within 24 hours. Other examples are the deviations in the movements of a magnetic needle, the ionization phenomena of the atmosphere, the incidence of cosmic rays, etc., all of which vary with location.

The physical experience of homogeneity is reproduced in pure geometry, plane as well as solid, by the fact that no preferred points or directions appear in any of its propositions. In pure geometry, moreover, the property of homogeneity is completely independent of physical measurement. This is true both in the Euclidean and non-Euclidean geometries. For example, on the surface of a sphere (the model for the romantic non-Euclidean geometry), there are no preferred points or directions [**28**].

Since the nature of a concept becomes clearer by considering examples in which it does not hold, we shall give some instances of non-homogeneity. These will be restricted to two-dimensional cases for simplicity. One example is the surface of the earth, which is flattened at the poles. We recall that this affects the measurement of *large* areas of land in the vicinity of the equator, and introduces certain deviations in comparison with measurements in the northern or southern latitudes. There are also other surfaces, such as the triaxial ellipsoid, or the surfaces of Plate I, pictures 3–6, on which the origin and the initial direction of a construction determine its further course. The sum of the angles of a triangle would differ with the location of the triangle; so would the contraction index and similar measurements. The non-Euclidean index would thus be a function of position. These are models of non-homogeneous non-Euclidean two-dimensional geometries, which are much more general than the homogeneous classical and romantic non-Euclidean geometries.

There are also non-homogeneous three-dimensional non-Euclidean geometries, and a natural question would be whether the geometry of physical space is of the non-homogeneous non-Euclidean variety. We must content ourselves at this point with merely stating that this eventuality cannot be excluded, although its verification would require extremely delicate measurements.

The foundations for a general theory of such geometries were laid by Riemann in the middle of the last century in his introductory lecture at Göttingen. Riemann's work was in some respects foreshadowed by Gauss' famous paper on surfaces published thirty years before. But Riemann's work was much more general and abstract than Gauss', and not confined to two dimensions.

Riemannian geometry is a very general $n$-dimensional non-Euclidean geometry (see Chapter VI for a discussion of dimension). To the non-mathematician, this freedom from a definite number of dimensions may be an uncomfortable abstraction, but Riemann's lecture was of the utmost significance in the development of mathematics.[10]

Now, due to a development in the history of science, four-dimensional space achieved a certain particular significance. The reason for this is of course no longer a matter of pure mathematics, but involves physical considerations, which are not entirely geometric. This turn of events was due to the theory of relativity. In addition to the three spatial coordinates used to determine the position of a point, it introduced time as a fourth coordinate. The four-dimensional space-time (see Chapter VI) is a Riemannian non-homogeneous geometry with a variable non-Euclidean index [29]. But physical theories are outside our scope, and these remarks must suffice. Nevertheless, Riemann himself had in mind the application of his geometric theory to the physical world.

Just as it is impossible to realize the significance of a composer by reading

[10] Many mathematical relations and concepts become completely clear only when they are stated for arbitrary dimension number $n$. Such are, for example, the formulas for the distance between two points and the cosine of an angle in $n$-dimensional space.

about his life without hearing his works, so it is difficult to appreciate Riemann's significance in the history of mathematics without a technical examination of his work. This is particularly difficult in his case because the fields of mathematics which he developed are quite different from those usually taught to nonmathematicians in the schools. We shall therefore have to be satisfied with the barest indications. The general theory of geometry which was later to be so extensively developed, and whose foundations Riemann sketched in his lecture[11] was only one of his great achievements.

His total work is characterized by three main features. First, he introduced a geometric point of view into a broad field of mathematics which had previously been dominated almost completely by arithmetic methods [**31**] (his doctoral dissertation was along these lines).[12] Second, he had a clear insight into the need for a rigorous foundation for the theory of real numbers and analysis (see Chapter VIII). Without such rigor, the subtle problems which were arising more and more often in modern mathematical research could not be precisely stated and solved [**32**]. Third, he had a profound insight into the branches of physics in which those fields of higher mathematics which had developed out of the differential and integral calculus could be fruitfully applied.

Riemann's theory of non-Euclidean geometry was influenced a great deal by its relationship to physics. Moreover, he had investigated many special physical problems: Nobili color bands and the distribution of electricity, heat conduction and the mechanics of the ear, air waves and the motion of liquids. He was even concerned with epistemological problems. It might also be of interest, in view of our discussion of the subject, to mention that one of his papers on prime number theory was responsible for very important developments in the problem of the distribution of the primes.

In discussing Felix Klein's lectures, we mentioned the modern period in the history of mathematics which began with Gauss (see Chapter IX). Dividing this modern age into two periods, we may say that Riemann and Dedekind put their stamp on the second period, which extends to our day.

They were close friends. Dedekind, five years the younger, did not die

[11] The lecture, *Ueber die Hypothesen, welche der Geometrie zu Grunde liegen* was first published posthumously. See {2; p. 272}. The theory of Riemannian manifolds has been developed in great detail (and in full rigor) by many mathematicians from the time of Riemann through the present day [**30**].

[12] In connection with Chapters IV and XI, where we mentioned that topology is one of the newer branches of mathematics, it may be of interest to note that Riemann introduced topological considerations into geometry. A complete theory of the topology of surfaces was not developed until much later, but the germ of such a theory is already to be found in a fragment of a paper by Riemann discovered posthumously (see {2; p. 479}) and also in a paper by Riemann's friend Enrico Betti (1823–1892), for whom the Betti groups of algebraic topology are named.

until the First World War, but Riemann died much earlier. Born in 1826 in Hannover, Bernhard Riemann was the second child of a minister. As a boy he was educated by his father. His talent for arithmetic and geometry had become apparent when he was ten. After two years at the Lycée in Hannover, he came to Lüneburg in 1842, where the director of the school lent him mathematical works, many of which Riemann read in a few days. At the age of 20, he entered the University of Göttingen as a student in philology and theology at the wish of his father. But the elder Riemann soon gave his son permission to follow his chosen subject. Between 1847–1849, Riemann attended the University of Berlin, a mathematical center at the time. He was there during the revolution of 1848, and as a member of the student corps, served as a guard at the Palace for two days.

Riemann received his doctorate in 1851. His dissertation, important for the development of function theory, has already been mentioned. A post at the Observatory would have helped him financially, but Gauss, at that time 72, felt that a man of Riemann's ability would be wasting his talents in routine duties. Riemann himself, however, always a shy, modest man, was inclined to doubt his ability, and was always ready to recognize the merits of others. He was always grateful for the help he received, particularly from Wilhelm Weber and Dirichlet. At the latter's recommendation, he received a stipend in 1855, and in 1857 was promoted to University lecturer. Now he was able to care for his three sisters, who had moved to Göttingen to be with him. Two years later, when Dirichlet died, he succeeded to Gauss' chair, which Dirichlet had occurpied for only four years. But he had already contracted tuberculosis, and he died in Italy in 1866 [**33**].

*Notes to Chapter XIV*

## SPACE CURVATURE

**1** (p. 305). For example, a student of mathematics soon learns to distinguish between infinite sequences and infinite series; or between the "continuity" of a straight line and the continuity of a function.

**2** (p. 308). An example is the following proposition due to Charles Julien Brianchon (1783–1864): Let $K$ be a conic section (circle, ellipse, parabola or hyperbola). Let $T_1, \cdots, T_6$ be any six distinct tangent lines to $K$, numbered in order as $K$ is traversed in a definite sense. Denote the points of intersection of $T_1, T_2$ by $P_1$, of $T_2, T_3$ by $P_2, \cdots$, of $T_6, T_1$ by $P_6$; so that $P_1, \cdots, P_6$ are the vertices of a hexagon whose sides lie on the tangent lines. Then the three lines $P_1P_4, P_2P_5, P_3P_6$ intersect in one point.

Another example is the determination of the length of a cycloid by Christopher Wren (1632–1723). A cycloid is the curve described by a fixed point $P$ on the circumference of a wheel as the wheel rolls along a straight line $L$ in the plane. The length of the cycloid between two consecutive contacts of $P$ with $L$ is $4d$, where $d$ is the diameter of the wheel. Wren is the architect who rebuilt St. Paul's cathedral after the great fire of London in 1666.

**3** (p. 308). There are propositions which are equivalent to the axiom of parallels (in the presence of the other Euclidean axioms) and which can therefore be substituted for it. In fact, Euclid did not take the axiom of parallels as his fifth axiom in Book I of the *Elements*, but used instead the following (sometimes known as the 11th axiom): If two lines are intersected by a third line, and the sum of the two interior angles on one side of the third line is less than two right angles, then the first two lines intersect on that side of the third line. See {3}.

**4** (p. 308). It is also impossible to extend a straight line on the surface of the earth indefinitely.

**5** (p. 309). A similar idealization is to be found in the assumption that the positive integers form an unending sequence.

**6** (p. 309). George Berkeley says in his *Principles of Human Knowledge* that the ten thousandth part of the diameter of the earth exists, but that that part of an inch does not. See {4}. Moreover, the length of light waves sets a lower limit on the measurement of distances.

**7** (p. 311). This characterization of the mathematical nature of theoretical astronomy is an idealization. In practice, the calculations are themselves approximate.

**8** (p. 312). See {5}, {6}, {7}.

**9** (p. 313). Other equilibrium figures have been studied mathematically, with no immediate practical application in mind, except perhaps with the hope that they might be applicable in cosmology.

**10** (p. 313). See {8}. A remark on p. 95 of vol. 1 of this work assigns to mathematical theories the task of deriving the logical consequences of a set of assumptions.

**11** (p. 313). In mathematics, the classical and romantic non-Euclidean geometries are called hyperbolic and elliptic geometries, respectively, and Euclidean geometry is referred to as parabolic geometry. The names, however, have nothing to do with the familiar conic sections to which they refer. It was for this reason that we did not wish to use the technical names here. Later, we shall refer to the classical and romantic geometries also as geometries of negative and positive type, respectively, in connection with certain intrinsic measurements which can be carried out in each geometry. The geometry of positive type is also known as Riemannian geometry, but we shall not use this name since it actually refers to a much more general type of geometry than the one we have in mind at the moment. We shall refer to this more general Riemannian geometry in connection with Riemann's Habilitationsvortrag.

**12** (p. 314). The unique historical position of the axiom of parallels was due to the long held belief that it was not independent of the other four axioms, that is, that it could be derived from the other four. For centuries, many mathematicians tried to show that this was so. Their efforts could not, of course, be successful, but they were not in vain, since they eventually led to the discovery of the non-Euclidean geometries.

**13** (p. 314). The difference between Euclidean and this type of non-Euclidean geometry can be illustrated in the following way. On the line $g$ (Fig. 155) consider a sequence of points $A' < B' < C' < \cdots$ and the lines joining these points to the point $P$. These lines approach a line $h'$ through $P$ which has no point of intersection with $g$. Now consider a sequence of points $A'' > B'' > C'' > \cdots$ on $g$ and the lines joining these points to $P$. These lines approach a line $h''$ through $P$ which again has no point of intersection with $g$. Now in the Euclidean geometry it is assumed that $h'$ and $h''$ are two sides of the same line $h$, so that there is only one parallel to $g$ through $P$. In the non-Euclidean geometry we are considering, however,

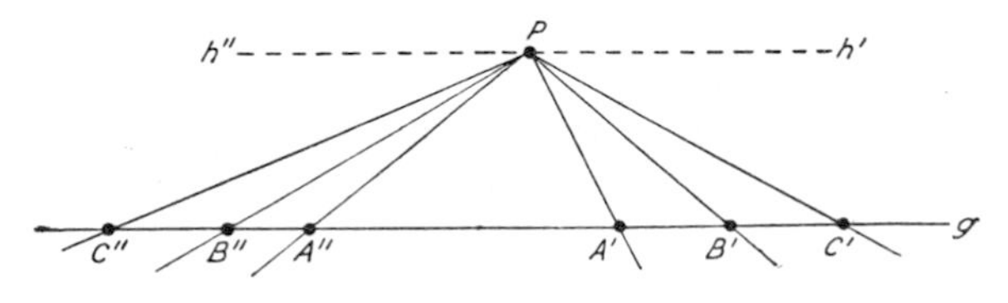


Fig. 155

it is assumed that $h'$ and $h''$ are *not* the same line, that if $P$ is close enough to $g$ the angle between $h'$ and $h''$ is small but not zero. In other words, if $P$ is close enough to $g$, none of the lines included in the angle between $h'$ and $h''$ intersect $g$.

**14** (p. 315). The picture which comes immediately to mind is that of the surface of a sphere, on which every two great circles intersect, so that there are no parallel great circles. Also the great circles have finite length. However, the geometry of the sphere is *not* equivalent to that of the romantic non-Euclidean geometry, although this is often erroneously stated to be the case (see Note 16). The geometry of the sphere is also often erroneously called Riemannian geometry, because Riemann mentioned it in his Habilitationsvortrag, but of course what he developed was a much more general and abstract theory (see Note 11).

**15** (p. 318). A critical reader may perhaps object that even in the thickest fog our three-dimensional bodies and measuring instruments would involve us in the surrounding space. This objection is valid because of the vagueness of the language I have used. The only alternative would be to start at the beginning, to state definitions and theorems precisely and to prove the theorems, a course it would not be feasible to follow in a book of this nature.

**16** (p. 319). Note that an infinite number of great circle arcs of equal length pass through two antipodal points on a sphere. But the great circle arcs are the straight lines or geodesics on a sphere. Hence the *whole* sphere cannot be a model for the non-Euclidean geometry of positive type, since it, like Euclidean geometry, satisfies the axiom which requires that precisely one line pass through two distinct points. As a matter of fact, the projective plane obtained by identifying antipodal points on the surface of a sphere makes a more faithful model for a geometry of positive type, but it is not as simple intuitively as the sphere.

**17** (p. 319). Like the spheres, the pseudo-spheres also have a non-Euclidean index (although it is not quite so simple to state). It is easy to imagine that if the surface of Fig. 154 were to be enlarged a thousand times, a triangle with sides one inch long would be hardly distinguishable from a plane triangle, whereas the difference between the two is obvious on the scale of Fig. 154.

**18** (p. 320). The circumference of the circle on the sphere is $2\pi R \sin \alpha$, where $R$ is the radius of the sphere, $\alpha = (r/R\pi)(180)$ degrees and $r$ is the length of the path on the sphere (in our case $r = 10$ and $R = 100$).

**19** (p. 320). Curiously enough, it was thought at one time that it would not be possible to use instruments made according to the principles of Euclidean geometry to measure the deviation between physical space and Euclidean geometry.

**20** (p. 320). We refer to the formulas of spherical trigonometry. In geodetic surveys of large areas, the oblateness of the earth must also be taken into account (see Chapter II, Note 2).

**21** (p. 321). In the plane or on a sphere the circumference of a circle depends only on the radius, but not on the center of the circle. But on other surfaces, such as an ellipsoid, the circumference of a circle is also a function of its center.

**22** (p. 321). As on a sphere, the circumference of a circle on a pseudo-sphere is independent of the center.

**23** (p. 321). In Chapter II we noted that on a curved surface there are, in general, points of positive, points of negative and points of zero curvature (see Chapter II, Notes 15 and 18 for points of zero curvature). There are certain general relations between the curvature at a point and intrinsic measurements in a neighborhood of the point.

**24** (p. 322). We use this example of surface measurement in three-dimensional space as a possibility of distinguishing between Euclidean and non-Euclidean space in order to preserve the analogy with the two-dimensional case (measurement on a curved surface). In practice, however, it is hardly likely that such measurements could be carried out. There are of course many other ways of checking the physical validity of Euclidean geometry; one such way is to measure the sum of the angles of a sufficiently large triangle.

**25** (p. 322). We referred to the decrease in the area of a surface in a non-Euclidean geometry of positive type as a contraction. Similarly, if the area increases (as it will in a geometry of negative type), we can call this a magnification; the corresponding indexes can then be referred to as the contraction or the magnification indexes. Better still, they could be called positive or negative non-Euclidean indexes.

**26** (p. 322). This is not to be confused with the four-dimensional space-time world mentioned in Chapter VI.

**27** (p. 323). See Chapter VI for a discussion of dimension. Mathematically, there is no difficulty in considering "curved" subspaces (analogous to curved surfaces) of spaces whose dimension is greater than three.

**28** (p. 323). This is also true on a pseudo-sphere in so far as intrinsic properties of the surface (and not imbedding properties) are concerned.

**29** (p. 324). The theory of relativity of Albert Einstein (1879–1955) was originally concerned with electro-magnetic phenomena and optics; in this special theory, the velocity of light played a special role. The general theory of relativity, which came later, included also the laws of inertia and the theory of gravitation. But the masses which obey the law of gravitation are not uniformly distributed in space, as is obvious, say, from the contrast between the great mass of the sun and the vast stretches of empty space in the solar system. This obvious remark makes it clear that the non-Euclidean space of the theory of relativity must be assumed to be non-homogeneous; it also suggests why the behavior of light rays in the neighborhood of a large mass like the sun would be different than in empty space and leads to one of the possible experimental verifications of the theory of relativity.

**30** (p. 325). Among many others, we might mention Christoffel, Ricci, Levi-Civita, Schouten, Weyl and Herglotz. See {9}.

**31** (p. 325). We refer to (complex) function theory, in which the main interest has shifted from elliptic functions and theta functions to Riemann surfaces, analytic manifolds and conformal mappings.

**32** (p. 325). We note in particular Riemann's paper {2; p. 227} on trigonometric series, which extended Dirichlet's work in this field.

**33** (p. 326). Riemann's gravestone was later incorporated into the wall of the cemetery at Biganzolo. His remains could no longer be found in 1906. See {10}.

# POSTSCRIPT

The series of problems we have discussed could easily have been extended. For instance, we could have included Dido's problem: When Dido was shipwrecked on what is known today as the coast of Tunis, she asked the ruler of the land for as much territory as could be encompassed by the hide of a cow as asylum for herself and her shipmates. When this apparently modest request was granted, she cut a hide into thin strips and made a belt of considerable length which she stretched from one point on the coast to another, thus gaining the whole coastal area bounded by the strip. It was in this way that Carthage was founded.

Mathematically, Dido's problem is concerned with the following question: What is the maximum area which can be encompassed or bounded by curves of a given length; in other words, what shape must a curve of given length have in order to bound the greatest possible area? Dido's problem, as well as other related problems, led to the development of a new branch of mathematics, the calculus of variations. Many of the great mathematicians from the time of the brothers Bernoulli to the present have contributed to this field; among them, Hilbert [1] (1862–1943), Hadamard (1865–) and Carathéodory (1873–1950).

We could, therefore, have included some problem in the calculus of variations [2]. Or, we might have discussed the fundamental problem of the integral calculus: the determination of the path of a motion if the velocity at every point of the path is known; or, conversely, the fundamental problem of the differential calculus: the determination of the velocity along a path if the path is known. A consideration of the differential and integral calculus, which now has a somewhat different form but is essentially the same as that created by Newton and Leibniz, would have led us into a field which has been of the utmost importance in the development of mathematics as well as in science and technology.

We could also have considered problems in the theory of probability, such as the needle problem, problems connected with card games, the Petersburg problem [3], or problems arising from the Mendelian laws of heredity. It might have been of interest to discuss Poincaré's recurrence theorem or the ergodic theory, on which much recent work has been done [4]. Another interesting topic would have been the theory of knots and the unsolved problems of this theory [5].

But no matter how the problems might have been selected, whether by taste or inclination or by richness of content, we must bear in mind that the great majority of mathematical problems, both solved and unsolved, are automatically excluded from a book such as this for one very simple reason: Merely to understand these problems and their significance, quite apart from the research done on their partial or complete solution, requires a mathematical knowledge and sophistication which take several years for even talented students to acquire. We were, therefore, necessarily prohibited from giving an account of the present state of mathematical research and its goals. We had to be content with demonstrating that mathematics is not, and never was, a collection of dead material; that today, as in the past, it is rich in problems which have an irresistible attraction for those with the inclination and ability to pursue them, and that the people who do so number among them the best minds of the age. From the cases of some of those who have solved some of these difficult problems, we know how taxing, but also stimulating, the process can be [6].

Our discussion has not paid much attention to the applications of mathematics in science and technology. The reason for this is that the problems of applied mathematics [7] are for the most part not simple and presuppose a great deal of technical background. In the applied fields it is often necessary to make use of branches of mathematics which go far beyond the scope of undergraduate instruction. We must bear in mind that the boundaries of mathematics have been considerably extended in the last two thousand years, and especially in the two and a half centuries since the creation of the differential and integral calculus [8]. Aspiring mathematicians must now study the mathematical literature scattered through the mathematical journals [9]. Although at one time the mind of a Leibniz could absorb all the knowledge of his time, all the branches of mathematics have grown to such an extent that only a few especially gifted mathematicians can master several of these fields.

Most of the fields of mathematics, a large part of which owe their origin to a thirst for pure knowledge of men of genius, have applications to science. On the other hand, many of the deepest problems which have concerned and continue to concern mathematicians [10] have no immediate bearing on practical problems. But, just as we are proud of the creations of our great musicians, so do we honor the incomparable achievements of Gauss, Dirichlet, Dedekind, Cantor, Riemann and Hilbert.

In the final analysis, all the branches of science are directly or indirectly inter-connected. The experimental physiological research of Galvani initiated our knowledge of electricity. The calculus of variations developed in connection with problems in the theory of light, and was in turn applied by Hamilton to mechanics. The theory of complex numbers, a branch of pure mathematics, was recently used by my colleague Carathéodory in completing research on optical instruments {13}. The once purely theoretical extension of geometry to more than three dimensions later proved highly useful in mechanics (for example, in describing the motion of a rigid body which has six degrees of freedom by means of a curve in 6-dimensional space, or in 7-dimensional space if the time is taken into account).

It is thus impossible to foretell when some apparently useless bit of knowledge may become of decisive practical significance. As the famous physicist Boltzmann once said, nothing is more practical than theory. But theory must have inner reserves if it is to serve science and technology as it has in the past. Any limitation of pure research to what is momentarily practical would cripple its development and prove a great disservice to posterity. For, after all, we must not only transmit our store of knowledge, we must also give those who follow the capability of increasing it.

# NOTES TO POSTSCRIPT

**1** (p. 332). Carathéodory, in his short lively tribute {1} gives a good picture of Hilbert, "who for more than a generation has been recognized the world over as the foremost mathematician of his time."

Hilbert's lecture *Mathematical Problems* {2} delivered at the First International Mathematical Congress in Paris in 1900 is especially well known to and esteemed by mathematicians. In this lecture he posed 23 difficult and significant problems. The majority of these were solved in the following decades.

For an account of Carathéodory's life and work see {3}.

**2** (p. 332). Dido's problem is known as the isoperimetric problem. As I was writing these lines (November 1944), my colleague Carathéodory suggested that I might wish to include a discussion of this problem on the basis of a recent paper by Alexander Dinghas and Erhard Schmidt {4}.

Carathéodory emphasizes in his paper {5} that the term *calculus of variations* was first used in 1850 to describe problems such as Dido's.

**3** (p. 332). For the needle and Petersburg problems see {6}. For card problems see {6; p. 1090} and {7}. For a stability theorem in the theory of Mendelian heredity see {8}.

**4** (p. 332). The famous French mathematician Henri Poincaré (1854–1912) was for many years foremost in the fields of pure mathematics, theoretical astronomy and physics. Poincaré's "last theorem" (a fixed point theorem which arose in connection with his work on periodic solutions of differential equations), which he himself was not able to prove, was proved by G. D. Birkhoff in 1913 {9}.

For Poincare's recurrence theorem see {10}.

**5** (p. 332). For the theory of knots see {11}. Parts of {11} require more technical knowledge than we have so far presupposed.

Readers with a fondness for number theory will perhaps miss a discussion of Waring's problem (solved by Hilbert in 1909); or the Goldbach conjecture, which has not been proved or disproved up to this time, although a great deal of work has been done by Hardy, Littlewood, Schnirelmann and others.

**6** (p. 333). Thus, Felix Klein's great work on automorphic functions, in which he competed with Poincaré, took such a toll of his strength, that he devoted himself afterwards mainly to his lectures, publication of the *Encyklopädie der mathematischen Wissenschaften*, the advancement of applied mathematics and the adaptation of the mathematical curriculum to the new advances in mathematics.

**7** (p. 333). The distinguished mathematician Carl Runge (1856–1927) of

Göttingen once protested against the term "applied mathematics," since it gives the mistaken impression that applied mathematics is a field separate from pure mathematics, whereas in his view it is merely pure mathematics applied to astronomy, physics, chemistry, biology, etc. This was the theme of a paper I addressed to students of mathematics {12}.

**8** (p. 333). For example, in the period 1930–1935, publications in mathematics, excluding text books, totaled about 40000 pages. These papers appeared in more than 50 technical and approximately 100 academic journals published throughout the world. The volume has increased since the last war. Reviews of all mathematical papers now appear in the German *Zentralblatt für Mathematik und ihre Grenzgebiete* (this goes back to 1929 but was suspended during the war), the American *Mathematical Reviews* (which goes back to 1940) and the Russian *Referativnyĭ Zhurnal* (during the last 10 years or so).

**9** (p. 333). For a comprehensive view of the whole field of mathematics (up to 1935) see the *Encyklopädie der mathematischen Wissenschaften*, a work of 23 volumes founded by Felix Klein to which about 200 mathematicians from all over the world contributed during a period of 40 years. The first volume appeared in 1898, the last in 1935. The changes in mathematics since then have been so great that a second series of the Encyklopädie is now being issued. Both series require a mathematical background of the reader.

**10** (p. 333). Examples are the Riemann hypothesis on the zeros of the Riemann zeta function, problems in the theory of functions of several complex variables (which, however, is now beginning to acquire importance in theoretical physics) and the topological classification of manifolds of dimension greater than two.

# REFERENCES

NOTE. For convenience, the books and journals (including encyclopedias) which are referred to more than once are listed at the beginning. They will be cited by using the abbreviations indicated. References to journals will be made by listing the name of the journal (or its abbreviation), volume number (if any) in bold face, year in parenthesis and the page numbers of the paper cited.

## BOOKS


AHRENS, W. E. M. G.

[A] *Mathematische Unterhaltungen und Spiele*, 2 vols. Leipzig: Teubner, 1918.

CAJORI, FLORIAN

[C] *A History of Mathematical Notations*, 2 vols. Chicago: Open-Court, 1928–1929.

[$C_1$] *A History of Mathematics*. New York: Macmillan, 1919.

CANTOR, M.

[Ca] *Vorlesungen über Geschichte der Mathematik*, 3 vols. Leipzig: Teubner, 1880.

CARATHÉODORY, C.

[Car] *Gesammelte Mathematische Schriften*. München: Beck, 1954–1957.

DIRICHLET, G. LEJEUNE

[D] *Werke*, 2 vols. Berlin: Reimer, 1889–1897.

GAUSS, C. F.

[G] *Werke*. Leipzig: Teubner, 1870–1919.

HAUPT, O.

[H] *Einführung in die Algebra*, 2 vols. Leipzig: Akademische Verlagsgesellschaft, 1929; 2nd ed., 1954.

HECKE, E.

[He] *Vorlesungen über die Theorie der Algebraischen Zahlen*. Leipzig: 1922; in reprint, New York: Chelsea, 1948.

KLEIN, F.

[K] *Vorlesungen über die Entwicklung der Mathematik im* 19. *Jahrhundert*, 2 vols. Berlin: Springer, 1926–1927 (Die Grundlehren der mathematischen Wissenschaften, Bd. 24–25); in reprint, New York: Chelsea, 1950.

LEGENDRE, A. M.

[L] *Théorie des Nombres*, 4th ed. Paris: Hermann, 1908.

LUCAS, ÉDOUARD

[Lu] *Récréations Mathématiques*, 4 vols. Paris: Gauthier-Villars, 1882.

PERRON, O.

[P] *Algebra*, 2 vols. Leipzig: de Gruyter, 1927 (Göschens Lehrbücherei, Bd. 8–9); 2nd ed., 1933; 3rd ed., 1951.

[$P_1$] *Irratitonalzahlen*. Berlin and Leipzig: de Gruyter, 1921 (Göschens Lehrbücherei, Bd. 1); 2nd ed., 1939; 3rd ed. 1943. In reprint, New York: Chelsea.

SCHUBERT, H.

[S] *Mathematische Mussestunden*, 2nd ed. Leipzig: Göschen, 1900; in translation, *Mathematical Essays and Recreations*. Chicago: Open-Court, 1898.

SMITH, D. E.

[Sm] *History of Mathematics*, 2 vols. Boston: Ginn, 1923–1925; in reprint, New York: Dover, 1958.

TROPFKE, JOHANNES

[T] *Geschichte der Elementar-Mathematik*, 7 vols. Berlin and Leipzig: 1921.

## JOURNALS

[J1] Bayerische Akademie der Wissenschaften. Mathematisch-Naturwissenschaftliche Klasse. Sitzungsberichte. (München)
[J2] Encyklopädie der Mathematischen Wissenschaften.
[J3] Encyclopédie des Sciences Mathématiques, Édition Française. Paris-Leipzig, 1906.
[J4] Jahrbuch über die Fortschritte der Mathematik.
[J5] Jahresbericht der Deutschen Mathematiker Vereinigung. (Stuttgart)
[J6] Journal für die Reine und Angewandte Mathematik. (Berlin)
[J7] Journal of the London Mathematical Society.
[J8] Königliche Gesellschaft der Wissenschaften zu Göttingen. Math.-Physik. Klasse. Nachrichten.
[J9] Königliche Preussische Akademie der Wissenschaften. Math.-Naturwiss. Kl. Abhandlungen.
[J10] Mathematische Annalen. (Berlin-Göttingen-Heidelberg)
[J11] Wiener Akademie der Wissenschaften. Mathematisch-Naturwissenschaftliche Klasse. Sitzungsberichte.
[J12] Zeitschrift für Angewandte Mathematik und Mechanik.
[J13] Zeitschrift für Mathematik und Physik.

*Chapter I*

1. Tropfke: [T; vol. 1, p. 96].
2. Kraitchik, Maurice: *Recherches sur la Théorie des Nombres*. Paris: Gauthier-Villars, 1924; pp. 131–191.
3. Lehmer, D. N.: *List of Prime Numbers*. Washington, D. C.: Carnegie Institution, Publication No. 165, 1914.
4. Burckhardt, J. Ch.: *Table des Diviseurs*. Paris: Courcier, 1816, 1817.
5. Cajori: [$C_1$; p. 368].
6. Seelhoff, P.: [J13; **31** (1886), 178]. This reference is taken from Tropfke [T; vol. 1, p. 101].
7. Fauquembergue, E.: *L'Intermédiaire des Mathématiciens*, vol. 24, 1917; p. 33. See also Tropfke [T; vol. 1, p. 101], where, however, the number is not given explicitly.
8. Hardy, G. H. and E. M. Wright: *An Introduction to the Theory of Numbers*. Oxford: The Clarendon Press, 1938; pp. 4, 11, 233.
9. Heiberg, Johan Ludwig: *Litteraturgeschichtliche Studien über Euklid*. Leipzig: Teubner, 1882. We are indebted to Heiberg for a pioneering edition of Euclid: Heiberg, J. L.: *Euclidis Elementa*. Leipzig: Teubner, 1883–1888.
10. Tannery, Paul: *Euclide*. Grande Encyclopédie, vol. XVI, pp. 723–724. Reprinted in
Tannery, Paul: *Mémoires Scientifiques*. Toulouse-Paris: E. Privat, 1915; vol. 3, pp. 362–366.
11. Pauly-Wissowa: Real Encyclopädie der Class. Altertumwissensch., vol. 11, 1907; the article *Eukleides*.
12. Heath, T. L.: *A History of Greek Mathematics*, 2 vols. Oxford: The Clarendon Press, 1921; vol. 1, pp. 354–476.
13. Enriques, F.: *Gli Elementi d'Euclide e la Critica Antica e Moderna*, 4 vols. Rome: 1925.
14. Gercke, Alfred and Eduard Norden: *Einleitung in die Altertumwissenschaft*,

3 vols. Leipzig and Berlin: Teubner, 2nd ed. 1912–1914, 3rd ed. 1922; vol. 2, part 2, the article by A. Rehm and K. Vogel: *Exakte Wissenschaften* (esp. pp. 5 and 49).
15. Smith: [Sm; vol. 1, p. 102 ff.].
16. Heath, T. L.: *The Thirteen Books of Euclid's Elements*, 3 vols., 2nd ed. Cambridge: The University Press, 1926; in reprint, New York: Dover, 1956.
17. Tropfke: [T; vol. 1, p. 97; vol. 4, pp. 135–136].
18. *Über die Stäckelschen Lückenzahlen nebst kleinen Randbemerkungen zur Verteilung der Primzahlen*, [J1; (1944), 21–39]. See pp. 21–28.
*Verallgemeinerung einer Meissner-Stäckelschen Vermutung über die Verteilung der Primzahlen*, [J1; (1944), 69–73].
19. *Tafel der Primzahl-Zwillinge unter* 300000, [J1; (1947)].

*Chapter II*

1. Hahn, H. and H. Tietze: *Einführung in die Elemente der höheren Mathematik*. Leipzig: S. Hirzel, 1925; p. 271. (For an English reference see: Johnson, R. E. and F. L. Kiokemeister: *Calculus*, 3rd ed. Boston: Allyn and Bacon, 1964; pp. 497–506.)
2. Weyl, Herman: *Raum, Zeit, Materie*. Berlin: Springer, 1918; § 17 and the discussion of straight lines preceding it. For an English translation, see Weyl, H.: *Space—Time—Matter*. New York: Dover, 1952.
3. Tietze, H.: *Mathematische Analyse des Raumproblems* (Lectures delivered in Barcelona and Madrid). Berlin: 1923.
4. Herglotz, Gustav: *Über die scheinbaren Helligkeitsverhältnisse eines planetarischen Körpers mit drei ungleichen Hauptaxen*, [J11; **111** (1902), Abt. IIa].
5. Blaschke, Wilhelm: *Vorlesungen über Differentialgeometrie*. Berlin: Springer, 1921; vol. 1, § 81, pp. 142–143; 2nd ed. (1924), pp. 143–144; 3rd ed. (1930) or 4th ed. (1945), pp. 211–212.
6. Comptes Rendus de l'Acad. des Sciences, Paris: **188** (1929[2]), 295, 534; **189** (1930[1]), 269. For reviews of these papers see [J4; **55** (1929), 315–316].
7. Lusternik, L.: *Sur quelques méthodes topologiques dans la géométrie différentielle*, Atti del Congresso Internazionale dei Matematici, Bologna, 1928; vol. IV, Bologna, 1931; p. 294.
8. Lusternik, L.: *Kürzeste Linien, eine Einführung in die Variationsrechnung*. Berlin: Deutsche Verlag der Wissenschaften, 1957. For an English translation see Supplementary References, VIII, *1*.
9. [J6; **158, 160**]; [J10; **99**]; Mathematische Zeitscrift, **28;** [J5; **37,** Abt. 2].
10. Leja and Wilkosz: Annales de la Soc. Polon. de Math., **2** (1923).
11. Dürer, Albrecht. *Vnderweysung der messung mit zirckel und richtscheyt in Linien ebnen vnnd gantzen corporen*. Nürnberg, 1525; Book 4. See Tropfke [T; vol. 7, p. 53; vol. 2, p. 61].

*Chapter III*

1. *Zur Analyse der Lineal- und Zirkel-Konstruktionen* I, [J1; (1944)]. This paper is connected with an earlier note: [J11; **118** (1909), Abt. IIa, 735–757].
2. Enriques, F.: *Fragen der Elementargeometrie*, Teil II: *Die geometrischen Aufgaben, ihre Lösung und Lösbarkeit*. Leipzig and Berlin: Teubner, 1907; article VII by A. Conti, § 10, p. 227 ff.
3. Vahlen, K. T.: *Konstruktionen und Approximationen in systematischer Darstellung*.

Leipzig and Berlin: Teubner, 1911. For further references see [J2; vol. III, part 1, 2nd half, article III AB8 by J. Sommer, p. 772].
4. Perron, O.: *Die Winkeldreiteilung des Schneidermeisters Kopf*, [J1; (1929), 341]. Perron, O. *Eine neue Winkeldreiteilung des Schneidermeisters Kopf*, [J1; (1933), 439].
5. Vogel, F.: *Über die Näherungskonstruktionen für die Dreiteilung eines Winkels*, Zeitschrift für den mathematischen und naturwissenschäftlichen Unterricht, **62** (1931), 145–155.
6. Perron: [P; vol. 2, 2nd ed., § 34, p. 176; vol. 2, 3rd ed., § 37, p. 196].
7. Haupt: [H; vol. 2, 2nd ed., p. 398].
8. Birkhoff, G. and S. MacLane: *A Survey of Modern Algebra*. New York: Macmillan, 1950; pp. 389–390.
9. See Enriques (Ref. Note 2): Article IV by G. Castelnuovo; article V, § 3, by Enriques; article VII, § 10, by A. Conti.

*Chapter IV*

1. Klein: [K; vol. 1, p. 117].
2. Möbius, A. F.: *Der baryzentrische Calcul, eine neues Hilfsmittel zur analytischen Behandlung der Geometrie*. Leipzig: Barth, 1827.
3. Möbius, A. F.: *Gesammelte Werke*. Leipzig: 1885–87.
4. Möbius, A. F.: *Lehrbuch der Statik*. Leipzig: 1843.
5. Cantor: [Ca; vol. 2, p. 617, Note 3 and p. 619].
6. Ahrens: [A; vol. 2, Ch. XVIII, § 2, esp. p. 215].
7. Ringel, G.: *Bestimmung der Maximalzahl der Nachbargebiete auf nichtorientierbaren Flächen*, [J10; **127** (1954), 181–214].
8. Kempe, A. B.: *On the geographical problem of the four colours*, American Journal of Mathematics, **2** (1879), 193–200.
9. Heawood, P. J.: *Map-colour-theorem*, The Quarterly Journal of Pure and Applied Mathematics, **24** (1890), 332–338. For a review of this paper see [J4; **22** (1890)].
10. Heffter, L.: *Über das Problem der Nachbargebiete*, [J10; **38** (1891), 477–508].
11. Ringel, G.: *Farbensatz für orientierbare Flächen vom Geschlecht $p > 0$*, [J6; **193** (1954), 11–38].
12. Lucas: [Lu; p. 21 ff.].
13. Ahrens: [A; vol. 2, Ch. XVI, § 5, p. 183 and Ch. XVII, p. 196 ff.]; [J2; vol. 1, part 2, article IG1, no. 7, pp. 1089–1090].
14. Gauss: [G; vol. VIII, p. 271 ff.].
15. Tietze, H.: *Ein Kapitel Topologie, zur Einführung in die Lehre von den verknoteten Linien*. Hamburg. Math. Einzelschriften, Heft 36 (1942).
16. Stäckel, P.: *Die Entdeckung der einseitigen Flächen*, [J10; **52** (1899), 598–600].
17. Scheffers, G.: *Einführung in die Theorie der Flächen*. Leipzig: 1902; 2nd ed., 1913. See p. 41 of the 2nd ed.
18. Tietze, H.: *Der Richtungssinn und seine Verallgemeinerung*, [J5; **29** (1920), 95–123].
19. Tietze, H.: *Einige Bemerkungen über das Problem des Kartenfärbens auf einseitigen Flächen*, [J5; **19** (1910), 155–159].
20. Franklin, P.: *A six colour problem*, J. Math. Massachusetts, **13** (1934), 363–369.
21. Kagno, I. N.: *A note on the Heawood color formula*, J. Math. Massachusetts, **14** (1935), 228–231.
22. Bose, R. C.: *On the construction of balanced incomplete block designs*, Annals of Eugenics, **9** (1939), 353–399.

23. Coxeter, H. S. M.: *The map colouring of unorientable surfaces*, Duke Mathematical Journal, **10** (1943), 293–304.
24. Ringel, G.: *Farbensatz für nichtorientierbare Flächen beliebigen Geschlechtes*, [J6; **190** (1952), 128–147].
25. Ringel, G.: Arch. Math., **4** (1953), 137–142.
26. See Ref. Note 7.
27. Guthrie, F.: Proc. Royal Soc. Edinburgh, **10** (1878–1880), 728.
28. Stäckel, P.: [J13; **42** (1897), 275].
29. Dixon, A. C.: The Messenger of Mathematics, **32** (1903), 82.
30. Tietze, H.: *Über das Problem der Nachbargebiete im Raum*, Monatshefte f. Math. und Physik, **16** (1905), 211–216.
31. Besicovitch, A. S.: *On Crum's problem*, [J7; **22** (1947), 285–287].

*Chapter V*

1. Hessenberg, Gerhard: *Transzendenz von e und π. Ein Beitrag zur höheren Mathematik von elementaren Standpunkt aus*. Leipzig and Berlin: Teubner, 1912.
2. Tropfke: [T; vol. 4, pp. 195–238].
3. Schubert: [S; vol. 1, p. 39].

*Chapter VI*

1. [J1; (1945/1946), March 16, 1945, Point 2, p. 7*; (1947), Dec. 5, 1947, Point 3].
2. Peano, G.: *Sur une courbe, qui remplit toute une aire plane*, [J10; **36** (1890), 157].
3. Hilbert, D.: *Über die stetige Abbildung einer Linie auf ein Flächenstück*, [J10; **38** (1891), 459].
4. Sommerfeld, A.: Jahrbuch der Akad. der Wiss. in Göttingen (1943/1944), 87–92.
5. Brouwer, L. E. J.: *Über den natürlichen Dimensionsbegriff*, [J6; **142** (1913), 146–152].
6. Sperner, E.: *Neuer Beweis für die Invarianz der Dimensionszahl und des Gebietes*, Abh. Math. Sem. Univ. Hamburg, **6** (1928), 265–272.
7. Hurewicz, W.: *Über eine topologisches Theorem*, [J10; **101** (1929), 210–218].
8. [J2; article III AB13 by Tietze and Vietoris in v. III, part 1, 2nd half (Heft 10)].

*Chapter VII*

1. Legendre, A. M.: *Recherches d'analyse indeterminée*, Histoire de l'Académie des Sciences, Paris, 1785 (appeared in 1788). This reference is given in Landau, E.: *Handbuch der Lehre von der Verteilung der Primzahlen*. Leipzig and Berlin: Teubner, 1909; in reprint, New York: Chelsea, 1953; vol. 1, p. 7; vol. 2, p. 934.
Dirichlet, G. L.: *Beweis des Satzes, dass jede unbegrenzte arithmetische Progression, deren erstes Glied und Differenz ganze Zahlen ohne gemeinschaftlichen Factor sind, unendlich viele Primzahlen enthält* (Proof of the theorem that every infinite arithmetic progression whose first term and difference are relatively prime integers contains an infinite number of primes), [J9; (1837), 45–81]. Reprinted in Dirichlet [D; v. 1, pp. 313–343].
3. Bericht über die Verhandlungen der Preuss. Akad. der Wiss. (1937), 108–110.
4. Legendre, A. M.: *Essai sur la Théorie des Nombres*, 2nd ed. Paris: Courcier, 1808; p. 404. See also Legendre [L; vol. 2, p. 77].
5. Kummer, E. E.: Abhandlungen der Kgl. Akad. der Wiss. zu Berlin (1860). Reprinted in Dirichlet [D; vol. 2, pp. 309–344].

6. Minkowski, H.: *Dirichlet und seine Bedeutung für die heutige Mathematik*, [J5; **14** (1905), 149–163].
7. Klein: [K; vol. 1, pp. 96–100].
8. See Landau (Ref. Note 1), vol. 2, pp. 646–647.
9. [J1; (1944), 69, 75]; Abhandlungen der Bayer. Akad. der Wiss., New Series, **55**.
10. [J2; vol. II, part III (1923), article by Bohr and Cramér, pp. 791, 804].

*Chapter VIII*

1. Menninger, Karl: *Zahlwort und Ziffer*. Breslau: F. Hirt, 1934; p. 239.
2. van der Waerden, B. L.: *Science Awakening*. Groningen: Noordhoff, 1954; p. 52. See also Supplementary References, II.
3. Cajori: [C].
4. Tropfke: [T; vol. 1, pp. 12–99].
5. Cantor: [Ca; vol. 1].
6. Kaye, G. R.: *Indian Mathematics*. Calcutta and Simla: Thacker, Spink & Co., 1915.
7. J. a. Proc. As. Soc. Bengal, **8** (1912).
8. Scientia, **25** (1919) (Bologna), No. 81, 1.
9. Wieleitner, Heinrich: Unterr.-Blättern f. Math u. Naturw., **25** (1919).
10. Ahrens: [A; vol. 1, Ch. III; vol. 2, pp. 319–333].
11. Variété, Paris, Librairie Gallimard, 32[e] éd., pp. 21–27.
12. Hecke: [He].
13. Dedekind, Richard: *Gesammelte mathematische Werke*, 3 vols. Braunschweig: Vieweg, 1930–1932.
14. [J2; vol. 1, part 1, p. 48 ff.].
15. [J3; t. 1, vol. 1, article I3 by Pringshein and Molk, p. 133 ff.].
16. See Ref. Note 14, pp. 56–58.
17. Nachrichten der K. Gesellschaft der Wissenschaften zu Göttingen, Geschäftl. Mitteilungen, 1917.
18. Klein: [K; vol. 1].
19. Carathéodory: [Car; vol. V, pp. 401–402].
20. Perron: [$P_1$].
21. Smith: [Sm; vol. 1, p. 137].
22. See Ref. Note 23.
23. *Sonya Kovalevsky: Her Recollections of Childhood*, translated from the Russian by Isabel F. Hapgood; with a biography by Anna Carlotta Leffler, translated from the Swedish by A. M. C. Bayley; and a biographical note by Lily Wolfsohn. New York: Century, 1895.
24. van der Waerden, B. L.: *Nachruf auf Emmy Noether*, [J10; **111** (1935), 469–476].
25. Weyl, Hermann: *Emmy Noether*, Scripta Math., **3** (1935), 201–220.

*Chapter IX*

1. Tropfke: [T; vol. 4, p. 181 ff.].
2. Scholz, Arnold: *Einführung in die Zahlentheorie*. Berlin: de Gruyter, Sammlung Göschen, Bd. 1131, 1939; p. 32.
3. [J3; t. 1, vol. 3, fasc. 1, pp. 51–52].
4. Klein, F.: *Vorträge über ausgewählte Fragen der Elementargeometrie*, ed. by F. Tägert. Leipzig, 1895; p. 13. English translations: *Famous Problems of Elementary Geometry*. New York: Dover; New York: Chelsea, 1962. The Chelsea edi-

tion contains in addition expository material on determinants (Sheppard), combinatory analysis (MacMahon) and Fermat's last problem (Mordell). See Supplementary References, IX.
5. Intelligenzblatt der Allg. Litteraturzeitung Nr. 66, 1 Juni 1796; p. 554 = Gauss [G; vol. X[1], p. 3].
6. [J5; **41** (1932)].
7. Kosmos: (1938), Heft 10, p. B39.
8. Gauss: [G; vol. V, p. 580].
9. Astronomische Nachrichten, **18** (1841).
10. Klein: [K].

*Chapter X*

1. Cantor: [Ca; Chs. 17, 19, 23, 29, 33].
2. Tropfke: [T; vol. 3, p. 35 ff.].
3. Perron: [P; vol. 2, p. 51; or vol. 2, 2nd ed., p. 66].
4. Cantor: [Ca; vol. 2, Ch. 64, pp. 442–456, 461–472, 474–477, 497–498].
5. Smith: [Sm; vol. 2, pp. 459–464].
6. Cajori: [C; vol. 1, p. 96 ff.].
7. Cajori: [$C_1$; 1897 ed., pp. 143–145].
8. Cantor. [Ca; vol. 3, Ch. 105, pp. 555–556 and Ch. 106, p. 583].
9. Gauss: [G; vol. III[2], p. 17].
9a. Burckhard, H.: *Die Anfänge der Gruppentheorie und Paolo Ruffini*, [J13; **37** (1892), Suppl. p. 119].
10. [J2; vol. I, part 1, article IB3c, d by O. Hölder: *Galoische Theorie mit Anwendungen*, No. 18, p. 504].
11. Klein: [K; vol. 1, p. 101].
12. Sarton, G.: *Évariste Galois*, Osiris, **3**, part 1 (1937), 241–259.
13. *Oeuvres Mathématiques d'Évariste Galois*, Journal de Mathématiques Pures et Appliquées, **11** (1846), 381–444.
14. [J3; t. 1, v. 1, article I1 (H. Schubert, J. Tannery, J. Molk), note 188, p. 56].
15. Perron: [P; vol. 2, Ch. 2].
16. Haupt: [H; vol. 1, Ch. 15].
17. van der Waerden, B. L.: *Moderne Algebra*, 2 vols. Berlin: Springer, 1930–1931; 2nd ed., 1937; 4th ed., 1955. In translation: *Modern Algebra*, New York: Ungar, 1949. See vol. 1, Ch. 7.
18. The Scientific Monthly, **13** (1921), 363–375.
19. Dupuy, Paul: Annales de l'École Normale, **13** (1896), 197–266. Reprinted in Cahiers de la Quinzaine, 5[e] serie, 2[e] cahier, Paris, 27 Octobre, 1903.

*Chapter XI*

1. Ahrens: [A; vol. 2, Ch. XVI, § 5, p. 183 ff.].
2. Tietze, H.: *Ein Kapitel Topologie*, Hamburger Math. Einzelschriften, Heft 36, 1942; p. 7 and 37 ff.
3. Kempe, A. B.: *On the geographical problem of the four colours*, American Journal of Mathematics, **2** (1879), 193–200.
4. Kempe, A. B.: Nature, **21** (26.II.1880), No. 539.
5. Kempe, A. B.: Proc. of the London Mathematical Society, **10** (1878–1879).
6. Story, W. E.: *Note on Mr. Kempe's paper on the geographical problem of the four colours*, American Journal of Mathematics, **2** (1879), 201–204.

7. Proc. Royal Geographical Society, **1**, 259.
8. Heawood, P. J.: Quarterly Journal of Mathematics, **24** (1890); **29** (1898).
9. Heawood, P. J.: *On extended congruences connected with the four-colour map theorem*, Proc. of the London Math. Soc., **33** (1932), 253–286.
   Heawood, P. J.: *Failures in congruences connected with the four-colour map theorem*, ibid. **40** (1936), 189–202.
10. Heawood, P. J.: *Note on a correction in a paper on map-congruences*, [J7; **18** (1943), 160–167].
   Heawood, P. J.: *Note on a correction in a paper on map-congruences*, [J7; **19** (1944), 18–22].
11. Dirac, G. A.: *Map-colour theorems*, Canadian Journal of Mathematics, **4** (1952), 480–490. See also: Dirac, G. A.: *Percy John Heawood*, J. London Math. Soc., **38** (1963), 263–277. This contains a bibliography of 40 papers.
12. Ratib, I.: Proc. Math. and Phys. Soc. of Egypt, **2** (1946), No. 4, 1944.
13. Ratib, I. and C. E. Winn: Congrès International des Mathématiciens, Oslo, 1936.
14. Veblen Oswald: *Analysis Situs*. New York: American Mathematical Society, Colloquium Publications, vol. $V^2$, 1922.
15. Kerékjártó, B. v.: *Vorlesungen über Topologie*, Bd. I. Berlin: Springer, 1923.
16. König, D.: *Az Analysis Situs Elemei* I. Budapest: 1918.
   Weyl, H.: *Analysis Situs Combinatorio*, Rev. Mat. Hisp. Amer., **5** (1923); **6** (1924).
   Tietze, H.: *Vorträge über Analysis Situs*. Hamburger Mathematische Einzelschriften, Heft 2 (also in Abh. a. d. Math. Seiminar d. Hamburg Univ., Bd. 2).
17. Levi, F.: *Geometrische Konfigurationen mit einer Einführung in die kombinatorische Flächentopologie*. Leipzig: Hirzel, 1929.
   Lefschetz, S.: *Topology*. New York: American Mathematical Society, Colloquium Publications, vol. XII, 1930.
   Reidemeister, K.: *Einführung in die kombinatorische Topologie*. Braunschweig: Vieweg, 1932; in reprint, New York: Chelsea.
   Seifert, H. and W. Threlfall: *Lehrbuch der Topologie*. Leipzig and Berlin: Teubner, 1934; in reprint, New York: Chelsea.
   Alexandroff, P. and H. Hopf: *Topologie*, Bd. I. Berlin: Springer, 1935; in reprint, Ann Arbor, Mich.: Edwards Bros.
   Bourbaki, N,: *Éléments de Mathématique*, Livre III (*Topologie Générale*). Paris: Hermann, 1947–1953.
   Kuratowski, C.: *Topologie* I, II. Warsaw: 1952.
   For more recent books on topology, see Supplementary References, XI.
18. Klein: [K].
19. [J2; vol. III, part I, 1st half, article III AB3 by M. Dehn and P. Heegard, Abschnitt A, No. 2, p. 174 ff., Note 47 ff.]. For more recent references to the literature, see [J2; v. III, part I, 2nd half, article III AB13 by H. Tietze and L. Vietoris, p. 221, Note 227a]. See also Supplementary References, XI: Berge, Ore and Cairns.

*Chapter XII*

1. Cantor: [Ca; vol. 1, pp. 276–278].
2. Tropfke: [T; vol. 1, p. 5, 6; vol. 2, p. 59].
3. Hankel, H.: *Zur Geschichte der Mathematik im Altertum und Mittelalter*. Leipzig: Teubner, 1874; p. 7.
4. Smith, D. E.: *History of Mathematics:* v. 1, *General Survey of the History of Elementary Mathematics*. Boston: Ginn, 1932; p. 5.

5. Cajori: [C; vol. 1].
6. Weyl, H.: *Die Stufen des Unendlichen*. Jena: Fischer, 1931; p. 14.
7. Carathéodory, C.: *Vorlesungen über reelle Funktionen*. Leipzig and Berlin: Teubner, 1918; 2nd ed., 1927; in reprint, New York: Chelsea; p. v.
8. Hausdorff, F.: *Grundzüge der Mengenlehre*. Leipzig: de Gruyter, 1914; in reprint, New York: Chelsea; Ch. 3, § 2, pp. 47–51.
9. Pascal, E.: *Reportorium der höheren Mathematik* (German edition), 2nd ed. Leipzig and Berlin: Teubner, 1910; vol. 1, 1st half, Ch. 1 (by H. Hahn), § 5, p. 17 ff.
10. von Staudt: *Beiträgen zur Geometrie der Lage*, Heft I. Nürnberg: 1756; § 8, Von der Menge der Elemente, p. 86 ff.
11. Reye, Th.: *Die Geometrie der Lage*, 5th ed. Leipzig: 1909; Abt. 1, p. 19 ff.
12. Enriques, F.: *Vorlesungen über projektive Geometrie* (German edition). Leipzig: Teubner, 1903; Ch. 1, § 1, p. 8.
13. Dedekind, Richard: *Was sind und was sollen die Zahlen?*, 6th ed., 1930. Reprinted in:
    Dedekind, Richard: *Gesammelte mathematische Werke*. Braunschweig. Vieweg, 1930–1932; vol. 3, p. 335 ff. See § 5, Remark No. 64 and the definition of finite sets in the Foreword to the 2nd ed. of *Was sind und was sollen die Zahlen?* For an English translation see Part II of:
    Dedekind, Richard: *Essays on the Theory of Numbers: I. Continuity and Irrational Numbers. II. The Nature and Meaning of Numbers*. New York: Dover, 1963.
14. Russell, Bertrand: *Introduction to Mathematical Philosophy*. London: Allen and Unwin; New York: Macmillan, 1919, 1924.
15. Perron, O.: *Die Lehre von den Kettenbrüchen*. Leipzig and Berlin: Teubner, 1913; 2nd ed., 1929. See also Supplementary References, VI: Khinchin (*Continued Fractions*), Olds.
16. Legendre, A. M.: *Zahlentheorie* (German edition of *Théorie des Nombres*), vol. 1, 2nd ed. Leipzig: Teubner, 1893; p. 18 ff.
17. Weber, H. and J. Wellstein: *Encyklopädie der Elementar-Mathematik*, vol. 1. Leipzig: 1903; Abschnitt 15, §§ 78 ff., p. 256 ff.
18. Pringsheim, A.: *Vorlesungen über Zahlen- und Funktionenlehre*, vol. 1. Leipzig and Berlin: Teubner, 1921; Abt. 3, Abschnitt IV, pp. 88–114.
19. Perron: [$P_1$; p. 29 ff.].

*Chapter XIII*

1. Gesellschaft der Wissenschaften zu Göttingen, Geschäftliche Mitteilungen (1908), Heft 1. See also:
    *Preisausschreiben der Kgl. Gesellschaft der Wissenschaften zu Göttingen für den Beweis des Fermatschen Satzes*, [J10; **66** (1909), 143–144].
    *Bekanntmachung der Gesellschaft der Wissenschaften zu Göttingen vom* 1. *September* 1919, [J10; **80** (1921), 84].
2. Dickson, L. E.: *History of the Theory of Numbers*, 2 vols. Washington: Carnegie Institution, 1919–1920.
3. Cajori: [C].
4. Valéry, Paul: *La crise de l'esprit*, Variétés, 32ᵉ ed., Librairie Gallimard, Paris; p. 24 ff. See esp. p. 27, pp. 47–48.
5. *Les Grands Courants de la Pensée Mathématique:* in the collection *L'Humanisme Scientifique de Demain*.
6. Diophantus: *Opera*, ed. by P. Tannery, 2 vols. Leipzig: Teubner, 1893–1895; vol. 1, pp. 90–92.

7. Tannery, P.: [J3; t. 1, vol. 3, fasc. 1, art. I 15, p. 28].
8. Tropfke: [T; vol. 3, p. 111 ff.].
9. Cantor: [Ca; vol. 1, p. 646 and pp. 672–675].
10. Braunmühl, A. v.: *Vorlesungen über die Geschichte der Trigonometrie*, 2 vols. Leipzig: Teubner, 1900–1903; vol. 1, p. 54 ff.
11. Lucas: [Lu].
12. Ball, W. W. Rouse: *Mathematical Recreations and Problems*. London: 1893; reprint of 11th ed. with corrections, New York: Macmillan, 1962.
13. Schubert: [S].
14. Ahrens: [A].
15. Ahrens, W.: *Altes und Neues aus der Unterhaltungsmathematik*. Berlin: 1918.
16. Kraitchik, M.: *La Mathématique des Jeux ou Récréations Mathématiques*. Bruxelles: Stevens Frères, 1930 In English translation: *Mathematical Recreations*. New York: Dover, 1953.
17. Kowalewski, Gerhard: *Alte und neue mathematische Spiele*. Leipzig: Teubner, 1930.
18. [J2; v. 1, part 2, article IG1, p. 1080 ff.].
19. Fermat, Pierre de: *Oeuvres de Fermat*, publiées par les soins de MM. Paul Tannery et Charles Henry. Paris: Gauthier-Villars, 1891–1896.
20. Bolletino di Bibliografia e di Storia delle Scienze Matematiche e Fisiche, published by B. Boncampagni, Roma; t. XII, p. 477–568, 619–740.
21. Legendre, A. M.: *Zahlentheorie* (translated from the 3rd French edition of Théorie des Nombres by H. Maser). Leipzig: Teubner, 1893; art. 326 and 327, p. 5 ff.
22. Hofmann, J. E.: *Studien zur Zahlentheorie Fermats*, Abh. d. Preuss. Akad. d. Wiss. Math.-naturwiss. Klasse, (1944), No. 7, p. 9.
23. [J3; t. 1, vol. 3, fasc. 1 (1906), art. I15 (P. Bachmann and E. Maillet), p. 36, Notes 192, 193].
24. Cahen, E.: *Théorie des Nombres*. Paris: Hermann, 1924; vol. 2, p. 598.
25. Landau, E.: *Vorlesungen über Zahlentheorie*, 3 vols. Leipzig: Hirzel, 1927; vol. 3, section 2 on Fermat's conjecture, part 12, Ch. 1, § 3, Satz 901, pp. 211–214.
26. Gauss: [G; vol. II, p. 398].
27. [J3; t. 1, vol. 3, fasc. 1 (1906), p. 36, 37].
28. Dirichlet: [D; vol. 1, p. 38, 39].
29. [J2; v. 1, part 2 (1900/04), p. 634, Note 106; p. 714, Note 31].
30. Klein: [K; vol. 1].
31. Hilbert, D.: *Die Theorie der algebraischen Zahlkörper*, [J5; **4** (1897), 175–546]; see p. 532 ff.
32. K. Hensel's speech in memory of Kummer: [see Dickson (Ref. Note 2), vol. 2, pp. 738–744]. See also Dirichlet [D; vol. 2, p. 254 ff.].
33. Nörlund, N. E.: *Vorlesungen über Differenzenrechnung*. Berlin: Springer, 1924. Knopp, K.: *Theorie und Anwendung der unendlichen Reihen*, 3rd ed. Berlin: Springer, 1931.
34. Selfridge, T. L., C. A. Nicol and H. S. Vandiver: Proc. Nat. Ac. Sc. USA, **41** (1955), 970.
35. Hecke: [He].
36. Dirichlet, Peter Gustav Lejeune: *Vorlesungen über Zahlentheorie*, edited and with supplements by R. Dedekind. Braunschweig: Vieweg, 2nd–4th eds., 1871, 1879, 1894. See Supplement XI.
37. Waltershausen, W. Sartorius v.: *Gauss zum Gedächtnis*. Leipzig: 1856. Cited in Cajori [$C_1$; (1897), p. 248].

38. Cajori: [$C_1$; (1897), p. 249, 250].
39. Wolf, Rudolf: *Biographen zur Kulturgeschichte der Schweiz*, 4 vols. Zürich: Orell Füssli, 1858–1862.
40. *Festschrift zur Feier des 200. Geburtstages Leonhard Eulers*, herausgegeben von d. Berlin. math. Ges. Leipzig and Berlin: 1907; Abhandlungen zur Geschichte d. Math. mit Einschluss ihrer Anwendungen, Heft 25, p. 14.
41. *Nouvelle Biographie Générale*, 40 vols. Paris: Firmin Didot Frères, 1862–1870.
42. *Encyclopedia Britannica*. Edinburgh: Adam and Charles Black.

*Chapter XIV*

1. Stäckel, P. and Fr. Engel: *Die Theorie der Parallellinien von Euklid bis Gauss*. Leipzig: 1895.
2. Riemann, B.: *Gesammelte mathematische Werke*. Leipzig: Teubner, 1876; 2nd ed., 1892; in reprint, New York: Dover, 1953.
3. Euklid: *Die Elemente*. Ostwald's Klassiker der exakten Wissenschaften, No. 235, part I, p. 3.
4. Cantor: [Ca; vol. 3, p. 714].
5. Tietze, H.: *Über das Schicksal gemischter Populationen nach den Mendelschen Vererbungsgesetzen*, [J12; **3** (1923), 362–393].
6. Tietze, H.: *Zuschrift an den Herausgeber*, [J12; **5** (1925), 88]. See the papers of Weinberg mentioned in this letter to the editor.
7. Behr, J. v.: *Mendelismus*, [J10; **100** (1928), 722–751].
8. Boltzmann, Ludwig: *Vorlesungen über Gastheorie*, 2 vols. Leipzig: Barth, 1896–1898.
9. Laue, M. v.: *Die Relativitätstheorie*, 2 vols. Braunschweig, Vieweg, 1921; §§ 6–12, pp. 42–135.
10. [J5; **31** (1922), section 2, p. 26].

*Postscript*

1. [J1; (1943)]; reprinted in Carathéodory [Car; vol. 5, pp. 101–105].
2. [J8; (1900), pp. 253–297]; *Sur les problèmes futurs des Mathématiques* (translated by Laugel), Congrès International des Mathématiciens, 1900, Paris (1902), pp. 58–114.
3. Carathéodory: [Car; vol. 5, p. 409 ff. and pp. 387–408 for autobiographical material]. See also [J1; (1950), 85–101].
4. Dinghas, Alexander and Erhard Schmidt: *Einfacher Beweis der isoperimetrischen Eigenschaft der Kugel im n-dimensionalen euklidischen Raum*, [J9; (1943), No. 7 (Berlin 1944)].
5. Carathéodory, C. *The beginning of research in the calculus of variations*, Osiris, **3** part 1 (1937), 224–240.
6. [J2; vol. 1, part 2, pp. 754, 765].
7. Tietze, H.: *Über gewisse Umordnungen von Permutationen und ein zugehöriges Stabilitätskriterium*, [J5; (1943)]. Four Notes on the above paper [J1; (1943)].
8. See Ch. XIV, Ref. Note 5.
9. Birkhoff, G. D.: *Proof of Poincaré's geometric theorem*, Transactions of the American Mathematical Society, **14** (1913), 14–22. See also Bulletin de la Société Math. de France, **42** (1914).
10. Wintner, A.: *The Analytical Foundations of Celestial Mechanics*. Princeton, N. J.: Princeton University Press, 1941; p. 91 ff.

11. Tietze, H.: *Ein Kapitel Topologie: Zur Einführung in die Lehre von den verknoteten Linien*. Hamburger mathematische Efinzelschriften, Bd. 36 (1942).
12. Tietze, H.: *Über angewandte und reine Mathematik*, Feldpostbrief der naturwissenschaftlichen Fakultät der Universität München, Folge 1, 1943.
13. Carathéodory, C.: *Die Fehler höherer Ordnung der optischen Instrumente*, [J1; (1943)].

# SUPPLEMENTARY REFERENCES

(Paperback editions are indicated by (P).)

## I. GENERAL

Aleksandrov, A. D. et alt. (eds.): *Mathematics: Its Content, Methods and Meaning*, 3 vols. Cambridge, Mass.: MIT Press, 1965.
Courant, R. and H. Robbins: *What Is Mathematics?* New York: Oxford, 1941.
Hardy, G. H.: *A Mathematician's Apology*. New York: Cambridge, 1940.
Henkin, L. et alt.: *Retracing Elementary Mathematics*. New York: Macmillan, 1962.
Hess, A. L.: *Mathematics Projects Handbook*. Boston: Heath. (P)
Jones, B. W.: *Elementary Concepts of Mathematics*. New York: Macmillan, 1963.
Klein, F.: *Elementary Mathematics From an Advanced Standpoint*, 2 vols. New York: Dover. (P)
Meschkowski, H.: *Ways of Thought of Great Mathematicians*. San Francisco: Holden-Day, 1964. (P)
Rademacher, H. and O. Toeplitz: *The Enjoyment of Mathematics*. Princeton: Princeton University Press, 1957.
Saaty, T. L. (ed.): *Lectures on Modern Mathematics*, 2 vols. New York: Wiley, 1963, 1964.
Singh, J.: *Great Ideas of Modern Mathematics*. New York: Dover, 1959. (P)
Stabler, E. R.: *Introduction to Mathematical Thought*. Reading, Mass.: Addison-Wesley, 1953.
Steinhaus, H.: *Mathematical Snapshots*, 2nd rev. ed. New York: Oxford, 1960.

## II. HISTORY AND BIOGRAPHY

Aaboe, A.: *Episodes From the Early History of Mathematics*. New York: Random House, 1964. (P)
Bell, E. T.: *Men of Mathematics*. New York: Simon & Schuster, 1937. (P)
Bourbaki, N.: *Éléments d'Histoire des Mathématiques*. Paris: Hermann, 1960. (P)
Eves, H.: *An Introduction to the History of Mathematics*. New York: Holt, 1964.
Hardy, G. H.: *Ramanujan: Twelve Lectures on His Life and Works*. New York: Chelsea.
Struik, D. J.: *A Concise History of Mathematics*, 2 vols. New York: Dover, 1948. (P)
van der Waerden, B. L.: *Science Awakening*. New York: Wiley. (P)

## III. COLLECTIONS OF PROBLEMS

*Hungarian Problem Books*, I, II. New York: Random House. (P)
Salkind, C. T. (ed.): *The Contest Problem Book*. New York: Random House. (P)
Shklarsky, D. O. et alt.: *The USSR Olympiad Problem Book*. San Francisco: Freeman, 1962.
Steinhaus, H.: *One Hundred Problems in Elementary Mathematics*. New York: Pergamon, 1962.
Ulam, S.: *Collection of Mathematical Problems*. New York: Wiley, 1960.
Ulam, S.: *Problems in Modern Mathematics*. New York: Wiley. (P)
Yaglom, A. M. and I. M. Yaglom: *Challenging Mathematical Problems With Elementary Solutions*. San Francisco: Holden-Day, 1964. (P)

## IV. LOGIC AND FOUNDATIONS


Christian, R. R.: *Introduction to Logic and Sets*. New York: Blaisdell, 1963. (P)
Dubisch, R.: *Lattices to Logic*. New York: Blaisdell, 1964. (P)
Gödel, K.: *The Consistency of the Continuum Hypothesis*. Princeton: Princeton University Press, 1940. (P)
Goodstein, R. L.: *Mathematical Logic*. New York: Ungar.
Halmos, P. R.: *Algebraic Logic*. New York: Chelsea, 1962.
Hilbert, D. and W. Ackermann: *Principles of Mathematical Logic*. New York: Chelsea, 1959.
Kleene, S. C.: *Introduction to Metamathematics*. Princeton: van Nostrand, 1952.
Landau, E.: *Foundations of Analysis*. New York: Chelsea, 1951.
Lightstone, A. H.: *The Axiomatic Method: An Introduction to Mathematical Logic*. Englewood Cliffs: Prentice-Hall, 1964.
Mendelson, E.: *Introduction to Mathematical Logic*. Princeton: van Nostrand, 1964.
Nagel, E. and J. R. Newman: *Gödel's Proof*. New York: New York University Press, 1958. (P)
Nidditch, P. H.: *Development of Mathematical Logic*. New York: Macmillan. (P)
Novikov, P. S.: *Elements of Mathematical Logic*. London, Oliver, 1963.
Quine, W. V. O.: *Mathematical Logic*, rev. ed. Cambridge, Mass.: Harvard University Press, 1951. Also New York: Harper. (P)
Ramsey, F. P.: *Foundations of Mathematics*. Paterson, N. J.: Littlefield. (P)
Rosenbloom, P. C.: *Elements of Mathematical Logic*. New York: Dover, 1950. (P)
Sominskii, I. S.: *The Method of Mathematical Induction*. New York: Blaisdell, 1962. (P)
Spreckelmeyer, R.: *The Natural Numbers*. Boston: Health. (P)
*The Integers*. Boston: Heath. (P)
*The Rational Numbers*. Boston: Heath. (P)
*The Real Numbers*. Boston: Heath. (P)
*The Complex Numbers*. Boston: Heath. (P)
Stoll, R. R.: *Sets, Logic and Axiomatic Theories*. San Francisco: Freeman, 1961. (P)
Stoll, R. R.: *Set Theory and Logic*. San Francisco: Freeman, 1961.
Suppes, P.: *Introduction to Logic*. Princeton: van Nostrand, 1957.
Wilder, R. L.: *Foundations of Mathematics*. New York: Wiley, 1952.


## V. SET THEORY


Fraenkel, A. A.: *Abstract Set Theory*. Amsterdam: North Holland, 1961.
Halmos, P. R.: *Naive Set Theory*. Princeton: van Nostrand, 1961.
Hausdorff, F.: *Set Theory*. New York: Chelsea, 1962.
Huntington, E. V. *The Continuum*. New York: Dover. (P)
Kamke, E.: *Theory of Sets*. New York: Dover, 1950. (P)
Landin, J. and N. Hamilton: *Set Theory: The Structure of Arithmetic*. Boston: Allyn & Bacon, 1961.
Quine, W. V. O.: *Set Theory and Its Logic*. Cambridge, Mass.: Harvard University Press, 1964.
Suppes, P.: *Axiomatic Set Theory*. Princeton: van Nostrand, 1960.
Yarnelle, J. E.: *An Introduction to Transfinite Mathematics*. Boston: Heath. (P)
Zippin, L.: *Uses of Infinity*. New York: Random House. (P)

## VI. NUMBER THEORY

Bell, E. T.: *The Last Problem.* New York: Simon & Schuster, 1961.
Cohn, H.: *A Second Course in Number Theory.* New York: Wiley, 1962.
Corput, J. G. van der: *Démonstration Élémentaire du Théorème sur la Distribution des Nombres Premiers.* Amsterdam: Mathematisch Centrum, 1948. (P)
Davenport, H.: *The Higher Arithmetic: An Introduction to the Theory of Numbers.* New York: Harper, 1960.(P)
Davis, P. J.: *The Lore of Large Numbers.* New York: Random House, 1962. (P)
Dickson, L. E.: *History of the Theory of Numbers,* 3 vols. New York: Chelsea, 1952.
Dynkin, E. B. and V. A. Uspenskii: *Problems in the Theory of Numbers.* Boston: Health. (P)
Gelfond, A. O. and Linnik, Yu. V.: *Elementary Methods in Analytic Number Theory* (Russian). Moscow: GIFML, 1962.
Gelfond, A. O.: *Transcendental and Algebraic Numbers.* New York: Dover, 1960. (P)
Gelfond, A. O.: *The Solution of Equations in Integers.* San Francisco: Freeman, 1961. (P)
Jones, B.: *Modular Arithmetic.* New York: Blaisdell, 1964. (P)
Khinchin, A. Y.: *Three Pearls of Number Theory.* New York: Graylock, 1952. (P)
Khinchin, A. Y.: *Continued Fractions.* Chicago: University of Chicago Press, 1964. (P)
Landau, E.: *Elementary Number Theory.* New York: Chelsea, 1958.
Leveque, W. J.: *Elementary Theory of Numbers.* Reading, Mass.: Addison-Wesley, 1962.
Leveque, W. J.: *Topics in Number Theory,* 2 vols. Reading, Mass.: Addison-Wesley, 1956.
Niven, I.: *Numbers: Rational and Irrational.* New York: Random House, 1962. (P)
Niven, I.: *Irrational Numbers* (Carus Monograph 11). New York: Wiley, 1956.
Niven, I. and H. Zuckerman: *An Introduction to the Theory of Numbers.* New York: Wiley, 1960.
Olds, C. D.: *Continued Fractions.* New York: Random House. (P)
Ore, O.: *Number Theory and Its History.* New York: McGraw-Hill, 1948.
Rademacher, H. *Lectures on Elementary Number Theory.* New York: Blaisdell, 1964.
Shanks, D. *Solved and Unsolved Problems in Number Theory.* Baltimore: Spartan Books, 1964.
Vinogradov, I. M.: *Elements of Number Theory.* New York: Dover, 1954. (P)
Vorob'iev, N. N.: *Fibonacci Numbers.* New York: Blaisdell, 1961. (P)

## VII. ALGEBRA

### *A. General and Expository*

Albert, A. A. (ed.): *Studies in Modern Algebra* (MAA Studies in Mathematics, vol. 2). Englewood Cliffs: Prentice-Hall, 1963.
Ball, R. W.: *Principles of Abstract Algebra.* New York: Holt, 1963.
Birkhoff, G. and S. MacLane: *A Survey of Modern Algebra.* New York: Macmillan, 1953.
Chevalley, C.: *Fundamental Concepts of Algebra.* New York: Academic Press, 1956.
Deskins, W. E.: *Abstract Algebra.* New York: Macmillan, 1964.

Herstein, I. N.: *Topics in Algebra*. New York: Blaisdell, 1964.
Jacobson, N.: *Lectures in Abstract Algebra;* vol. 1: *Basic Concepts*. Princeton: van Nostrand, 1951.
Kelley, J. L.: *Introduction to Modern Algebra*. Princeton: van Nostrand, 1960. (P)
Kurosh, A. G.: *Lectures on General Algebra*. New York: Chelsea, 1963.
Lederman, W.: *Complex Numbers*. New York: Macmillan. (P)
Levi, H.: *Elements of Algebra*. New York: Chelsea, 1962.
McCoy, N. H.: *Introduction to Modern Algebra*. Boston: Allyn and Bacon, 1960.
Mostow, G. D. et alt.: *Fundamental Structures of Algebra*. New York: McGraw-Hill, 1963.
Sawyer, W. W.: *A Concrete Approach to Modern Algebra*. San Francisco: Freeman, 1959. (P)
van der Waerden, B. L.: *Modern Algebra*, 2 vols. New York: Ungar, 1953, 1950.
Yarnelle, J. E.: *Finite Mathematical Structures*. Boston: Heath. (P)
Zariski, O. and P. Samuel: *Commutative Algebra*, 2 vols. Princeton: van Nostrand, 1958, 1960.

*B. Linear Algebra and Matrix Theory*

Gelfand, I. M.: *Lectures on Linear Algebra*. New York: Wiley, 1961.
Halmos, P. R.: *Finite-Dimensional Vector Spaces*, 2nd ed. Princeton: Princeton University Press, 1958.
Jacobson, N.: *Lectures in Abstract Algebra;* vol. 2: *Linear Algebra*. Princeton: van Nostrand, 1953.
Munkres, J. R.: *Elementary Linear Algebra*. Reading, Mass.: Addison-Wesley. (P)
Schreier, O. and E. Sperner: *Introduction to Modern Algebra and Matrix Theory*. New York: Chelsea, 1951.

*C. Group Theory*

Alexandroff, P. S.: *An Introduction to the Theory of Groups*. New York: Stechert-Hafner, 1961.
Grossman, I. and W. Magnus: *Groups and Their Graphs*. New York: Random House. (P)
Hall, M.: *The Theory of Groups*. New York: Macmillan, 1959.
Kurosh, A.: *Group Theory*, 2 vols. New York: Chelsea, 1959–60.
Papy, G.: *Groups*. New York: St. Martin's Press, 1964.
Wielandt, H.: *Finite Permutation Groups*. New York: Academic Press, 1964. (P)
Zassenhaus, H.: *The Theory of Groups*. New York: Chelsea, 1958.

*D. Galois Theory*

Artin, E.: *Galois Theory*, 2nd ed. Notre Dame: University of Notre Dame Press, 1948. (P)
Jacobson, N.: *Lectures in Abstract Algebra;* vol. 3: *Theory of Fields and Galois Theory*. Princeton: van Nostrand, 1964.
Postnikov, M. M.: *Fundamentals of Galois Theory*. Groningen: Noordhoff, 1962.

*E. Algebraic Number Theory*

Pollard, H.: *Theory of Algebraic Numbers* (Carus Monograph 9). New York: Wiley, 1950.
Weiss, E.: *Algebraic Number Theory*. New York: McGraw-Hill, 1963.

### *F. Homological Algebra*

Jans, J. P.: *Rings and Homology*. New York: Holt, 1964. (P)

## VIII. ANALYSIS

### *A. Elementary Precalculus and Calculus*

Apostol, T. M.: *Calculus*, 2 vols. New York: Blaisdell, 1961–62.
Bristol, J. D.: *The Concept of a Function*. Boston: Heath. (P)
*Graphing Relations and Functions*. Boston: Heath. (P)
Hardy, G. H.: *Pure Mathematics*. New York: Cambridge, 1959. (P)
Hilton, P. J.: *Differential Calculus*. New York: Macmillan. (P)
Johnson, R. E. and F. L. Kiokemeister: *Calculus*, 3rd ed. Boston: Allyn and Bacon, 1964.
Markushevich, A. I.: *Areas and Logarithms*. Boston: Heath. (P)
Miller, N.: *Limits*. New York: Blaisdell, 1964. (P)
Natanson, I. P.: *Summation of Infinitely Small Quantities*. Boston: Heath. (P)
Niven, I.: *Calculus: An Introductory Approach*. Princeton: van Nostrand, 1961.
Sawyer, W. W.: *What Is Calculus About?* New York: Random House. (P)
Shervatov, V. G.: *Hyperbolic Functions*. Boston: Heath. (P)
Shilov, G. E.: *How to Construct Graphs;* Natanson, I. P. *Simplest Maxima and Minima Problems*. Boston: Heath. (P)

### *B. Advanced Calculus*

Apostol, T. M.: *Mathematical Analysis: A Modern Approach to Advanced Calculus*. Reading, Mass.: Addison-Wesley, 1957.
Bartle, R. G.: *The Elements of Real Analysis*. New York: Wiley, 1964.
Buck, R. C.: *Advanced Calculus*. New York: McGraw-Hill, 1956.
Dieudonné, J.: *Foundations of Modern Analysis*. New York: Academic Press, 1960.
Khinchin, A. Y.: *Eight Lectures on Mathematical Analysis*. Boston: Heath. (P)
Nickerson, H. et alt.: *Advanced Calculus*. Princeton: van Nostrand, 1959. (P)

### *C. Functions of a Real Variable*

Bellman, R. (ed.): *Collection of Modern Mathematical Classics: Analysis*. New York: Dover. (P)
Buck, R. C. (ed.): *Studies in Modern Analysis* (MAA Studies in Mathematics, vol. 1). Englewood Cliffs: Prentice-Hall, 1962.
Burkill, J. C.: *The Lebesgue Integral*. Cambridge: Cambridge University Press, 1951. (P)
Gelbaum, B. R.: *Counterexamples in Analysis*. San Francisco: Holden-Day, 1964.
Hewitt, E.: *Theory of Functions of a Real Variable*. New York: Holt, 1960.
Hyslop, J. M.: *Real Variables*. New York: Wiley, 1960.
Kolmogorov, A. N. and S. V. Fomin: *Elements of the Theory of Functions and Functional Analysis;* vol. 1: *Metric and Normed Spaces;* vol. 2: *Measure. The Lebesgue Integral. Hilbert Space*. New York: Graylock, 1957, 1961.
McShane, E. J. and T. Botts: *Real Analysis*. Princeton: van Nostrand, 1959.
Royden, H. L.: *Real Analysis*. New York: Macmillan, 1963.
Williamson, J. H.: *Lebesgue Integration*. New York: Holt, 1962. (P)

### *D. Functions of a Complex Variable*

Cartan, H.: *Elementary Theory of Analytic Functions.* Reading, Mass.: Addison-Wesley, 1963.
Knopp, K.: *Elements of the Theory of Functions.* New York: Dover, 1953. (P)
Knopp, K.: *Theory of Functions*, 2 vols. New York: Dover, 1948, 1952. (P)
Knopp, K.: *Problem Book in the Theory of Functions*, 2 vols. New York: Dover, 1952. (P)
Pennisi, L. L.: *Elements of Complex Variables.* New York: Holt, 1963.
Saks, S. and A. Zygmund: *Analytic Functions.* New York: Hafner, 1952.
Thron, W. J.: *Introduction to the Theory of Functions of a Complex Variable.* New York: Wiley, 1953.

### *E. Sequences and Series*

Green, J. A.: *Sequences and Series.* New York: Macmillan, 1958. (P)
Hirschman, I. I.: *Infinite Series.* New York: Holt, 1962. (P)
Knopp, K.: *Infinite Sequences and Series.* New York: Dover, 1956. (P)
Markushevich, A. I.: *Infinite Series.* Boston: Heath. (P)

### *F. Inequalities*

Beckenbach, E. and R. Bellman: *An Introduction to Inequalities.* New York: Random House, 1961. (P)
Kazarinoff, N. D.: *Analytic Inequalities.* New York: Holt, 1961. (P)
Kazarinoff, N. D.: *Geometric Inequalities.* New York: Random House, 1961. (P)
Korovkin, P. P.: *Inequalities.* New York: Blaisdell, 1961. (P)

### *G. Differential, Difference and Integral Equations*

Agnew, R.: *Differential Equations*, 2nd ed. New York: McGraw-Hill, 1960.
Apostol, T. M.: *A Brief Course in Ordinary Differential Equations.* New York: Blaisdell, 1964.
Burkill, J. C.: *Theory of Ordinary Differential Equations.* New York: Wiley, 1956.
Edzard, G and. H. Reuter: *Elementary Differential Equations.* New York: Macmillan. (P).
Goldberg, S.: *Introduction to Difference Equations.* New York: Wiley. (P)
Garabedian, P. R.: *Partial Differential Equations.* New York: Wiley, 1964.
Greenspan, D.: *Theory and Solution of Ordinary Differential Equations.* New York: Macmillan, 1960.
Hurewicz, W.: *Lectures on Ordinary Differential Equations.* New York: Wiley, 1958. (P)
Petrovsky, I. G.: *Lectures on Partial Differential Equations.* New York: Wiley, 1955.
Petrovskii, I. G.: *Lectures on the Theory of Integral Equations.* New York: Graylock, 1957.
Pontryagin, L.: *Ordinary Differential Equations.* Reading, Mass.: Addison-Wesley, 1962.

### *H. Fourier Series. Special Functions*

Artin, E.: *The Gamma Function.* New York: Holt. (P)
Hardy, G. H. and W. Rogozinski: *Fourier Series.* Cambridge: Cambridge University Press, 1956. (P)

Rainville, E. D.: *Special Functions*. New York: Macmillan, 1960.
Rogozinski, W.: *Fourier Series*. New York: Chelsea, 1959. (P)

*I. Calculus of Variations*

Akhieser, N. I.: *Calculus of Variations*. New York: Blaisdell, 1962.
Bliss, G. A.: *Calculus of Variations* (Carus Monograph 1). Chicago: University of Chicago Press. (P)
Gelfand, I. M. and S. V. Fomin: *Calculus of Variations*. Englewood Cliffs: Prentice-Hall, 1963.
Kryzhanovskii, D.: *Isoperimetry*. Boston: Heath. (P)
Lyusternik, L. A.: *Shortest Paths: Variational Problems*. New York: Macmillan, 1965.

## IX. GEOMETRY

Argunov, B. I. and M. B. Balk: *Geometric Constructions in the Plane*. Boston: Heath. (P)
Argunov, B. I. and L. A. Skornyakov: *Configuration Theorems*. Boston: Heath. (P)
Boltyanskii, V. G.: *Equivalent and Equidecomposable Figures*. Boston: Heath. (P)
Blumenthal, L. M.: *A Modern View of Geometry*. San Francisco: Freeman, 1961. (P)
Borsuk, K. and W. Szmielew: *Foundations of Geometry: Euclidean Geometry, Bolyai-Lobachevskian Geometry, Projective Geometry*. New York: Wiley, 1960.
Coxeter, H. S. M.: *Introduction to Geometry*. New York: Wiley, 1961.
Coxeter, H. S. M.: *Regular Polytopes*. New York: Macmillan, 1963. (P)
Dubnov, Ya. S.: *Mistakes in Geometric Proofs*. Boston: Heath. (P)
Eggleston, H. G.: *Convexity*. New York: Cambridge, 1958.
Fetisov, A. I.: *Proof in Geometry*. Boston: Heath. (P)
Golovina, L. I. and I. M. Yaglom.: *Induction in Geometry*. Boston: Heath. (P)
Hilbert, D.: *Foundations of Geometry*. La Salle, Ill.: Open-Court. (P)
Hilbert, D. and S. Cohn-Vossen: *Geometry and the Imagination*. New York: Chelsea, 1952.
Hobson, E. W. et alt.: *Squaring the Circle. Ruler and Compasses. The Theory and Construction of Non-differentiable Functions. How to Draw a Straight Line*. New York: Chelsea.
Klee, V.: *Combinatorial Geometry in the Plane*. New York: Holt. (P)
Klein, F. et alt.: *Famous Problems of Elementary Geometry. From Determinant to Tensor. Introduction to Combinatory Analysis. Three Lectures on Fermat's Last Theorem*. New York: Chelsea, 1962. (P)
Kostovskii, A. N.: *Geometrical Constructions Using Compass Only*. New York: Blaisdell, 1962. (P)
Lopshits, A. M.: *Computation of Areas of Oriented Figures*. Boston: Heath. (P)
Lyusternik, L. A.: *Convex Figures and Polyhedra*. New York: Dover. (P) Also, Boston: Heath. (P)
Meschkowski, H.: *Noneuclidean Geometry*. New York: Academic Press, 1964. (P)
Moise, E. E.: *Elementary Geometry From an Advanced Standpoint*. Reading, Mass.: Addison-Wesley, 1963.
Prenowitz, W. and H. Swain: *Congruence and Motion in Geometry*. Boston: Heath. (P)
Russell, B.: *Essay on the Foundations of Geometry*. New York: Dover. (P)
Smogorzhevskii, A. S.: *The Ruler in Geometric Constructions*. New York: Blaisdell, 1962. (P)
Valentine, F. A.: *Convex Sets*. New York: McGraw-Hill, 1964.

Wylie, C. R.: *Foundations of Geometry*. New York: McGraw-Hill, 1964.
Yaglom, I. M. and V. G. Boltyanskii: *Convex Figures*. New York: Holt, 1961.
Yaglom, I. M.: *Geometric Transformations*. New York: Random House. (P)
Zetel', S. I. *Geometry of the Straightedge and Geometry of the Compass*. Boston: Heath. (P)

## X. DIFFERENTIAL GEOMETRY

Flanders, H.: *Differential Forms*. New York: Academic Press, 1963.
Guggenheimer, H.: *Differential Geometry*. New York: McGraw-Hill, 1963.
Kreyszig, E.: *Differential Geometry*. Toronto: University of Toronto Press, 1959.
Pogorelov, A. V.: *Differential Geometry*. Groningen: Noordhoff, 1959.
Springer, C. E.: *Tensor and Vector Analysis with Applications to Differential Geometry*. New York: Ronald, 1962.
Struik, D. G.: *Differential Geometry*, 2nd ed. Reading, Mass.: Addison-Wesley, 1961.
Thomas, T. Y.: *Concepts From Tensor Analysis and Differential Geometry*. New York: Academic Press, 1961.

## XI. TOPOLOGY

### *A. General Topology*

Arnold, B. H.: *Intuitive Concepts in Elementary Topology*. Englewood Cliffs: Prentice-Hall, 1962.
Bushaw, D.: *Elements of General Topology*. New York: Wiley, 1963.
Gaal, S.: *Point Set Topology*. New York: Academic Press, 1964.
Hall, D. and G. L. Spencer: *Elementary Topology*. New York: Wiley, 1955.
Hocking, J. G. and G. S. Young: *Topology*. Reading, Mass.: Addison-Wesley, 1961.
Hu, S. T.: *Elements of General Topology*. San Francisco: Holden-Day, 1964.
Kelley, J. L.: *General Topology*. Princeton: van Nostrand, 1955.
Kuratowski, K.: *Introduction to Set Theory and Topology*. Reading, Mass.: Addison-Wesley, 1962.
Mendelson, B.: *Introduction to Topology*. Boston: Allyn and Bacon, 1962.
Newman, M. H. A.: *Elements of the Topology of Plane Sets of Points*. New York: Cambridge, 1961. (P)
Patterson, E. M. N.: *Topology*. New York: Wiley, 1956.
Pervin, W. J.: *Foundations of General Topology*. New York: Academic Press, 1964.
Sierpinski, W.: *General Topology*. Toronto: University of Toronto Press, 1961.
Simmons, G. F.: *Introduction to Topology and Modern Analysis*. New York: McGraw-Hill, 1963.

### *B. Combinatorial and Algebraic Topology*

Aleksandrov, P. S.: *Elementary Concepts of Topology*. New York: Dover. (P)
Aleksandrov, P. S.: *Combinatorial Topology*, 3 vols. New York: Graylock, 1956, 1957, 1960.
Berge, C.: *The Theory of Graphs and Its Applications*. New York: Wiley, 1962.
Bourgin, D. G.: *Modern Algebraic Topology*. New York: Macmillan, 1963.
Cairns, S. S.: *Introductory Topology*. New York: Ronald, 1961.
Crowell, R. H. and R. H. Fox: *Introduction to Knot Theory*. Boston: Ginn, 1963.
Dynkin, E. B. and V. A. Uspenskii: *Multicolor Problems*. Boston: Heath. (P)

Fréchet, M. et Ky Fan: *Introduction à la Topologie Combinatoire*. Paris: Vuibert, 1946. (P)
HILTON, P. J.: *An Introduction to Homotopy Theory*. Cambridge: Cambridge University Press, 1953. (P)
Hocking, J. G. and G. S. Young. See *A*.
Hu, S. T.: *Homotopy Theory*. New York: Academic Press, 1959.
Newman, M. H. A.: See *A*.
Ore, O.: *Graphs and Their Uses*. New York: Random House. (P)
Pontryagin, L. S.: *Foundations of Combinatorial Topology*. New York: Graylock, 1952.
Wallace, A. H.: *Introduction to Algebraic Topology*. New York: Pergamon, 1957.

### *C. Differential Topology*

Auslander, L. and R. E. MacKenzie: *Introduction to Differentiable Manifolds*. New York: McGraw-Hill, 1963.
Munkres, J. R.: *Elementary Differential Topology*. Princeton: Princeton University Press, 1964. (P)

## XII. PROBABILITY AND STATISTICS

Bartlett, M. S.: *Introduction to Stochastic Processes*. New York: Cambridge. (P)
Cramér, H.: *The Elements of Probability Theory and Some of Its Applications*. New York: Wiley, 1955.
Cramér, H.: *Mathematical Methods of Statistics*. Princeton: Princeton University Press, 1946.
Dynkin, E. B. and V. A. Uspenskii: *Random Walks*. Boston: Heath. (P)
Feller, W.: *Probability Theory and Its Applications*, 2nd ed. New York: Wiley, 1957.
Gnedenko, B. V. and A. Y. Khinchin: *Elementary Introduction to the Theory of Probability*. San Francisco: Freeman, 1961. (P)
Gnedenko, B. V.: *Theory of Probability*. New York: Chelsea, 1962.
Kemeny, J. G. and J. L. Snell: *Finite Markov Chains*. Princeton: van Nostrand, 1959.
Khinchin, A. Y.: *Mathematical Foundations of Information Theory*. New York: Dover. (P)
Kolmogorov, A. N.: *Foundations of the Theory of Probability*. New York: Chelsea, 1956. (P)
Loève, M.: *Probability Theory*, 3rd ed. Princeton: van Nostrand, 1963.
Uspensky, J. V.: *Introduction to Mathematical Probability*. New York: McGraw-Hill. (P)
Yaglom, A. M. and I. M. Yaglom: *Probability and Information*. Boston: Heath. (P)

## XIII. THEORY OF GAMES AND COMPUTING MACHINES

Barsov, A. S.: *What is Linear Programming?* Boston: Heath. (P)
Bell, D. A.: *Intelligent Machines: An Introduction to Cybernetics*. New York: Blaisdell, 1962. (P)
Bristol, J. D.: *An Introduction to Linear Programming*. Boston: Heath. (P)
Hilton, A. M.: *Logic, Computing Machines and Automation*. Washington, D. C.: Spartan Books, 1963.
Trakhtenbrot, B. A.: *Algorithms and Computing Machines*. Boston: Heath. (P)
Uspenskii, V. A.: *Some Applications of Mechanics to Mathematics*. New York: Blaisdell, 1961. (P)

Venttsel', E. S.: *An Introduction to the Theory of Games*. Boston: Heath. (P)
von Neumann, J. and O. Morgenstern: *Theory of Games and Economic Behavior*. New York: Wiley. (P)

## XIV. RELATIVITY

Bergmann, P. G.: *Introduction to the Theory of Relativity*. Englewood Cliffs: Prentice-Hall, 1942.
Einstein, A.: *The Meaning of Relativity*, 5th ed. Princeton: Princeton University Press, 1955.
Einstein, A. and L. Infeld: *The Evolution of Physics*. New York: Simon & Schuster. (P)
Einstein, A.: *Relativity: The Special and General Theory*. New York: Crown. (P)
Einstein, A. et alt.: *The Principle of Relativity:* 11 *Papers on Relativity*. New York: Dover. (P)
Gamow, G.: *Mr. Tompkins in Wonderland*. New York: Cambridge, 1940.
Lieber, L. R.: *The Einstein Theory of Relativity*. New York: Farrar and Rinehart, 1945.
Rainich, G. Y.: *The Mathematics of Relativity*. New York: Wiley, 1950.
Rindler, W.: *Special Relativity*. New York: Wiley, 1960.
Schrödinger, E.: *Space-Time Structure*. New York: Cambridge, 1950.

# LIST OF PAPERS FROM THE AMERICAN MATHEMATICAL MONTHLY


1. Archibald, R. C.: *Gauss and the regular polygon of seventeen sides.* **27**(1920), 323–326.
2. Arnold, B. H.: *A topological proof of the fundamental theorem of algebra.* **56**(1949), 465–466.
3. Ayres, W. L.: *Some elementary aspects of topology.* **45**(1938), 88–92.
4. Batchelder, P. M.: *Waring's problem.* **43**(1936), 21–27.
5. Bell, E. T.: *Successive generalizations in the theory of numbers.* **34**(1925), 55–75.
6. Bell, E. T.: *Suggested readings in connection with the above.* **34**(1927), 195–196.
7. Bing, R. H.: *Elementary point set topology.* **67**(1960), #7, Part II, 1–58.
8. Birkhoff, G.: *What is a lattice?* **50**(1943), 484–487.
9. Birkhoff, G. D.: *What is the ergodic theorem?* **49**(1942), 222–226.
10. Bliss, G. A.: *The evolution of problems in the calculus of variations.* **43**(1936), 589–609.
11. Botts, T.: *Convex sets.* **49**(1942), 527–535.
12. Brahana, H. R.: *The four-color problem.* **30**(1923), 234–243.
13. Cajori, F.: *Origin of fourth dimension concepts.* **33**(1926), 397–406.
14. Carmichael, R. D.: *Some recent researches in the theory of numbers.* **39**(1932), 139–146.
15. Copeland, A. H.: *Fundamental concepts of the theory of probability.* **48**(1941), 522–530.
16. Dieudonné, J.: *Recent developments in mathematics.* **71**(1964), 239–248.
17. Doob, J. L.: *What is a stochastic process?* **49**(1942), 648–653.
18. Evans, H. P. and S. C. Kleene: *A postulational basis for probability.* **46**(1939), 141–148.
19. Funkhauser, H. G.: *A short account of the history of symmetric functions of roots of equations.* **37**(1930), 357–368.
20. Gödel, K.: *What is Cantor's continuum problem?* **54**(1947), 515–525.
21. Graves, L. M.: *What is a functional?* **55**(1948), 467–472.
22. Grosswald, E.: *A proof of the prime number theorem.* **71**(1964), 736–743.
23. Hempel, C. G.: *On the nature of mathematical truth.* **52**(1945), 543–556.
24. Henkin, L.: *On mathematical induction.* **67**(1960), 323–338.
25. Hille, E.: *Gelfond's solution of Hilbert's seventh problem.* **49**(1942), 654–661.
26. Klee, V. L.: *A characterization of convex sets.* **56**(1949), 247–249.
27. Kline, J. R.: *What is the Jordan curve theorem?* **49**(1942), 281–286.
28. Langer, R. E.: *What are eigen-werte?* **50**(1943), 279–287.
29. MacDuffee, C. C.: *What is a matrix?* **50**(1943), 360–365.
30. MacLane, S.: *Symbolic logic.* **46**(1939), 289–296.
31. Martin, W. T.: *Functions of several complex variables.* **52**(1945), 17–27.
32. Menger, K.: *What is dimension?* **50**(1943), 2–7.
33. Montgomery, D.: *What is a topological group?* **52**(1945), 302–307.
34. Morse, M.: *What is analysis in the large?* **49**(1942), 358–364.
35. Niven, I.: *The transcendence of pi.* **46**(1939), 469–471.
36. Ore, O.: *Pascal and the invention of probability theory.* **67**(1960), 409–419.
37. Polya, G.: *Heuristic reasoning and the theory of probability.* **48**(1941), 450–465.

38. Quine, W. V.: *New foundations for mathematical logic.* **44**(1937), 70–80.
39. Rado, T.: *What is the area of a surface?* **50**(1943), 139–141.
40. Rosenthal, A.: *The history of calculus.* **58**(1951), 75–86.
41. Scherck, P. and M. Kwizak: *What are tensors?* **58**(1951), 297–305.
42. Stone, M.: *The revolution in mathematics.* **68**(1961), 715–734.
43. Ulam, S. M.: *What is measure?* **50**(1943), 597–602.
44. Vandiver, H. S.: *Fermat's last theorem: its history and the nature of the known results concerning it.* **53**(1946), 555–578.
45. Veblen, O.: *On the transcendence of pi and e.* **11**(1904), 219–223.
46. Whyburn, G. T.: *What is a curve?* **49**(1942), 493–497.
47. Widder, D. V.: *What is the Laplace transform?* **52**(1945), 419–425.
48. Wilder, R. L.: *The nature of mathematical proof.* **51**(1944), 309–323.
49. Wilder, R. L.: *Some unsolved problems of topology.* **44**(1937), 61–70.
50. Zassenhaus, H.: *What is an angle?* **61**(1954), 369–378.

# INDEX